P9-DEP-014

GEOLOGY OF PETROLEUM

The quality of the materials used in the manufacture of this book is governed by continued postwar shortages.

GEOLOGY OF
PETROLEUM

BY

WILLIAM HARVEY EMMONS, Ph. D.

*Professor and Head of Department of Geology and Mineralogy, University
of Minnesota; Director, Minnesota Geological Survey; Formerly
Geologist, Section of Metalliferous Deposits, United
States Geological Survey*

SECOND EDITION
NINTH IMPRESSION

WITHDRAWN FROM
J. EUGENE SMITH LIBRARY
EASTERN CONN. STATE UNIVERSITY
WILLIMANTIC, CT 06226

McGRAW-HILL BOOK COMPANY, INC.

NEW YORK AND LONDON
1931

Copyright, 1921, 1931, by the
McGraw-Hill Book Company, Inc.

— — — —

Printed in the United States of America

*All rights reserved. This book, or
parts thereof, may not be reproduced
in any form without permission of
the publishers.*

Composition by the Maple Press Company, York, Pa.
Printed and bound by Comac Press, Inc., Brooklyn, N. Y.

553,28
Em67g

1/27/51

PREFACE

I wish to thank geologists and others interested in petroleum for the kind reception which they accorded the first edition of "Geology of Petroleum." The development of oil fields moves so rapidly that the volume was somewhat out of date before it came from the press, but nevertheless I hope that it has served a useful purpose. In the preparation of the second edition all chapters of the book have been rewritten and reset, and the book is greatly enlarged. About half of the illustrations have been discarded and some 350 maps, cross sections, and other illustrations have been added.

As in the first edition the treatment is confined strictly to the geology of petroleum, natural gas, and associated materials. Nothing is included on geophysical prospecting. The book is intended to serve primarily as a textbook and secondarily as a brief compendium or manual relating to the geology and deposits of oil-bearing areas. Essentially all of the world's oil fields are briefly treated, with references to the important literature.

Because the book is designed as a manual as well as a textbook, certain small fields are included which might otherwise have been omitted. Some pages, particularly on the Mid-Continent and Rocky Mountain fields, will make rather dreary reading for the general student of the subject. The material is arranged, however, so that certain detailed descriptions may be omitted in classroom work without much loss and the larger fields may be emphasized.

In the ten years that have passed since the publication of the first edition of "Geology of Petroleum," great progress has been made in the use of geology in the discovery and development of oil and gas deposits. This progress was made largely as a result of careful and wise organization and use of data gathered by surface and subsurface work over wide areas by the geologists of operating companies. Not only has this work resulted in the discovery of numerous oil fields, but it has led to a much more nearly accurate interpretation of the geologic history of the world. The increasingly scientific methods used by the petroleum geologists are bringing to the science of geology an abundance of stratigraphic and structural data. This particularly is true of sub-

v

15735

surface studies which are revealing conceptions of geology unsuspected from earlier work confined to surface exposures.

Great reserves of oil have been developed. This has resulted from (1) a better use of geologic data, (2) the use of better drilling machinery and of improved cutting tools and, especially, the development of heavier and better rotary systems which make it possible to drill deeper, and (3) economic conditions favorable to the profitable search for new oil fields.

Commercially the oil situation has changed; a few years ago economists feared that the oil supplies of the United States would be seriously depleted in only a score or two score of years. The industry is now struggling with oversupply brought on by the discovery of some of the largest oil fields ever found in the United States; by greatly increased gasoline yields resulting from continued improvement in refining technology; and by the temporary yet widespread general economic depression. More is heard today of overproduction than of conservation. To one looking even a short time ahead, however, there seems to be more need of conservation and a wise use of reserves than ever before. Many of the greatest fields in the Mid-Continent region are developed in the lowest beds that are known to contain oil. Drilling within the past ten years has developed vast reserves in these deep beds, but the drill has encountered and often drilled through the lowest or oldest beds that contain oil anywhere in the world. No geologic work, however skillful, and no improvement in drilling methods, however revolutionary, will make it possible to develop oil below the beds that are now producing oil in many of the greatest fields in Oklahoma, Kansas, and Texas. New fields may be developed on other structures, but the future production of these deep fields can come only from the deposits that are now known. A list of the fields that have been fully developed or explored and in which the deepest possible reservoir rocks have been penetrated is an impressive exhibition. Although new fields are being developed, the production in many of the greatest fields is trending downward away from the peak. Meanwhile, the use of oil products, stimulated by very low prices, is increasing. Even admitting further improvement in technology, it is a rational conclusion that a few decades will see a serious shortage of oil, especially in North America where development and exhaustion have gone ahead more rapidly than in other continents.

I have endeavored suitably to acknowledge by footnote references the chief sources of information. I wish to thank particularly Mr. A. I. Levorsen, who read critically the section on the Mid-Continent field;

Mr. Gail F. Moulton, who read the section on Illinois and Indiana; and Mr. W. B. Wilson, who read portions of the chapters on the general subject. Maps and a section of Venezuela fields were supplied by Mr. H. J. Wasson. Data on the Oklahoma City field were supplied by Messrs. Hubert E. Bale, J. B. Umpleby, and Charles Taylor. I wish also to thank for many courtesies Messrs. Frank R. Clark, L. L. Foley, John H. Nelimark, and J. M. Brown; and in connection with the preparation of drawings Messrs. Henry R. Norman, Lloyd F. Kernkamp, and W. W. Wetzel.

W. H. EMMONS.

MINNEAPOLIS, MINN.,
March, 1931.

CONTENTS

CONTENTS

CHAPTER XVI

CHAPTER XVII

CHAPTER XVIII

CHAPTER XIX

CHAPTER XX

CHAPTER XXI

CHAPTER XXII

GEOLOGY OF PETROLEUM

CHAPTER I

INTRODUCTION

GENERAL OCCURRENCE OF PETROLEUM

Petroleum, or rock oil, is an inflammable mixture of oily hydrocarbons that exudes from the earth or is pumped up and is used extensively for generating heat, light, and power and for lubricating machinery.

Asphaltum is a solid bitumen, and maltha a semifluid bitumen; both are residues formed by the partial evaporation or inspissation of petroleum.

Natural gas, or rock gas, is an aeriform mixture that is found at or beneath the surface of the earth and is used as an illuminant, for fuel, for making carbon black (soot), and for generating power. Natural gas is commonly associated with petroleum.

Petroleum and natural gas are formed by the decomposition of plant and animal remains that have been buried with sedimentary beds. They are almost never found in commercial quantities in igneous rocks, in metamorphosed rocks, or in fresh-water sediments not associated with marine strata. They generally originate in muds, clays, shales, marls, or limestones. Petroleum and natural gas cannot ordinarily accumulate in shales in large amounts, because in such rocks adequate openings are generally not available. As a rule they accumulate in sands or sandstones associated with clays or shales, or in porous limestones and dolomites. In age the petroleum-bearing strata range from Ordovician to Recent.

Salt water is generally associated with petroleum and is believed to be sea water that filled the pores of the sands when they were laid down in the sea. Waters from oil-bearing strata differ from sea water in concentration and in composition, but there are reasons for supposing that changes have taken place since the original sea water was stored in the rocks. Not all oil-bearing strata are saturated with salt water; some contain very little water, and in certain fields the oil is floated on water that contains very little salt.

In folded rocks saturated with petroleum, natural gas, and water, the oil is generally found above the water, and the gas is found above the oil occupying the top of an anticline. The rearrangement is due to gravity.

1

Most strata that contain petroleum are folded. At some places they are only gently folded; in others they are thrown into sharp folds, the beds dipping 20 to 30 degrees or more. In consolidated rocks, such as shales, sandstones, and limestones, which have been intensely deformed by faulting and close folding, oil is generally not found in large amounts. In unconsolidated series of rocks, such as clays, marls, and sands, large accumulations are known in areas of highly complicated structures. In some regions unconsolidated oil-bearing rocks have been intensely faulted and overturned, yet they retain large accumulations of petroleum.

Not all reservoirs are on anticlines. Any body of porous rock sealed above in any manner may, under certain conditions, supply a reservoir for the accumulation of either petroleum or natural gas. Many of the oil fields are on monoclines, on which are developed secondary folds, such as anticlines, synclines, domes, and structural terraces. In rocks that are highly saturated with oil and water, the oil gathers in domes, if any are available, but accumulation takes place also in plunging anticlines where these are sealed up the dip of the axis by impervious material.

Oil accumulates also in reservoirs that are formed by monoclines sealed up dip: by the sand lensing out or becoming impervious; by hardening of the oil to form a tar plug; by faults; by intrusions; or by later beds that lie unconformably on the older ones.

If the porous strata in areas of folded structures are not saturated with oil and water, the oil will descend on the folds until it occupies the flanks of synclines, and, if no water is present, it tends to move to the bottoms of synclines.

Although many valuable oil pools have accumulated on monoclines and, in the absence of much water, near the axes of synclines, yet, in general, the outstanding structural feature of oil- and gas-producing rocks is the anticline. Briefly stated, the conditions that are necessary for the formation of a considerable accumulation of oil, are:

1. A rock with openings to serve as a reservoir.
2. An impermeable cover to prevent escape of oil.
3. Strata containing organic matter to provide sources of oil.
4. A suitable elevated structure to facilitate separation of oil, water, and gas.

USES

In its crude state petroleum is used extensively for fuel. It has a high evaporating power per unit of weight and is in demand for use under locomotive and marine boilers. The heavy oils are used for fuel more generally than the lighter oils, because, as a rule, the heavy oils will not yield such valuable products. Crude oils are used also in the Diesel internal combustion engine. Heavy crude oils are used also for road dressing and for making building paper and roofing.

In refining petroleum, it is broken up by a process of distillation into many products, including petroleum ether, gasoline, naphtha, kerosene, lubricating oils, vaseline, paraffin wax, and petroleum coke. Each of these materials has a variety of uses. Ether is used as a cooling agent and for priming internal-combustion engines in cold weather. Gasoline is used as fuel in internal-combustion engines, for cleaning cloth and other substances, and as a solvent of oil and grease. Naphtha is used for approximately the same purposes and much commercial gasoline is a mixture of gasoline and naphtha. Kerosene is used principally for illumination and as a fuel for tractors. Lubricating oils are the heavy viscous products obtained by refining petroleum. They are used for lubricating machinery and, when highly refined, for medicinal purposes, especially as laxatives. Paraffin wax is used for making candles, for sealing preserved fruits and vegetables, and as a preservative. It is used also for medicinal purposes, especially in the treatment of burns. Petroleum coke is used in metallurgic processes, as a fuel, and for making carbons for batteries and arc lights.

Many petroleum refineries do not produce all the products mentioned. Some "topping plants" distill off the lighter products, such as may be used as fuel for internal-combustion engines, and sell the heavier residues for fuel oil or for road dressing.

Asphalt is formed in nature by the drying up of petroleum, chiefly where it exudes at the surface. It is used for making pavements, roofings, and other building materials. Some oils, on refining, yield an artificial asphalt that is much like the natural product and is used for similar purposes.

The demand for gasoline is greater than the amount that would be obtained by "straight" distillation of the petroleum produced, but the demand for the heavy oils that would remain from the distillation of gasoline is far less than the amount that would be available. By "cracking" crude oil, a much larger amount of gasoline is obtained from the crude oil. In cracking the oil it is heated to a high temperature in a still, under considerable pressure. The large molecules of the hydrocarbons which boil only at high temperatures are cracked or broken down into smaller molecules that vaporize at low temperatures. This fluid is run through stills and the gasoline is driven off. Petroleum coke is formed by the cracking process and also considerable gas remains in the gaseous state after cooling, but much more gasoline is produced than by ordinary distillation.

In the process of hydrogenation of oil, the crude oil is heated to high temperatures under pressure, and hydrogen is introduced in the presence of a catalyst. There is a rearrangement of the carbon and hydrogen of the heavy hydrocarbon molecules and also an addition of hydrogen to form smaller molecules with lower boiling points. This method of treatment is more expensive than the cracking process but yields much more gasoline.

GEOGRAPHIC DISTRIBUTION OF PETROLEUM

The table[1] on page 6 shows the production of various oil-producing countries of the world (Figs. 1, 2). The Western Hemisphere has pro-

Fig. 1.—Map showing main oil fields of Western Hemisphere.

duced 77 per cent and the Eastern Hemisphere 23 per cent of the world's oil. North America has produced 74.8 per cent and South America 2.2 per cent. Europe has produced 17.2 per cent, Asia 5.7 per cent, and Africa 0.1 per cent. The Northern Hemisphere has produced about 97 per cent of the world's oil. The production of the United States in 1927 was 71.5 per cent of that of the world. In 1928 it was estimated to

[1] REDFIELD, A. H.. Federal Oil Conservation Board *Rept.* 3, Appendix C, p. 53, 1929.

be 68.2 per cent. With the great developments now carried on in Venezuela, Colombia, Persia, Iraq, and in the East Indies the percentage of production of the United States will probably decline.

GEOLOGIC DISTRIBUTION OF PETROLEUM

Kinds of Strata Containing Oil and Gas.—The world's petroleum comes from sedimentary beds, practically all of it from sands, sandstones, conglomerates, porous limestones, and dolomites. The deposits the world over are held in by coverings of shale, clay, or marl. The producing beds almost without exception are marine strata or strata of fresh-water

FIG. 2.—Map showing main oil fields of Eastern Hemisphere.

origin that are closely associated with marine strata. The organic material from which the oil is derived finds lodgment in clays and marls when they are deposited, and the oil accumulates in sands and other porous rocks that are associated with the clays and marls. The bodies of strata most common in oil fields are those in which thick shales, clays, or marls alternate with relatively thin sands.

Geologic Age of Strata Producing Oil.—Oil is found in strata ranging from Ordovician to Pleistocene. On following tables the geologic distribution of the oil in the chief producing countries is shown. The greatest range of distribution is that shown by North America where oil occurs in large amounts in Ordovician and also in Late Tertiary beds and in most of the systems between them. In western Canada the chief deposits of oil are in Mississippian limestone. In Mexico, Cretaceous and Comanchean limestone are most productive. Practically all of the oil produced in northern South America is from Tertiary rocks. At Comodoro Rivadavia, Argentina, large amounts of oil come from the Cretaceous beds and, in western Bolivia and Argentina, Paleozoic rocks have produced some oil. The oil of Europe has come chiefly from Tertiary strata, except the oil of Germany which is derived almost entirely from Mesozoic rocks, the small production of England which is derived from Mississippian rocks, and a small part of the Galician oil which is from Cretaceous rocks. The bulk of the European oil is from Pliocene beds which contain the great deposits of the Baku field, Russia. In the great plains of Russia, west of the Ural Mountains, asphaltic deposits are abundant and there are probably large deposits of oil in Paleozoic strata, but thus far relatively small amounts of oil have been discovered.

WORLD'S PRODUCTION OF PETROLEUM IN 1926 AND 1927, AND FROM 1857 TO 1927[1]

,Country	1926		1927		1857 to 1927	
	Barrels	Per cent	Barrels	Per cent	Barrels	Per cent
United States.............	770,874,000	70.3	901,129,000	71.5	10,341,675,000	65.4
Russia[2]..................	64,311,000	5.9	77,018,000	6.1	2,246,960,000	14.2
Venezuela.................	36,911,000	3.4	63,134,000	5.0	137,944,000	0.9
Mexico...................	90,421,000	8.2	64,121,000	5.1	1,465,048,000	9.3
Persia....................	35,842,000	3.3	39,688,000	3.1	258,090,000	1.6
Roumania.................	23,314,000	2.1	26,368,000	2.1	274,240,000	1.7
Netherlands East Indies.....	21,243,000	1.9	25,967,000	2.1	362,662,000	2.3
Colombia.................	6,444,000	0.6	15,002,000	1.2	23,645,000	0.2
Peru.....................	10,519,000	1.0	10,135,000	0.8	82,794,000	0.5
Argentina.................	7,851,000	0.7	8,630,000	0.7	43,208,000	0.3
British India.............	8,011,000	0.7	7,878,000	0.6	181,709,000	1.2
Poland...................	5,844,000	0.5	5,342,000	0.4	207,779,000	1.3
Trinidad..................	5,278,000	0.5	5,712,000	0.5	38,641,000	0.3
British Borneo (Sarawak)...	4,942,000	0.4	4,943,000	0.4	30,647,000	0.2
Japan and Taiwan..........	1,785,000	0.2	1,700,000	0.1	54,894,000	0.3
Egypt....................	1,188,000	0.1	1,267,000	0.1	15,439,000	0.1
Germany..................	653,000		663,000		18,596,000	
France...................	478,000		504,000		4,370,000	
Canada...................	364,000		477,000		26,734,000	
Ecuador..................	214,000	0.2	537,000	0.2	1,455,000	0.2
Sakhalin..................	181,000		440,000		806,000	
Czechoslovakia............	150,000		149,000		938,000	
Italy.....................	48,000		54,000		1,358,000	
Others...................	28,000		225,000		954,000	
Total.................	1,096,894,000	100.0	1,261,083,000	100.0	15,820,586,000	100.0

[1] Compiled by L. M. Jones, U. S. Bur. Mines.
[2] Not including Sakhalin, which is shown separately.

In the Emba field, north of the Caspian Sea, large amounts of oil are found in Jurassic strata. The oil from the other important Asiatic fields is from Tertiary rocks, except in the Ferghana region where some of the oil is said to be derived from Cretaceous beds. Two small fields in China produce oil from pre-Tertiary beds.

AGE OF BEDS PRODUCING OIL IN UNITED STATES

Age	Appalachian	Kentucky	Ohio	Indiana	Illinois	Michigan	Kansas	Oklahoma	Texas	New Mexico	Louisiana and Arkansas	Rocky Mountains	San Joaquin, Calif.	Santa Maria, Calif.	Ventura, Santa Clara	Los Angeles basin
Pleistocene																
Pliocene									+		+		+	+	+	+
Miocene									+		+		+	+	+	+
Oligocene									+		+	+			+	
Eocene									+		+	+	+		+	
Cretaceous									+	+	+	+	+			
Comanchean								+	+		+	+				
Jurassic												+				
Triassic												+				
Permian								+	+	+		+				
Pennsylvanian	+	+	+	+	+		+	+	+			+				
Mississippian	+	+	+	+	+	+	+	+				+				
Devonian	+	+	+	+	+	+		+								
Silurian		+	+		+			+								
Ordovician		+	+	+	+		+	+	+							

Age of Beds Producing Oil in Part of Western Hemisphere

Age	Alaska	Ontario	Western Canada	Tampico, Mexico	Tuxpam	Tehuantepec	Barbados	Trinidad	Venezuela	Colombia Coast	Magdalena Valley	Ecuador	Peru	Bolivia	Argentina
Pleistocene															
Pliocene															
Miocene	+?					+		+	+	+?	+?		+		+
Oligocene	+				+	+		+	+	+?	?	+	+		
Eocene					+?		+	+?	+	+?	+		+		
Cretaceous			+	+	+?			?							+
Comanchean			+	+	+										
Jurassic	+		+											?	+
Triassic															
Permian															
Pennsylvanian														+?	
Mississippian			+												
Devonian		+	+											+?	+?
Silurian		+													
Ordovician		+													

Age of Beds Producing Oil in Part of Eastern Hemisphere

Age	England	Alsace, France	Hanover, Germany	Czechoslovakia	Galician Poland	Roumania	Italy	Baku, Russia	Grozny, Russia	Maikop, Russia	Emba, Russia	Egypt	Algeria
Pleistocene													
Pliocene						+	+	+					
Miocene				+	+	+	+	+	+	+		+	+
Oligocene		+			+	+				+			
Eocene					+	+	+					+	+?
Cretaceous			+		+		+?					+	
Comanchean			+										
Jurassic			+								+		
Triassic			+										
Permian													
Pennsylvanian	+												
Mississippian	+												

Age	Cheleken Island	Naphtha Dagh	Ferghana	Irak	Persia	Punjab	Assam	Burma	Sumatra	Java	Borneo	Japan	Sakhalin	New Zealand
Pleistocene														
Pliocene									+		+		+	+
Miocene	+?	+?		+	+	+	+	+	+	+	+	+		
Oligocene				+	+		+	+			+?			
Eocene			+			+?		+			?			
Cretaceous			+											

CHAPTER II

SURFACE INDICATIONS OF PETROLEUM AND MATERIALS ASSOCIATED WITH IT

Indications of oil deposits include oil and the materials that have been formed by the drying of oil—asphaltum, gilsonite, paraffins, maltha, etc.—as well as the common associates of oil, such as bituminous rock, gas, salt water, and in certain regions sulphur and its compounds and acid waters. Mud volcanoes and in some regions mud dikes, indicating the existence of mud volcanoes that have been eroded, are evidence of gas. In places "paraffin dirt" has been found above deposits of oil or gas. Any indication of oil or gas is to be interpreted in connection with its geologic setting, namely, the rock column, the structure, and the degree of metamorphism shown in associated beds that may be present.

Distribution.—Oil springs or asphaltites are found in many oil fields and are generally regarded as favorable indications. The springs may

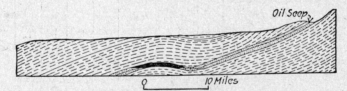

Fig. 3.—Sketch showing oil seeps at outcrop of petroliferous stratum and an accumulation of oil and gas (black) many miles away down the dip from the outcrop.

exude at outcrops of the oil sands or limestones in which the oil is stored (Fig. 3), or they may exude from fault fissures, joints, or other conduits in beds that cover the oil-bearing stratum. Where oil exudes from the oil-bearing stratum, the springs merely indicate that the stratum is

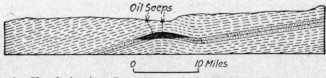

Fig. 4.—Sketch showing oil seeps at crest of fold above oil accumulation.

petroliferous and that the deposits are being scattered. Petroleum deposits commonly are not situated below the points of issue, but in some regions they are down the dip many miles away, at places where the structure is favorable for retaining oil. In some regions these evidences

10

of oil are found at the crests or on the flanks of anticlines, where the oil has seeped through the cover of the reservoir (Fig. 4). Where the hydrocarbons escape through fissures or joint planes, valuable deposits may occur not far away or even directly below their places of issue.

Oil Seeps.—Oil seeps are evidences that oil exists in the region in which they are found, though in many regions that contain oil seeps considerable drilling has not disclosed important supplies—for example, the fields on the northwest coast of Newfoundland, on Gaspe Peninsula, Quebec, and near Albert, New Brunswick. Most of the large oil-producing regions of the world, however, contain oil seeps at one place or another, although numerous individual pools in these regions do not lie below the seeps. Many oil seeps are associated with springs of water. In some there is merely a slight iridescent film or "rainbow" of oil above the water. Such a film resembles somewhat the film of iron oxide that covers some pools of water, and iron oxide films have been mistaken for oil films. The iron oxide film differs from the oil film, however, in that it is brittle and will break if the water is agitated, whereas the oil film will not. In many oil springs the oil on the water forms a considerable layer. At some places it is collected by laying a blanket on the pool. The blanket absorbs the oil and is wrung out and the oil recovered. In other springs the oil is skimmed off.

When the amount of oil from a well or pool is very small, it is sometimes difficult to ascertain whether or not a steady flow of oil exists. Pools of water contaminated with oil that has been used to lubricate machinery or for other purposes have been mistaken for oil springs. The petroleum of springs is generally heavy, because it has suffered evaporation or oxidation or both, and that of some springs resembles lubricating oil in appearance, but often tests or analyses will show whether the oil of a spring is in the natural state or whether it is a product of refining.

Solid Bitumens.—Asphaltite is a general term applied to solid asphaltic hydrocarbons. Between oil and asphalt there are all stages, grading from the liquid to the solid state. Many of the solid hydrocarbons have been described and named as distinct species. These include gilsonite, uintaite, elaterite, wurtzilite, albertite, grahamite, and many others. They vary greatly in composition; most of them are mixtures of hydrocarbons. Ozokerite is largely paraffin and is an important source of that material.

Asphalts, as already stated, are formed by the inspissation or drying out of petroleum. They may be regarded as the residual products of natural distillation in which the more volatile fluids are generally scattered. The process is commonly attended by the oxidation of certain constituents, and the oil becomes less readily inflammable.

Bituminous Rocks.—Sandstones and limestones at many places are filled with dried or partly dried petroleum. There are all gradations between impure asphalts and bituminous sandstones. The bituminous material in some beds is formed from petroleum that has risen in springs. An example is that of the "gum beds" of Oil Spring, Ontario. In others the bituminous material is that which has remained in the beds after they have been drained of oil.

Many petroliferous strata contain at their outcrops a little residual bituminous matter that is not evident on inspection of the outcrop, although the rock if broken under water may yield an iridescent film of oil.

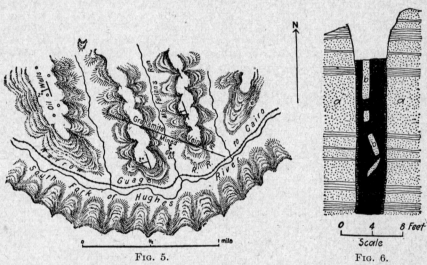

FIG. 5.   FIG. 6.

FIG. 5.—Sketch showing grahamite vein in Ritchie County, West Virginia. (*After Eldridge.*)

FIG. 6.—Sketch of gilsonite dike, Duchesne Mine, Uinta Basin, Utah. The gilsonite is black; *a*, sandstone walls of dike; *b*, fragments of sandstone in dike. (*After Eldridge.*)

Bituminous Dikes.—Bituminous dikes (Figs. 5, 6) are formed where petroleum enters fissures and becomes hardened before it reaches the surface. The process of hardening is brought about by the loss of the more volatile constituents and by oxidation. Such dikes, during their formation, probably feed gas and oil springs at the surface.

Ozokerite, or mineral wax, is a native bitumen with a paraffin base. It is essentially paraffin. It is found in Galicia, in England, on Cheleken Island in the Caspian Sea, in the Salt Creek region of Wyoming, and in the Uinta basin in Utah. It is supposed to be formed by the drying out of paraffin oil. Considering its origin, its occurrence at depths of nearly 2,000 feet at Boryslaw, Galicia, is noteworthy (Fig. 7).

TEST FOR OIL IN ROCKS

(*After Woodruff*)

1. Select a representative specimen of rock to be tested. It is generally advisable to obtain several samples as large as 1 to 5 pounds each.

2. Break them up, and thoroughly mix the pieces. If the samples consist of sand, mix the sand.

3. Dry the sample on a plate in the sun or over a radiator. Do not dry it over a fire; to do so may drive the oil from the rock or sand.

4. Crush the sample to a powder. Mix the powder. Loose sand does not need to be crushed.

5. Place about a tablespoonful of the sample in a bottle. Pour chloroform or carbon tetrachloride over the sample until it is thoroughly saturated and there is about half a tablespoonful of the liquid above the crushed rock or sand. Cork the bottle, but not too tightly. Shake occasionally for 15 or 20 minutes.

6. Place a white filter paper in a glass funnel over a white dish.

7. Pour the contents of the bottle into the funnel. After the liquid has passed through, place the white dish in a window where the liquid can evaporate.

8. Examine the filter paper. If the rock contains more than a trace of oil, there will be a brown or black ring on the filter paper.

9. After the liquid in the dish has evaporated, examine the remaining substance. It is the petroleum which was in the rock.

Apparatus for Testing

One dinner plate on which to dry specimens.

Some means for crushing rock.

One or more bottles, 4- or 6-ounce size, with corks, in which to treat the rock.

Chloroform or carbon tetrachloride.

One glass funnel 3 or 4 inches in diameter.

Two dozen round filter papers, 6 inches in diameter.

Two or more white dishes.

Gas Seeps.—Gas accompanies the oil that issues at many oil springs. There are also many gas seeps where no oil issues. Because the gas is colorless and some of it odorless, gas seeps are not so easily recognized as oil seeps. Many of them have been recognized where the gas issues as bubbles in pools of water or by explosions of the gas resulting from accidental ignition. Where the gas is under pressure and the seep is in a sand or soft sandy earth, the movements of the sand or clay particles may lead to the discovery of gas. The issue of gas under pressure may build up small mounds, or mud volcanoes on the surface, which are easily recognized. Where heavy lethal gases issue in depressions,

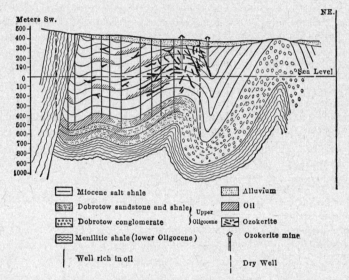

Fig. 7.—Profile through Boryslaw oil field, Galicia, showing ozokerite veins above an anticline. Horizontal and vertical scales are the same. (*After Zuber.*)

animals exposed to them are killed, and the remains mark the places of accumulation.

The gases that issue at the surface of the earth include chlorine, nitrogen, carbon dioxide, carbon monoxide, sulphurous compounds, methane, and other hydrocarbons. Chlorine, nitrogen, and carbon dioxide have little significance as surficial indications of petroleum. They are not inflammable, and they issue in regions where volcanic processes are active or have recently been active, and elsewhere. Carbon monoxide is not ordinarily abundant in gas seeps, although a little may be present associated with other gases. Carbon monoxide and methane are the "fire damp" of coal mines. The hydrocarbon gases are commonly associated with oil and are more significant as indications of oil than carbon dioxide and carbon monoxide. Helium is found in some natural gases.

The most common constituent of natural gases is methane. Methane gas, however, is not all associated with petroleum deposits. It is "marsh gas," which forms in peat bogs or anywhere that vegetation is decaying. The "will-o'-the-wisp" of the marshes and swamps is burning methane. In many fields, however, methane is associated with petroleum. Commonly, the methane contains also small amounts of other gases. In some fields ethane, propane, and butane are associated with methane. These and heavier hydrocarbon gases are generally regarded as evidence that the gas is petroleum gas—that is, that it is associated with oil—and, if the structure of the beds is favorable, their presence warrants drilling for oil at a structurally lower point below the gas reservoir.

The presence of ethane, propane, and butane in gas is generally regarded as a favorable indication of petroleum, because these substances are found in a great many gases that are associated with oil. Nevertheless, their presence is not an infallible indication. One or more of the hydrocarbon gases heavier than methane were found in a sample of natural gas collected in 1917 in a glacial-lake deposit that is covered with lacustrine clay in southern Minnesota. On the other hand, a gas from the Caddo field, Louisiana, showed on analysis no hydrocarbon except methane, although the sand that yielded the gas contains oil in the part of the field where the gas sample was taken.

Natural gas carries gasoline vapors much as air carries water vapor. Gas under great pressure is less likely to carry the gasoline vapors than gas under less pressure. When a boring penetrates a reservoir containing oil and gas under great pressure, the gas immediately expands and moves toward the hole, carrying the oil with it. As there is less resistance to the movement of the gas it moves faster and is exhausted first. When the pressure is high, the dry gases absorbed in the oil are liberated, but as pressure decreases the wet gases liquefied and dissolved in the oil also are released. A dry gas issuing under great pressure is more likely to be associated with oil than a dry gas issuing under low pressure.

Sulphurous gases and sulphur are associated with many petroleums and in smaller proportions with some natural inflammable gases. The sulphur gases include sulphur dioxide and hydrogen sulphide, both of which are easily detected by their odor. The gases accompanying the oil at Spindletop field, near Beaumont, Texas, were poisonous, possibly owing to the presence of sulphur compounds. These gases deposited sulphur on the Spindletop dome, and it was the occurrence of such deposits that led to the drilling of this field in a search for commercial deposits of sulphur.

Sulphur gases are found at the surface of many of the salt-dome deposits of Texas and Louisiana. Because sulphur, hydrogen sulphide, and sulphur dioxide are widely dispersed in nature and occur in places far removed from petroleum deposits, they are generally of uncertain value as indications of oil, although in some areas their presence is regarded as significant.

Paraffin Dirt.—The so-called "paraffin dirt" of the Gulf Coast oil fields[1] has been considered an indication of the presence of oil and gas. The term has been applied to clay soils with a texture which has been described as "curdy" or "rubbery." When moist the material breaks after the fashion of "green" cheese. It is rubbery under compression but does not resemble rubber in tenacity or cohesion. In the field it resembles "art gum." When dry the material ranges from hard clods to a horny mass. The moist material ranges in color from dark brown in the specimens rich in organic matter to grayish in specimens containing more inorganic matter. It has a characteristic "swampy" or "mucky" odor when wet. According to Brokaw, the place of paraffin dirt among the evidences of oil and gas rests on the possibility that it may indicate gas-saturated soils in which gas inhibits oxidation, and, obviously, such soils are present in the vicinity of gas seeps. It does not follow that every gas seep is accompanied by paraffin dirt, nor is paraffin dirt an infallible sign of a gas seep. Most paraffin dirt probably contains no paraffin.

Mud Volcanoes.—Gas issuing at the surface may carry with it particles of sand and clay which are deposited at the place of issue. Continuation of the process will build up a "pimple," mound, or cone. The process goes on generally in unconsolidated rocks, especially in the presence of water. If the wet clay or mud seals over the place of issue, gas accumulates under pressure, and, when the pressure is sufficient, it blows off the seal with violence, imitating on a small scale the eruption of a volcano. In arid countries these mounds are built to considerable heights. The Bog-Boga mud volcano, in the principal oil district of the Baku region, Russia, is more than 100 feet above the plateau on which it stands. In many Tertiary oil fields where the rocks are unconsolidated mud volcanoes are numerous.

Mud Dikes.—Mud dikes that cut across the strata are found in some oil fields. They are supposed to have filled the vents through which gas issued to form gas seeps or mud volcanoes. Such dikes are found in Burma oil fields. What are undoubtedly mud dikes occur in the Huron shales of the gas field around Cleveland, Ohio. Dikes are formed also by clay squeezed into fissures.

Oil Shales.—As oil shales are commonly said to be the original sources of petroleum and gas, their presence is usually regarded as a favorable indication. There are many regions, however, in which oil shale is present and oil deposits seem to be wanting.

Salt-water Seeps.—Salt water is associated with petroleum in practically every large oil-producing region in the world. Salt seeps

---

[1] BROKAW, A. D., An Interpretation of the So-called Paraffin Dirt of the Gulf Coast Oil Fields, Am. Inst. Min. Eng. *Bull.* 136, pp. 947–950, 1918.

are found in many oil fields. Many salt licks, or places where animals congregate to lick the salt from the earth or rocks, are formed of drying brine. Where the brine is associated with oil, the animals' feet become oil soaked, and it is said that oil seeps have been discovered by men observing oil on the feet of pigs that had returned from their range. Large quantities of bones are found in some such places. These are evidently the remains of animals that drank at springs which possibly were salty. Brine and rock salt are among the most widely distributed materials and occur at many places far removed from oil fields. The presence of salt water may suggest the possibility of petroliferous strata, but it has no certain significance, as many oil pools have been found where no salt springs issue and many salt springs issue at places remote from oil fields.

Sulphur and Sulphur Compounds.—Sulphur or sulphur compounds are found in the petroleum of many fields and in the salt water that is associated with the petroleum. Sulphurous gases have been mentioned. Some of them deposit native sulphur and on oxidation yield sulphuric acid. In the Spindletop oil field of the Gulf Coast region, sulphur was found in the soil, and the discovery well was drilled as an exploration for sulphur. At Sour Lake, also in the Gulf Coast field, acid waters were among the surface indications that led to drilling. Sulphur and acid waters, like salt and salt water, are widely distributed in the earth. It is only in certain surroundings that they are of interest as indications that suggest the possible presence of petroleum.

CHAPTER III

OPENINGS IN ROCKS, RESERVOIR ROCKS, AND COVERING STRATA

SIZES OF OPENINGS

Openings may be classified with respect to their size and with respect to their origin. With respect to size, they may be placed in three groups—supercapillary, capillary, and subcapillary.

Supercapillary openings are those in which water obeys the ordinary laws of hydrostatics. For water at ordinary temperatures, tubes with holes more than 0.508 millimeter in diameter or sheet openings more than 0.254 millimeter wide are supercapillary.

Capillary openings are tubes with holes less than 0.508 and greater than 0.0002 millimeter in diameter, or sheet openings between 0.254 and 0.0001 millimeter wide. In these water does not obey the ordinary laws of hydrostatics but is affected by capillary attraction. Water will not circulate so freely in such openings because of the greater friction along the walls. Hot water may move through such openings more readily than cold, however, and under pressure either hot or cold solutions may be forced through capillary openings.[1]

Subcapillary openings include tubes with holes less than 0.0002 millimeter in diameter and sheet openings less than 0.0001 millimeter wide. In these the attraction of the molecules of the solid extends across the open space. Water may enter such openings, but it tends to remain as if fixed to the walls, prohibiting further entrance of solutions. Circulation of solutions at ordinary temperatures through such openings is therefore very slow.

If two rocks have equal amounts of pore space—supercapillary in one and subcapillary in the other—the one with the larger openings will afford more favorable conditions for the movement of fluids. Muds, clays, shales, and rock powders, which contain exceedingly minute openings, are the great natural barriers to circulation, although, under sufficient pressure, fluids are forced through them.

ORIGIN OF OPENINGS

With respect to their origin, openings in rocks are classified as follows:

Primary Openings:

    Intergranular spaces.
    Bedding planes.

[1] VAN HISE, C. R., U.S.G.S. Mon. 47, p. 135, 1904. The figures given above are only approximations. See MEINZER, O. E., U.S.G.S. Water Supply Paper 494, p. 18, 1923.

Vesicular spaces.
Submicroscopic spaces.

Secondary Openings:

Openings formed by solution.
Shrinkage cracks due to dehydration, cooling, etc.
Openings due to force of crystallization.
Openings due to the thrust of solutions.
Openings due to the greater earth stresses.

PRIMARY OPENINGS

Intergranular Spaces in Sedimentary Rocks.—The pore spaces in sedimentary rocks constitute a percentage of the volume of the rock ranging from less than 1 up to 25 or even more. According to Buckley,[1] the Dunnville sandstone of Wisconsin has a pore space of 28.28 per cent. Many sandstones have 20 per cent or more. As shown by Slichter,[2] the size of the grains does not determine the amount of pore space; a fine-grained rock may be as porous as a coarse conglomerate. Figure 8 shows a pile of balls arranged in the most compact manner possible; Fig. 9 shows the space between the balls of Fig. 8. It is obvious that if these balls were increased or decreased in size the changes would affect similarly the spaces between them. The amount of space depends principally upon the assortment of grains and the system of packing. If small grains fill in the spaces between large grains, the porosity is obviously diminished. The fact that very fine material will not permit the free movement of fluids is not due to the absence of openings but to the small size of the openings. In rocks with subcapillary openings fluids tend to remain fixed to the rock particles. The pore spaces of the coarsely granular rocks, such as sandstone, are more likely to serve as reservoirs for fluids than those in fine-grained rocks, such as shales. Clay particles are small, and, because many are flat, they pack closely. Moreover, colloidal matter in clay and shale tends to decrease permeability. Under sufficient pressure, however, fluids will be driven through even clays and shales.

Bedding Planes.—Bedding planes are due to the assortment or sizing of material during transportation and deposition. On account of the assortment of grains, there is also a different arrangement of the pore spaces in the different beds.[3] Consequently, even in a nearly homogeneous rock, the different beds commonly have different degrees of permeability. Fluids moving along the beds may follow the most

[1] BUCKLEY, E. R., Building and Ornamental Stones of Wisconsin, Wis. Geol. and Nat. Hist. Survey *Bull.* 4, pp. 225, 403, 1898.

[2] SLICHTER, C. S., Theoretical Investigation of the Motion of Ground Waters, U. S. Geol. Survey *Nineteenth Ann. Rept.*, pt. 2, p. 305, 1899.

[3] KING, F. H., Principles and Conditions of the Movements of Ground Water, U. S. Geol. Survey *Nineteenth Ann. Rept.*, pt. 2, p. 135, 1899.

Fig. 8.—Spheres packed in the most compact manner possible.   The face angles are 60 and 120 degrees.   (*After Slichter.*)

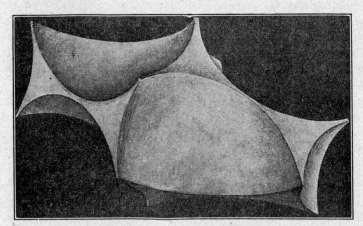

Fig. 9.—Cast showing pore space in a mass of spheres packed in the most compact manner possible.   (*After Slichter.*)

permeable layer, but fluids moving across them must traverse also the most impermeable layers. Fluids will therefore pass along beds more readily than across them.

Vesicular Spaces.—Magmas generally contain included fluids. When the magmas are erupted and flow out upon the surface, pressure is relieved and the fluids expand and escape as gases. If they expand when the lavas are in a sticky or viscous condition and near the point of solidification, the openings due to expansion are preserved. The openings due to expanded gases in lavas, unlike the pores in sandstone, are generally not connected and therefore do not offer continuous passages to fluids.

Submicroscopic Spaces.—The denser rocks, which appear solid, contain, nevertheless, small amounts of pore space. A granite, which under the microscope has no visible openings, will absorb a small amount of water in the cold. Shales contain numerous openings, but these do not permit the ready passage of fluids, because they are largely subcapillary. Under pressure, however, fluids are forced into or through subcapillary openings.

SECONDARY OPENINGS

Openings Formed by Solution.—In soluble rocks, like limestones and dolomites, large openings may be formed by solution and by removal of rock matter. Solution usually proceeds by enlarging smaller openings, such as joints, bedding planes, or fissures. These openings may become the principal drainage channels of the country, and the solution cavities along them may be developed on an enormous scale. As a rule solution is more active above the water level, but large cavities have been found considerably below the present water level. Where an ancient drainage surface is buried by later strata, solution cavities may be found at great depths.

Openings Due to Shrinkage.—Shrinkage may be caused by dolomitization, dehydration, cooling, and other processes. If a fairly pure limestone is changed to dolomite without addition of carbon dioxide, a shrinkage of about 12 per cent takes place. The porosity of some dolomites is assumed to be due to shrinkage. Cracks due to shrinkage in drying are common. Cooling cracks are formed soon after the solidification of igneous rocks, before they have cooled to the temperatures of the surrounding rocks.

Openings Due to the Force of Crystallization.—The force which crystallizing matter exerts on the containing walls has been assumed to be sufficient to push the walls apart.[1] If this force so operates, it would be supposed that a solution, having once gained entrance to a fissure,

[1] BECKER, G. F., and A. L. DAY, The Linear Force of Growing Crystals, Wash Acad. Sci. *Proc.*, vol. 7, pp. 282–288, 1905.

however narrow, could enlarge the fissure while it was being filled. This process does not produce open spaces but is assumed to widen those already formed. Becker and Day performed experiments to ascertain the strength of such a force and found it to be of the same order as the crushing strength of crystals. Harris[1] appealed to the force of crystallization to account for the salt domes of the Gulf Coast region, but, as these domes were developed, it became evident that the salt cores of the domes had been thrust upward by tectonic forces during folding of the regions containing them.

Openings Due to Greater Stresses.—The openings that are due to the greater stresses attending the deformation of the earth are the seats of the larger number of the world's metalliferous deposits. Such openings, however, are less significant in connection with the origin of the bitumens. Many dikes of ozokerite, gilsonite, and other bitumens have formed by the drying out of petroleum in great fractures. Few metalliferous veins filling openings in rocks are longer or wider than the great gilsonite dikes of the Uinta basin, Utah. In some regions that yield petroleum, fissures and zones of fracturing have served as passages between the strata in which the petroleum and gas originated and the strata in which they accumulated. In a few regions the fissures in rocks serve as the petroleum and gas reservoirs.

RESERVOIR ROCKS

General Character.—The reservoirs that contain oil and gas are the pore spaces in sands, sandstones, and sandy marls and the pores, solution cavities, and fissures in limestones, dolomites, and other sedimentary rocks. Oil is found in fissures in indurated shale and igneous rocks, but such occurrences are comparatively rare.

In the Appalachian geosyncline, including the gas-bearing area in western New York, there are 56 horizons that contain oil and gas. Most of these are sandstones of fine grain with an average porosity[2] of 16 per cent. Four are limestones, including the Trenton, Niagara, Corniferous, and Greenbrier. The limestones are of wide extent and may be traced over large areas. The Clinton, Big Injun, and Berea sands also are extensive, but most of the other sands are more restricted. On the flanks of the Cincinnati arch, in the Lima-Indiana field, the oil is found in the Trenton limestone of Ordovician age, and in Kentucky the oil is found in several limestones of Paleozoic age. In Michigan the chief reservoir rocks are the Dundee and the Traverse limestones and Berea sandstone. In Illinois, western Indiana, and western Kentucky oil

---

[1] HARRIS, G. D., Oil and Gas in Louisiana, with a Brief Summary of Their Occurrence in Adjacent States, U. S. Geol. Survey *Bull.* 429, p. 8, 1910.

[2] VER WIEBE, W. A., Tectonic Classification of Oil Folds in the United States, Am. Assoc. Pet. Geol. *Bull.*, vol. 13, pp. 409–440, 1929.

is found at 22 horizons, several of which are limestone. The most productive portion of the region is in southern Illinois where the oil is found mainly in sandstones and in the McClosky "sand" which is an oolitic limestone. In Kansas and Oklahoma, north of the Arbuckle Mountains, there are present 35 or more oil- and gas-producing horizons. Of these, eight or more are limestones. The main production of southern Oklahoma is from sands.

In north-central Texas much oil is derived from both sandstones and limestones. In the Balcones fault region the main production is from sands, although at Thrall the oil is in a tuff of igneous origin, at Lytton Springs it is in fractured serpentine, and at Luling it is in limestone. In western Texas large amounts of oil are found in limestone. In the Panhandle the oil is derived from limestone and from "granite wash," a residuary material above a granite core. In Louisiana the main production is from sands. In the Gulf Coast region most of the fields produce from sandstones, although valuable deposits are found also in limestones.

In the Rocky Mountains region the oil is derived mainly from sands, but important deposits of oil are found in the Madison limestone in the Kevin-Sunburst field, and in the Embar limestone in many fields in Wyoming. At Florence, Colorado, the oil is found in fractured shale and at Salt Creek, Wyoming, considerable oil is from fractured shales. In California the oil is obtained almost exclusively from sands. These sands are included in clays and shales and differ from the sands of most other fields in the United States in that they are less persistent and can not be correlated over such large areas. In many of the California fields the individual sand members are not correlated even over a single field, but are grouped in sand zones. In certain fields the sand-bearing groups have aggregate thicknesses of 2,000 feet or more. In Casmalia field, Santa Maria district, California, oil is found in fractured shales.

Mineral Composition of Reservoir Rocks.—The sands that form the reservoirs of sandy strata range from fine sands to the pebbles of conglomerate. Few data are available regarding the mineral character of sands as shown by microscopic study. Most petroliferous sands consist mainly of quartz, but, in some, feldspar, mica, and chlorite are present. Pyrite is often abundant. Some petroliferous sands contain fragments of heavy residual minerals such as magnetite, garnet, ilmenite, amphibole, and monozite. In certain sands the quartz grains are "frosted" by attrition which gives the surfaces of the grains the appearance of ground glass.[1] According to Galloway, quartz grains rounded in

[1] SHERZER, W. H., Criteria for the Recognition of the Various Types of Sand Grains, Geol. Soc. Am. *Bull.*, vol. 21, pp. 625–662, 1910.

GALLOWAY, J. J., The Rounding of Grains of Sand by Solution, *Am. Jour. Sci.*, vol. 47, pp. 270–280, 1919.

DAKE, C. L., The Problem of the St. Peter Sandstone, *Bull.* Missouri School Mines and Met., vol. 6, No. 1, pp. 185–186, 1921.

water are pearly, not glassy, like freshly broken quartz, nor "frosted" as are wind-blown sands. The frosted surface is commonly believed to be due to the action of winds at some stage in the formation of the grain.

Many minerals, on altering, yield clay. The fine particles of kaolin and the colloidal matter that is present in many clays tend to seal openings between the original mineral particles Many of the ferromagnesian minerals form clay readily on weathering. These are more abundant in basic rocks than in acidic rocks like granites. Sands derived from basic rocks are generally less porous than sands derived from acidic rocks. Woodruff states that certain sands of Cuba are derived largely from gabbro fragments and that they have altered partly to clay, which fills the pores and limits their capacity. It is noteworthy, however, that fragments of limburgite, a rather basic rock, are found in the reservoir rock of Thrall field, Texas, and that basic igneous rocks, in part tuffs and volcanic sands, constitute part of the reservoir at Furbero, Mexico.

The porous limestones that form reservoirs include dolomites and also limestones that are not high in magnesium. The pore spaces of limestone are believed to be developed largely by solution.

Capacities of Oil Sands.—The amount of petroleum and natural gas a reservoir will hold depends upon its size and its porosity. The porosity of a fractured rock varies greatly because of differences in size and irregular spacing of fractures. Porous sands, on the other hand, are comparatively regular. The most porous sands are those that are made of comparatively uniform grains and free from clay. Cementation by silica, lime carbonate, iron oxide, or other substance will decrease porosity. An experienced driller can generally estimate the porosity of a sand by its "feel." If it is loose and free from cement and clay particles, its porosity is likely to be high. Other tests include touching it with the tongue or blowing through it to ascertain porosity. Chemical tests will reveal any trace of oil. The amount of lime carbonate is easily estimated by treatment with acid.

The porosity of a sand does not depend upon size of grain; a fine sand may have pore space less than, equal to, or greater than a coarse one. Uniformity of grains, shape of grains, and arrangement or system of packing affect porosity. If spheres of uniform size are packed in the closest possible manner (Figs. 8, 9), the pore space between them is 25.95 per cent by volume. If the spheres are of different sizes, the pore space is less, because the small particles fill the spaces between the large ones. If the particles are of irregular or angular shape, the porosity may be greater or less than that of a system of uniform spheres, but if the material is highly angular, with no flat particles, the porosity is likely to be greater. Figure 10 shows porous sands.

A specimen of the Wall Creek sand, which is the principal petroleum-bearing stratum in the Salt Creek field, Wyoming, collected by Wegemann

in the Powder River field just west of Salt Creek, under tests made by
C. E. Van Orstrand, showed a porosity of 25.8 per cent. Tests of the
porosity of the Nacatoch sand, member of the Navarro formation,
Mexia-Groesbeck field, Texas, showed porosity from 16.6 to 34.2 per
cent, and the average was 25.5 per cent. The oil- and gas-bearing
sandstone of Petrolia, Texas, showed a porosity ranging from 18.5 to 27
per cent. Fragments of the third sand at Oil City, Pennsylvania, were

(A) Hoing sand, Colmar field, Illinois.   (B) Producing sand of the Cushing field.

(C) Grains of sand from sandstone shown in B, magnified.

Fig. 10.—Photographs of oil sands. (*From A. W. Lauer, Econ. Geol.*)

tested by Carll, who estimated them to be capable of absorbing 7 to 10
per cent of their bulk without pressure and probably 12.5 per cent under
pressure. Gardner estimated the porosity of the Bartlesville sand of
Oklahoma to be 20 per cent. The porosity of some of the sands of Baku,
Russia, according to Thompson, is 25 per cent or more.

The size of the grains of a sand does not appear to limit its porosity.
In many parts of the Sunset-Midway field, California, according to
Pack, more than 80 per cent of the oil sands are smaller than 200 mesh.
Of five samples of oil sands from Russian fields tested by Thompson,

nearly all of the material passed through a screen measuring 80 meshes to the inch, and all of one sample passed through one measuring 200 meshes to the inch.

Clay particles between sand grains greatly reduce porosity. The small clay particles fill the pores, and some clay is in a jelly-like colloidal state which is relatively impervious.

Sands grade into muds and sandstones into shales. Muds and shales are made up principally of fine sand grains and clay. Very thin sands in thick series of shales are likely to be filled with clay and impervious to oil and water. Sands that were laid down far out from shore lines are commonly less porous than sands deposited near shore.

The estimation of production by utilizing saturation as a factor has been worked out by Washburne.[1] He estimates that the porosity of sand ranges from 0 to 20 per cent and notes that field determinations of surface samples generally show lower porosity than those of buried sands, probably because near the surface calcium carbonate is deposited in some of the openings. In one determination the deep sands showed one-fourth greater porosity than the same sand at the surface. Washburne estimates for two samples 60 and 75 per cent saturation, the volumetric remainder, 40 and 25 per cent, respectively, being assigned to gases and water. The amount of oil extracted is, according to Washburne, 60 to 80 per cent, the higher figure for gas-rich oils in sands pumped to a vacuum. Sands with heavy oils may yield considerably less.

Oil sands are rarely uniformly porous. Porous layers are interbedded with less porous ones. These layers are commonly called "benches." The First Wall Creek sand of Salt Creek, Wyoming, which is about 136 feet thick, consists of a porous bench 80 to 100 feet thick, below which are about 20 feet of relatively impervious strata consisting of either shale or hard calcareous sand. Below the latter is a porous sand 20 feet thick. The Second Wall Creek sand which is from 20 feet to 100 feet thick, includes shale and bentonite, which separate the sand members or benches.

The porosity of porous limestones cannot be estimated, so readily as that of sand because the pores in limestone are more diverse in size and not so regularly spaced. Enlarged sections of the Trenton limestone showing the nature of the pores are illustrated in Fig. 11, after Orton.

Limestone Reservoir Rocks.—The porous limestones that form reservoirs include dolomites and limestones low in magnesium. The Trenton limestone of the Lima-Indiana oil field is dolomitic where it contains oil, and Orton maintained that its porosity is due to dolomitization. It is said that replacement of limestone to form dolomite results in forming about 12 per cent pore space when carbon dioxide remains

[1] WASHBURNE, C. W., Estimation of Oil Reserves, Am. Inst. Min. Eng. *Trans.*, vol. 51, p. 645, 1915.

unchanged in the replacement "molecule by molecule." It is now known, however, that replacement does not take place molecule by molecule but by solution and deposition in openings so small that there is no collapse of the original structures.[1] Phinney, who studied the Lima-Indiana field after Orton, stated that the openings in the limestone are due to loss of substance and not to substitution. Bownocker confirmed Orton's observations and showed that the limestone where oil bearing is dolomitic and that the magnesium content of the limestone decreases downward.

Fig. 11.—Enlarged sections of Trenton limestone showing nature of pores. (*After Orton.*)

So many oil fields have been found in which the limestone is dolomitic that there seemed to be some basis for Orton's theory. Mylius,[2] studying the oil fields of Illinois, and Jillson, those of Kentucky, noted that the numerous limestone reservoir rocks are found at old erosion surfaces. Studies of other oil fields have shown that many limestone reservoirs are below unconformities, and that the most porous parts of the limestone are generally within a few score feet of the old erosion surfaces, just as solution cavities and cave systems today are found mainly within a few score feet of the present erosion surfaces. Solution takes place chiefly in the vadose zone above the ground-water level and, consequently,

[1] Emmons, W. H., "Principles of Economic Geology," pp. 218–223, 1918.
[2] For references to papers see descriptions of the field mentioned.

solution cavities are generally within 300 or 400 feet of the surface or less, except in arid climates and in areas of considerable relief where the level of ground water lies deep. If the beds overlying the limestone were formed under arid conditions, and especially if they were laid down on a hilly topography, the reservoirs in the limestone may be expected to extend several hundred feet below the ancient buried surface.

As already stated, the magnesium content of the Trenton limestone in Ohio decreases with depth. R. K. Richardson showed in a series of analyses that the Asmari limestone, which is the reservoir rock of the Persian oil field, becomes less dolomitic with depth. Weak acid dissolves lime carbonate more readily than magnesium carbonate, and it is probable that earth acids remove $CaCO_3$ from erosion surfaces more readily than $MgCO_3$, thus making the limestone porous and increasing the proportion of $MgCO_3$ in the limestone.

Many fields in which limestone[1] is a reservoir rock have recently been developed. Howard states that probably 95 per cent of the limestones owe their porosity to weathering. In Ohio, Indiana, Michigan, Ontario, Illinois, Kentucky, and Tennessee, practically every limestone reservoir lies within 100 feet of an unconformity. In Kansas oil is found in limestone at and near old buried eroded surfaces in many fields, including Coffeyville, Eldorado, Elbing, Peabody, and Slick. In Oklahoma such fields include Blackwell, Garber, North Braman, Billings and Morrison, Cushing, Healdton and many others.

In north-central Texas some of the oil is won from the Marble Falls limestone which possibly was eroded before burial. In the South Bend field, Young County, the Marble Falls limestone which is not dolomitic yields oil.

In the Yates, McElroy, and Hendricks fields of western Texas, the oil is obtained mainly from the Permian Big Lime and most of the oil comes from horizons near ancient erosion surfaces. In the Luling field, Texas, the main reservoir rock is the Edwards limestone which is porous and dolomitic near an ancient erosion surface.

In the Rocky Mountains fields oil is obtained from the Madison limestone in the Kevin-Sunburst field, Montana, where the limestone has been exposed to weathering probably on an ancient arched low hill that was eroded, buried, and refolded to form the Sweet Grass arch. The Embar limestone which carries oil in many fields in Wyoming is found below an old erosion surface. In the oil fields at Tampico-Tuxpam district, Mexico, much of the oil is found in limestone near a buried erosion surface. Many other examples of limestone reservoirs are mentioned on following pages describing the oil fields.

---

[1] HOWARD, W. V., A Classification of Limestone Reservoirs, Am. Assoc. Pet. Geol. *Bull.*, vol. 12, pp. 1153–1161, 1928.

Residuary Rocks.—Where cherty limestone is weathered, the lime carbonate is removed, leaving a mantle of insoluble chert. These fragments in the Joplin zinc district are called "chat." In some of the oil fields of Kansas and Oklahoma the very open and porous chert breccia forms reservoirs for oil. In many of the fields producing oil from eroded surfaces of limestone, the reservoirs in residual chert above the limestone are of considerable importance.

Fissures.—In a few regions considerable deposits of oil and gas are found in fissures in shales. In Florence, Colorado, the main reservoirs are in fractured shales that are essentially free from sands. In the Salt Creek field, Wyoming, the chief deposits are in sands, but much oil has been derived from fractured shales. In the Casmalia district, Santa Maria region, California, oil is obtained in part from fractured shales, and on the Thirty-five anticline, a subdistrict of Sunset-Midway district, California, the location of the oil appears to be due in part to fracturing.

Reservoirs in Igneous Rocks.—In the Lytton Springs oil field, Texas, in the Totumo field, Venezuela, and in a few other fields, oil is found in fissures in igneous rock.

COVERINGS OF RESERVOIRS

Kinds of Covering Strata.—Nearly all the strata that form petroliferous reservoirs are covered by argillaceous rocks. Paleozoic reservoirs are generally covered by shales; Mesozoic reservoirs by shales, clays, or marls; Cenozoic reservoirs by clays or marls, or, where the strata have become indurated, by shales. Although the shales and marls are almost everywhere the cap rocks of oil fields, there are other rocks which are sufficiently impervious to form cappings. Shaly sandstones, at places, supply coverings, and, commonly, the base of a shale group above an oil-sand group is a sandy shale or shaly sandstone. In the Cabin Creek district, West Virginia, the cap rock is a hard quartzite (Berea). In the Colmar field, Illinois, the Hoing oil sand is capped by limestone. In these and other fields where the cap rock is not shale, the argillaceous rocks are generally present not far above the cap rocks.

In certain fields the covering shales are somewhat indurated and considerable fractures have formed in them. This is true of cap rocks of Boryslaw, Galicia, and Salt Creek field, Wyoming. In these and other fields ozokerite and other bitumens have formed by hardening of the oils and have sealed the fractures.

Thickness of Covering Strata.—The thickness of the covering that is necessary to retain a petroleum deposit depends upon the gas pressure that exists in the deposit. If the covering is a soft pliable rock that will not fracture, it is more effective than an indurated, brittle, or jointed rock. Most of the large petroleum deposits developed are relatively deep.

They are held down by adequate covers of clays or shales that fracture with difficulty and close the fractures that are made in them.   Some oil fields, however, are developed very near the surface.   The Drake well at Titusville, Pennsylvania, encountered oil at a depth of only 69 feet and yielded oil at the rate of 25 barrels daily.   Flowing wells have been

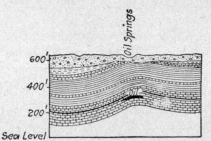

FIG. 12.—Section of Oil Springs dome, Ontario, showing thin cover cap holding in oil under high gas pressure.   (*Based on sketch by Williams.*)

brought in less than 100 feet below the surface.   A well-known shallow oil field is the one in Lambton and Middlesex Counties, southwestern Ontario (Fig. 12).   The producing stratum is the porous limestone, which is covered by about 400 feet of shales, limestone, and glacial drift. The shales are soft and very pliable and are referred to by the drillers as "soapstone."   Flowing wells shooting high in the air and producing from 3,000 to 6,000 barrels a day each were obtained in this field.

CHAPTER IV

SOME PROPERTIES OF PETROLEUM, GAS, AND OIL-FIELD WATERS

PETROLEUM

Color.—Most crude oils are opaque except in very thin bodies. As a rule, the color of thin layers in light passed through them is brown, although some oils are red and others yellow. The light oil obtained in the Calgary field, Alberta, is a pale lemon yellow. A little white oil has been found in the Los Angeles field, California, and considerable quantities of pale straw-colored or "white" oil are recovered in the Surakhani field in the Baku region, Russia. White oils are supposed to result from the natural filtration of petroleum through clay. Sumatra, according to Thompson, yields large quantities of volatile crude oil having the color of port wine.

By reflected light most crude oils have a greenish cast. Some, however, are yellow or black, or of the same color as when seen in transmitted light. The greenish cast of crude oil in reflected light frequently serves to distinguish it from some products of refining, which have a bluish fluorescence.[1]

Odor.—Oils from different fields have different and fairly constant odors. The Pennsylvania oils smell like gasoline. California oils, which have less odor, smell like coal tar. Some East Indian oils smell like oil of cedar. The Lima-Indiana oil has the disagreeable odors of sulphur compounds.

The odors of oils have been used to assist in ascertaining their origin. According to Clapp, in order to determine the characteristic odor of an oil, samples should be prepared in narrow bottles, stoppered, half filled with the oil. The oil is shaken vigorously so as to impart its odor to the air above the oil in the bottle, and if this gives the odor of hydrogen sulphide, a strong solution of caustic potash is added and the oil shaken until the odor of sulphide of hydrogen disappears. Many California oils, shaken with caustic potash solution, will give an odor of pyridine. In a second sample the odor should be noted after similar treatment with dilute sulphuric acid.

Density.—The value of an oil in general is suggested by its weight, or specific gravity. As a rule, light oils will yield larger proportions

---

[1] CLAPP, F. G., "Petroleum and Natural Gas Resources of Canada," Canada Dept. Mines, Mines Branch, vol. 1, p. 47, 1914.

of the more valuable products, such as gasoline and kerosene. The specific gravity of an oil is its weight divided by that of the weight of the same volume of distilled water taken as 1.000. In foreign countries the decimal gravity scale is extensively used, but in the United States the Baumé scale is used. That is an arbitrary scale in which the weight of water is placed at 10°, the degrees increase as the weight of the liquid decreases. Thus, the lighter an oil the higher the number on the Baumé scale. The U. S. Bureau of Standards uses the following formula[1] for converting degrees Baumé into the decimal standard:

$$° \text{Baumé} = \frac{140}{\text{specific gravity of liquid}} - 130$$

The density is taken at 60° F.

The A.P.I. gravity scale adopted by the American Petroleum Institute, the U. S. Bureau of Mines, and the U. S. Bureau of Standards is coming into more general use. The following formulae may be used to change one scale to another:

$$\text{A.P.I. gravity} = 1.01071 \times ° \text{Baumé} - 0.107142$$

$$\text{A.P.I. gravity} = \frac{141.5}{\text{specific gravity at 60° F.}} - 131.5$$

The gravity of oil is taken by a hydrometer at a temperature of 60° F., or if taken at another temperature, it is corrected to correspond to a reading at 60°. The hydrometer is placed in the oil so that it sinks of its own weight. It should not be pushed down and allowed to rise.[2] It should be allowed to remain in the oil about 5 minutes and any foam on top of the oil may be dispersed by adding a drop of gasoline or alcohol.[3]

Viscosity.—The viscosity of oil varies with its specific gravity. It is measured by ascertaining the time it takes a given amount of the oil to flow through a small opening in a viscosimeter. The instruments used are the Engler and Saybolt viscosimeters. A unit often used is the Engler unit, obtained by dividing the time of the outflow of 200 c.c. of the oil by the time of outflow of the same quantity of water at 20° C.

The determinations are of interest, especially to pipe-line companies and all others who transport oil through pipes. Some oils are so thick that it is found practicable to heat them to decrease their viscosity. The lubricating properties of oils are closely related to their viscosity.

Composition.—Petroleums are mixtures of compounds of carbon and hydrogen, generally with impurities consisting of sulphur and nitrogen

---

[1] Used for liquids lighter than water.

[2] GODDE, A. H., Production Records and Methods of Measuring Fluid, Summary of Operations California Oil Fields, Calif. Div. Mines, vol. 13, No. 6, pp. 5–10, December, 1927.

[3] The U. S. Bureau of Standards, Washington, D. C., supplies gravity conversion tables.

compounds.   Hydrocarbons of the following series have been discovered in petroleum.[1]

$$C_nH_{2n+2} \qquad\qquad C_nH_{2n-6}$$
$$C_nH_{2n} \qquad\qquad C_nH_{2n-8}$$
$$C_nH_{2n-2} \qquad\qquad C_nH_{2n-10}$$
$$C_nH_{2n-4} \qquad\qquad C_nH_{2n-12}$$

The compounds most frequently appearing, according to Hoefer, belong to the first or paraffin series, the second or olefine series, and the fifth or aromatic (benzene) series.   Of these the paraffins are much the most abundant in both natural gas and petroleum.

PROPERTIES OF HYDROCARBONS OCCURRING IN NATURAL GAS[1]

	Formula	Molecular weight	Boiling point, degrees Fahrenheit	Critical temperature, degrees Fahrenheit	Critical pressure, pounds per square inch	Specific gravity liquid (water = 1)
Methane......	CH_4	16	−256	−139.6	736.5	0.415
Ethane........	C_2H_6	30	−119.4	+ 95.0	665.8	0.446
Propane.......	C_3H_8	44	− 47.4	206.5	662.8	0.536
Butane........	C_4H_{10}	58	+ 32.5	307.5	522.0	0.600
Pentane.......	C_5H_{12}	72	97.7	387.0	486.6	0.633
Hexane.......	C_6H_{14}	86	156.2	454.1	441.9	0.667

[1] MILLER, H. C., "Function of Natural Gas in the Production of Oil," p. 196, 1929.

Oils are commonly classified as those with asphaltic base and those with paraffin base.   Asphaltic oils yield on distillation a dark asphaltic residue. Paraffin oils on distillation yield light-colored paraffins that do not dissolve in solvents that dissolve asphalts.   Oils that contain paraffin arc more easily refined than those that contain asphalt.   In general, asphaltic oils sell at a lower price than paraffin oils.   Many oils contain both asphalt and paraffin.

In ordinary work, oil is analyzed to ascertain what fractions may be obtained from it by distillation rather than exactly what chemical compounds are present.   The standard method of analysis, Engler's method, is described by Day[2] as follows: 100 c.c. of the crude oil, measured at 60° F., is delivered into a distilling bulb holding about 125 c.c.   The thermometer used is a nitrogen thermometer reading to 550° C.   The condenser tube is 75 centimeters long and has an inclination of 75 degrees from the horizontal.   The point of initial boiling is taken when the first drop of oil falls from the condenser tube into the receiving flask. The fraction between the initial boiling point and 150° C. (302° F.)

[1] HOEFER, H., Das Erdoel, p. 54, 1906.
[2] DAY, D. T., The Production of Petroleum in 1913, U. S. Geol. Survey Mineral Resources, 1913, pt. 2, 1123, 1914.

constituting the gasoline fraction, and the fraction between 150° and 300° C. (572° F.), constituting the kerosene fraction, are examined for specific gravity. The residuum is weighed, its specific gravity taken, and the volume calculated.

Sulphur in Oil.—Sulphur or its compounds are found in the petroleum of most fields, although in some oils they are present in very small amounts. Sulphur is only one of many compounds that make up oil, but it is of great interest because of the expense of removing it in refining oils. The sulphur is probably derived from the bodies of plants and animals, many of which contain sulphur, and from the sulphates of sea water which was buried with the oil. The sulphur is present as the element dissolved in oil and as complicated compounds which have not been thoroughly studied. In the Lima-Indiana[1] field it occurs as methyl sulphide $(CH_3)_2S$. There are probably scores of sulphur compounds in oil. There seems to be no clear relationship between the amount of sulphur in the oil and its age or depth. Some of the oldest oils, such as oils of the Lima-Indiana field (Ordovician), are high in sulphur, whereas oil in rocks of about the same age is "sweet" or practically free from sulphur, as is the "Wilcox sand" oil of Oklahoma. The Paleozoic oils of Pennsylvania are low-sulphur oils, while the oil in the McClosky oolitic limestone of Illinois, which is of Mississippian age, is high in sulphur. The oils in Permian rocks of west Texas fields are generally very high in sulphur. The oil of the Embar (Permian) and Sundance (Jurassic) formations of Wyoming also are high in sulphur. The oils of the Cretaceous rocks of the Rocky Mountains region in general are relatively low in sulphur. In California many of the oils in Tertiary rocks are high in sulphur. The oil of Huntington Beach is exceptionally high.

A considerable number of oils in limestone reservoirs are high in sulphur. These include oils of the Lima-Indiana field, the oil of the McClosky oolitic limestone in southeastern Illinois, the oil of the Embar limestone of Wyoming, the cap-rock oils of certain salt domes of Texas and Louisiana, oils of west Texas, certain oils of the Tampico region, Mexico, and many others. On the other hand, many oils in limestone are low in sulphur. These include the oils of Lambton County, Ontario, many Kentucky oils, oils in the Paleozoic limestones of Oklahoma and Kansas, the oils of the Madison limestone, Kevin-Sunburst field, Montana, and many others.

Relations of Oils in One Sand and Depth.—In certain fields oil is drawn from the same sand at different depths; in other fields it is drawn from different sands at different depths. Where oil is drawn from the same sand at different elevations on a dome, it is commonly found that the oil near the top of the dome is richer in natural gas than the oil low

[1] MABREY, C. F., and A. W. SMITH, *Am. Chem. Jour.*, vol. 13, pp. 233–243, 1891.

on the dome.   That is true in the Salt Creek field, Wyoming, and in a less striking degree in certain other fields.   In certain domes the oil is much lighter near the top of the dome than it is near the base of the oil deposit.   The chief cause for this difference is probably gravity.   The heavy oil may move downward, forcing the light oil up, or the segregation may be brought about by gas which is carried to the top of the dome

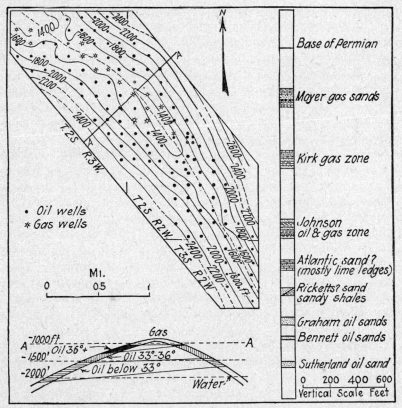

FIG. 13.—Map and cross sections Graham oil field, Oklahoma. (*After Tomlinson and Storm.*)   The section *AA* shows gas, oil, and heavy oil, in Johnson sand.

because of its light weight.   It carries light oil with it and that makes the oil near the top of the structure lighter and that remaining low on the dome heavier.   If water is mixed with the oil, this water generally increases toward the bottom of the pool, and if oil is emulsified with water, the emulsion is likely to be more abundant with depth than it is near the surface.   In the Sunset-Midway field, California, there is evidence also that a chemical reaction has taken place between the edge water and oil so that very heavy oil or tar is found where water and oil come together.   This is observed both above the oil deposit and at its base.   This formation of heavy oil or tar does not take place to the same extent in most fields and in many fields it has not been noted.

The Graham[1] field is in southern Oklahoma southwest of the Arbuckle Mountains.   The field in 1921 was producing 15,000 barrels of oil daily, together with considerable gas.   The oil is derived from several sands of Pennsylvanian age which lie on a dome.   The oils range in gravity from 27 to 43° Bé.   The oils of the deeper sands are lighter than those nearer the surface but in a single sand (Fig. 13) the lighter oils are found near the top of the dome above the heavier oils.   This relation is noted in several sands but is best shown in the Johnson sand.   The oil-gas contact is nearly level but the oil-water contact extends farther down on the west slope.   Oil above 36° Bé. is confined to the upper part of the fold.   Below the light oil zone is one with a gravity between 33 and 35.9° Bé., and below that, next to edge water, oil with gravity below 33° Bé.

Relations of Oils in Different Sands and Depth.—In many fields oil is found in several sands lying one below the other.   In a few fields the oil is lighter in the higher sands.   That is true of the Grass Creek field in Wyoming, where the Embar limestone yields a heavy dark oil, whereas the Cretaceous sands above it produce a light oil.   In the Salt Creek field, Wyoming, the oil in the First Wall Creek sand is a little lighter than the oil in the Second sand below it.   In the Glenpool field, Oklahoma, the Wilcox sand produces a heavy oil, whereas the oil in the Pennsylvania sands is lighter.   The shallow oil of Eldorado, Kansas, according to Fath, was as light or lighter than the deeper oil of the Stapleton zone.   In some of the fields of Baku, Russia, a very light oil is found at places nearer the surface than the heavier oils.   In the latter field it is believed that the very light oil is derived in some manner from the heavy oil, because the light oil is of local occurrence.   Although there is no universal rule, it is much more generally true that oils of a series of petroliferous beds are lighter in the older and deeper rocks than they are in the younger beds of a series.   That is true in scores of fields in Oklahoma, where oil of medium gravity is found in Pennsylvanian sands, and, in the same fields at greater depths, very light oil is found in older beds.   In the Big Lake field, Texas, medium gravity oil is found in the higher strata and a very light oil at a depth of about 8,525 feet.   In California, in several fields, heavy oils are produced near the surface and in depth lighter oils are found.

In the Sanga Sanga field, Dutch Borneo, a heavy oil is found at shallow depths, a lighter oil in lower beds below it, and in still lower beds a light paraffin oil.   In the Nishiyama field, Echigo Province, Japan, light oil is found below heavy oil.

[1] TOMLINSON, C. W., and W. STORM, The Graham Field, Oklahoma, Am. Assoc. Pet. Geol. *Bull.*, vol. 8, pp. 593–620, 1924.

Exceptions notwithstanding, there are so many oil fields that show light gravity oils below heavier oils, that there must be a commonly prevailing reason for this relationship. It is probably not due to age. The oldest beds which contain large oil deposits east of the Mississippi River in the United States are Ordovician limestones which contain the medium gravity oil in the Lima-Indiana field. In Oklahoma, however, the Wilcox sands and Arbuckle limestone of Ordovician age carry very light oils in large amounts. Passing to the other end of the geologic column, the very light and the heavy oil of Baku, Russia, are in beds of Pliocene age. The kind of reservoir rocks seems to be of little significance, for both light and heavy oils are found in limestone and in sandstone, regardless of age. One hypothesis is that older oils which have been deeply buried have been broken up by pressure and heat and at places have supplied the lighter derivatives.

GAS

Natural gas is associated with practically all petroleums. It rises to the higher points of reservoirs and is absorbed in the oil. Under the high pressures that exist in some fields, considerable quantities are absorbed. Expansion of gas pushes the oil out of the interstices of the rocks and causes it to flow in wells. Gas pressure causes wells to spout oil and salt water. Even in wells that are pumped, the gas generally forces the oil to the bore.

Although practically all oils are associated with inflammable gas, there are at many places issues of gas that are not associated with oil. The gas that forms in swamps and marshes has been mentioned. In Minnesota, in sands below glacial clay, gas is found in quantities sufficient for lighting houses. Swamp gas is generally methane or "marsh gas."

Hydrocarbons in Natural Gas.—The predominating hydrocarbons in natural gases are the light members of the paraffin series, chiefly methane and ethane; with these carbon dioxide and nitrogen are commonly found. Propane and butane are present in many gases, and small amounts of pentane and hexane vapor are present in some. The value of gas for gasoline extraction depends on its content of propane, butane, and the vapor of pentane, hexane, and heptane.[1] By compression, refrigeration, or solution in heavy mineral oil, some butane and most of the heavier hydrocarbons are condensed, and these, when mixed with naphtha from the refineries, may be utilized as motor fuel.

[1] ROGERS, G. S., U. S. Geol. Survey *Prof. Paper* 117, p. 23, 1919.

ANALYSES OF NATURAL GAS[1]

Oil field	County	State	CO_2	O_2	N_2	Total paraffins	Total	CH_4	C_2H_6	Gross heating value per cubic foot at 0° C. and 760 millimeters pressure, B.t.u.	Specific gravity (air = 1)
Santa Maria.	Santa Barbara	California	15.5	0.2	1.4	82.9	100.0	62.7	20.2	1,044	0.81
Torrey......	Ventura	California	6.8	0.0	3.4	89.8	1u0.0	54.2	35.6	1,240	0.81
Coalinga....	Fresno	California	11.1	0.0	0.9	88.0	100.0	88.0	0.0	937	0.66
McKittrick..	Kings	California	30.4	0.0	2.4	67.2	100.0	66.2	1.0	724	0.85
West Los Angeles...	Los Angeles	California	1.0	0.1	5.2	93.7	100.0	91.0	2.7	1,019	0.60
Sunset......	Kings	California	10.5	0.0	1.8	87.7	100.0	87.7	0.0	934	0.66
Fullerton....	Orange	California	1.7	0.0	2.1	96.2	100.0	86.7	9.5	1,100	0.63
Kern River..	Kern	California	6.5	0.0	1.2	92.3	100.0	84.3	8.0	1,047	0.66
	Clarion	Pennsylvania	0.0	0.0	1.1	98.8	100.0	96.4	2.5	1,073	0.57
	Forest	Pennsylvania	0.0	0.0	1.0	99.0	100.0	70.8	28.2	1,279	0.70
	Clarion	Pennsylvania	0.0	0.0	1.7	98.3	100.0	80.5	17.8	1,189	0.65
	Butler	Pennsylvania	0.0	0.0	0.9	99.1	100.0	53.3	45.8	1,420	0.78
	Armstrong	Pennsylvania	0.05	0.0	1.45	98.5	100.0	81.6	16.9	1,184	0.64
Hogshooter..	Osage	Oklahoma	1.1	0.0	4.6	94.3	100.0	94.3	0.0	1,004	0.58
	Creek	Oklahoma	2.4	0.0	1.8	95.8	100.0*	64.1	31.7	1,273	0.74
	Barren	Kentucky	2.5	0.0	1.3	93.3	100.0†	23.6	69.7	1,548	0.91
	Barren	Kentucky	2.6	0.0	5.1	92.3	100.0	44.1	48.2	1,367	0.84
	Grand	Utah	3.6	0.0	5.6	90.8	100.0	90.8	0.0	967	0.61
	Grand	Utah	3.5	0.0	6.5	90.0	100.0	90.0	0.0	959	0.62

[1] U. S. Bur. Mines *Bull*. 88, p. 21, 1915.
* H_2S, 2.9 per cent.
† H_2S, 0.1 per cent.

Carbon Dioxide and Nitrogen in Natural Gas.—Natural gas commonly contains carbon dioxide, and in certain gases it is the most abundant constituent. A well at Walden, Colorado, which has produced 500 barrels of oil per day, yielded also 30,000,000 cubic feet of gas containing 83 per cent CO_2 and 17 per cent N. Large gas wells yielding CO_2 are drilled in Carbon County and in Emery County, Utah. A well in Colfax County,[1] New Mexico, yielded 250,000 cubic feet of gas per day of the following composition: carbon dioxide, 67 per cent; oxygen, 4.1 per cent; nitrogen, 28 per cent; methane 0; ethane 0. A well in Mora County, New Mexico, yielded 5,000,000 cubic feet: carbon dioxide, 90 per cent; oxygen, 2.2 per cent; nitrogen, 7.8 per cent; methane, 0; ethane 0. Lang

[1] LANG, W. B., Unusual Natural Gases, Am. Assoc. Pet. Geol. *Bull*., vol. 10, pp. 1176–1177, 1926.

suggests the probability that these gases have resulted from the action of igneous rocks on limestone.

Helium in Natural Gas.—Helium[1] is found in the natural gases of many fields in the United States. In the Petrolia field, Texas, in Potter County, Texas, and near Dexter, Kansas, it is found in considerable amounts. According to Ruedemann and Oles, it is probably derived from the decomposition of uranium and other radioactive minerals, which are found in pegmatites in central Texas and which are probably present in sedimentary rocks of the main helium-bearing gas regions. The greatest supply of helium is in the gas of the Bush dome, Potter County, Texas, where there are large reserves of gas containing 2 per cent helium and in a well in Colorado some 60 mi. southeast of Pueblo. The gas of this well contains 7 per cent helium. A well in Emery County, Utah, yields a non-inflammable gas containing considerable helium. Lind[2] has shown that electric discharges or radioactive compounds convert methane to oily matter consisting of higher hydrocarbons. Since helium, which is a product of radioactivity, is found in certain gases that are associated with oil this suggests that the conversion of methane to oil may have operated where favorable conditions existed in the earth. Helium is a very light gas and is suitable for filling aircraft. It is heavier than hydrogen, but it is not inflammable.

OIL-FIELD WATERS

The water above the oil sand is commonly termed "top water"; the water in the oil sand at the edge of the oil pool and below the oil is

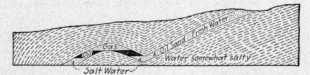

Fig. 14.—Sketch showing a common relationship of oil, gas, salt water, water somewhat salty, and fresh water. The circulation of fresh ground water sweeps out the brine near the surface and dilutes it in depth.

termed "edge water"; and the water below the oil sand is termed "bottom water." A bottom water of one sand may be top water of another. As already stated, nearly all oil deposits rest upon water, and in nearly all oil fields the water carries salt (Fig. 14). Even where the rocks are

[1] ROGERS, G. S., Helium-bearing Natural Gas, U. S. Geol. Survey *Prof. Paper* 121, pp. 1–109, 1921.

RUEDEMANN, P., and L. M. OLES, Helium—Its Probable Origin and Concentration in the Amarillo Fold, Texas, Am. Assoc. Pet. Geol. *Bull.*, vol. 13, pp. 799–810, 1929.

[2] LIND, S. C., The Origin of Terrestrial Helium and Its Association with Other Gases, *Proc.* Nat. Acad. Sci., vol. 11, pp. 772–779, December, 1925.

not saturated with water and the oil is found near the bottom of synclines, there is commonly some salt water. A list of the oil fields in which salt water is encountered in the oil sands includes practically all oil fields in which the oil sands carry water.

In certain oil fields samples of water are taken and analyzed with a view to identifying sands.[1] The waters of different sands have different compositions in some fields, whereas the waters in the same sands show less variation. If samples of water are taken at various depths as wells are drilled, in certain fields a sudden change in composition or in concentration may justify the inference that the well has encountered a fault or an unconformity.

Because marine sedimentary rocks are generally present in oil-bearing systems of strata, it is inferred that the salt water is residual sea water that was trapped in the rocks at the time when the oil or the materials from which the oil is derived were laid down. This is a rational assumption, for in many oil fields no bodies of salt are evident such as might have supplied salt to ground water. Nevertheless, the analyses of many oil-field waters do not approach very closely in composition the average composition of sea water. This is shown by the tables that follow.

ANALYSES OF OIL-FIELD WATERS
(Parts per million)

	1	2	3	4	5	6	7	8	9
Chloride	19,410	77,340	42,120	15,742	91,537	108,990	93,706	152,100	15,743
Sulphate	2,700	730	43	2,797	499	455	1,022	319	
Carbonate	70			84					
Bicarbonate			672	140	52	43	48		412
Sodium	10,710	31,950	21,867	10,385	47,844	54,363	49,939	73,620	9,340
Potassium	390	650							
Calcium	420	13,260	182	700	7,834	10,560	7,341	17,700	553
Magnesium	1,300	1,940	19	288	1,553	2,390	1,540	2,541	147
Silica			16	6				30	
Fe, Al			15	16				300	
Total	35,000	125,870	64,934	30,158	149,319	176,801	153,596	246,610	26,200

1. Mean of 77 analyses of ocean water. Challenger Expedition, Dittmar, analyst. Carbonate is in part bicarbonate. Newby and others, "Structures of Typical American Oil Fields," vol. 2, p. 435, 1929.

2. Bradford, Pennsylvania, sand water at south end of Bradford field. Newby and others, *op. cit.*

3. Clark County, Illinois, "Trenton" limestone. Mylius. Ill. Geol. Survey *Bull.* 54, p. 712, 1927.

4. Lawrence County, Illinois, Buchanan sand (Mississippian) Mylius, *op. cit.*

5. Seminole City field, Oklahoma, Seminole sand, average of 3 analyses by L. C. Case. Levorsen, "Structure of Typical American Oil Fields," vol. 2, p. 349, 1929.

6. St. Louis field, Oklahoma, "Wilcox" sand 4,242 feet deep. L. C. Case, analyst. Levorsen *op. cit.*

7. Searight field, Oklahoma, Hunton limestone water, average of 2 analyses by L. C. Case. Levorsen *op. cit.*

8. Garber, Oklahoma, Layton sand. Gish and Carr, "Structure of Typical American Oil Fields," voi. 1, p. 189, 1929.

9. Mexia, Texas, Woodbine sand east part of field. Lahee, "Structure of Typical American Oil Fields,' vol. 1, p. 376, 1929.

[1] PARKS, E. M., Water Analysis in Oil Production and Some Analyses from Poison Spider, Wyoming, Am. Assoc. Pet. Geol. *Bull.*, vol. 9, pp. 927–946, 1925.

ANALYSES OF OIL-FIELD WATERS

(Parts per million)

	1	2	3	4	5	6	7	8
Chloride..............	2,670	153	2,850	304.7	143	11	196	20,421
Sulphate..............	trace	....	....	13.0	79	627	41	
Carbonate.............	696	....	....	1,362.3	144	31		
Bicarbonate..........	5,120	2,866	10,028	1,238.0	1,903	301	1,588	162
Sodium...............	4,125	1,148	6,256	1,237.2	1,012	427	745	11,176
Potassium............				2.7	trace	....	....	86
Calcium..............		10		7.6	4.3	9	....	1,100
Magnesium............	16	10	7	3.6	trace	4	....	503
Silica...............				16.4	22	26	16	
Fe, Al...............				1.5				
Total...............	12,627	4,187	19,141	4,187.0	3,307.3	1,436	2,586	33,448

1. Salt Creek, analysis 18, First Wall Creek sand east side field, after Young and Estabrook, "Petroleum Development and Technology in 1925."

2. Salt Creek, analysis 15, First Wall Creek sand west side field, after Young and Estabrook, *op. cit.*, p. 256.

3. Salt Creek, analysis 44, Second Wall Creek sand west side near oil, *idem*.

4. Grass Creek, Wyoming, Frontier sand. Hewett, U. S. Geol. Survey *Prof. Paper* 145, p. 89 (mountainward).

5. *Idem*, basinward.

6. Poison Spider, Wyoming, Dakota sandstone. Parks, Am. Assoc. Pet. Geol. *Bull.*, vol. 9, p. 941, 1925. Sodium includes potassium.

7. *Idem*, Sundance No. 4. Sodium includes potassium.

8. Sample Sunset-Midway, California, Rogers, U. S. Geol. Survey *Prof. Paper* 117, p. 65. Contains I, 29, NO_3, 45.

According to Rogers,[1] in the Midway-Sunset field, California, the reaction of water with the oil results in a reduction of sulphate in the water to sulphide or to sulphur and in oxidation of the oil. The oil absorbs the sulphur and thus the sulphate is decreased in the water. The oil probably oxidizes in part, supplying CO_2 which forms carbonates and bicarbonates in the water. As a result of these reactions, chloride becomes relatively more abundant, carbonates become much more abundant, and sulphates are practically eliminated in the waters. The oils near the water become richer in sulphur and heavier and are probably more highly oxidized. It is noteworthy that tar sands seal the oil reservoir near the surface, and also that tar sands are found below the oil where water of the edge-water zone probably reacted with the oil. These tar sands were probably not formed by escape of light constituents of oil, for such constituents would not have escaped downward. Evidently, the tar was formed by water reacting on oil.

[1] ROGERS, G. S., The Sunset-Midway Oil Field, California, Chemical Relations of the Oil, Gas, and Water. U. S. Geol. Survey *Prof. Paper* 117, pt. 2, pp. 1–103, 1919.

Briefly, it appears probable that the waters of oil fields are residual sea waters that have been changed (1) by reaction with oil and gas, and (2) by dilution with ground water. These changes must take place very slowly, for even in domes on the flanks of mountains, where the water circulation is probably under considerable head, the chlorides commonly remain in the deep ground water suggesting that the sea water or its salts have not yet been eliminated. Moreover, if an oil and sea water react rapidly to form tar, it appears very probable that the reaction would be completed in the sea or in the oil sands during the processes of the accumulation of oil and that the sands would more commonly contain tar without oil.

The mechanism of the reactions by which sulphates are reduced in the presence of oil is not understood. There are no experimental data to support the theory that reduction takes place by simple chemical reactions. Bastin[1] has shown that the reactions are probably biochemical. According to Bastin, the reduction is brought about by bacteria with the generation of hydrogen sulphide. Sulphate-reducing bacteria have been found in river muds, sewage, soils, and sands to depths of 37 meters, black muds of ocean bottoms, and deep bottom muds of the Black Sea. Sulphate-reducing bacteria have been identified by Bastin in waters from oil sands of Paleozoic age in Illinois and from Tertiary beds of California. The waters carrying the bacteria are low in sulphates. In the Midway-Sunset oil field, California, water as deep as 3,090 feet was found to contain abundant sulphate-reducing bacteria. Sulphate-reducing bacteria break up the sulphate radical and utilize its oxygen. Organic matter which is necessary for their life is presumably supplied by the oil. Inoculation of the waters takes place when the beds are laid down, for muds of ocean bottoms are found to contain the bacteria. Inoculation probably takes place also after the oil and water are segregated, for in many fields there is communication between the surface of the earth and the oil deposit, as is shown by pressure relations.

The waters of Salt Creek, Wyoming, have been carefully studied. The Salt Creek oil field is located on a great dome that lies southeast of the Big Horn Mountains and is 40 miles north of Casper. The dome has about 1,400 feet of closure and the bulk of the oil production which was about 206,000,000 barrels to the end of 1928, has come from the First and Second Wall Creek sands of the Frontier formation (Upper Cretaceous). A chemical survey of the waters of the First sand[2] shows that they are low in calcium and magnesium and are nearly free from sulphate. They are essentially sodium bicarbonate waters with considerable sodium

[1] Bastin, E. S., The Problem of the Natural Reduction of Sulphates, Am. Assoc. Pet. Geol. Bull., vol. 10, pp. 1270–1299, 1926.

[2] Young, H. W., and E. L. Estabrook, Waters of the Salt Creek Field, Wyoming, "Petroleum Development and Technology in 1925," pp. 255–264, 1926.

chloride. Iodine is present in small amounts. The rocks dip east from the Big Horn Mountains and the First Wall Creek sand crops out about 15 miles west of the field. On the east and south sides of the dome, where the water is farther from the outcrop of the sand, the concentration is much higher than on the north and west sides. This is shown by Fig. 15 after Young and Estabrook. The Cl, Na, and HCO$_3$ radicals all increase notably toward the oil deposit. On the west side of the field these radicals are practically wanting in the waters a short distance

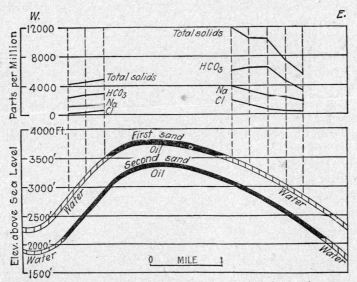

Fig. 15.—Cross section through Salt Creek dome showing changes in composition of water in the First Wall Creek sand which is the upper sand shown. The water is more concentrated on the east side of the field than on the west side and, on both flanks of the dome the concentration decreases away from the oil. The lower sand is the Second Wall Creek sand. (*Redrawn from figure by Young and Estabrook.*)

from the oil. The steeply dipping beds on the west side of the field were evidently more easily flushed out than the more protected and more gently dipping beds on the east side that lie farther from the outcrop. On both sides of the field, however, there is an increase in concentration of salts in the waters of the First Wall Creek sand toward the oil blanket in the sand. The Second sand contains a higher concentration of salts than the First sand, but the waters are of the same general character. Movements of underground water in Salt Creek field were studied by F. B. Taylor. Dyes were introduced in 4-ounce cartridges in wells of the Teapot dome, and samples of water in offset wells to the north of the reserve were tested for the substances used which included methyl orange, fluoresceine, and other dyes.[1] His experiments showed that waters are moving northward toward the Salt Creek dome.

[1] Taylor, F. B., *Oil Weekly*, vol. 49, p. 52, May 18, 1929.

In the Salt Creek field the oil is in Cretaceous and older rocks and probably has been subjected to changes for a long time. Due to the head, there is a vigorous circulation of water near the oil fields. The high carbonate-chloride ratio in the waters of Salt Creek and the low concentration compared to sea water suggest extensive changes due to reactions of the oil with water and to dilution due to the downward movement of surface waters. The amount of sulphur in the oil is not very high (0.2 per cent) which may be due to the large amount of dilution of salt water by fresh water rather than to reaction of oil with salt water.

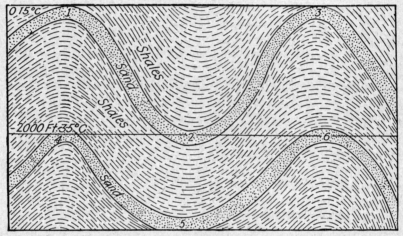

FIG. 16.—Diagram illustrating movement of hot water or of heat from troughs to crests of folds.

In the Grass Creek[1] field, Wyoming, the waters are alkaline and the prevailing salts are sodium carbonates and sodium bicarbonates, although chlorides and some sulphates are present also. In other fields in Wyoming also, as shown by Parks, the prevailing salts are carbonates.

Temperatures.—Temperature readings in several oil fields show that the highest temperatures at a given depth are found on the anticlines. Temperature readings in wells and mines show that temperatures increase downward, but that they show great differences in the rates of increase. The average increase is about 1° C. per 100 feet. If, in a homogeneous rock, the mean temperature at the surface is 15° C. it would be about 35° C. at 2,000 feet. Rocks are poor conductors of heat, but water and oil are good conductors. In a syncline at 2 and 5 (Fig. 16) any transfer of heat along the sands filled with liquids would be to higher levels, because connection would be along the beds. Heat moves from places of high temperature to places of lower temperature, and the temperatures at 1, 4, 3, and 6 would be increased by movement of heat

[1] HEWETT, D. F., U. S. Geol. Survey *Prof. Paper* 145, p. 89, 1926.

from 2 to 5. Communication at points along the crests of the anticlines would be along the beds with places that are deeper and therefore hotter. The temperature at 4 would be higher than the temperature at 2, although they are at the same depth.

In certain reservoirs the temperature of the oil near edge water appears to be notably higher than the temperature of the oil away from the water. As the end of production approaches, the temperature of the oil increases and, finally, hot water follows the oil. The conductivity of water is much greater than that of oil, and the specific heat of water is higher than that of oil. The sudden rise in temperature of the oil near edge water is probably due to transfer of heat from water to the oil and to slower transfer of heat in the oil. The expansion of gas cools associated fluids. Commonly, the oil near edge water is free from gas; consequently, the oil near edge water would not be cooled by expansion of gas.

Parks,[1] studying the waters of oil fields near Casper, Wyoming, found that in the wells making the most water in proportion to oil the water was at the highest temperature, suggesting that the water came from below. In California fields a rise in the temperature of oil or of oil and water issuing from a well commonly arouses a fear that the well will soon go to water. Where there is upward movement of water in a well, the water will usually be hotter than normal.

In the Tampico-Tuxpam oil field of Mexico, many wells have produced millions of barrels of oil flowing naturally to the end of production. In the final stages, after the temperature of the oil increases, the flow of oil is replaced by a flow of an emulsion of oil and water, and, finally, hot salt water appears and in some of the wells the water has continued to flow for considerable periods.

Salts in Oil Wells.—Salt water is not only carried out of wells by oil but also gases carry it as spray. These gases are under high pressure, and, when they are released, they expand and become cooler. Decrease in temperature or evaporation may cause the salts to be deposited in the reservoir rocks or in well casings.

In wells of the Saratoga and Batson[2] oil fields, Texas, barite pisolites, larger than the mesh of the screens in the wells, are found in considerable quantities. These were formed since the screens were set. According

[1] PARKS, E. M., Am. Assoc. Pet. Geol. *Bull.*, vol. 9, p. 943, 1925.

[2] MOORE, E. S., Oolitic and Pisolitic Barite from Saratoga Oil Field, Texas, Geol. Soc. Am. *Bull.*, vol. 25, pp. 77–79.

BARTON, D. C., and S. L. MASON, Further Notes on the Barite Pisolites from Batson and Saratoga Oil Fields, Am. Assoc. Pet. Geol. *Bull.*, vol. 9, pp. 1294–1295, 1925.

SUMAN, J., The Saratoga Oil Fields, Texas, Am. Assoc. Pet. Geol. *Bull.*, vol. 9, p. 275, 1925.

to Barton and Mason, the pisolites of Batson are flat and 5 to 8 milli-meters in diameter, and 2 or 3 millimeters thick. They are built around magnetic iron oxide, probably pipe scale.

Expanding gases will absorb water of a solution and cause the salt in the solution to be precipitated. According to Mills and Wells[1] who studied the deposits formed in well casings, there is a definite order of change in the proportion of the dissolved constituents in the waters. Carbon dioxide and other gases are lost from the solutions. Calcium, magnesium, and iron separate as carbonates, and, under favorable conditions, sodium and minor amounts of calcium and magnesium separate as chlorides. Where waters from different beds meet, reactions may take place resulting in precipitation of various compounds. In these ways wells may be salted up and, by leaking of gas, reservoir rocks and fractures may become locally cemented.

[1] MILLS, R. V., and R. C. WELLS, The Evaporation and Concentration of Waters Associated with Petroleum and Natural Gas, U. S. Geol. Survey *Bull.* 693, pp. 1–103, 1919.

CHAPTER V

ORIGIN OF PETROLEUM

The chief hypotheses that have been proposed to account for the origin of petroleum are

Inorganic:
  a. Reactions of water with metallic carbides.
  b. Reactions of carbon dioxide and water with metals.

Organic:
  a. Decomposition of organic matter before and during burial.
  b. Decomposition and distillation of organic matter after burial.

Inorganic Theories.—The first hypothesis proposes to account for petroleum by the action of water on metallic carbides such as calcium and iron carbides.[1] The reaction of water with calcium carbide will generate acetylene gas, and with iron carbide water will generate hydrocarbons like some of the hydrocarbons of the oil series. Metals such as sodium and potassium will, under certain conditions, react with CO_2 and water to form hydrocarbons.[2] Metallic carbides and alkali metals are not known to exist in the earth, but they are very unstable and, if they did exist they would be destroyed in the crust of the earth by reactions with water. If they do exist, they are high-temperature products and therefore associated with volcanic phenomena. Because most of the oil fields of the earth are not closely associated with volcanic phenomena and because some of the greatest oil fields are far removed from igneous centers, the inorganic theory to account for the formation of petroleum is discarded by practically all investigators.

Organic Theories.—According to the organic theories, oil is derived from parts of plants and animals that are buried in the sea. One theory is that the oil generated from decaying organic matter is deposited as oil in muds, clays, and marls and accumulates later in sands and porous limestone. It has been shown by Stuart[3] that fine particles of clay surround globules of oil and sink and hold them below water. Haseman[4]

[1] BERTHELOT, M., Sur l'Origine des Carbures et des Combustibles Mineraux, *Compt. Rend.*, No. 63, pp. 949–951, 1866.

[2] MENDELIEF, D., Entstehung und Vorkommen des Mineralöls, Abstract by G. Wagner, *Deut. Chem. Ges. Ber.*, vol. 10, p. 229, 1877.

[3] STUART, M., The Sedimentary Deposition of Oil, *Records* Geol. Survey India, vol. 40, pp. 320–330, 1910.

[4] HASEMAN, J. D., The Humic Acid Origin of Asphalt, Am. Assoc. Pet. Geol. *Bull.*, vol. 5, pp. 75–80, 1921.

has noted asphalt in modern beds near Haseman, Florida.   Such deposits of asphalt he believes are formed from "humic acids" brought down by rivers and precipitated by sea water.   Near Fallon, Nevada, in recent sediments of Lake Lahontan,[1] a well was sunk 935 feet deep.   Oil spots appeared in the sludge water at 5 horizons all within 297 feet of the surface.   Sands of Lake Lahontan contain bitumens of which 5 per cent is soluble in chloroform and, according to Jones, many samples of Lahontan sands carry oil that may be extracted with chloroform.   Moore[2] cites an example of a brackish lake in Russia in which the algae contained 3.5 per cent of oil.   According to Rae, "ulmo-humic acids," derived from the decomposition of plant and animal remains and carried to the sea by river waters, are precipitated along with silica by sea water[3] in which salts are electrolytes.

Trask,[4] who is making a systematic study of the distribution of oil and fatty materials in sediments, found that solvents, which extract oil, dissolved an average of 0.06 per cent of the material of modern sediments collected on the Pacific Coast.

Takahashi[5] found a substance like the so-called "humic acid" in marine muds.   These data indicate that oil may be deposited directly as oil, in sediments now forming; quantitatively, however, they are not particularly impressive.   Future work may show that oil is much more abundant in sediments than is indicated by the observations that have been made.   Thus far, analyses that have been made have shown that modern sediments will yield to distillation between temperatures of 350 to 500° C. many times as much oil as may be dissolved from them by solvents.

By distillation modern sediments yield noteworthy amounts of oil. Takahashi[6] found that sediments of the Kohoku lagoon will yield 0.5 gallon of oil per ton.   Trask[7] found that sediments taken from shallow water of Pamlico Sound off the coast of North Carolina yield as much

[1] JONES, J. C., Suggestive Evidence on the Origin of Petroleum and Oil Shale, Am. Assoc. Pet. Geol. *Bull.*, vol. 7, pp. 67–72, 1923.

[2] MOORE, E. S., "Coal," pp. 176–177, 1922.

[3] RAE, COLIN, Organic Material in Carbonaceous Shales, Am. Assoc. Pet. Geol. *Bull.*, vol. 6, pp. 333–341, 1922.

GAVIN, M. J., Oil Shale, U. S. Bur. Mines *Bull.* 210, pp. 144–149, 1922.

[4] TRASK, P. D., Results of Distillation and Other Studies of the Organic Nature of Some Modern Sediments, Am. Assoc. Pet., Geol. *Bull.*, vol. 11, pp. 1221–1230, 1927.

[5] TAKAHASHI, J. R., Preliminary Report on the Origin of California Petroleum, *Econ. Geol.*, vol. 22, p. 146, 1927.

[6] TAKAHASHI, J. R., The Marine Kerogen Shales of Japan, *Science Repts.*, Tôhoku Imp. Univ., ser. 3, vol. 1, No. 2, pp. 53–156, 1923.

[7] TRASK, P. D., *op. cit.*, pp. 1223–1229; also Oceanography and Oil Deposits, Trans. Am. Geophys. Union Nat. Research Council *Bull.* 61, pp. 235–240, 1927; The Potential Value of Recent American Coastal and Inland Deposits as Future Source Beds of Petroleum, Am. Assoc. Pet. Geol. *Bull.*, vol. 12, pp. 1057–1068, 1928.

as 2.7 gallons of oil per ton. Samples from the deep part of Lake Maracaibo yielded 2 gallons of oil per ton, and samples from Great South Bay, New York, and from Laguna Sinamaica, Venezuela, yielded 1.5 gallons per ton. Samples from the limestone-forming areas near Cuba yielded 2 gallons per ton. An algal deposit from Mud Lake, an inland lake 20 miles northeast of Ocala, Florida, yielded 28 gallons per ton. Some samples yielded practically no oil and, in general, samples of clays and silts yielded more oil than sands.

Bacterial Decomposition.—A theory that is accepted by many investigators is that there are two stages[1] in the formation of petroleum from organic material. In one biochemical processes predominate; in the other dynamochemical processes. Petroleum is believed to be derived from remains of plants, especially from those of low orders yielding waxy, fatty, gelatinous, or resinous substances, and from animal matter. The organic matter was deposited on the sea bottom, in estuaries or not far from shore and in lakes. Through the action of anærobic bacteria it is changed, the cellulose probably being altered and the waxes and fats set free. That plants of low orders, when distilled, can yield petroleum was demonstrated by Renault.[2] Prominence is given to such plants in the contributions by Dalton, White, and Winchester.

The probability that bacterial action plays a part in the reaction that yields petroleum was brought forward by Morrey.[3] That the source of the material is principally muds, marls, and shales is evident from the association of shales, clays, and limestones with oil-bearing strata.

The anærobic bacteria are active probably as soon as the mud containing organic material is deposited Any oily matter which they set free could accumulate even on the sea bottom, for fine particles of clay surround globules of oil and sink them or hold them below water. Bastin has shown that bacteria live at great depths and under heavy pressure.[4] Bacterial decomposition probably goes on long after the organic muds are buried and may go on at considerable depths. It is known that the oil blankets in many oil fields are in contact with salt water that is in equilibrium with ground water and is therefore connected by water, essentially, with the surface of the earth. This is evident from the fact

[1] DALTON, W. H., On the Origin of Petroleum, *Econ. Geol.*, vol. 4, pp. 603–631, 1909.

WHITE, DAVID, Some Relations in Origin Between Coal and Petroleum, Wash. Acad. Sci. *Jour.*, vol. 5, pp. 189–212, 1915; Late Theories Regarding the Origin of Oil, Geol. Soc. Am. *Bull.*, vol. 28, pp. 727–734, 1917.

[2] RENAULT, B., Houille et Bacteriaces, Soc. Hist. Nat. Autun. *Bull.*, vol. 9, pp. 475–500, 1896; *Compt. Rend.*, vol. 117, p. 593, 1893.

[3] MORREY, C. B., and EDWARD ORTON, Origin of Oil and Gas, Ohio Geol. Survey *Bull.* 1, p. 313, 1903.

[4] BASTIN, E. S., The Problem of the Natural Reduction of Sulphides, Am. Assoc. Pet. Geol. *Bull.*, vol. 10, pp. 1270–1299, 1926.

that the pressure of the gas above the oil is approximately equal to the weight of a column of water as high as the hole is deep. In such a field where there is communication with the surface through water, bacterial contamination from the surface is very probable. If ground water can sweep oil out of a sand, as it doubtless has in areas of strong head, it could also sweep bacteria into the sand. Whether or not the bacteria could enter the organic shales which are the sources of oil of the reservoirs is uncertain, yet it appears probable.

Effect of Pressure.—The results of experiments designed to show the effect of pressure on oil shale are conflicting. McCoy[1] and Trager[2] obtained small amounts of oil from shale that had been subjected to high pressure. Van Tuyl and Blackburn[3] placed in a steel cylinder a sample of oil shale from a mine near Elko, Nevada, that was capable of yielding by heat 42 gallons of oil to the ton. After applying a pressure of 35,714 pounds to the square inch to the sample, it was found that approximately the same amount of oil could be dissolved from it by chloroform as was dissolved in another sample that had been ground in a mortar to pass an 80-mesh screen. McCoy,[4] discussing these experiments, states that the grinding of the shale may have made as much material soluble as the high pressure test. He describes a series of experiments by Brainerd in which oil shale was repeatedly ground and leached and after each grinding, more of the kerogen in the shale became soluble. Calculations showed that the increased solubility was not due to exposure of new surfaces of shale to the solution but presumably to kerogen converted into soluble matter by friction. McCoy believes that petroleum is produced from organic matter by differential movements at times of faulting and fissuring of source beds, but appears to doubt the quantitative importance of the process. He believes that oil deposited in marine sediments would tend to become waxlike with age due to reaction with gas and with connate waters. The favorable effect of faulting and folding is not due entirely to generation of oil by pressure. In order that considerable accumulation of oil should take place, according to McCoy, favorable structural conditions would have to develop in the sediments before the oil solidified. Faulting and jointing would bring about such conditions so that the oil could move from the source beds into reservoir sands. Diastrophic movements taking place soon after the deposition

---

[1] McCoy, A. W., Notes on Principles of Oil Accumulation, *Jour. Geol.*, vol. 27, pp. 252–262, 1919.

[2] Trager, E. A., Kerogen and Its Relation to Oil Shale, Am. Assoc. Pet. Geol. *Bull.*, vol. 8, pp. 301–311, 1924.

[3] Van Tuyl, F. M., and C. O. Blackburn, The Effect of Rock Flowage on the Kerogen of Oil Shale, Am. Assoc. Pet. Geol. *Bull.*, vol. 9, pp. 158–160, 1127, 1925.

[4] McCoy, A. W., A Brief Outline of Some Oil Accumulation Problems, Am. Assoc. Pet. Geol. *Bull.*, vol. 10, pp. 1015–1034, 1926.

of source beds would favor migration and preservation of the oil. This view has been stated also by van Waterschoot van der Gracht.[1]

Experiments by Hawley[2] show that oxidation renders part of the material of oil shale soluble in chloroform and shearing and grinding apparently aid oxidation. Further than that, pressure does not appear to aid in the solution of the organic matter of shales.

Distillation.—Kerogen is the oil-producing substance of oil shale. Only small percentages of it are dissolved by solvents, such as carbon bisulphide and chloroform, and certain experiments show no solution whatever, but, on heating, it gives off large amounts of bituminous materials that may be dissolved. It is suggested that kerogen results from bacterial action on organic matter and McCoy suggests that kerogen forms from oils that are deposited with the sediments and changed by reaction with connate waters and gases. From this view, however, others dissent. The distillation of kerogen or of organic material has been long accepted by many as the chief process to account for the origin of petroleum.

The theory that petroleum is generated by natural distillation under geothermal and dynamic influences from organic matter buried in sediments was first suggested by Newberry[3] and Orton.[4] Laboratory experiments that support this theory include those of Warren and Storer,[5] who prepared from menhaden oil a calcium soap which on distillation yielded a mixture of hydrocarbons like kerosene. Engler[6] distilled directly from menhaden oil the paraffins from pentane to nonane. Day[7] obtained by distilling a mixture of fresh herring and pine wood a product that yielded on redistillation a residue like gilsonite, and by distilling herring alone he obtained one like elaterite.

Engler[8] obtained hydrocarbons by the distillation of vegetable oils. The theory that oil is derived principally from animal remains was

[1] VAN DER GRACHT, W. A. I. M. VAN WATERSCHOOT, Sind jetzt Muttergesteine kuenftiger Erdoellagerstaetten in Bildung begriffen? *Petroleum Z.*, vol. 25, pp. 183–191, 1929.

[2] HAWLEY, J. E., Generation of Oil in Rocks by Shearing Pressures, Am. Assoc. Pet. Geol. *Bull.*, vol. 13, pp. 303–366, 1929; vol. 14, pp. 451–481, 1930.

[3] NEWBERRY, J. S., Devonian System, Ohio Geol. Survey, vol. 1, p. 160, 1873.

[4] ORTON, EDWARD, The Origin and Accumulation of Petroleum and Natural Gas, Ohio Geol. Survey, vol. 6, p. 74, 1888.

[5] WARREN, C. M., and F. H. STORER, Examination of a Hydrocarbon Naphtha Obtained from the Products of the Destructive Distillation of Lime Soap, Acad. Arts and Sci. *Mem.*, ser. 2, vol. 9, p. 177, 1867.

[6] ENGLER, C., Zur Bildung des Erdöls, *Deut. chem. Ges. Ber.*, vol. 21, p. 1816, 1918.

[7] DAY, W. C., The Laboratory Production of Asphalts from Animal and Vegetable Materials, *Am. Chem. Jour.*, vol. 21, pp. 478–499, 1899.

[8] ENGLER, C., Cong. Internat. du Pétrole, p. 20, Paris, 1900.

supported by Engler[1] and by Hoefer,[2] both well known for their investigations of the origin of petroleum.

Trask's analyses of modern sediments show that oil begins to form
by distillation at temperatures between 350° and 450° C.   In recent
years much oil has been found in late Tertiary rocks that seem to have
suffered little or no metamorphism and doubt is expressed as to whether
distillation could account for such deposits.   Some of the most productive
deposits in the world are found in Pliocene rocks that are not well consolidated and are not altered by heat near the oil deposits.   On the other
hand, many fields contain, associated with the oil, natural gas under
high pressures, and much of the gas carries oil that is separated from
gas and utilized.   It is possible that certain oils have been distilled from
source beds at moderately high temperatures and that the gas has
moved along the beds to places where temperatures and pressures are
lower.   It is possible also that, given time enough, distillation will
take place at lower temperatures than is indicated by the experiments
yielding oil by distillation of kerogen.

Organic muds are acted on by heat and pressure.   Heat is increased
by burial.   The normal increment of heat of the earth's crust is about 1°
C. for every 100 feet.   The temperature of a deposit that has been
buried 2 miles deep would be raised about 100° C., and by folding the
heat would probably be increased considerably, due to friction which
results from movements of the beds.   Rich[3] has emphasized this feature
of the genesis of petroleum, and changes in character of oils due to heat
and pressure are implied by the carbon ratio theory of White.[4]   This
theory holds that important oil deposits rarely exist in areas where the
metamorphism of associated strata is sufficient to change the coals to a
stage where the carbon ratio of the coal exceeds 70 per cent.

Both the theory of the distillation of oil and the carbon ratio theory
have been questioned.[5]   It is stated that only the lighter oils will volatilize at the temperatures to which the organic muds are usually subjected.
It is not known what these temperatures are, yet it appears unlikely that
they are normally sufficient to volatilize the heavier oils.   Even moderate

[1] ENGLER, C., Zur Geschichte des Bildung des Erdöls, Deut. chem. Ges. Ber., vol.
33, pp. 7–21, 1900.

[2] ENGLER, C., and H. HOEFER, Das Erdoel, vol. 2, 1909.

[3] RICH, J. L., Generation of Oil by Geologic Distillation during Mountain Building,
Am. Assoc. Pet. Geol. Bull., vol. 11, pp. 1139–1150, 1927.

[4] WHITE, D., Some Relations in Origin between Coal and Petroleum, Wash. Acad.
Sci. Jour., vol. 5, pp. 189–212, 1915.

[5] WASHBURNE, C. W., Some Physical Principles of the Origin of Petroleum,
Am. Assoc. Pet. Geol. Bull., vol. 3, pp. 345–362, 1919.

RUSSELL, W. L., Is the Geologic Distillation of Petroleum Possible?   Am. Assoc.
Pet. Geol. Bull., vol. 13, pp. 75–84, 1929.

REEVES, F., The Carbon Ratio Theory in the Light of Hilt's Law, Am. Assoc.
Pet. Geol. Bull., vol. 12, pp. 795–823, 1928.

heat, however, will greatly increase the mobility of oil, and moderately hot water will liquefy certain waxy solids. It is probable that the generation and movement of oil take place in part by natural distillation due to heat of the earth and the increase of heat by friction, and that movement takes place also by reason of an increase of fluidity due to an increase in temperature. It is probable also that some heavy oil is carried as minute globules of heavy liquid in gas and in the vapor of the lighter constituents of petroleum.

While the mechanism of the generation and accumulation of oil from organic muds is not fully understood, it is certain that the process is slow and generally incomplete. This conclusion is warranted by the fact that beds which have been folded and subsequently eroded are capable of giving up oil to strata that are subsequently laid down upon the folded beds unconformably. Exploration in recent years has shown that oil deposits are very commonly at and above unconformities. At some places it appears certain that the source beds are included in the strata that lie below the unconformity, yet the accumulations of oil in the reservoir rocks above the unconformity are of the first order of magnitude. The beds below the unconformity must have continued to supply oil to the overlying rocks long after they were folded and eroded and during a second period of less intense folding.

Briefly, it is probable that oil in sediments is generated from organic matter before the time the beds containing the organic matter are deposited and also after the beds are deposited; that part of the generation of oil is very slow; that the later stages of the development are aided by heat and pressure; and that accumulation takes place both by distillation and by movements of oil in the liquid state.

Source Beds.—Because practically all important oil-bearing series of rocks include marine strata, it is believed that marine conditions are favorable for the development of oil. Nevertheless, oil shales which are commonly regarded as source beds are largely non-marine. The Green River oil shales contain fresh-water shells at places, and these shales, according to Winchester,[1] are probably sources of the great bituminous dikes that are found associated with the shales in the Uinta basin of Utah.[2] It is noteworthy that oil was formed in recent times in the sediments of Lake Lahontan which, however, was a salt lake in the later stages of its development. An algal alkaline lake in Florida, studied by Trask, contains sediments that are very high in material that yields oil. Certain boghead coals, which are rich in material that on distillation yields oil, are fresh-water deposits. On the other hand,

---

[1] WINCHESTER, D. C., Oil Shale of the Uinta Basin, Northeastern Utah, U. S. Geol. Survey *Bull.* 691, pp. 27–50, 1919.

[2] Professor Charles Schuchert suggests that the basin in which the Green River shales were deposited may have been salt at a certain stage of its history.

practically all commercial oil accumulations are in or near series of marine strata which may have been the sources of supply. Salt waters which are generally believed to be the altered products of sea waters are closely associated with nearly all deposits of oil. Why oil deposits are, in general, of marine origin is not known. It may be that bacteria that liberate oil from associated cellulose thrive best in sea water or, possibly, certain fresh-water bacteria consume oil. It is not unlikely that sea water which contains salts that precipitate colloids aids in the deposition of organic matter that is converted to oil.

Association of Oil and Coal.—It has been suggested[1] that oil is derived from the materials that form coal. "Coal oil" and kerosene distilled from petroleum are nearly related with respect to their physical properties. Pictet and Bouvier[2] distilled from a coal from Montrambert, Loire, a tar in which they found $C_{10}H_{20}$ and $C_{11}H_{22}$, hydrocarbons identical with some that are separated from petroleums.

Coal has been formed in the main from vegetable matter deposited in fresh water. If vegetable matter deposited in fresh water can yield oil, a close association of coal and oil deposits would be expected. Methane gas is commonly associated with coals, and it is reasonable to suppose that heavier hydrocarbons also might be derived from coal-forming materials. They are formed when coke is made from coal. If there is a close generic relation between the formation of coals and the formation of oils, one should expect frequently to find oil-soaked coals and coal measures impregnated with oil, and also coal or lignite in the oil measures. The great coal-producing strata of the earth generally are not the oil-producing strata. Many of the oil-producing strata are, nevertheless, lignitic or closely associated with highly lignitic beds—more generally in Europe and Asia than in North America.

In Pennsylvania oil is found in large amounts in Devonian strata far below any important beds of coal. In Oklahoma the great deposits of oil in Ordovician beds are generally separated from the coal-bearing strata by thick beds of limestone and shales. In California no important beds of coal are found in the oil fields.

In brief, the organic materials that have formed coals and lignites may have contributed fractions that have accumulated as deposits of petroleum and gas. It is improbable, however, that the principal coal deposits have formed from the materials that have contributed the principal petroleum deposits. This is shown at many places by the presence of barren sands between the oil sands and coal beds. There are probably in all fields, moreover, other sources of organic matter adequate to have supplied petroleum.

[1] CUNNINGHAM-CRAIG, E. H., Origin of Oil and Shale, Roy. Soc. Edinburgh *Proc.*, vol. 36, pp. 44–86, 1916.

[2] PICTET, A. and M. BOUVIER, Ueber die Distillation der Steinkohle Unter Vermindertem Druck, *Deut. chem. Ges. Ber.*, pp. 33–42, 1913.

Petroleum in Beds Formed under Arid Conditions.—Many petroliferous strata are closely associated ,with red beds, salt, and gypsum—
strata that are assumed to have formed under arid conditions. This
association is noteworthy, for arid conditions generally are not favorable
to the accumulation of organic remains. Salt and gypsum in the main are
formed in arms of the sea or precipitated in closed basins, such as do not
exist in moist climates. Most marine organisms, moreover, will perish
in salt solutions that are highly concentrated. Practically all the oil-
bearing series that contain beds formed under arid conditions include
also, associated with red beds, salt, and gypsum, bodies of marine strata
containing organic matter or remains of organic bodies, which may have
supplied material for the formation of petroleum. Strata formed under
arid conditions doubtless supply the favorable reservoirs rather than the
sources of organic matter that yields petroleum.

Shore-line Relations.—The beds that are assumed to be the sources
of oil in the various oil fields of the world show a great range with respect
to shore-line relations.[1] The commonest types of source beds are doubtless of shallow-water origin. Many oil shales show abundant evidence
of deposition in shallow water. Important source beds include silts,
shales, and limestones, and, among the latter, coral reefs and other
limestone reefs appear to have been important sources. In Burma and
in the Sunda islands many of the oil fields lie in great deltas of Tertiary
age, and nearly all of the geologists who have described these fields
regard deltaic conditions as peculiarly favorable for the formation of
both the source and reservoir beds. Trask[2] showed that oil, or materials
from which oil may be distilled, is much more abundant in fine-grained
rocks, such as clays, than in silts and sands. The relatively high yields of
limy oozes indicate that certain limestones also may be important sources
of oil. Deposits laid down relatively near shore are likely to be richer in
organic matter than those laid down far from land. Even if the continental shelf is far from shore, however, it is possible that the sediments
deposited on it may be of high organic content. Much organic matter
of the sea is derived from plankton, and when the continental shelf
is far from shore, plankton may be plentiful above it. Since plankton[3]
has nearly the weight of sea water, it does not require much current to
move it. If the shallow sea bottom is subject to wave action or to
currents, therefore, plankton particles are likely to be moved to deeper
water where they can not be washed out, and thus they accumulate,

[1] WHITE, D., "Treatise on Sedimentation," by W. H. Twenhofel and others, p.
302, 1926.

THIESSEN, R., Origin and Composition of Certain Oil Shales, *Econ. Geol.*, vol.
16, pp. 289–300, 1921.

[2] TRASK, P. D., Am. Assoc. Pet. Geol. *Bull.*, vol. 12, pp. 1057–1068, 1928.

[3] Plankton: floating or drifting organisms of the sea, either plants or animals,
as distinguished from coast and bottom forms.

probably in considerable amounts, in deep water; presumably they are swept into the abyssal depths beyond the continental platform.

Deposits formed in regions subject to considerable tidal action do not seem to be good source beds, since, according to Trask, they contain little organic matter. On the continental platform off the coast of the state of Washington, the sediments now forming have a relatively low organic content, although the surface waters of this region are rich in diatoms which are killed during certain parts of the year by influx of fresh water. Samples of sandy silt taken 25 miles from land in this area at a depth of 110 meters produced only 0.1 gallon of oil per ton. The storms that occur in this region agitate the sea bottom and prevent the accumulation of the remains of the diatoms. In this connection the studies of Goldman are noteworthy. In the bottom of the Potomac River near its mouth there is a large depression in which black mud rich in organic matter accumulates. This material gives off hydrogen sulphide on decomposition and the finer material is richest in organic matter.[1]

Source Organisms.—According to Engler and Hoefer[2] the remains of animals, particularly the remains of fishes, are important sources of petroleum. Clark[3] mentions calculations by Szajnocha which show that the annual catch of herring on the northeast coast of Germany could yield in 2,560 years as much oil as Galicia had produced (1900) if half the fats were converted into oil. Near Bloomington, Indiana, the St. Louis limestone contains gastropod casts that carry petroleum which, according to Reeves,[4] is probably indigenous to the fossil. Lahee[5] found in Argentina shells of cephalopods which, when broken open, show residues of grahamite or rafaelite.

Foraminifera shells are commonly abundant in organic sediments and Foraminifera are regarded as possible sources of oil. Cushman[6] observes that certain Foraminifera, *Iridia diaphana*, placed in a dish overnight left their shells and in the morning were found as naked masses swimming freely. In their method of growth these bodies appear to form new tests. Thus, as noted by Stipp,[7] a large proportion of tests

[1] GOLDMAN, M. I., "Black Shale" Formation in and about Chesapeake Bay, Am. Assoc. Pet. Geol. *Bull.*, vol. 8, pp. 195–201, 1924.

[2] ENGLER, C., and H. HOEFER, *Das Erdoel*, vol. 2, p. 91, 1909.

[3] CLARK, F. W., The Data of Geochemistry, U. S. Geol. Survey *Bull.* 770, p. 749, 1924.

[4] REEVES, J. R., Am. Assoc. Pet. Geol. *Bull.*, vol. 9, p. 667, 1925.

[5] LAHEE, F. H., Note on the Origin of Petroleum, Am. Assoc. Pet. Geol. *Bull.*, vol. 8, pp. 669–671, 1924.

[6] CUSHMAN, J. A., Monograph on the Foraminifera of the North Pacific Ocean, U. S. Nat. Museum *Bull.* 71, p. 7, 1910; also, Shallow-water Foraminifera of the Tortugas Region, Carnegie Inst. Wash., vol. 17, p. 8, 1922.

[7] STIPP, T. F., The Relation of Foraminifera to the Origin of California Petroleum, Am. Assoc. Pet. Geol. *Bull.*, vol. 10, pp. 697–702, 1926.

observed in strata probably were empty of animal tissue at the time of burial.

In normal life processes organic matter is consumed by animal organisms in large amounts, and the soft parts of animal organisms are likely to be devoured before burial. If, however, sudden changes of conditions result in the death of large numbers of organisms, the preservation of their remains by burial is probable. It is believed that at certain places death results from sudden influx of fresh water into the sea, and it has been suggested that the dessication of salt water in closed basins results in death of organisms of the basin. This theory has been suggested to account for the origin of oil deposits that are not infrequently found to be associated with salt, red beds, and gypsum.

Vegetable matter is commonly assumed to be an important source if not chief source of petroleum. This, as already noted, is emphasized by the studies of White, Thiessen, Winchester, and others already cited. Redwood[1] states that the salt marshes of Sardinia are sometimes covered with sheets of seaweed which are in process of decomposition into an oily substance resembling petroleum. The fact that iodine is found in seaweeds and also in the waters of certain oil fields is significant in this connection. Stuart[2] believes that the oils of Burma have formed largely from oils that were in the trunks of heavy logs rich in resin, and that the oil was expressed after burial of the logs and particularly during their petrifaction and silicification. Diatoms are believed to be important sources of oil, and they are abundant in strata that are closely associated with oil in many oil fields. Algae are believed to be important sources of oil.

In connection with the agency of diatoms in the generation of oil, the observations at Copalis Beach,[3] Washington, 60 miles north of the Columbia River, are instructive. Diatoms live in great numbers off the shallow beach, particularly *Aulacodiscus kittoni*, which is a centric marine diatom floating at the surface (Fig. 17). At intervals the diatoms die in great numbers and green masses of their remains are washed up by the waves. The epidemics follow the rainy season or a heavy rain when the sea water is diluted by fresh water, and they reach a maximum when the rain is followed by bright sunshine. The diatom remains, dried, contain 78.7 per cent of siliceous material and 2.07 per cent of oil which was extracted by ether. The oily matter represents 9.7 per cent of the total non-siliceous material of the diatom.

Fig. 17.—A diatom, magnified 250 diameters. (*Photograph by G. D. Hanna.*)

[1] REDWOOD, B., "A Treatise of Petroleum," vol. 1, p. 184, 1922.

[2] STUART, MURRAY, "The Geology of Oil, Shale, and Coal," pp. 60–78, London, 1926; *Econ. Geol.*, vol. 9, pp. 594–597, 1914.

[3] BECKING, L. B., C. F. TOLMAN, H. C. McMILLAN, J. FIELD, and T. HASHIMOTO, Preliminary Statement Regarding the Diatom "Epidemics" at Copalis Beach, Washington, and an Analysis of Diatom Oil, *Econ. Geol.*, vol. 22, pp. 356–368, 1927.

When the living diatom was placed in fresh water, the shell broke apart and the chlorophyl bodies came out. The plastids, that is, the small bodies of protoplasm in the cells, in 5 minutes had swollen so that their diameters were doubled. Oil began to ooze out, and in 45 minutes the process appeared to be complete. Thus it appears that the osmotic pressure of the cell sap breaks the shell and drives out the oil, which lodges in surrounding colloidal material.

As shown above, oil may be generated by the chlorophyl bodies enclosed in a diatom test by a purely biogenetic process, as well as by bacterial decay and destructive distillation, and, as stated by Tolman,[1] the energy necessary for the chlorophyl to break up carbon dioxide and water and form organic compounds of higher energy content comes from sunlight which "activates" chlorophyl.

In California there are beds of diatomite hundreds of feet thick, consisting essentially of diatom tests and of their fragments. At places opal is associated with the diatomite and locally replaces it. This opal, according to Tolman, is secreted largely by diatoms. Although they contain oil, diatoms do not contain the substances that are found in California oils. Experiments have been made to ascertain the decomposition products of diatoms under conditions of anærobic bacterial decay. These products include carbon dioxide, methane, and hydrogen sulphide, but none of the higher hydrocarbons are identified.[2] The data now available are inconclusive as regards the part played by diatoms.

In the Echigo oil fields in Japan, as pointed out by Iki[3] and by Takahashi,[4] the oil has probably been derived from dark shales, and these shales contain abundant diatoms. As noted by Takahashi, the most flinty shales are diatomaceous. These shales were probably not deposited in deep water but near the shore in sheltered parts of the sea. The studies of the genesis of the petroleum deposits of the oil fields of Japan have great significance because in some of the fields the oil series rests unconformably on igneous rocks, and it appears improbable that pre-Tertiary strata have contributed oil to the reservoirs. In view of the fact that many investigators regard the organisms of low orders as particularly prolific sources of petroleum, the high yield of oil from an algal inland lake near Ocala,[5] Florida, is significant.

---

[1] TOLMAN, C. F., Biogenesis of Hydrocarbons by Diatoms, *Econ. Geol.*, vol. 22, pp. 454–474, 1927.

[2] HEALD, K. C., Report of the Committee on Studies in Petroleum Geology, p. 16, May 3, 1930 (mimeograph sheets).

[3] IKI, T., Some Studies of the Stratigraphy of the Tertiary Formation in the Echigo Oil Field, Japan, *Jour. Geol. and Geog.*, vol. 1, pp. 9–90, 1922.

[4] TAKAHASHI, J. R., The Marine Kerogen Shale from the Oil Fields of Japan, *Science Repts.* Tôhoku Imp. Univ., ser. 3, vol. 1, No. 2, pp. 63–156, Sendai, 1922.

[5] TRASK, P. D., Am. Assoc. Pet. Geol. *Bull.*, vol. 12, p. 1066, 1928.

In any theory that is proposed to account for the origin of oil, quantitative relations are important. Arnold, Anderson, and Johnson[1] noted, long ago, that most of the oil deposits of California are associated with great thicknesses of beds containing large amounts of diatoms which it was supposed supplied the oil. The most common source appears to be the Monterey shale of Miocene age. Subsequent work has supported the theory in the main, although in the oil fields in Pliocene strata in the Los Angeles basin this relation is not so clearly shown. According to Cunningham, the oil in Pliocene strata in the Los Angeles basin originated in the Pliocene strata in organic shales which are relatively poor in diatoms, and he believes that the oil is derived from material that was carried into the basin by the rivers[2] and deposited in sea water in Pliocene time.

In conclusion it may be said that oil is derived from organic matter of both animal and vegetable origin, marine and non-marine, and that it is probably derived from the remains of many kinds of plants and animals. The almost constant association of oil with salt water supports the theory that most oil deposits, if not all of them, have accumulated in the sea.

[1] ARNOLD, R., and R. ANDERSON, Geology and Oil Deposits of the Coalinga District, California, U. S. Geol. Survey *Bull.*, 398, 1910.

——— and H. R. JOHNSON, Preliminary Report on the McKittrick Oil Region, U. S. Geol. Survey *Bull.* 406, 1910.

[2] CUNNINGHAM, G. M., Were Diatoms the Chief Source of California Oil? Am. Assoc. Pet. Geol. *Bull.*, vol. 10, pp. 709–721, 1926.

CHAPTER VI

MAPS AND LOGS

STRUCTURAL CONTOUR MAPS

Structural contour maps are used extensively in mapping oil fields. They show approximately, by contours, the position of a bed or horizon over the entire area mapped, and one familiar with their use may picture the structure from them at a glance. As a rule, it is not possible to map a bed or horizon over a large folded area. At some places it may be removed by erosion; at others it may be concealed. Its outcrops are mapped and their elevations noted at many places, with the dip and strike (Fig. 18). Its positions in wells also are recorded. Where it has

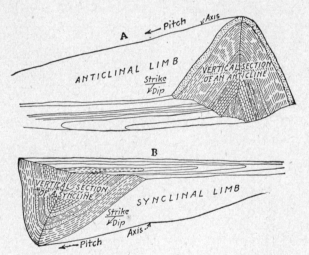

FIG. 18.—Sketches showing parts of folds. (*After Willis.*)

been removed by erosion, any bed below it that is now exposed is noted, and the former position of the bed to be mapped is estimated from its distance above the exposed bed in the geologic column as determined within or near the area.

If the structure is domatic the contours will "close," or pass all the way around the dome. Such a fold is called a "closed fold." Figure 19a is a sketch showing elevations of the same stratum or horizon at different places; Fig. 19b is a sketch of the same area with structural contours drawn to connect points of equal elevation. It outlines an elongated dome, or anticline, with at least 30 feet of closure. Figure 20 is a

60

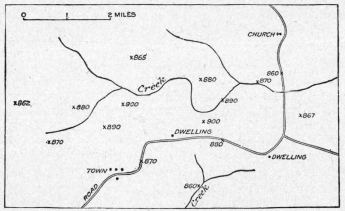

FIG. 19*a*.—Sketch map showing elevation of the same stratum at different points in feet above sea level marked by crosses. (*After Gardner.*)

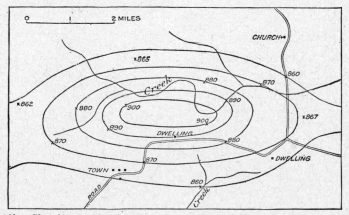

FIG. 19*b*.—Sketch map showing elevations of same stratum at different points marked by crosses as in Fig. 19*a*. The structure contours are drawn connecting points of equal elevation, thus outlining an elongated dome. (*After Gardner.*)

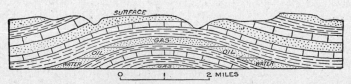

FIG. 20.—Lengthwise section of elongated dome shown in Fig. 19*a*, vertical scale greatly exaggerated. (*After Gardner.*)

lengthwise section of the anticline, in which the vertical scale is greatly exaggerated.

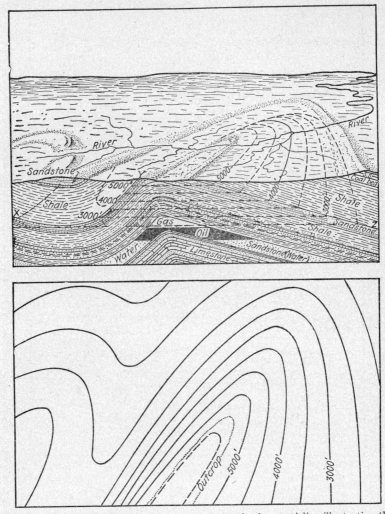

Fig. 21.—Upper figure is a cross section and sketch of an anticline illustrating the use of structure contours. Lower figure is a structure contour map of the same anticline. The structure contours are drawn on top of the sandstone *XYZ*. (*After Hewett & Lupton, with additions.*)

In ordinary mapping of beds having complicated structure, it is not regarded good practice to use a vertical scale on the cross-section that is different from the horizontal scale, because it gives a distorted picture of the structure. For mapping flat-lying rocks, however, this practice is necessary. In some fields the folds are so low that they can not be shown on a true scale. If a contour map is used to depict the structure, together with the section, the amount of exaggeration is instantly apparent.

In some fields the relation of oil and gas accumulations to structure is very close. On the presence of a closure of 30 feet may depend the

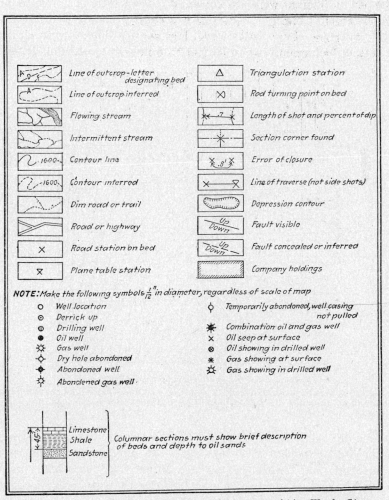

FIG. 22.—Symbols commonly used on field maps. (*After Woodruff.*)

localization of 30 feet of sand saturated with oil or gas. The mapping is done as accurately as is possible with instruments of precision.

Small domes like that shown in Fig. 19 are typically developed in the oil fields of Oklahoma and Kansas. In fields in mountainous countries the structural features are larger and the dips steeper. Figure 21 shows a sketch and cross-section of an anticline with a contour map.

It is desirable that as far as practicable the same symbols be used on different maps. Figure 22 is a chart, prepared by E. G. Woodruff, showing symbols that are commonly used.

When the true direction of dip of a bed and the differences in elevations of the bed in different wells are known, it is frequently desirable to determine the amount of dip. Figure 23 is a chart prepared by F. H. Lahee for this purpose. Suppose two well logs show a difference in elevation of a certain bed amounting to 30 feet to a mile in a direction N. 40° E.

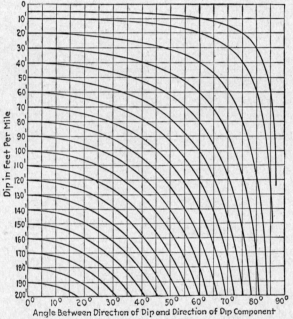

Fig. 23.—Chart for determining the amount of true dip, when components are known, on lines oblique to line of dip. Horizontal lines represent true dip, curved lines represent dip components. (*After Lahee.*)

The true dip is known to be N. 80° E. The angle between the true dip and the dip component is 40 degrees. The intersection of the vertical line marked "40°" with the curve marked "30'" indicates that the amount of the true dip in the area between the two wells is about 40 feet to the mile.

In recent years geophysical methods have come into wide use in connection with prospecting for oil and mapping oil-bearing areas. The data obtained by these methods are interpreted and used in connection with other geological data.

CONVERGENCE

In certain areas groups of strata thin out or converge in one direction and become thicker or diverge in the opposite direction. Thus they form wedges and at places such wedges lie above an oil sand. If such a wedge is present between the rock mapped at the surface and the producing sand, it is obvious that the structure at the producing horizon will be different from that shown at the surface.[1] A dome shown in the surface

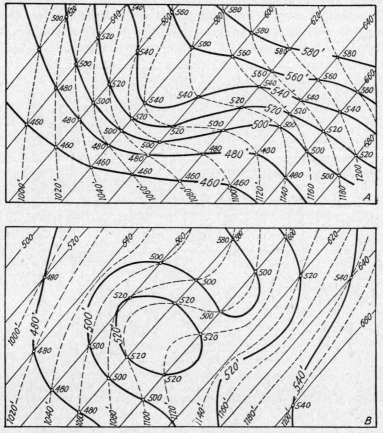

Fig. 24.—Maps showing effects of convergence on two types of folding. Structure of beds at surface shown by light dashed lines, convergence by light solid lines, structure of lower formation (oil sand), by heavy solid lines. Elevation on broken line, minus interval on convergence line, equals elevation on heavy line. In the upper figure the anticline plunging nearly at a right angle to the direction of convergence shows a terrace up dip, but the structure does not close with depth. In Fig. *B*, the anticline plunges in the direction of the convergence and shows a terrace up dip; with depth the open structure becomes closed. (*After Levorsen.*)

beds may be wanting at the horizon of the oil sand. An open anticline plunging in the direction of the regional dip, and particularly one that plunges below a flatter part of the axis, may indicate a closed structure or dome below the plunging anticline. The convergence of the strata is

[1] Levorsen, A. I., Convergence Studies in the Mid-Continent Region, Am. Assoc. Pet. Geol. *Bull.*, vol. 11, pp. 657–682, 1927.

commonly regular and the amount is often known over state-wide areas. In such areas the convergence sheet is generally made up on tracing cloth for the interval between the stratum that is mapped at the surface and the deep-lying oil sand. The elevation of the latter at any point may be ascertained by subtracting the amount of the interval from the elevation of the outcropping bed. Thus, by determining a large number of points showing the position of the oil sand, it is possible to draw contours show-

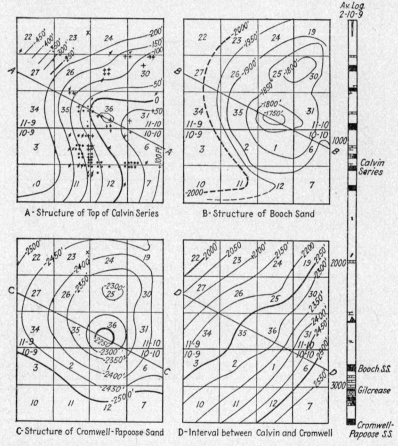

Fig. 25.—Sketches showing structure of Garrison field, Okfuskee County, Oklahoma. (*After Levorsen.*)

ing the structure of the latter. In Figs. 24a and 24b the light dotted lines show the attitude of the bed mapped, the light solid lines show the convergence, and the heavy solid lines show the attitude of the lower beds. Both of these figures show gentle plunging anticlines or structural noses. In the upper figure the nose shown on the dotted line plunges nearly at right angles to the direction of the convergence. The structure of the deep horizon is indicated by the heavy solid line and shows merely a similar structure but dipping in a different direction. In the lower figure the anticline dips northwest in the direction of the convergence and it flattens up dip. The deep sand, when contoured, shows a dome.

In parts of Oklahoma and in north-central Texas there is a great convergence to the northwest between the Upper Pennsylvanian and Mississippian strata. In Fig. 25a, Garrison field, 5 miles south of Okemah, Okfuskee County, Oklahoma, the top of the Calvin series is

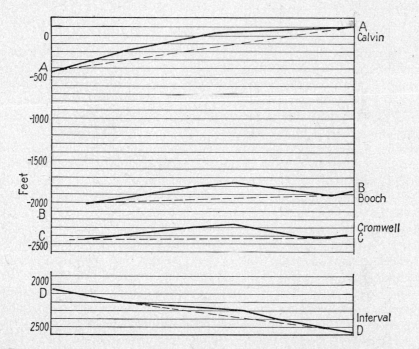

Fig. 26.—Cross section, Garrison field, Okfuskee County, Oklahoma on lines shown on Fig. 25. Section AA on top of Calvin series shows the axis of an anticline plunging northwest and becoming flat up dip; BB is drawn on the Booch sand across the dome, Fig. 25B. The beds between the Calvin and Booch formations increase to the southeast; CC on the Cromwell sand is drawn across the dome Fig. 25C; DD shows the amount of convergence or interval between the Calvin and Cromwell formations which is shown also on Fig. 25D. The folding of the Calvin is almost as much as the folding of the Cromwell sand, the difference being the small fold shown on DD. (*After Levorsen.*)

mapped near the surface. Figure 25d is the convergence map of the interval between the Calvin series and Cromwell sand. Figure 25b shows the structure of the Booch sand and Fig. 25c shows the structure of the Cromwell-Papoose sand. The horizons of both of these sands are indicated in the section at the right of the figure. By subtracting the amount of the interval Fig. 25d from the elevation of the Calvin Fig. 25a, the structure of the Cromwell-Papoose sand (Fig. 25c,) may be drawn. If, as appears probable, the Calvin series was essentially flat when it was deposited, then Fig. 25d may be regarded as showing the structure of the Cromwell sand when the Calvin series was deposited. At that time the Cromwell had a nearly uniform southeast dip about 95 feet per mile. Cross-sections (Fig. 26) show the Calvin, Booch, and Cromwell sands. Note the increasing plunge of the Calvin to the northwest and the dip of the lower sands to the southeast below the area where the Calvin sand is nearly flat lying. The Calvin sand is folded almost as much as the Cromwell sand, the difference being the small fold shown in the section of the convergence (Fig. 25d).

WELL LOGS

In mapping the geology of an oil field use is made of both the surface exposures and the information obtained by drilling. In areas covered by mantle rock the wells supply most of the detailed information. Where an anticline is found exposed and plunging and where the upper end is concealed, it is desirable to ascertain whether the concealed end rises and brings an oil sand to the hard-rock surface below the mantle rock, or whether it also plunges so as to form a dome or closed structure. This information may be gained by pitting or by drilling shallow holes with the diamond drill. It is common practice for oil companies to engage geologists or micropaleontologists to study the cuttings of wells as they are drilled and to identify the sands by studying the fossils or by making separations and detailed investigations of the sands. Core samples are taken for study. Most well records, however, are the logs of drillers and the geologist must utilize the drillers' records and interpret them as accurately as possible. As a rule, the well records of a field have been taken by several drillers working for different companies. In general, there is a courteous exchange of information between the companies, but there is no standard practice of logging wells among drillers.

The driller's log depends principally upon the erudition of the driller and his previous experience. He often carries the names of rocks encountered in one district to another perhaps far removed and in different surroundings. The rocks encountered with the cable or impact drill may be recorded differently when encountered with the rotary drill which progresses by abrasion.

A "hard rock" is generally one that is hard to make progress in. If the cable system is used, a stratum of gypsum might be classed as a hard rock because it is elastic and not readily broken by blows, whereas a hard brittle limestone which is easily drilled would be classed as "soft." The gypsum would be classed as soft if the rotary system is used, because it is readily cut, whereas the limestone which resists abrasion would be hard.[1]

---

[1] KNAPP, A., Rock Classification from the Oil-driller's Standpoint, *Mining Met.* Sec. 26, No. 158, pp. 1 6, February, 1920.

"Slates" are reported in most logs of wells that are driven through argillaceous rocks that are more consolidated than clays or soft shales. Oil sands are rocks that contain oil, whether sands, sandstones, limestones, or dolomites.

With the rotary drill, a formation is "sticky" which cuts in large pieces that adhere to the bit and drill pipe. A formation that is sticky with the rotary is usually sticky with the cable tools. On the other hand, formations are encountered in which the cable tools stick, owing either to the elasticity of the formation or to the fact that the drilled-up particles do not mix readily with the water in the hole and settle so quickly as to stick the bit. These formations might not appear sticky to the rotary driller.

The term "sandy" may be used accurately by the cable-tool driller. He obtains samples of the formation, through which he passes, of sufficient size to determine the relative amount of sand to clay or sand to shale in any formation. In the case of the rotary drill, this term is misleading. The rotary well is drilled with the aid of a "mud" of varying density. It is usually a mixture of clay, sand, and water. Mud often contains as high as 40 to 50 per cent sand. As stated by Knapp, any change in the density of the mud changes its capacity to carry sand. Even a small shower falling on the slush pit will change the density enough to cause some of the suspended sand to be precipitated. These properties of the mud lead to error in the observation of the formation. If a clay formation containing a moderate amount of sand is encountered while drilling in a mud low in sand content, the mud will absorb most of the sand, which will not settle out in the overflow ditch, and its presence in the formation will not be noted if not felt by the action of the bit in drilling. If, some time later, the mud is thinned by adding water, this sand will appear in the overflow and may be attributed to a formation many feet below the one from which it actually originated.

The so-called "jigging" action of the rising column of mud on the sand or cuttings also leads to misinterpretation. The deeper the drill the finer the sand in cuttings brought to the surface by mud. As stated by Knapp, the coarser particles are pounded into the walls of the well or broken.

A change in the speed of pumping the mud also causes a change in the amount and size of the cuttings that appear at the surface. Thus, in the case of the rotary, "sandy" may have little or no meaning when applied to a formation. The term "sandy" is often used in contradistinction to "sticky." A formation that drills easily and is not sticky is often recorded as sandy because sand tends to decrease stickiness.

A wet specimen, fresh from the hole, has a different color from the same specimen dried. Many specimens, when dried, bleach. Many of them air slack or oxidize. The terms "light" and "dark" should be used only for the extremes.   They are, in general, relative.   A sample of wet shale examined under an electric light might appear darker than in daylight.

Clay is readily recognized by the "feel of the bit" while drilling with either cable tools or rotary.   To some drillers all clay is gumbo while to others gumbo is only sticky clay.   Some clays have the property of cutting in large pieces but do not adhere excessively to the bit and drill pipe and are designated as "tough."

Free uncemented sand is easily recognized by the feel of the tools in both systems of drilling.   "Packed sand" is a sand that is slightly cemented with some soft, easily broken, cementing material, such as calcium carbonate.   It cuts, when drilled with a rotary, with much the same feeling as when cutting crayon with a knife.   The cementing material is dissolved or broken before reaching the surface, so that the driller finds only sand in the overflow.   A microscopic examination of sands from the overflow often shows cementing material to be present when not suspected by the action of the bit.

A quicksand is one that caves or sticks the tools; a heaving sand is one that rises in the bore.   A "shell" may be the test of an organism or a thin layer of any kind of sedimentary rock.

With the development of the rotary drill the examination of cuttings has become increasingly important.   When this drill is used the hole is filled with a mud which commonly weighs about 11 pounds per gallon. The rotary string is a rotating tube with a cutting device at the end. The purpose of the heavy fluid is to increase the pressure on the walls of the bore and thus to prevent caving, and also it has the effect of making the weight of the string of rotary tools lighter than it would be if the hole were filled with water.   The pressure of thousands of feet of heavy fluid is so great that an oil sand or gas sand might be encountered and passed through without its discovery unless oil or gas is under very high pressure.   The cuttings of the rotary bit are carefully washed to free them from mud.   Samples are taken every few feet and examined microscopically.   The sample from the bottom of the well consists of cuttings from many beds from near the bottom of the bore.   These are examined for the presence of new material that has not previously appeared in the samples.   The new material is from the lowest bed represented.

Survey of Holes.—Holes drilled by the diamond drill, rotary drill, or cable tools are rarely straight.   Many of them flatten out and some tend to wander from the perpendicular in several planes.   Most shallow diamond-drill holes are nearly straight but even moderately deep ones often curve 40 degrees or more, especially when started at a considerable angle to beds.   Frequently, in tilted rocks they change direction so that they tend to cut beds at right angles.   Great changes in direction may take place in diamond-drill holes of small gage between 500 and 1,000 feet deep.

There are several devices for the survey of holes. Some use bottles half filled with hydrofluoric acid. The bottles are placed in the drilling tube, and; after they are lowered in the hole, they are allowed to rest until the acid etches a line where its upper surface comes to rest. Other devices make a record at various depths on a photographic film. These and similar devices may be used in wells drilled by rotary and cable tools. The practice of surveying deep holes is becoming well established in certain areas.

There is a device also that records the direction from which fluids are moving to the bottom of a well. This consists of a magnetic needle which shows the orientation of the instrument, a vane which registers the direction of movement, and a fluid which solidifies after the device comes to rest.

CHAPTER VII

ACCUMULATION OF PETROLEUM

Water, oil, and gas in porous strata tend to arrange themselves in accordance with their density—the oil above the water and the gas above the oil (Fig. 27). In folded rocks that are saturated with water, oil, and gas, the oil and gas rise to the crests of the upfolds, or anticlines,

Fig. 27.—Section through Bartlesville sand, Cushing field, Oklahoma. (*After Beal.*)

and the water is found on the flanks of the anticlines and in synclines. If the rocks are dry, the oil is found low on the folds or in synclines. If some water is present, the oil floats on the water and will be found low on the anticlines, its position depending on the amount of water present. On monoclines that are sealed, the oil rises above the water and the gas above the oil.

THE ANTICLINAL THEORY

The theory of gravitational arrangement according to density is generally referred to as the anticlinal theory. This theory was formulated as a result of work in the Appalachian field of the United States and in the Ontario field. It is doubtful, however, whether the theory meets as many difficulties in any other large oil field in the world as in the Appalachian region, where many of the sands are not saturated with water. In these sands the oil is found far down on the flanks of the anticlines and in synclines. At some places, especially in the well-known fields in Pennsylvania near Pittsburgh, these sands are very productive, and it was natural that the theory should have met a lack of enthusiasm where pronounced exceptions to it were so prominently displayed.

The fact that oil, gas, and water will separate by gravity was first noted in America[1] by Andrews[2] and by Hunt.[3] Andrews had studied

---

[1] Engler and Hoefer state that Oldham recognized a connection between the anticline and oil accumulation at Yenangyaung in 1855 (*Das Erdoel*, Band 2, p. 18).

[2] ANDREWS, E. B., Rock Oil, Its Relations and Distribution, *Am. Jour. Sci.*, 2d ser., vol. 32, pp. 85–91, 1861.

[3] HUNT, T. S., Notes on the Geology of Petroleum or Rock Oil, *Canadian Naturalist*, vol. 6, pp. 241–255, 1861.

the Burning Springs-Volcano anticline of West Virginia, and Hunt the Petrolia and Oil Springs domes of Lambton County, Ontario. In these localities the segregation of oil and its accumulation at the tops of domes is very marked.

Alexander Winchell and J. S. Newberry gave the theory a more definite form. Winchell[1] based his conclusions chiefly on the relations he had observed in Ontario, and Newberry[2] on the areas in western Pennsylvania, West Virginia, and eastern Ohio. In the years immediately following these discussions the theory made little progress. The fields of Pennsylvania were then being developed, and in these fields many of the accumulations are in synclines. Lesley[3] and his associates of the Pennsylvania Geological Survey opposed the anticlinal theory. The theory was discredited in many quarters, because so many exceptions to it had been found. I. C. White[4] revived it, worked out many problems nearly related to it, and was probably the first investigator in the United States to use it in a practical way.

Orton agreed with White as to his main contention and soon after the discovery of oil in the Trenton fields of Ohio and Indiana made a survey of the fields and found that accumulations were on or near anticlinal axes and on terraces or "arrested anticlines," where there was a flattening of the northward dip of the strata.[5] Later, Orton published a monograph on the Lima-Indiana field.[6] In this paper he amplified his former discoveries and presented a map,[7] which is probably the first contour map drawn for the purpose of showing structure in an oil field. This report marks a decided advance in geologic methods applied to mapping the structure of oil fields. It was followed by a series of brilliant papers by men engaged in the survey of the Appalachian oil region by the United States and Pennsylvania geological surveys under the direction

[1] WINCHELL, ALEXANDER, On the Oil Formation in Michigan and Elsewhere, *Am. Jour. Sci.*, 2d ser., vol. 39, p. 352, 1865; Something About Petroleum, "Sketches of Creation," Harper & Brothers, 1870; also notes, in appendix, about initial production of Ontario wells.

[2] NEWBERRY, J. S., Devonian System, Ohio Geol. Survey, vol. 1, p. 160, 1873.

[3] LESLEY, J. P., Geology of the Pittsburgh Coal Region, Am. Inst. Min. Eng. *Trans.*, vol. 14, pp. 654–655, 1886.

ASHBURNER, C. A., The Production and Exhaustion of the Oil Regions of Pennsylvania and New York, Am. Inst. Min. Eng. *Trans.*, vol. 14, pp. 419–428, 1886; The Geology of Natural Gas, Am. Inst. Min. Eng. *Trans.*, vol. 14, p. 434, 1886.

[4] WHITE, I. C., The Geology of Natural Gas, *Science*, vol. 6, June 26, 1885; Petroleum and Natural Gas, W. Va. Geol. Survey, vol. A, pp. 48–64, 1904 (a reprint and amplification of the first paper).

[5] ORTON, EDWARD, The Origin and Accumulation of Petroleum and Natural Gas, Ohio Geol. Survey, vol. 6, p. 94, 1888.

[6] ORTON, EDWARD, The Trenton Limestone as a Source of Petroleum and Inflammable Gas in Ohio and Indiana, U. S. Geol. Survey *Eighth Ann. Rept.*, pt. 2, pp. 475–662, 1889.

[7] *Op. cit.*, pl. 55, opp. p. 548.

of Campbell.　These reports and the structural contour maps accompanying them have shown that oil and gas occur at the tops of structural
uplifts in saturated rocks and lower in unsaturated rocks.　Woolsey[1]
in 1906 noted that the oil was found high in anticlines where the beds
contain water and in the hollows of synclines where they do not.　F. G.
Clapp[2] and Stone and Clapp[3] investigated further the occurrence and
relations of oil, gas, and water in unsaturated synclines.　Griswold and
Munn[4] in 1907 made a detailed report on a large area in southwestern
Pennsylvania in which the oil in the saturated rocks, the Big Injun sand,
and beds above it, was found in the higher parts of anticlines, and that
in the unsaturated rocks, the Hundred-foot sand, and those below it,
on the flanks of anticlines and in synclines (Fig. 86).　They suggested the
hypothesis that the unsaturated rocks had formerly been saturated
and partly drained.　Later, Reeves[5] reviewed the problem and stated
that the unsaturated rocks in the Catskill of the Devonian are a fresh-
water or terrigenous series that was probably dry when buried below the
sea.　Recently, marine fossils were found in certain of the Devonian
beds in the Appalachian region and Reeves' suggestion loses some of its
force.

During the development of the California oil fields, Arnold and
his associates worked out the structural details of accumulations.　They
found that the principal oil pools are on anticlines and monoclines sealed
with asphalt or by faults.[6]

Later, the structural relations in the Illinois fields were found to
accord with the gravitational theory.　The accumulations of the Kansas,
Oklahoma, Texas, Louisiana, and Wyoming fields were found to be in
accord with it, except where the rocks are dry.　Some of the deposits
are found in sealed monoclines or terraces, but the gravitational arrange-

[1] Woolsey, L. H., Economic Geology of the Beaver Quadrangle, Pennsylvania,
U. S. Geol. Survey *Bull.* 286, p. 81, 1906.

[2] Clapp, F. G., Economic Geology of the Amity Quadrangle, Pennsylvania, U. S.
Geol. Survey *Bull.* 300, pp. 1–145, 1907.

[3] Stone, R. W., and F. G. Clapp, Oil and Gas of Greene County, Pennsylvania,
U. S. Geol. Survey *Bull.* 304, pp. 79–82, 1907.

[4] Griswold, W. T. and M. J. Munn, Geology of the Steubenville, Burgettstown,
and Clayville Quadrangles, Ohio, West Virginia, and Pennsylvania, U. S. Geol.
Survey *Bull.* 318, 1907.

[5] Reeves, Frank, The Absence of Water in Certain Sandstones of Appalachian
Oil Fields, *Econ. Geol.*, vol. 12, pp. 354–378, 1917.

[6] Arnold, Ralph and Robert Anderson, Geology and Oil Resources of the Coalinga District, California, U. S. Geol. Survey *Bull.* 398, pp. 1–354, 1910.

——— and H. R. Johnson, Preliminary Report on the McKittrick-Sunset Oil
Region, Kern and San Luis Obispo Counties, California, U. S. Geol. Survey *Bull.*
406, pp. 1–225, 1910.

Eldridge, G. H., and Ralph Arnold, The Santa Clara Valley, Puente Hills,
and Los Angeles Districts, Southern California, U. S. Geol. Survey *Bull.* 309, pp. 1–263,
1907.

ment[1] is in general clearly expressed. Nearly every report on an oil field in any country that has been published in recent years discusses the relations of the accumulation to structure.

The differences in the surface tension of oil and water cause them to separate, the oil and gas occupying the large spaces and the water the small ones. This segregation, as pointed out by Washburne,[2] attends gravitational separation, and its influence has been noted in many fields.

The development of the anticlinal theory in Europe and Asia parallels that in North America. Engler and Hoefer[3] state that a relation between the oil deposits of Burma and the anticline was noted by Oldham as early as 1855. The fields of Western and Central Europe are generally complicated by faulting and those of Germany and Roumania are generally developed around salt cores. Consequently, the controlling features of accumulation often were not made clear until development was well advanced. In certain fields in Galicia, however, the relation of oil accumulation to anticlines is obvious. In Russia, Burma, Netherlands India, and Japan the anticlines are strong and well defined, and the relations of the oil fields to their axes are convincingly shown in nearly all large fields. The adoption of the theory made rapid progress in Russia and Asia, where no great synclinal accumulations of oil corresponding to those of the Appalachian region in the Western Hemisphere are known. Consequently, many of the oil companies operating in the eastern fields accepted the anticlinal theory in the earlier days with more enthusiasm than certain companies operating early in the Appalachian fields. The construction of the structural contour maps which are generally used in connection with the delineation of anticlines and domes was perfected in North America, and they are still more generally used in North America than elsewhere. That is largely because the sands that are productive in the fields first developed in North America are more generally persistent than the sands of the Tertiary fields of Russia and Asia. In most of the pre-Tertiary fields in North America individual sands may be identified over considerable areas, and their structure may be shown on contour maps.

Various theories have been proposed as corollaries to the anticlinal theory. Of these the hydromotive theory of Munn is perhaps the best known.[4] He suggests that bodies of water in motion carry the oil with them. If the water moved downward or laterally, it could carry the oil

[1] CLAPP, F. G., Revision of the Structural Classification of Petroleum and Natural Gas Fields, Geol. Soc. Am. *Bull.*, vol. 28, pp. 553–602, 1916.

[2] WASHBURNE, C. W., The Capillary Concentration of Gas and Oil, Am. Inst. Min. Eng. *Bull.* 93, pp. 2365–2378, 1914.

[3] ENGLER, C., and H. HOEFER, *Das Erdoel*, Band 2, p. 18.

[4] MUNN, M. J., The Anticlinal and Hydraulic Theories of Oil Accumulation, *Econ. Geol.*, vol. 4, pp. 509–529. 1909.

State Teachers College Library
Willimantic, Conn.

with it, and the oil carried down would tend to float into any higher structural features it encountered and accumulate in them. The higher folds would serve as oil traps raised above the passageways of water and oil. If, in depths below the higher folds, the sands were for any reason impermeable, the downward flow would turn to a horizontal course and larger volumes of water might pass below the oil trap, giving greater opportunities for segregation.

Johnson[1] suggests that the oil is carried through the sands as films on globules of gas. Daly[2] appeals to pressures generated as a result of diastrophic movement. According to Beckstrom and Van Tuyl,[3] compaction of the sediments due to gravity is a cause of migration of oil. These methods of segregation probably assist gravitational separation to some extent.

There is reason to suppose that the temperatures of the oil measures have, in general, been higher than they are now.[4] Hot waters flow from many wells. Oil loses viscosity with increase of temperature and would be less readily adsorbed by grains of sand. At depths of 6,000 feet some oils would be no more viscous than water. If a vessel is filled with sand that is saturated with oil and the bottom perforated so that all the oil that can be removed by gravity will drain out, much oil will remain in the sand. If air is blown through the sand, more oil will be removed. If water, hot water, and superheated water are successively passed through, additional oil will be carried out with each. The water of oil fields is probably rarely as hot as steam, but efficiency to overcome adhesion is aided, doubtless, by high temperature. An increase of temperature of only 50° C. will decrease the density of oil appreciably, increasing the difference in density between oil and water.

A series of experiments was made in the geological laboratory of the University of Minnesota, in which gas was introduced into an oil-soaked sand in a closed system. Tubes about 6 feet long were bent to form anticlines of which the limbs had slopes of about 15 degrees (Fig. 28). These were filled with sand which had been mixed with oil, sea water, and light gasoline. The tube was completely filled with the mixture and allowed to remain a considerable period, as shown by Fig. 28b. No segregation took place except locally, where the oil gathered into small

[1] JOHNSON, R. W., The Accumulation of Oil and Gas in Sandstone, Science, new ser., vol. 35, pp. 458–459, 1912.

[2] DALY, MARCEL, Water Surfaces in the Oil Fields, Am. Inst. Min. Eng. Trans., vol. 59, pp. 557–563, 1918.

[3] BECKSTROM, R. C., and F. M. VAN TUYL, Am. Assoc. Pet. Geol. Bull., vol. 12, pp. 1049–1055, 1928.

[4] WASHBURNE, C. W., The Role and Fate of Connate Water in Oil Sands, Am. Inst. Min. Eng. Trans., vol. 51, p. 607, 1915.

drops. Subsequently, the system was warmed so that the gasoline was vaporized.[1]

After 48 hours a considerable segregation of oil, gas, and water had taken place (Fig. 28c). The gas occupied the highest part of the tube D, and rested on oil C, C', which in turn rested on salt water B, B'.[2] The space occupied by the gas represents air spaces which it was not possible to eliminate in charging the water and the oil-soaked sand in the tube, together with the space made available by the gas pressure forcing liquids into small cracks of the sand.

The method of segregation is due principally to gravity. Gravity, however, will not operate in the absence of gas, because adhesion is great

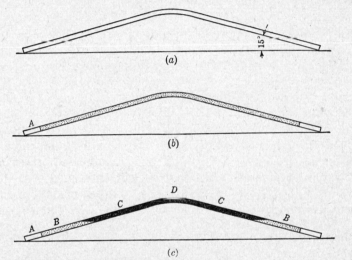

FIG. 28.—Experiment illustrating accumulation of oil and gas in sand. (a) tube, 6 ft. long; (b) same with sand, oil and water; (c) same as (b), gas added.

enough to hold the oil tightly to the sand. The gas generated presses on both oil and water, but the oil being lighter is pushed up farther and rides above the water. It is clear that little oil is carried by the gas as films on gas bubbles, because the amount of oil is much greater than would be required to form films. A small amount of gas seems to be as effective as a large amount, provided the pressure is sufficient. That the pressure is effective, rather than the movement of the gas, is clear from other experiments. The system was set up exactly as is shown in Fig. 28, but the tube was arranged to represent a syncline rather than

[1] These experiments were made by introducing ether, light gasoline, or CO_2 into the system. When CO_2 was used the CO_2 was generated in the tubes by introducing limestone and acid. The results appear to be the same whatever gas is introduced. (W. H. E.)

[2] THIEL, G. A., Gas an Important Factor in Oil Occurrence, *Eng. Mining Jour.*, vol. 109, p. 888, 1920.

an anticline.   Gas was introduced at one end only.   The gas rose on the limb near the end of the tube, the oil below the gas, and water segregated below the oil.   On the other limb oil rose above the water.   A terrace was set up, the end being bent so that two arms sloped approximately

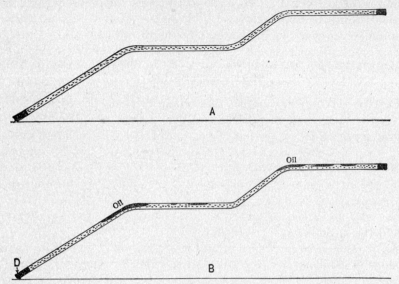

Fig. 29.—Experiment illustrating accumulation of oil on terraces. A, sand saturated with oil and water; B, same after gas under pressure is generated in system. The oil segregated near bends and in flat part of the tube but ultimately most of the oil rose to the higher terrace where it was sealed in above.

15 degrees.   Between the two arms the tube was level, as it was also at the upper end.   After being charged with oil-soaked sand, sea water, and gas, the oil rose to the first level of the terrace and remained several days.   Subsequently, it moved up the higher inclined arm to the flat

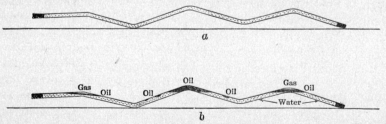

Fig. 30.—Diagrams illustrating accumulation of oil and gas in sand. a, Tube filled with sand saturated with oil and water; b, same tube after gas was generated at both ends. The finer grains of sand were carried toward the roof of the reservoir and caused small accumulations of oil to remain low on the central upfold.

portion of the tube.   There was a strong tendency for the maximum accumulation to remain in the flat part of the tube nearest the bent limb. In certain experiments bodies of oil remained for many days on the slopes of the tubes, although the bulk of the oil rose above the water (Fig. 29). It was found that particles of fine sand and clay had been carried up with the oil and had filled the pores between the sand. The experiment is believed to represent the method of accumulation of certain oil deposits that are formed on terraces. In another experiment three anticlines are shown (Fig. 30). Gas was generated at the ends of the tube only, yet the oil rose in each of the three folds.

SEGREGATION OF OIL AND WATER DUE TO DIFFERENCES IN THEIR SURFACE TENSION

Surface tension is the tension of a liquid by virtue of which it acts as an elastic enveloping membrane, tending always to contract to the minimum area. It is best exemplified in films freed from liquid masses, as in soap bubbles, and in the formation of drops. It is commonly explained as due to the fact that while molecules in the interior of the liquid are attracted in all directions, and are thus in equilibrium, those on the surface have no neighbors outside to balance the attraction of those within and are consequently acted upon by a resultant force tending toward the interior.

As a result of surface tension, water and oil will be drawn into small openings of capillary size, regardless of the force of gravity. Examples are the movements of water into a sponge or the rise of oil in a lamp wick. The surface tension of a water-air surface is about 75.6 dynes per centimeter at 0° C. and 72.8 dynes at 20° C. Washburne[1] states that the surface tension of salt water, such as is found in oil fields, is 79 dynes per centimeter. Washburne found also that Pennsylvania crude oil (specific gravity 0.852) had a tension of 24 dynes at 20° C.[2]

As water has about three times the surface tension of crude oil, capillary action must exert about three times as much pull upon it. The amount of the capillary pull varies inversely as the diameter of a pore. Hence, the constant tendency of capillarity is to draw water rather than oil into the smallest openings, displacing the gas and oil in them. Gas can not be drawn into capillary openings by surface tension, hence water can force it out of the fine pores without resistance. As stated by Washburne, gas is, therefore, most quickly and completely gathered in the largest openings available. Capillarity, moreover, resists the movement of water from fine to large pores more than it resists the movement of oil and gas from them. Thus water will enter fine capillaries about three times as readily as oil, and it encounters about three times as much

[1] WASHBURNE, C. W., The Capillary Concentration of Gas and Oil, Am. Inst. Min. Eng. *Trans.*, vol. 50, pp. 829–842, 1914.

[2] The movements of oil and water in quartz sand, due to differences in surface tension, are probably similar to movements in contact with glass. In clayey containers the results may be quantitatively different. Exact data are not available.

capillary resistance in leaving them. Consequently, oil and gas are concentrated in the largest openings, as the largest openings have the least capillary power.

Capillary action is not exerted in supercapillary openings. As water is most readily removed from such openings by capillary action in the surrounding material, they are most readily filled with oil and gas.

Differences in capillary attractions decrease with increase of temperature and with increase of depth. With an increase of 1° C. per 30

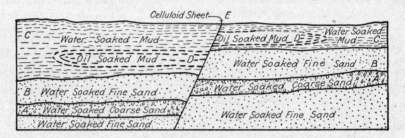

Fig. 31a.

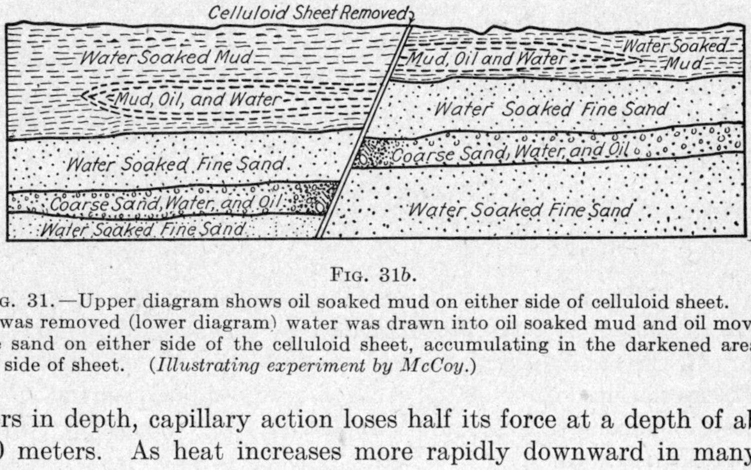

Fig. 31b.

Fig. 31.—Upper diagram shows oil soaked mud on either side of celluloid sheet. After sheet was removed (lower diagram) water was drawn into oil soaked mud and oil moved to coarse sand on either side of the celluloid sheet, accumulating in the darkened areas on either side of sheet. (*Illustrating experiment by McCoy.*)

meters in depth, capillary action loses half its force at a depth of about 5,000 meters. As heat increases more rapidly downward in many oil fields than the normal increase, it is probable, according to Washburne, that capillary force decreases one-half at depths of 3,000 or 4,000 meters. Because the surface tensions of all but the lightest hydrocarbons decrease much less rapidly than that of water for each increment of temperature, the surface tension of water does not have such great excess over that of oil at these depths. Hence, it is probable that the capillary concentration of oil and gas must all be effected within 4,000 or 5,000 meters of the ground surface. Oil in deeper strata must remain diffused in the shales, if that was its original distribution, unless it was concentrated in the sands at some former period when the strata concerned were closer to the surface.

If oil-soaked mud is placed near water-soaked sand, the oil will move to the sand. McCoy[1] placed in a glass box a water-soaked sand bed (*B*, Fig. 31) in which was a layer of coarser sand *A*. Above the sand was placed water-soaked mud *C*, containing a layer of oil-soaked mud *D*. Two series of these beds at different levels were separated by a celluloid sheet *E*, representing a fault. Within one hour after removal of the sheet, oil began to collect in the layer of the sand having the largest pores, and it continued to do so for several hours until the porous sand was nearly filled on each side of the plane representing the fault (Fig. 31*b*). Water, by capillary action, had partly replaced the oil in the oil-soaked mud.

In the Sewickley quadrangle, near Pittsburgh, Pennsylvania,[2] oil is produced from the Catskill sands (Devonian) and from the 100-foot sand near or above the top of the Devonian. The 100-foot sand is from 30 to 125 feet thick and is saturated with salt water. The sand is of medium grain and porosity and contains lenses of coarse sandstone and conglomerate which are much more porous than the surrounding sand. The porous lenses are a mile long, more or less, and a few feet thick. Practically all the oil is concentrated in them. The country is thrown into very gentle folds, and nearly all the lenses or "pay streaks" that contain oil are in the higher parts of the anticlines. The oil is associated with gas under pressure and with salt water. Down the dip and in synclines the pay streaks generally carry water only. Some of the wells have flowed as much as 2,000 barrels of oil a day. This area is shown in the accompanying map (Fig. 32). The section in Fig. 33 illustrates the occurrence of oil on anticlines in the pay streaks. The pools lower on the flanks of anticlines and in synclines in the sands below the 100-foot sand (Fig. 32) are noteworthy.

UNCONFORMITIES

Accumulations of oil and gas are found at unconformities in many districts. Unconformities are favorable situations for accumulation for many reasons.

1. Soluble rocks, such as limestone, exposed to weathering become porous by solution and provide suitable reservoirs for accumulation of oil. Such accumulations in limestone as already stated, are very common. They are found in the Trenton field of Ohio and Indiana, in many fields in Kentucky and Illinois, in Oklahoma and Kansas, in the Kevin-Sunburst field, Montana, in the main oil fields of Persia, and in other fields.

[1] McCoy, A. W., Notes on Principles of Oil Accumulation, *Jour. Geol.*, vol. 27, pp. 252–262, 1919.

[2] Munn, M. J., Studies in the Anticlinal Theory of Oil and Gas Accumulation, *Econ. Geol.*, vol. 4, pp. 141–157, 1909.

2. At places insoluble residuary material is broken up and is accumulated near the surface below an ancient erosion plain. Such rocks are porous and provide suitable reservoirs for oil.   The oil deposits in detrital granite at the Hurghada field in Egypt and above the buried mountains

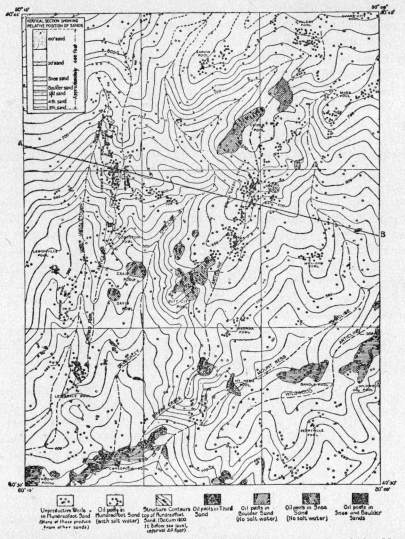

Fig. 32.—Map showing oil wells in Sewickley quadrangle, Pennsylvania. (*After Munn.*)

of the Panhandle, Texas, are noteworthy.   In certain fields in Kansas and Oklahoma oil is found in chats or broken chert that has accumulated during weathering at the top of the Boone formation.

3. The rocks above an unconformity are generally shallow-water deposits and normally include sands and gravels which are laid down at

the base of the younger series. Such rocks are highly porous and offer good reservoirs. Examples are the Burgess sand in many fields in Oklahoma, the basal sands of the Etchegon formation in the McKittrick-Sunset field, California, etc.

In certain oil fields the oil has accumulated at and near unconformities for more than one of the reasons named above. It may be found in both the older and younger series, and, where the attitudes of the beds both above and below the unconformity are favorable, the accumulation at the unconformity may be very marked. The unconformities in such regions become the main loci of the deposits.

WATER FLUSHING

It is believed that oil and gas have been flushed out from domes that lie on monoclines in mountainous countries where there is often a

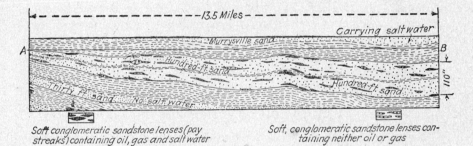

Fig. 33.—Section of Hundred-foot sand in Sewickley quadrangle, Pennsylvania, along line *AB*, Fig. 32. (*After Munn.*)

vigorous water circulation and at places where the water circulation is not greatly impeded by faulting of the oil-bearing domes. The composition and concentration of the waters in the oil sands below the oil have a close bearing on this problem, for, if the water on the flanks of the dome is dilute or carries only such salts as are commonly present in normal ground water, it is a natural inference that the oil field is in the path of a circulation from the outcrops of the sands. That is, if the water has diluted greatly the original water of the sand, it may also have carried away oil and gas.

An oil field that is connected by water with the outcrop is illustrated by Fig. 14. Fresh water descends from the surface and dilutes the salt water near the oil deposit, particularly near the side of the oil field that is on the up dip side of the region that is generally on the mountainward side of the fold.

No experiments are available to show that water may sweep oil from a dome when the water is moving along the flanks of the dome. The oil would have to move downward and away from the dome when it would

seem that its lighter gravity would hold it up.   Emulsions of oil and water
are commonly found near the contact of the two and the oil might move
in an emulsion.   The belief that oil is carried out of domes by water
rests chiefly on the fact that oil is absent from certain domes in mountainous countries, such as certain parts of Montana, Wyoming, and other
mountain states where ground water circulates readily, due to head, and
where domes containing sands that are known elsewhere to carry oil are
barren of oil and contain only water with low concentrations of salts.
Other domes contain gas but no oil.   It is a reasonable inference that in
certain fields oil has been swept out and that in others oil and also gas
have been carried away.   Water at 20° C. carries about 33 c.c. of methane
gas per liter at 1 atmosphere pressure.   The amount is small but probably increases directly with the pressure.   At 450 pounds pressure a
liter of water would dissolve a liter of gas measured at 15 pounds pressure.   It is probable that appreciable gas would be carried away if large
amounts of water moved by the gas deposit.   Bearing also on this problem is the relation of faulting to oil accumulation in mountainous countries.   Many of the large fields in Montana and Wyoming are faulted,
and it is believed that faulting impeded the movement of water and has
thus preserved the oil.   The important Rock River and Lance Creek
fields, Wyoming, however, do not show much faulting.

FRACTIONATION OF PETROLEUM IN CLAY

It has been suggested that some white oils and some very light oils
have been formed by the fractionation of petroleum that has passed
through clay.   When oil is mixed with fuller's earth and then displaced
with water, about two-thirds of the oil will pass out and one-third of the
oil will remain in the earth.   As shown by Day[1] and his associates, oil
passing through a dry fine clay (fuller's earth) loses its sulphur compounds, unsaturated compounds, and heavier components more readily
than its lighter ones.

When petroleum is allowed to rise in a tube packed with dry fuller's
earth, the fraction at the top of the tube is lighter than the one at the
bottom.   When water is added to fuller's earth that contains petroleum,
the oil which is displaced first differs in specific gravity from that which
is displaced afterward, when more water is added.   The paraffin hydrocarbons tend to collect in the lightest fraction at the top of the tube and
the unsaturated hydrocarbons at the bottom.

[1] DAY, D. T., Experiments on the Diffusion of Crude Petroleum Through Fuller's
Earth, *Science*, new ser., vol. 17, pp. 1007–1008, 1903.

GILPIN, J. E., and M. P. CRAM, The Fractionation of Crude Petroleum by Capillary Diffusion, U. S. Geol. Survey *Bull.* 365, pp. 1–33, 1908.

——— and O. E. BRANSKY, The Diffusion of Crude Petroleum Through Fuller's
Earth with Notes on its Geologic Significance, U. S. Geol. Survey *Bull.* 475,
pp. 1–50, 1911.

It has been suggested that the light oils of the Appalachian fields in Devonian and Carboniferous rocks have been derived from upward migration of heavier oils such as those found in Ordovician rocks in Ohio. This appears improbable according to Reeves,[1] since the fractionations in Day's experiments were made in dry fuller's earth and the sedimentary rocks between the Ordovician and the Devonian oil-bearing strata in the Appalachian region include water-bearing sands. If oil has passed through the sands they should now be saturated or partly saturated with oil.

[1] REEVES, F., U. S. Geol. Survey *Bull.* 786B, pp. 83–84, 1927.

CHAPTER VIII

STRUCTURAL FEATURES OF OIL AND GAS RESERVOIRS

RESERVOIRS IN ANTICLINES AND DOMES

Occurrence.—In accordance with the gravitational theory of accumulation, where reservoir rocks are saturated with salt water, oil will rise above the water and gas above the oil. On a fully developed, regular structural dome the normal arrangement would be a circular area of gas wells surrounded by a belt of oil wells, which, in turn, is surrounded by an area containing salt-water wells only. This ideal arrangement is not the most common one in oil fields, because most structural features are irregular in form, and oil sands rarely have uniform porosity. Gas and oil, moreover, in many fields occur together and issue simultaneously from wells drilled on tops of folds. In many folds water is not cleanly segregated from the oil. Many wells yield mixtures, some of them emulsions of oil and water. Size of pores also influences segregation. There is, nevertheless, in almost every great oil field in the world a distinct segregation of oil and gas in the higher parts of the uplifts.

In the Appalachian oil field of North America oil and gas are generally accumulated in anticlines, except in sands not saturated with water. The Venango group of western Pennsylvania is a prolific series of dry or partly dry sands in which much of the oil is found in synclines. In the Carboniferous strata above the Venango group oil is found in saturated rocks and accumulates near the tops of the anticlines. In the Volcano anticline of West Virginia the oil has accumulated near the crest of a dome. In the Lima-Indiana field of Ohio and Indiana, where oil is found in the Trenton limestone, the accumulation lies below or near a broad anticlinal axis. In Ohio the best yield is obtained below the arch and on terraces; in Indiana it is found on the north side of the arch, where the rocks dip northeast. The east branch of the axis of the Cincinnati anticline becomes essentially flat to the north of Lake Erie. To the south the limestone reservoir is sealed up dip because the limestone does not contain continuous openings. The oil and gas tend to accumulate near the axes of the anticline with gas above the oil, but the porosity of the limestone has greatly modified accumulation. That is true also in many of the oil fields of Kentucky and Tennessee, where the reservoir rocks are limestone.

In Illinois the principal producing wells are along the LaSalle anticline, especially in domes that are on and near the crest of the anticline,

STRUCTURAL CLASSIFICATION OF OIL AND GAS RESERVOIRS

1. Anticlines (closed) and domes. Appalachian and Lima-Indiana fields in part. Main fields of Illinois. Kansas: Eldorado, Peabody, Urschell, etc. Oklahoma: Garber, Blackwell, Tonkawa, Cushing, Seminole, St. Louis, Oklahoma City, Healdton, Hewett, etc. Texas: Breckenridge and many other fields of Bend arch regions, Panhandle region, West Texas Permian basin, Balcones region in part. Main fields of Louisiana and Arkansas. Chief Rocky Mountains and California fields. Canada, in western Ontario and Alberta. Many fields of Mexico and Venezuela. Main fields of Colombia, Peru, and Argentina. Main fields of Galicia, Russia, Persia, Irak, India, Burma, Sumatra, Java, Borneo, Japan, etc.

2. Monoclines sealed by:

    a. Sands lensing out up dip. Bradford, Pennsylvania, Clinton gas field, Ohio; Glenn Pool, Oklahoma; Archer County, north-central Texas, etc.

    b. Porosity diminishing up dip. Berea fields, Ohio; Burbank and Crinerville, Oklahoma; Monroe gas field and other fields, Louisiana; Smackover, Arkansas, in part; Osage, Wyoming; Lake Maracaibo, Venezuela, etc.

    c. Sands plugged by tar. Sunset-Midway and Coalinga, California; Lake Maracaibo, Venezuela, etc.

    d. Faulting of oil sand against impermeable rocks. Blackwell, Tonkawa, and Cromwell, Oklahoma; Balcones fault region, Texas, including Mexia group and Luling; Carolina-Texas field; Bellevue and certain other fields, Louisiana; Irma, Arkansas; Shannon, Wyoming; Mount Pozo and McKittrick, in part, California; Tuxpam, Mexico, in part; Peru; Pechelbronn, France; Hanover, Germany; Galicia, Roumania, Binagadi, Russia; around many salt domes in Louisiana, Texas, Germany, Roumania, etc.

    e. Igneous intrusions. Tampico, Mexico, in part.

    f. Unconformities. Many fields in Kansas, Oklahoma, Texas, Louisiana, Rocky Mountains, California, Mexico, Venezuela, France, Germany, Galicia, Russia, Persia, Netherlands India, Japan, etc.

3. Terraces. Certain fields in Pennsylvania, Ohio, and Indiana are on terraces but in most of them and probably in all of them the sands are sealed up dip, thus affording "closure" which prevents escape of oil and gas.

4. Synclines. Devonian and certain Carboniferous sands of Appalachian fields; unimportant fields in Rocky Mountains, etc.

5. Fissures.

    a. In shales. Parts of Salt Creek, Big Muddy, Pilot Butte, Wyoming; Florence, Colorado; part of McKittrick field, California, etc.

    b. In schists. Small occurrences in Santa Clara, California, and in Alaska.

    c. In igneous rocks. Lytton Springs, Texas; certain fields in Cuba; part of Furbero, Mexico.

in Lawrence, Crawford, Clark, and Cumberland counties. Some of the fields, however, are sealed up dip near a great unconformity.

In Kansas and eastern Oklahoma most of the oil comes from domes, but east of a line drawn north from Tulsa this relation in many of the fields is not clear. The great fields west of this line include Eldorado, Garber, Ponca, Tonkawa, Cushing, Oklahoma City, and a score of others, all of which are on domes. The Burbank and Glenn fields, however, are on monoclines sealed up dip.

In southern Oklahoma nearly all of the great fields are located on domes: Cement, Robberson, Fox, Graham, Healdton (Figs. 34, 35) Hewett, Empire, and others. Crinerville, however, is sealed up dip where the beds thin out or become impervious near a fault.

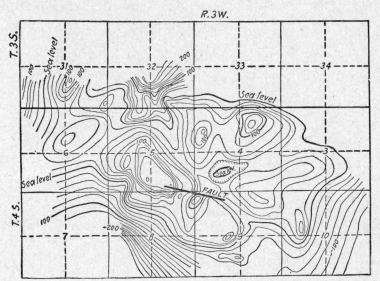

Fig. 34.—Structure map of Healdton field, Oklahoma. Contour interval 20 feet. (*After Wegemann and Heald.*)

In the great Panhandle region of Texas the oil and gas are on domes, and that is true also of the great fields of the Permian basin of west Texas. In north-central Texas many of the oil and gas fields are on domes, but a large number of important fields are developed on sand lenses that are sealed up dip, and in limestones that are locally permeable. In the Balcones fault region and in the Laredo (Reynosa Escarpment) area of south Texas many of the oil and gas deposits are along faults that seal the reservoir beds up dip and on low domes near faults. In the Lytton Springs field of the Balcones fault region the oil is in porous serpentine.

In northern Louisiana and southern Arkansas, oil or gas or both are found on domes in Caddo, Shreveport, De Soto-Red River, Homer, Cotton Valley, Bellevue, Smackover, Eldorado, and many other fields.

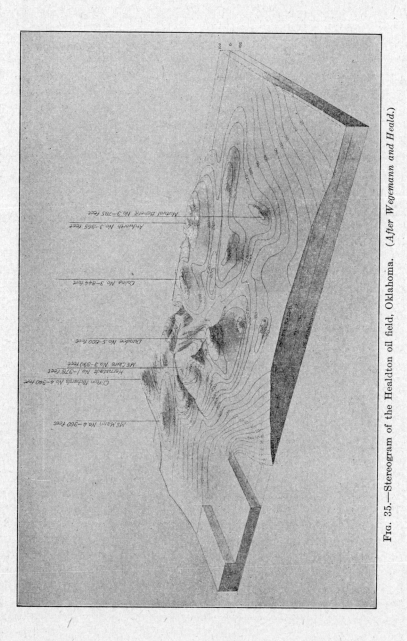

FIG. 35.—Stereogram of the Healdton oil field, Oklahoma. (*After Wegemann and Heald.*)

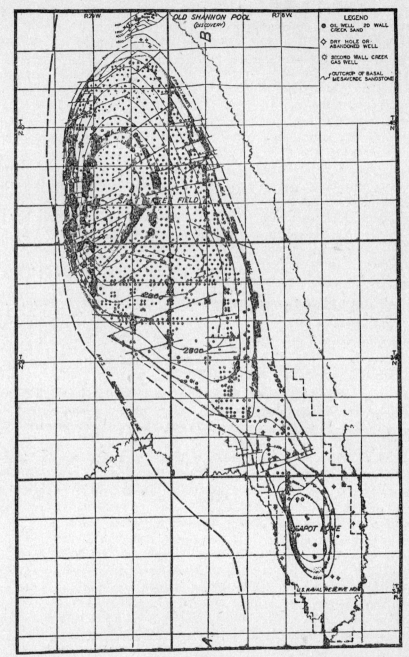

FIG. 36a.—Contour map showing structure of Salt Creek oil field, Wyoming, contoured on second Frontier Sand; contour interval 200 ft. datum sea level, all wells are not shown. (*After Beck, Wegemann, Rumsey, Clapp and others.*)

On the Gulf Coast in Texas and Louisiana oil is found in salt domes, many of which lie along axes of faulting and flexing.

In the Rocky Mountains region nearly all of the fields are on domes. The Kevin-Sunburst district, Montana, is on a great dome, but the accumulation is modified by porosity of the reservoir rocks. In the Bannatyne, Cat Creek, Big Lake, Soap Creek, and Elk Creek districts the oil is near the tops of domes and in the Glendive-Baker field gas is found on several domes on the Glendive anticline.

In the Big Horn basin, Wyoming, oil or gas is found on anticlines in about 25 fields; all of the important fields, including Grass Creek, Elk basin, Torchlight, Greybull, and Oregon basin are on domes. Other fields in Wyoming, located on domes, include Salt Creek (Fig. 36*a*), Big Muddy, Poison Spider, Lost Soldier, Rock Creek, the Lander group, and others. The great gas fields of Big Sand Draw and Baxter basin are on domes. On the southwest flank of the Black Hills oil is found in domes in the Lance Creek, Mule Creek, and other fields. The Osage field is on terraces.

1-Wall Creek Sandstone   2-Shannon Sandstone   3-Parkman Sandstone

Fig. 36*b*.—Generalized cross section of Salt Creek oil field on line *AB*, Fig. 36*a*. (*After Wegemann.*)

In Colorado oil is found on domes in the Wellington (Fort Collins), Walden, Moffat, Iles, Tow Creek, and other fields. In the Florence district which has produced about half of the yield of the state, the oil is found in fractured shale. In northwestern and southeastern New Mexico the oil is found on domes.

In California nearly all of the oil is found on anticlines and on monoclines where the latter are sealed up dip. The Coalinga field is divided into two parts, the Eastside and Westside. On the Westside the oil has accumulated on a monocline, where, at the outcrop, the oil sands are cemented with asphalt. On the Eastside the oil is concentrated below the Coalinga anticline. In the Kettleman Hills and in the Lost Hills districts, southeast of the Coalinga district, oil is accumulated on domes. In the North Belridge and Belridge districts the oil is found on anticlines and in the McKittrick district on anticlines, synclines, overturns, and on monoclines. The Midway district on the northeast flank of the Temblor Range is on a monocline on which subsidiary folds are developed. These folds have undulating crests, and the oil is obtained near the nodes of the crests. In Santa Clara and Santa Maria fields the most productive districts are on anticlines and domes. In the Los Angeles basin the greatest fields are on domes. These include Inglewood, Rosecrans, Dominguez, Long Beach, Alamitos, Seal Beach,

Huntington Beach, Santa Fe Springs, and others. Some of the Puente Hills fields and the Los Angeles fields are on sealed monoclines.

In Canada the greatest production has been derived from Lambton County, where the chief oil fields are located on domes (Figs. 37, 38).

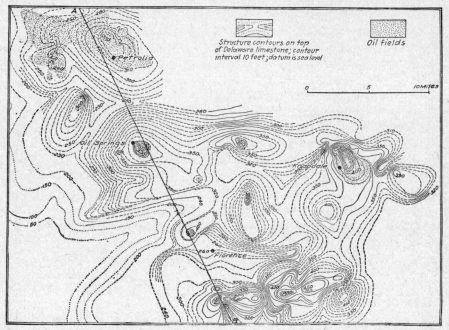

Fig. 37.—Sketch showing structure of principal oil region of Lambton County, Ontario. (*After Williams.*)

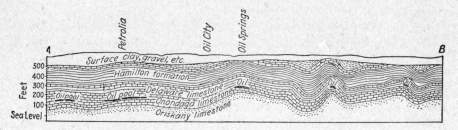

Fig. 38.—Cross section of Petrolia and Oil Springs oil fields, Lambton County, Ontario, along line *AB*, of Fig. 37. (*Redrawn from Williams.*)

In western Canada also the chief fields are on domes. The Sheep River field, Alberta, is most productive.

In Mexico in the Tampico-Tuxpam region the largest production is from the south part of the district, where nearly all of the oil is on a single anticlinal axis called the "Knife Edge." In the northern part of the region some of the fields are on domes and others probably are controlled by porosity, fissuring, and fracturing of the limestone. At Furbero oil is found in fractured shale and fractured igneous rock. In the fields of the Isthmus of Tehuantepec oil fields are developed above and on the flanks of salt domes.

In Trinidad the chief oil deposits are on anticlines and domes. In Colombia in the chief oil field, which is near Barranca Bermeja, the oil is accumulated on domes. In Venezuela a large number of oil fields are located on anticlines, but in the largest group, which is on the east side of Lake Maracaibo, the oil deposits are on monoclines sealed up dip by tar and by impervious beds, many of them at unconformities. In Peru the main deposits are on anticlines and domes and in blocks raised by complicated faulting. In the Commodoro Rivadavia field Argentina, the oil fields occupy low domes.

In England, Midlands region, the chief oil fields are on anticlines; in Pechelbronn, France, the chief accumulations of oil are against faults where the beds dip away from the faults. In the Hanover region, Germany, the main deposits are on the flanks of salt domes and anti-clines and the beds are commonly sealed by faults and at unconformities. In Czechoslovakia oil is found in domes. In Galicia large accumulations of oil are found on anticlines and domes, many of which are greatly complicated by thrust faulting and in some of the fields the beds are overturned. In Roumania the fields are chiefly on anticlines and elongated domes which have cores of rock salt. In Russia nearly all of the large fields are on anticlines and domes. These include Surakani, Balakhani, Sabunchi, Romani, Bibi Eibat, Sviatoi, Cheleken, Grozny, Dos-sor, Makat, and others. On the Binigadi anticline the beds are sealed up dip by faults, by tar and by lensing of sands. At Maikop important deposits lie in a sand-filled stream channel. In Persia and in Mesopotamia the chief deposits are on domes. In the Punjab and in Assam, India, and in Burma, the main deposits are on domes. In all of the great fields of Sumatra, Java, and Borneo the deposits are on anticlines or domes. In Japan the main deposits are on anticlines, although sand lenses and unconformities at places have localized production. In Sakhalin the deposits are on anticlines and domes. In Egypt the chief deposits are on domes.

Salt Domes.—In certain regions the prevailing structural features that have localized accumulation of oil and gas are domes and anticlines with cores of salt (Figs. 39, 40, 41). These fields include the Gulf Coast field of the United States, certain prospective fields in Utah, the Isthmus of Tehuantepec fields of Mexico, the fields near Hanover, Germany, and the principal oil and gas fields of Roumania, and gas fields of Transylvania. Salt domes and salt anticlines are generally very steep folds and, as a rule, there is much faulting around the salt cores. At many places the salt masses have been thrust up through muds and sands so

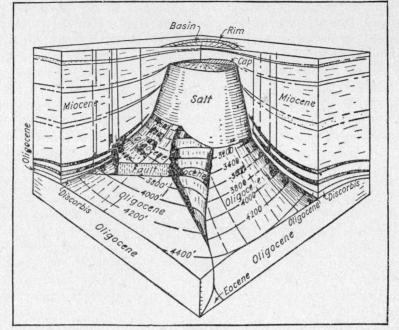

FIG. 39.—Perspective drawing of West Columbia salt dome, Texas. Depths in feet.
(*After Carlton.*)

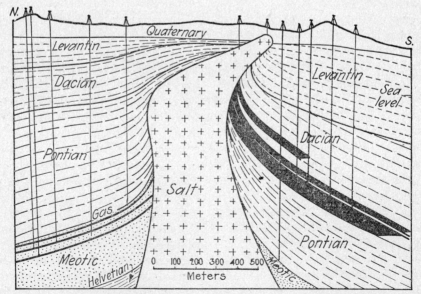

FIG. 40.—Geologic section across Moreni salt anticline, Roumania; oil sands, black. (*After
Cardas and Busyan.*)

that the salt and the older beds have passed by the younger beds along thrust faults.   The resulting structure is a kind of arm-in-sleeve arrangement which, in central Europe, is called "diaper structure."   This salt dome structure may be likened also to a short length of stove pipe standing upright, which represents the salt core, over which is fitted the pipe ring which is a frustrum of a cone and represents the beds.

There seems to be some peculiar property of the salt mass that lends itself to the formation of this structure.   It is generally believed that the salt moved as a fluid mass.   At places, however, the salt was probably crystalline and appears to have moved as a somewhat rigid and

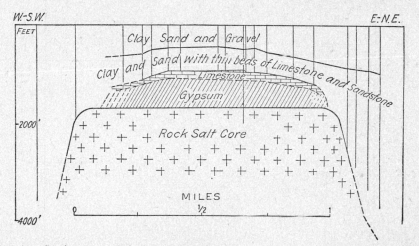

FIG. 41.—Section across Spindletop salt dome, Texas.   (*Data from Barton and Paxson.*)

spinelike mass through clays and poorly consolidated sands; a structure not unlike that of certain salt domes resulted in the Wankowa dome, Galicia, where the Inoceramus beds consisting largely of sandstones have been thrust through shales.   In certain fields, however, the salt probably moved as a wet fluid mass.   In certain of the salt-dome fields the oil measures form a true dome above the salt plug, in others oil is in the cap rock of the salt.   In a large number of them the top of the salt plug has been eroded and accumulations of oil are found around the flanks of the core, where the reservoir rocks are sealed against salt or against rocks that dip steeply away from the salt plug.

Arrangements of Domes.—From the foregoing summary it is evident that the majority of great oil and gas deposits of the world are on domes. The closure of a dome, as stated, is the difference in elevation between its highest point as measured on a certain bed on the dome and the highest point where the same bed begins to rise toward the surface. The closure of a dome is commonly different as measured on different beds.   This will be true where a converging series of strata lies between

the beds, or where the amplitude of a fold increases or decreases with
depth.   Anticlinal axes are rarely level.   As a rule they plunge in one
direction or the other.   If the axis continues to plunge in one direction
so that the oil sand rises to the surface, there would be no closure, and,

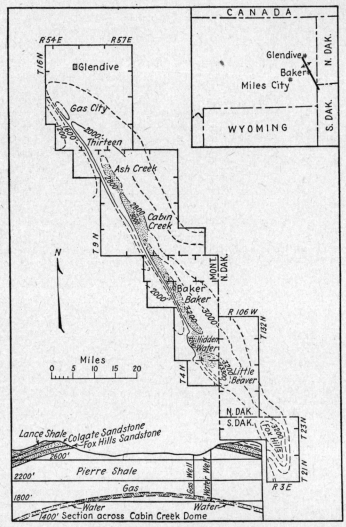

Fig. 42.—Cedar Creek anticline, southeastern Montana.   Contour lines show feet above
sea on top of Pierre Shale.   Gas bearing area is stippled.   (*After Moulton.*)

unless some kind of seal prevented it, the oil would escape from the sands
at the surface.   The anticline would not be an effective container.   On
the other hand, on a dome the impermeable cover would hold the oil in
the dome on all sides.

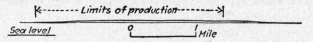

FIG. 43.—Section of Dropright dome, Cushing field, Oklahoma. Vertical and horizontal scale are the same. Shows curvature of Pawhuska limestone from northwest corner of section 5, to northwest corner of section 27 T. 8. N., R. 7. E. (*Data from Beal.*)

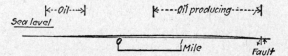

FIG. 44.—Section of De Soto-Red River field, Louisiana. Vertical and horizontal scale are the same. Shows curvature of Nacotosh sand from northwest corner of section 14 to fault in section 23. T. 13 N. R. 11 W. (*Data from Matson and Hopkins.*)

FIG. 45.—Section of Thrall field, Texas. Vertical and horizontal scale are the same. Shows curvature of oil-bearing rock. (*Data from Udden and Bybee.*)

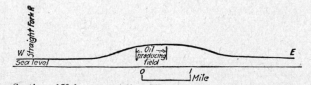

FIG. 46.—Section of Volcano anticline, West Virginia. Shows curvature of Washington coal bed from Straight Fork Creek through town of Volcano to Goose Creek. Vertical and horizontal scale are the same. (*Data from Hennen, West Virginia Geol. Survey.*)

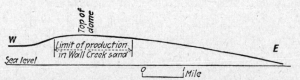

FIG. 47.—Section of Salt Creek dome, Natrona County, Wyoming. Shows curvature of Wall Creek sand from southwest corner of section 27, T. 40 N. R. 79 W. to southwest corner of section 26, T. 40 N. R. 78 W. Vertical and horizontal scale are the same. (*Data from Wegemann, U. S. Geol. Survey.*)

Where the axis of the anticline changes its direction of plunge from a high point on the axis, a dome will be formed. Thus, many domes are localized along anticlinal axes. A whole system of domes may be developed on a single fold with an undulating crest. Several domes are formed on the Glendive anticline, Montana, (Fig. 42) and on the Shoshone anticline near Lander, Wyoming (p. 497). It is very common for the long axes of the domes to lie approximately in line.

The amount of closure in different oil-bearing domes differs greatly. In certain fields in Kansas and Oklahoma the closure is less than 20 feet. In the Rocky Mountains region certain fields have closures of thousands of feet. Cross-sections of certain fields drawn true to scale are shown on Figs. 43 to 47. The oil and gas deposits may occupy only a small part of the closed area. Where domes are far apart, however, the gathering areas are greater and the deposits are likely to occupy larger areas.

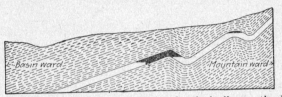

Fig. 48.—Ideal sketch showing oil accumulated principally on the lower anticline or the one on the basinward side of the larger fold; the accumulation is greatest on the basinward limb of the anticline. Black represents oil and gas.

Oil-bearing domes are generally elongated. As a rule one axis is considerably longer than the other. Anticlines and domes in general are formed by compressive stresses operating on the earth's crust. Many of them are minor mountain folds formed when the larger mountains were elevated. This is indicated by the parallelism of their longer axes to the axes of neighboring mountain folds. Domes are formed also by the upthrust of igneous masses and of salt masses. Certain investigators believe that oil-bearing domes are formed also by differential compaction of sediments laid down on buried hills. This subject is discussed on following pages.

Where rocks dip away from major uplifts, anticlines and domes are commonly found one below the other toward the central part of the basin. Often it is found that the lower domes are more productive than the higher ones (Fig. 48). That is because oil and gas escape more readily from the higher structures, for they are generally nearer the surface, and because the deeper domes, as a rule, have larger gathering areas. The lower domes in the Big Horn basin, as noted by Hewett and Lupton, are generally more productive than the higher ones, particularly in the Cretaceous beds which include the higher oil-bearing series. In the deeper Paleozoic beds of the basin this relation is not so clearly shown.

Segregation of Oil on Side of Gentle Dip.—Many anticlines and domes are not symmetrical and on such domes, as a rule, the maximum accumulation of oil and gas is on the side of lowest dip. If the edge-water line is a level line, there will be a greater area within a given contour on the side of the lowest dip. In general the side of gentle dip is the side toward the greatest gathering area and, consequently, the side

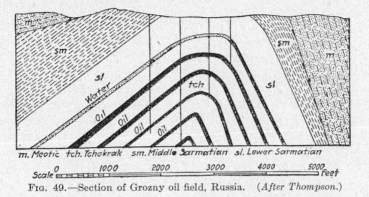

FIG. 49.—Section of Grozny oil field, Russia. (*After Thompson.*)

of greatest accumulation. Where several sands on a single structure are oil bearing, the difference is likely to be more marked. In many anticlinal folds the axial plane of the fold dips toward the gentle limb; consequently, the crest of the fold as measured on different beds will move with depth toward the gentle limb (Fig. 49). In certain fields, however, as at Fairport Kansas and Tonkawa Oklahoma, the axes shown

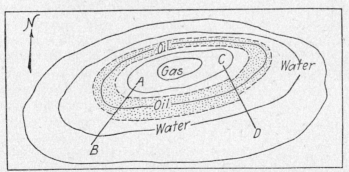

FIG. 50.—Map of dome showing oil-water contact at lower level on the south than on the north side. *AB* and *CD* represent impermeable areas.

in the lower rocks move toward the side of the fold that shows the steepest dip in the higher rocks.

In steep symmetrical domes, containing sands that are everywhere permeable, the contact between oil and water would normally be level. If higher at one point than at another, the water would descend by gravity and push the oil up where it is lowest. At many places, however, where gravitational separation is clearly indicated by the position of the accumulation with respect to the structure, the contact between the water and the oil is not level. This condition may be due to tightness of the sands in places, which prohibits free circulation of oil around the dome on nearly level lines. A difference could be established if communication were prevented at two places only. This is illustrated by Fig. 50 where the lines AB and CD represent impermeable areas. Oil segregated between these lines would not be free to move across them. The greatest accumulation would be on the side of the greatest gathering area.

RESERVOIRS IN MONOCLINES

A considerable number of oil and gas fields lie on monoclines that are sealed up dip in various ways. Monoclines may be sealed (1) where impervious rocks meet above the reservoir rock (Fig. 51); (2) where the sands become impervious by cementation of their interstices, or where the interstices were filled with clay particles when the sands were deposited (Fig. 52); (3) where the oil itself, at or near the surface, on drying, hardens to form asphalt (Fig. 53). In certain oil fields oil sands are sealed (4) at impervious fault planes (Fig. 54), where faults throw impervious rocks against reservoir rocks; (5) by igneous masses that cut across the oil-bearings beds; and (6) at unconformities. Oil fields are formed where a tilted eroded petroliferous series is covered unconformably by a later series. If permeable strata, such as conglomerates and sandstones, are laid down upon the petroliferous strata, the beds of the later series may carry oil (Fig. 55). If muds or clays cover the petroliferous bed, gas, oil, and water will more probably be segregated in the lower bed (Fig. 56). Reservoirs are found at uncomformities in many fields. It is obvious that monoclines sealed by impervious rocks joining above the reservoir rock and monoclines sealed by local cementation and at unconformities are discovered with greater difficulty than monoclines sealed by other processes. Oil pools in such positions are discovered, more often than otherwise, by wildcat drilling or by wells sunk for water.

Monoclinal Reservoirs Sealed by Shales above and under Oil Sands Joining up Dip.—Some oil sands are extensive, others are of small extent. They lap over older formations near shore and are overlapped by younger ones. Seaward they play out, their nature and extent depending upon the conditions existing at the time of their formation. Thus, many sands are of lenticular shape. Many of the world's great oil deposits are found in sands that play out up dip. They are sealed, and the escape of the oil and gas is prevented by the impermeable strata above them. In the Appalachian geosyncline many of the oil sands thin out toward the northwest. The land mass that supplied the sediments during Paleozoic time was southeast of the oil field. In eastern Ohio, where the "Clinton"

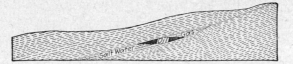

FIG. 51.—Sketch showing reservoir sealed by impervious rocks overlying and underlying the reservoir rock and joining above the reservoir.

FIG. 52.—Sketch showing reservoir sealed by tight sand. Black is oil and gas.

FIG. 53.—Sketch showing monoclinal reservoir sealed by asphalt.

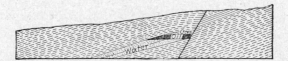

FIG. 54.—Sketch showing reservoir sealed by fault bringing oil sand against impervious rocks.

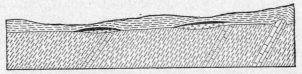

FIG. 55.—Sketch of section showing oil and gas (black) in porous deposits that rest unconformably on a tilted series of oil sands and carbonaceous shales.

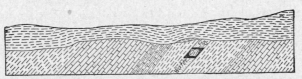

FIG. 56.—Sketch of section showing accumulation of oil and gas above water in a tilted bed overlain unconformably by an impervious bed.

sand thins out up dip toward the west, the sand plays out (Figs. 57, 58). The upper part of this sand contains gas under great pressure. From Cleveland southward to Jackson County, a distance of 170 miles, wells producing gas are sunk to this reservoir at many places. The general relations in the Appalachian field are illustrated by Fig. 58.

In Eastern Ohio oil and gas are found in the Berea sand, near the lower part of the Mississippian.[1] The Sunbury shales lie above the

FIG. 57. —Map showing location of "Clinton" gas field, Ohio. (*After Bownocker.*)

Berea and the Bedford shales below it. The Berea yields oil or gas in many counties.

Approximately along the area indicated by the line *XY* in Fig. 59, there is, according to Panyity, a noteworthy change in the character of the sedimentary rocks. East of the line and parallel to it, where the sand is thin and lenticular, the most productive fields are found. These include the fields of Barnesville, Temperanceville, Summerfield, Macksburg, Dudley, and others. East of the gas fields, down the dip, are the most productive Berea oil pools. In places where anticlinal structure

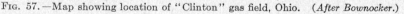

[1] PANYITY, L. S., Lithology of the Berea Sand in Southeastern Ohio and Its Effect on Production, Am. Inst. Min. Eng. *Bull.* 140, pp. 1317–1320, 1917.

is present the positions of the gas, oil, and water are in accord with the structural theory (Fig. 60). The controlling factor in most of these pools, however, is, according to Panyity, the western limit of the sand. West of the line *XY* there is a water-bearing sand. Near Byesville small gas pools are developed on minor uplifts above the water. The Corning pool is developed west of this line.

In the great Glenn pool, near Sapulpa, Oklahoma, the oil-bearing series dips west. The Bartlesville sand, which produces most of the oil, at places is more than 100 feet thick. Toward the east, as shown by Wilson,[1] the sand splits into thin layers and plays out, thus providing an effective seal. The isopach map[1] (Fig. 61) shows the thickness of the sand. The shaded portion of the map shows the main productive area. The sands become less permeable toward the thin edge of the wedge (Fig. 62), and little oil is found in areas where the sand is less than 25 feet thick.

In Venezuela, on the east shore of Lake Maracaibo, some of the world's greatest oil fields were discovered. These fields are not on structural domes, but the oil-bearing rocks which dip west lens out toward the east providing effective seals. Unconformities and tar plugs also seal some of the beds. Many other examples of oil-sand lenses could be named. In many regions the domatic structure and the lensing of the sands combine to control accumulation. In many fields sand lenses lie unconformably above older tilted beds. They play out against buried hills. Some of them are mentioned on following pages. In certain fields lenses of sand on monoclines are sealed up dip and also down dip where the lens wedges out. If there is no water in the lens the oil will accumulate near the bottom of the lens (Fig. 63).

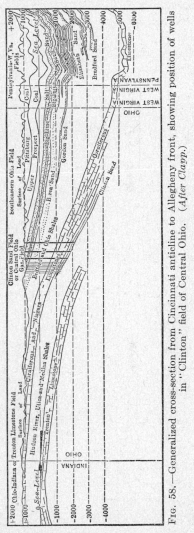

FIG. 58.—Generalized cross-section from Cincinnati anticline to Allegheny front, showing position of wells in "Clinton" field of Central Ohio. (*After Clapp.*)

[2] The isopach (same thickness) lines connect places where the Bartlesville sand **is** of equal thickness.

FIG. 59.—Sketch map showing position of certain oil pools in Berea sand in south-eastern Ohio. Oil is found in sealed monocline east of line *X-Y*. (*After Panyity.*) For section along *AB* and *CD* see Fig. 60.

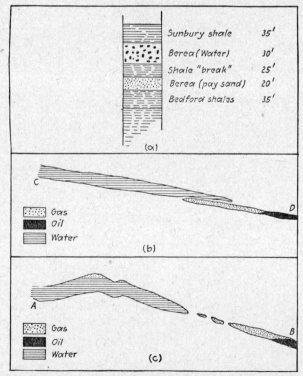

FIG. 60.—Sketch showing (*a*) section of Berea sand and adjacent strata Ohio; (*b*) reservoir in Berea sand on monocline (line *CD*, Fig. 59) and (*c*) reservoir in Berea sand on monocline and gas in anticline (on line *AB*, Fig. 59). (*After Panyity.*)

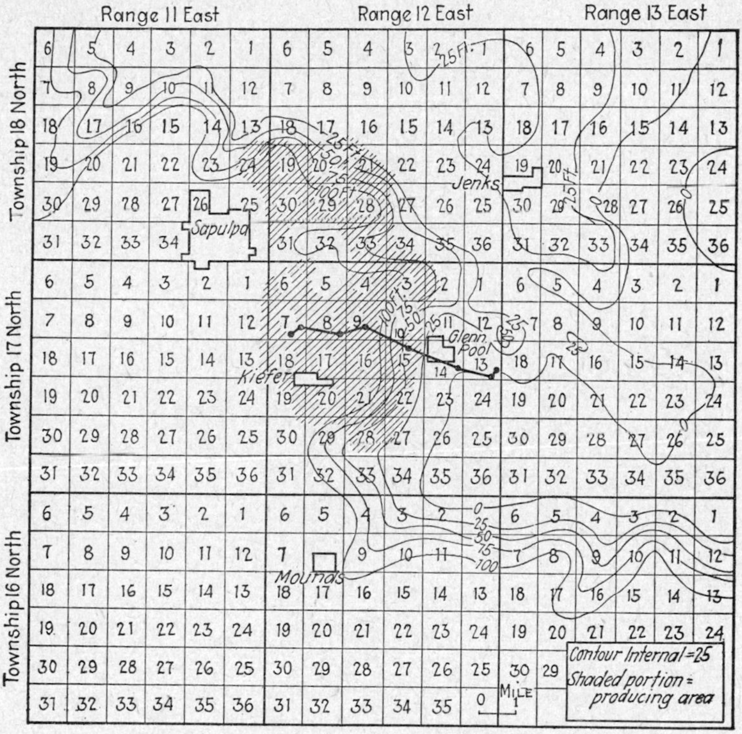

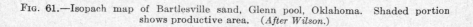

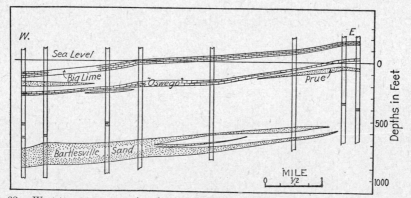

FIG. 61.—ISOPACH map of Bartlesville sand, Glenn pool, Oklahoma. Shaded portion shows productive area. (*After Wilson.*)

FIG. 62.—West to east cross section through Glenn pool, Oklahoma, showing sands pinching out up dip. Position of section is shown on Fig. 61. (*After Wilson.*)

Monoclinal Reservoirs Sealed by Impervious Areas above the Reservoirs.—Oil moves up dip.   If it reaches a place where the reservoir rock is impervious, it will accumulate.   Oil will not move readily through a sand that contains much clay.   When a sand is laid down, wave action near shore tends to wash out the clay and to carry it seaward to quiet waters, where it is deposited.   Thus, toward sea the sand may become so muddy that it will not allow free movements of fluids.   The oil sand may be made impervious also after it is laid down by the deposition of calcite, iron oxide, or other minerals in its pores.

Above the ground-water level limestones are readily dissolved and become porous.   Consequently, porous limestones are often found below

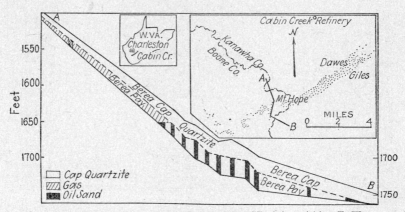

Fig. 63.—Cross section of Cabin Creek oil field, West Virginia.   (*After T. Wasson and I. Wasson.*)

ancient erosion surfaces.   Porosity is generally localized, however, and at places where the porous limestone gives way to impervious limestone, a seal for a reservoir is provided.

In the Burbank field, Oklahoma, the Burbank sand dips west at a low angle.   It is 50 to 80 feet thick and, according to J. M. Sands, has a porosity from 13.7 to 32.7 per cent.   To the east, however, it grades into sandy shale against which the oil, traveling up dip from the west, has accumulated.   At Crinerville, near Brock in southern Oklahoma, a reservoir is provided where, according to Powers, the oil sand plays out or becomes impervious up dip.   In the Osage field, Wyoming, on the west side of the Black Hills the reservoir is sealed up dip by impervious sands and by faulting.

In the Lima-Indiana field, as already stated, the oil and gas are found in the Trenton limestone on and near the branches of the axes of the Cincinnati arch.   This limestone is locally very porous, but toward the south porosity decreases and the openings are discontinuous.   In the Sweet Grass arch, in northern Montana, the chief oil deposits are accumulated in porous limestone on the flanks of a great dome. Since the oil and gas are wanting in the limestone at the crest of the dome, it is

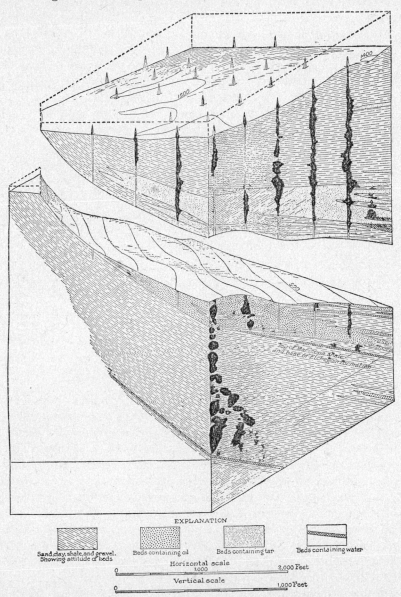

EXPLANATION

Sand, clay, shale, and gravel.
Showing attitude of beds

Beds containing oil

Beds containing tar

Beds containing water

Horizontal scale
0   1,000   2,000 Feet

Vertical scale
0   1,000 Feet

FIG. 64.—Stereogram showing reservoir sealed by asphalt forming in oil sand near the surface, Sunset-Midway field, California. (*After Pack, U. S. Geol. Survey.*)

inferred that its localization is controlled largely by porosity of the limestone. The lensing out of sands at unconformities is treated on a following page.

Monoclinal Reservoirs Sealed by Asphalt.—Certain reservoirs on monoclines are sealed above by tarry products that have resulted from hardening of the oil (Figs. 64, 65). Reservoirs containing heavier asphaltic oils are more generally sealed in this manner than reservoirs containing the lighter paraffin oils, although vents leading from reservoirs are known to contain both the asphaltic and the paraffin bitumens.

The best known fields of which the reservoir rocks are sealed by bitumens are the Coalinga field and the Sunset-Midway field of California. In both of these fields highly productive reservoirs are sealed by tar plugs. In the Sunset-Midway district[1] the reservoirs containing the oil are sealed

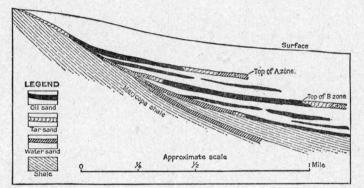

Fig. 65.—Diagram illustrating probable occurrences of water, oil and tar sands in part of Sunset-Midway oil field, California. Arrows indicate direction of movement of edgewater. (*After Pack.*)

up by tarry oil or tar which is formed by the interaction of the mineralized waters and the hydrocarbons that compose the oil. It is a reaction which results in the reduction of sulphate water to form sulphides and the addition of the sulphur or sulphides to the oil. Some of the oil sands of the fields on the east shore of Lake Maracaibo, Venezuela, are sealed near the surface by the deposition of asphalt.

Monoclines Sealed by Faults.—Some faults afford channels along which fluids escape. Other faults are accompanied by finely ground clay that seals the opening, making the fault impervious. Faults that cross shaly strata or other soft rocks are generally impervious. Some oil pools are on monoclines sealed up the dip by faults. In the Appalachian fields no monoclines of this character have been described. In Indiana certain minor fields appear to be connected with the Mount Carmel fault (Fig. 141) and in Illinois the Junction City dome is faulted on the west side of its crest. In Kentucky the Irvine field is developed along a faulted anticline, but at most places the reservoir has been sealed by folding, or by folding and faulting together. In Oklahoma faults

---

[1] PACK, R. W., The Sunset-Midway Oil Field, California, U. S. Geol. Survey *Prof. Paper*, 116, p. 87, 1920.

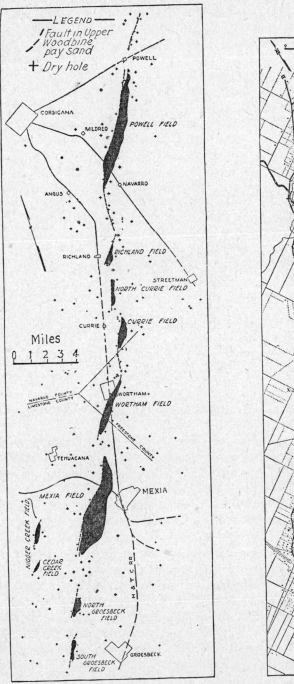

LEGEND
Fault in Upper Woodbine pay sand
+ Dry hole

POWELL

CORSICANA

MILDRED   POWELL FIELD

NAVARRO

ANGUS

Miles
0 1 2 3 4

RICHLAND   RICHLAND FIELD

STREETMAN

NORTH CURRIE FIELD

CURRIE   CURRIE FIELD

NAVARRO COUNTY
LIMESTONE COUNTY   WORTHAM

WORTHAM FIELD

FREESTONE COUNTY

TEHUACANA

MEXIA FIELD   MEXIA

NIGGER CREEK FIELD

CEDAR CREEK FIELD

H & T C R R

NORTH GROESBECK FIELD

SOUTH GROESBECK FIELD   GROESBECK

FIG. 66.   FIG. 67.

FIG. 66.—Map of Mexia-Powell fault zone, Texas.   (*After Lahee.*)
FIG. 67.—Map of Mexia fault zone Powell oil field Texas.   Contours show depth of
Woodbine pay below sea level.   The fault dips west.   *AB* shows fault at Woodbine pay;
CD at top of Austin formation; and *EF* at surface.   (*After Hill, Sutton and Lahee.*)

are common, and, in many of the productive domes, faults have influenced accumulation.   Some of the oil reservoirs in Wagoner County, Oklahoma, seem to be sealed by faulting.

In the Balcones fault region, north Texas (Figs. 66, 67, 68), most of the oil reservoirs are sealed by faults.   The Mexia fault zone of this region is traced 100 miles, is about 6 miles wide, and is marked by parallel overlapping normal faults which dip about 45 degrees and have displacements of from 100 to 700 feet.   The beds dip east, the faults dip west, and the hanging wall sides, moving downward, have dragged the beds of the footwall blocks so that low anticlines are formed in the footwall blocks. The oil is accumulated in the footwall blocks on domes on the anticlines, but the oil deposits at places extend lower than the closures of the domes. The oil is in the Woodbine sand which is sealed along the faults by impervious rocks, and large accumulations of oil are found in several fields including the Powell, Richland, Curry, Wortham, and Mexia.   At Luling, Texas, oil is similarly segregated in the footwall block along a west-dipping fault.   In the Carolina field, Laredo region, south Texas, oil is accumulated on a low dome bordered on the northwest by a fault.   An unusual feature of this field is the development of the dome on the hanging wall side of the fault. This fault, like those of the Mexia group,

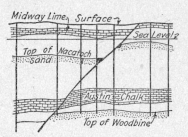

FIG. 68.—Section of Mexia oil field Texas.   (*After Pratt and Lahee.*)

is of the normal type.   In Louisiana and Arkansas many pools are bordered in part by fault seals.

In Wyoming in the Shannon pool, north of Salt Creek, the oil is accumulated in an anticline which plunges away from a fault.   Part of the oil in the Big Muddy pool has accumulated in a similar structure.

In the Whittier and Olinda fields, Puente Hills region, California, oil is accumulated in beds that dip away from a fault.   In the Los Angeles field, also, the accumulation of the oil is controlled in part by faulting on the up dip side of a reservoir.

In the Mount Pozo district, 16 miles north of Bakersfield, California (Fig. 69), the oil reservoir is sealed by a fault up dip.   In many other fields of California the oil measures are faulted and accumulation is modified by, or in part controlled by, faulting.

In Peru some of the largest accumulations of oil are in blocks that have apparently been raised by faulting.   In the Pechelbronn field, also, and in the Wietze field, Hanover region, Germany, the oil accumulations are found in beds that dip away from faults.   In Galicia and Roumania thrust faulting of the oil measures is pronounced and in some of the fields the reservoirs are sealed by faults.   In the Binigadi field, Baku

Peninsula, Russia (Fig. 70), large deposits of oil are accumulated in beds that dip away from faults. In the Tertiary oil fields of Asia faults are very common along the anticlines and domes on which the main reservoirs lie.

Monoclines Sealed by Igneous Intrusions.—In the Tampico-Tuxpam region, Mexico, oil accumulations are found in areas where dikes or other

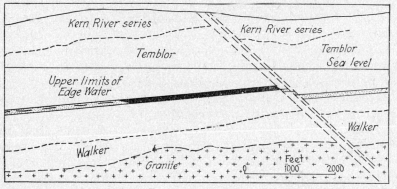

Fig. 69.—Cross section of Mount Pozo oil field, California, showing oil (black) sealed up dip by fault. (*After Wilhelm and Saunders.*) Horizontal equals vertical scale.

igneous bodies cut across petroliferous beds. As a rule the intrusion appears to have been attended by uplifting of the strata into domes.

Monoclines Sealed at Unconformities.—At many places tilted beds are covered by relatively flat-lying beds. Unconformities are favorable places for accumulation, because the younger deposits commonly include coarse sandstone or conglomerate near the base (Fig. 55). Some mono-

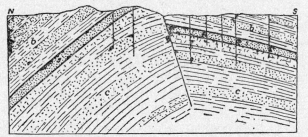

Fig. 70.—Cross section of Binigadi oil field, Russia. *b*, Freshwater beds, *s*, Spirialis beds.

clines are sealed by impervious beds that cover the tilted beds by overlapping them (Fig. 56).

If the underlying older strata contain sands or other porous rocks covered by shales and the sands become saturated with petroleum and water, the petroleum will rise toward the surface and be halted or diverted when it reaches the impervious cover. The zone of junction is rarely level, and accumulation is unequal at different places where the porous bed is covered.   If the junction is sealed at the high end by warping or at a place where the reservoir rock is tight, a trap is formed in which the oil or gas or both may find lodgment.

In Brenning basin, in the Douglas oil and gas field, near Douglas, Wyoming, the nearly flat White River (Tertiary) beds rest on tilted Cretaceous strata that include nearly all the beds of the Colorado and Montana groups (Cretaceous), which are productive elsewhere in Wyoming.   Barnett[1] states that the petroleum in migrating upward along bedding planes and through porous sandstone finds a barrier when it reaches the White River formation, so that oil and gas accumulate near the contact.   They penetrate the White River beds only where they encounter porous material or fault planes.

In the Healdton pool, south of the Arbuckle Mountains, Oklahoma, Pennsylvanian strata rest on steeply tilted Ordovician beds.[2]   A part of the Healdton oil was probably originally in the Ordovician beds, where they are covered by the Pennsylvanian shales.   The principal part of the output, however, is derived from Pennsylvanian rocks.

In the Madill pool, Oklahoma, just south of the Arbuckle uplift, folded Paleozoic sediments dip at high angles.   Above them are Comanche rocks that lie nearly flat.   The lowest member of the Comanche, the Trinity sand and gravel, is saturated with oil that is probably derived from the underlying Carboniferous strata,[3] which are highly productive in this region.

In the McKittrick-Midway-Sunset region, California, the Monterey (lower Miocene) and Santa Margarita formations, which lie in a conformable series, are tilted, and the McKittrick (upper Miocene) overlies them unconformably.[4]   The oil is believed to have originated in the diatomaceous shales of the Monterey and to have migrated to the sandy layers in the Monterey or to the sands and gravels of the unconformably overlying McKittrick formation.   Productive sands are found at the base of the McKittrick above the unconformity.

Oil is accumulated in the Misener sand at an unconformity in Oklahoma and at many other unconformities in Oklahoma.   These are mentioned on subsequent pages.

[1] BARNETT, V. F., The Douglas Oil and Gas Field, Converse County, Wyoming, U. S. Geol. Survey *Bull.* 541, p. 69, 1914.

[2] POWERS, SIDNEY, The Healdton Oil Field, Oklahoma, *Econ. Geol.*, vol. 12, pp. 594–606, 1917.

[3] TAFF, J. A., and W. H. REED, The Madill Oil Pool, Oklahoma, U. S. Geol. Survey *Bull.* 381, pp. 504–513, 1910.

HUTCHINSON, L. L., Rock Asphalt, Asphaltite, Petroleum, and Natural Gas in Oklahoma, Okla. Geol. Survey *Bull.* 2, p. 252, 1911.

[4] ARNOLD, RALPH, and V. R. GARFIAS, Geology and Technology of the California Oil Fields, Am. Inst. Min. Eng. *Bull.* 87, pp. 383–470, 1914.

Shoestring Sands.—Shoestring sands are commonly at unconformities. They are long, narrow, and relatively thick bodies of sand that are surrounded by clay, shale, or other relatively impervious material. As in sheets of sand, the gas accumulates above oil which is above water, and, if the sand is dry, the oil will lie in synclines, the gas under low pressure filling the high parts of the sand.

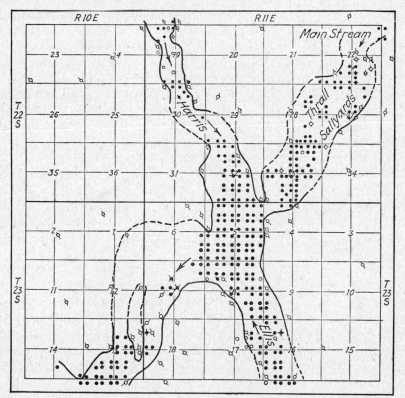

Fig. 71.—Sketch showing intersection of the Thrall-Sallyards and Harris-Ellis trends at the Seely pool, Greenwood County, Kansas. (*After Cadman.*) The sands are believed to fill channels of an ancient river and its tributaries.

Shoestring sands[1] are formed as (1) shore beaches and bars, (2) offshore bars, and spits, (3) filled river channels, (4) delta distributary channels. Shore beaches are characterized by crescentic outlines, by thickening of sand to landward and a slope seaward, and by thorough assortment of material. Offshore bars are thrown up at places where

[1] RICH, J. L., Shoestring Sands of Eastern Kansas, Am. Assoc. Pet. Geol. *Bull.*, vol. 7, pp. 103–113, 1923.

TWENHOFEL, W. H., "Treatise on Sedimentation," Baltimore, 1926.

JOHNSON, D. W., "Shore Processes and Shore Line Development," John Wiley & Sons, Inc.

waves drag on the sea bottom during storms. The material is finer and the sand more patchy and irregular. Such sands are likely to lie parallel to the shore and parallel to each other.

Filled river channels are characterized by dendritic plans (Fig. 71) and locally by meander curves. The base of the sand is commonly uneven as a result of scour and fill. Cross-bedding, poor assortment of material, muddy sands, and carbonaceous material are commonly noted. Such a sand is likely to lie nearly at right angles to beach and bar sands of the region.

Filled delta distributary channels are probably common sources of shoestring sands. The surrounding material consists of fine mud or very fine sand. Such a channel is characterized by narrowness and great length. The sand is relatively fine and uniform. The First Cow Run sand near Marietta, Ohio, according to Rich, is probably an example of such a deposit.

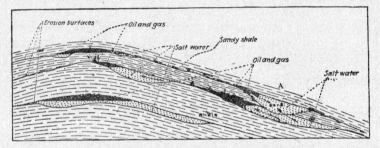

Fig. 72.—Ideal sketch through a dome, showing accumulations of oil and gas in sand-filled channels, and directions of migration. (*After Wallace Lee.*)

In eastern Kansas the Garnett[1] shoestring, southeast of Garnett, is about 30 to 50 feet thick and lies 30 feet below the top of the Cherokee shale. It is believed by some to be an old sand bar. The oil is in the parts of the sand where it lies across a syncline of the region and the gas where it crosses an anticline. If more water were present, the oil would probably be higher in the structure. Figure 72 illustrates oil and gas accumulated in sand-filled channels up dip on a dome.

Shoestring sands are found in the Sallyards[2] field, Greenwood and Butler counties, Kansas, at depths about 2,400 feet and 100 to 150 feet above the "Mississippi Lime" (Boone chert). The sand contains water and the oil is found on domes or high places in the sand. The sand is 140 feet thick and only about ½ mile wide. Berger states that the Sallyards sand is probably a bar formed offshore in the Pennsylvanian

[1] Rich, J. L., Shoestring Sands of Eastern Kansas, Am. Assoc. Pet. Geol. *Bull.*, vol. 7, pp. 103–113, 1923.

[2] Berger, W. R., The Relation between Structure and Production in the Sallyards Field, Kansas, Am. Assoc. Pet. Geol. *Bull.*, vol. 5, pp. 278–281, 1921.

sea.   Cadman, who studied the long narrow oil sands of Greenwood County in the area a few miles northeast of Sallyards,[1] concluded on the basis of the character of the sands and the absence of sea cliffs and the

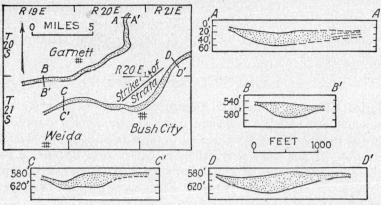

FIG. 73.—Plan and sections of shoestring sands near Garnett and Bush City Kansas. (*After Charles.*)

uneven bottoms of the sands that the Golden Lanes sands were deposited by streams working over a valley flat.   The main stream represented by the Thrall-Sallyards sand flowed southwest.   The stream represented by

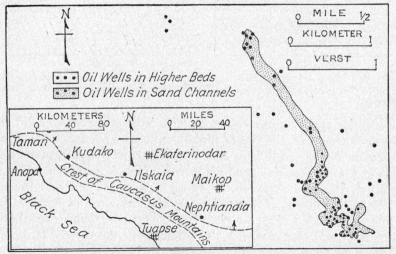

FIG. 74.—Type deposit of Maikop, Russia, oil field, showing accumulation of oil in an ancient river channel filled with sand.   (*After Charnoitsky.*)

the Harris sand flowing southeast joined it at the same place where the Ellis sand joins it from the southeast.

Near Bush City in eastern Kansas a shoestring sand curves so that the convex side of the curve points up dip (Fig. 73).   Tilting only has

[1] CADMAN, W. K., The Golden Lanes of Greenwood County, Kansas, Am. Assoc. Pet. Geol. *Bull.*, vol. 11, pp. 1151–1172, 1927.

taken place, yet owing to the curvature of the sand the structure of the reservoir is similar to that of a closed anticline.   Since some shoestring sands appear to be the sands that fill streams that flow over deltas, it would be supposed that they would be common in the Tertiary oil fields of Russia and Asia where deltaic conditions prevailed when many of the reservoir sands were formed.   Except the shoestrings of Maikop, Russia (Fig. 74), however, few examples are described.

BURIED HILLS AND ARCHES

Buried Hills and Differential Compaction.—As has been stated, oil is commonly accumulated at unconformities.   An angular unconformity illustrated by Fig. 75a may be domed to form an anticline as illustrated by Fig. 75b.   When wells were drilled in east-central Kansas on gentle anticlines, a buried mass of granite was revealed which extends practically across the state into Nebraska.   This mass is called the Nemaha buried granite ridge and it has been outlined by drilling for several hundred miles on strike.   Large oil fields are developed on or near its crest.

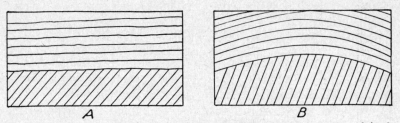

FIG. 75.—Diagrams illustrating unconformities.   *A*, tilted beds peneplained and covered by flat-lying beds.   *B*, tilted beds peneplained and covered by flat-lying beds and later arched.

Because this area was not known to have been much affected by great tectonic movements, the theory of differential compaction was proposed to account for the gentle folds that were formed above the granite ridge. It is well known that clays and muds contain much water when they are deposited, and that some of this water is squeezed out and the mud shrinks in the process of induration and the formation of shales.   Sand shrinks very little.   Suppose clays are deposited around and above a hill or ridge and that a sand is deposited above the clays.   If, by consolidation or compaction, the thickness of the clays is decreased, the sandstone will be let down more on the flanks of the hill than above its crest (Fig. 76), because more clay is present and shrinkage is greater on the flanks.   This would cause the layers of shale and sands within the shale to arch over the buried hill and form an anticline.   It has been suggested that bodies of sand, such as form beaches and bars, would tend to hold up parts of overlying clay beds and that folds would form above such sand masses.   Certain investigators have proposed the process of differential compaction to account for very gentle folds above sand reservoirs in areas of gentle structures, such as parts of the north-central Texas field.

The theory of differential compaction is simple and plausible and has received the support of high authority. Doubtless the process has served to accentuate certain folds, but when one seeks proof that great systems of anticlines are formed by differential compaction in the absence

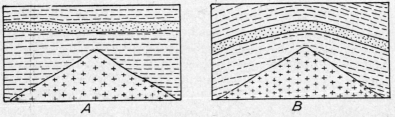

Fig. 76.—Diagrams illustrating an anticline formed by differential compaction. *A*, before compaction; *B*, after compaction of mud or shale by shrinking 20 per cent.

of tectonic movements, the proof is not convincing. The anticlines above the Nemaha granite ridge are commonly regarded as impressive examples of differential compaction, yet the Nemaha Ridge appears to end in central Iowa as a fault over 100 miles long with 300 feet of displacement of rocks no older than the rocks that are folded above the Nemaha Ridge in Kansas.

The criteria that are used to prove that folds have formed by differential compaction are difficult to apply in areas above granite. Fold-

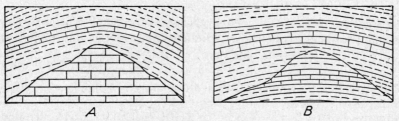

Fig. 77.—Diagrams illustrating buried hills reflected by folds formed by differential compaction. *A*, flat-lying beds are covered by folded beds; *B*, folded beds are covered by more steeply folded beds.

ing along the axis of a granite ridge may have raised the granite enough to account for the gentle arching of overlying beds. In sedimentary rocks, however, the proof may be found. If, as shown by Fig. 77, a buried ridge of flat-lying beds is covered by a series of folded beds, it appears probable that differential compaction has taken place. The same appears probable if the younger beds show more acute folds than the older beds. Even these criteria must be applied with caution, however, for rigid beds are often thrown into broader folds than softer yielding shales.

Reflected Buried Hills.—In many fields it is found that a series of gently folded rocks rests unconformably on a series of more highly folded rocks (Fig. 78). The upper series reflects in milder degree the structure of the underlying beds.[1] In general the minor folds in the intermontane lowland areas of the world are related tectonically to the great anticlinal mountain systems that commonly outline the geosynclines. Many mountain axes are known to have been loci of folding more than once and

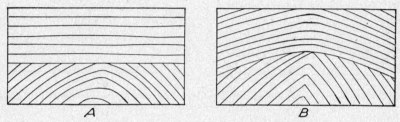

Fig. 78.—Diagrams illustrating: *A*, arched beds peneplained and covered by flat-lying beds; *B*, arched beds peneplained and covered by beds that later are arched above old axis.

that seems to be true of the minor axes also. If, as shown by Fig. 79, beds are deposited around the flanks of the masses of older rocks but do not extend over their tops, the structure is generally regarded as that of buried hills. The beds of the younger series, however, may be arched by movements that involved the older rocks, also, rather than by differential settling. Healdton, Robberson and Thomas, Oklahoma, are reflected buried anticlinal hills.

Arched Unconformities.—As already noted, unconformities for many reasons are favorable structures for accumulation of oil. The tilted

[1] BLACKWELDER, E., The Origin of Central Kansas Oil Domes, Am. Assoc. Pet. Geol. *Bull.*, vol., 4, pp. 89–94, 1920.

POWERS, S., Reflected Buried Hills and Their Importance in Petroleum Geology, *Econ. Geol.*, vol. 17, pp. 233–259, 1922.

———, Reflected Buried Hills in the Oil Fields of Persia, Egypt, and Mexico, Am. Assoc. Pet. Geol. *Bull.*, vol. 10, pp. 422–442, 1926.

NEVIN, C. M., and R. E. SHERRILL, Studies in Differential Compaction, Am. Assoc. Pet. Geol. *Bull.*, vol. 13, pp. 1–22, 1929.

MONNETT, V. E., Possible Origin of Some of the Structures of the Mid-Continent Oil Field, *Econ. Geol.*, vol. 17, pp. 194–200, 1922.

BRIDGE, J., and L. L. DAKE, Initial Dips Peripheral to Resurrected Buried Hills, Mo. Bur. Geol. and Min. Biennial *Rept.*, Appendix 1, pp. 1–7, 1928.

HEDBERG, A. D., The Effect of Gravitational Compaction on the Structure of Sedimentary Rocks, Am. Assoc. Pet. Geol. *Bull.*, vol. 10, pp. 1035–1072, 1926.

PARKS, E. M., Am. Assoc. Pet. Geol. *Bull.*, vol. 8, p. 705, 1924.

LEY, H. A., Am. Assoc. Pet. Geol. *Bull.*, vol. 8, pp. 445–453, 1924.

TEAS, L. P., Am. Assoc. Pet. Geol. *Bull.*, vol. 7, pp. 370–377, 1923.

petroliferous strata may be peneplained and covered with impermeable beds which will seal the reservoir. If the overlying strata are arched, the anticline is a favorable structure because any oil in the later beds may rise to the crest of the arch, and a large number of the older strata are in a position to contribute to the younger strata. If the beds of the later strata are parallel to the plain of unconformity, one infers that the lower beds were peneplained before burial.

Arched Peneplained Arches.—If a rod is bent, and, later, if pressure is applied, the rod will bend again at the same place. Similarly, axes of folded ranges have been the loci of folding at more than one period (Fig. 79b). Some have been folded many times. If beds are laid down upon a peneplained fold (Fig. 78a), accumulation of oil may take place in the upper beds near the arch from both sides. If the arch is folded a second time, any oil present is likely to accumulate on the arch from

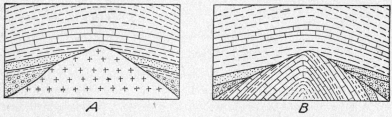

Fig. 79.—Cross sections of buried hills: *A*, granite hill with beds on its flanks that do not extend over top of hill; *B*, refolded buried anticlinal hill with beds on its flanks that do not extend over the top of the hill.

many beds of the lower series as well as from beds of the upper series. A dome showing two periods of folding, one in beds below and another in beds above the unconformity, is thus a very favorable structure, because it may draw oil from many beds and from large areas. Moreover, in consolidated beds faulting and fracturing are often localized at crests of anticlines, and thus openings may form that furnish pathways for the movement of oil. Some of the greatest oil fields developed are in areas that show arched unconformities with older beds arched before the later series was deposited. Examples are Garber, Oklahoma City, and Cushing, Oklahoma; Kevin-Sunburst, Montana; Shustar, Persia; Knife Edge field of Mexico, and many others. Some of these are buried hills. They were not eroded to base level before burial. Many domes, folded after burial are not buried hills. Figure 78b represents an arched peneplain. It is not a buried hill, for the hill raised by early folding was eroded before burial.

SUMMARY

Unconformities in General.—The beds that lie below or above unconformities are favorable places for accumulation of oil for many reasons already mentioned. With the development of certain fields in Kentucky, Ohio, Indiana, Illinois, Kansas, Oklahoma, west Texas, Panhandle of Texas, Montana, California, Venezuela, Peru, Persia, Netherlands India, Japan, and elsewhere, the importance of unconformities has become more and more evident.   The weathered surfaces

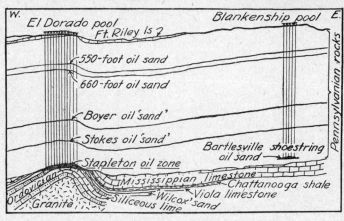

Fig. 80.—Cross section of El Dorado and Blankenship oil pools.   (*After Moore and Landes.*)

below unconformities or the coarser basal sediments above them supply reservoirs in many regions.   In most fields the unconformable relation is only one feature of the structure of the reservoir, for the unconformity lies above a dome, on a sealed monocline or other favorable structural feature.   The eroded, buried, anticlinal hill that has been refolded after burial appears to be a particularly favorable structure in which oil is found in the dome near the plane of the unconformity.   In many

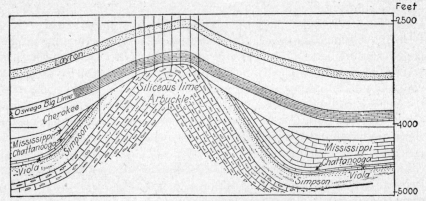

Fig. 81.—Generalized cross section Garber oil field Oklahoma. (*After S. K. Clark.*)

districts where oil is found near planes of unconformity, it is not known whether the oil originated in beds below or in beds above the erosion surface.   The oil is often in both systems of rocks.   There is a combination of doming, of the development of an unconformity, and of other favorable factors, and the importance of each can not easily be evaluated. A few examples of accumulation of oil in beds near unconformities are mentioned below.

In Ohio, Indiana, and Kentucky large accumulations of oil are found in limestone below unconformities. In Illinois in the main productive fields in the southeastern part of the state much of the oil is found in sands where a truncated tilted surface is covered by later beds (Fig. 146). In the great Eldorado field, Kansas, in Blackwell, Garber, Tonkawa, Oklahoma City, Cushing, Seminole, Robberson, and Healdton, Oklahoma, and in many other fields of Kansas and Oklahoma, in Caddo

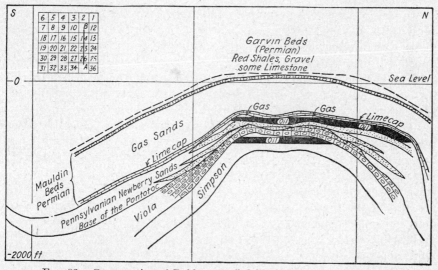

FIG. 82.—Cross section of Robberson oil field, Oklahoma. (*After Roth.*)

Parish, Louisiana, and elsewhere unconformities have played a prominent part in accumulation. In most of these fields the rocks were arched, eroded, buried, and arched again to form the complicated structures in which the oil is accumulated (Figs. 80, 81, 82). In some of these fields the oil is certainly on buried hills, because sands, residuary cherts, or other reservoir rocks found on the flanks of the domes are wanting on their summits, and the plane of unconformity shows more rise at the crest of the arch than the rise shown by the beds above the unconformity (Fig. 79). In other domes the unconformity shows a rise about equal to that of the beds above the unconformity (Fig. 78b), which shows that the ancient anticlinal hill was peneplained before burial. Low buried hills are shown by Figs. 81, 82.

In the Panhandle of Texas the oil and gas accumulated in limestone that was laid down on a granite ridge and later arched by folding approximately along the axis of the ridge. Oil and gas are accumulated also in granite wash which was laid down against the ridge and subsequently buried. In the great Yates field and in other fields of west Texas, the oil accumulated in domes that are buried hills. At Yates the oil-bearing limestone is very porous at and near the top of the dome, but in the basin away from the dome it is much less porous. This relation, as pointed out by Clark, is probably due to weathering of an upraised hill before burial. It is highly probable that the Kevin-Sunburst oil field has a nearly similar history. The Madison limestone was raised by folding; the Quadrant quartzite, if present above the arch, was removed from it; the limestone was weathered and the area was buried before the oil accumulated.

In California oil has accumulated at unconformities in the Coalinga, McKittrick-Sunset-Midway, and other districts. In the Coalinga district oil has accumulated at three different unconformities. In the Sunset-Midway district the oil-bearing series overlaps the Maricopa shale so that many sands play out against the shale and are overlapped by later sands, and the whole series is sealed up dip, in part by tar (Fig. 64).

Among the fields outside of the United States where unconformities play an important part in accumulation of oil is the great Knife Edge belt near Tuxpam, Mexico, which is one of the world's most productive regions. The oil is found in limestone along a buried ridge. In Venezuela in the oil fields on the northeast shore of Lake Maracaibo, which are among the world's most productive fields, the oil has accumulated on a monocline sealed by tar and sands lensing out up dip. The main oil-bearing strata are near the plane of an unconformity. In Peru large accumulations of oil have taken place near unconformities. In the Baku region, Russia, large amounts of oil are found near unconformities. In Persia much of the oil is in a porous limestone below an unconformity and probably on a buried hill. In Egypt some of the oil has accumulated at an unconformity. In Japan much of the oil is accumulated at unconformities. In the Kurokawa field in the Akita region the oil is on an anticline in local sands above an eroded surface of igneous rocks.

RESERVOIRS ON TERRACES

There are few large areas of the earth with rocks perfectly flat. As a rule the rocks dip away from a mountain fold to the bottom of a syncline where they rise again toward some other fold. Thus, the mountain folding affects essentially the entire area between the upfolded mountains. There are many areas, however, over which the rocks dip at very low angles. Some of these are belts of low dip that lie between belts of rocks that dip at higher angles. Where the rocks in all of the belts dip in the same general direction (Fig. 83), the area may show no

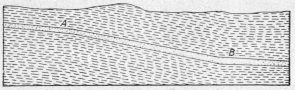

FIG. 83.—Ideal section showing position of oil accumulation on a terrace. If the oil migrates upward as it does in saturated rocks, it will tend to accumulate near *A*. If it migrates downward it will tend to accumulate near *B*.

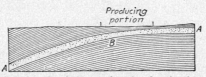

FIG. 84.—Ideal section of Gaines Pool, Pennsylvania, showing its relation to change of dip. *A*, oil sand; *B*, brink of terrace where oil has accumulated. (*After Fuller.*)

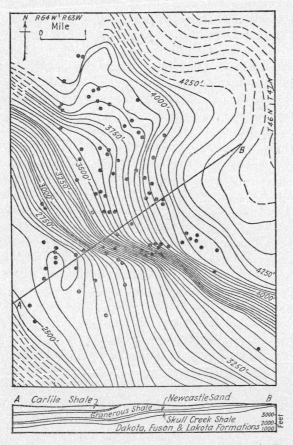

FIG. 85.—Map and cross section of the Osage oil field, Weston County, Wyoming. (*After Collier, U. S. Geol. Surv.*) Structure contours on upper bed of Newcastle sandstone.

anticline nor syncline. The area of nearly flat rocks between the areas of more highly tilted rocks is a structural terrace. Oil accumulations on terraces are found in the Gaines pool, Pennsylvania (Fig. 84), in the Osage district, Wyoming (Fig. 85), and elsewhere. In most and probably in all of the fields on terraces the reservoirs are sealed by lensing out, by tar, or in some other way, so that the terrace accumulation of oil is essentially like an accumulation on a monocline. It has been stated that, if the sands are saturated, the oil will move upward and lodge near the places where the bed flattens up dip (A, Fig. 83). If the reservoirs contain little water and oil moves downward, the accumulation may be located where the bed flattens downward (B, Fig. 83).

It is probable that all but the heavy oils will move in rocks that are almost flat, if gas is present in the system. It has been shown by experiments at the University of Minnesota that oil will move in tubes inclined less than one degree, even when the gas pressure is low. On the other hand, the oil moves more slowly at places where the tubes are flat than in places where the tubes are inclined (Fig. 29), and clay particles that are carried along with the oil in the experiments seem to accumulate more readily in the flat parts of the tubes. These clay particles tend to choke the sands and thus to halt the movement of the oil. It is noteworthy that in the experiment illustrated by Fig. 29, most of the oil ultimately rose to the top of the tube where it was sealed in.

The accumulation of oil on terraces is emphasized in much of the earlier literature on the geology of petroleum. Recent work, however, particularly the microscopic study of oil sands, has shown that in most fields where oil is found on terraces the sands become impervious up dip or in some other way are sealed up dip, thus closing in the oil-bearing structure. The Glenn field near Tulsa, Oklahoma, was once supposed by some to be due to a terrace structure but, as shown by Wilson, the oil-bearing sand pinches out up dip, thus affording an effective seal. There is no important field in the Mid-Continent region which is located on a terrace in which the oil sand is not sealed up dip. The Osage field, Wyoming, is on two terraces, but, as noted elsewhere, the oil sands become tight and are faulted up dip. The Gaines pool, Pennsylvania, is regarded as an accumulation due to the flattening of the oil-bearing sand, but no description of the sand outside of the area of oil accumulation is available. The general absence of important accumulations of oil on terraces, where no seal is provided up dip, emphasizes the conclusion that is now generally accepted, namely, that considerable oil accumulations are found only where they are sealed in, either on a dome or where impervious barriers prevent the movement and loss of the oil.

RESERVOIRS IN SYNCLINES

Oil is found in synclines in parts of the Appalachian region. In the Catskill strata in Pennsylvania and West Virginia petroleum and gas are found in sands between shales. These beds are not saturated with water. Reeves[1] states that these unsaturated beds, which are land sediments, had dried out before they were submerged in the sea and that the spaces of their reservoirs were filled with air. Later, when marine sediments were laid down above them, the oil evidently migrated into them, but not enough water to float the oil to the tops of folds. Some of the Missis-

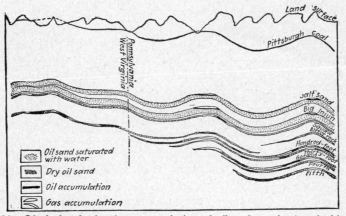

FIG. 86.—Ideal sketch showing accumulation of oil and gas in Appalachian region. The higher sands are saturated and oil and gas rise to crests of anticlines. The lower sands are not saturated and the oil and gas are found low on the flanks of the anticlines or in synclines. (*After Griswold and Munn.*)

sippian sands above the Devonian in Pennsylvania are saturated, and in them the oil and gas occur in anticlines. These features are illustrated by Fig. 86. Recently, marine fossils have been found in the unsaturated sands of the Bradford pool, New York and Pennsylvania, and in other oil fields of the Appalachian region in which the Devonian rocks are unsaturated. Thus Reeves' argument loses some of its force and no other theory has been proposed that satisfactorily accounts for the dry condition of the sands. The oil of the Cabin Creek district, West Virginia (p. 106), is found in a lens of Berea sand in a syncline. The sand is essentially dry and it is suggested[2] that the oil entered the sand as a gas during the Appalachian revolution and subsequently liquefied.

In southeastern Utah a little oil has been found in a syncline in the San Juan field. In the McKittrick district, California, a considerable

---

[1] REEVES, FRANK, The Absence of Water in Certain Sandstones of the Appalachian Oil Fields, *Econ. Geol.*, vol. 12, pp. 254–278, 1917.

[2] WASSON, T., and I. WASSON, Cabin Creek Field, West Virginia, Am. Assoc. Pet. Geol. *Bull.*, vol. 11, pp. 705–719, 1927.

concentration of oil is found in an overturned syncline (Fig. 87). In Galicia also oil is found in synclines in the Boryslaw field.

The large deposits of oil in well-defined synclines in consolidated rocks are in the Appalachian field. Most other fields in which large concentrations are found in synclines are in partly consolidated rocks that

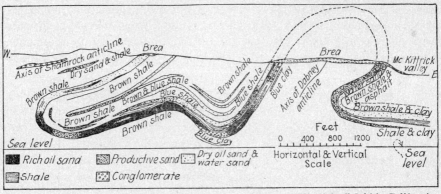

Fig. 87.—Hypothetical section across the south end of the McKittrick oil field in California. (*After Arnold and Johnson, U. S. Geol. Surv.*)

have been intensely deformed. Under such conditions as have already been noted, petroleum is apparently found in many different structural positions.

Some synclines are merely gentle sags near the crests of anticlines. Such sags may be saturated with oil or gas or both (Fig. 88). Others contain a little water near the axis of the sag. In still others the sand may be filled with water.

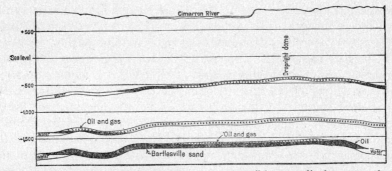

Fig. 88.—Section of Cushing field, Oklahoma, showing oil in a synclinal sag near the crest of an anticline. (*After Beal, U. S. Geol. Surv.*)

Where an oil-bearing bed is folded after oil has accumulated in the bed, oil would be expected to lie in both the downfolds and in upfolds. Such structures seem to be rare. Seminole, Oklahoma, has been cited as an example of such a field, but the structure was probably incorrectly interpreted owing to crooked holes.

RESERVOIRS FORMED BY FISSURES

Practically all consolidated rocks are jointed, and many of them are appreciably fractured. The earlier investigators of oil reservoirs in the Appalachian region laid much emphasis on fissures as containers of oil and gas. Later, when great fields in unconsolidated rocks were developed in Russia, in California, and elsewhere, it appeared less probable that fissures play so important a part, for in soft rocks fissures will close. The effect of openings formed by fracturing, and brecciation has been mentioned in connection with the discussion of reservoir rocks. Such openings doubtless add materially to the capacity of reservoirs in certain fields where oil occurs in consolidated pre-Tertiary rocks. In unconsolidated rocks of some Tertiary fields they are generally less effective. The capacity of fissures is attested by those that are filled with bitumens—some containing many millions of tons.

At Florence, Colorado, according to Washburne,[1] the principal reservoirs are fissures in the shale of the Pierre formation. This is a uniform shale, and in the lower part, which carries the petroleum deposits, no sands are present. Evidence that the oil lies in joints and fissures consists (a) of a correspondence in direction of the major joints in the rocks at the surface with the alignment of wells which have interfered with one another; (b) of the fact that many wells have been drilled within a few feet of one another without encountering oil at the same depth; (c) of the fact that gas struck in a shallow well often immediately ruins an adjacent well several hundred feet deeper by tapping the source of pressure; (d) of the fact that many wells drain adjacent wells that are shallower; (e) of the indication of vertical connection between the oil bodies shown by the marked increase in maximum pressure with depth; and (f) of the dissimilar pressures in adjacent wells of the same depth.

In the Salt Creek field, Wyoming,[2] considerable oil has been found in fissures in the Cretaceous shale. This region is a domatic uplift and yields oil from sands in elevated portions of the dome. West of the dome there is a great syncline with thick shale beds in which the oil sands carry only water. In nearly every well drilled in this field, according to Wegemann, some oil is found in the shale, a few wells having an initial production of as much as 1,500 barrels a day. The oil is not obtained from porous beds in the shale, and it is found in adjoining wells at different depths. The shale is so fine grained that it would not in itself constitute a reservoir for oil.

[1] WASHBURNE, C. W., The Florence Oil Field, Colorado, U. S. Geol. Survey *Bull.* 381, pp. 517–544, 1910.
[2] WEGEMANN, C. H., The Salt Creek Oil Field, Wyoming, U. S. Geol. Survey *Bull.* 670, p. 36, 1917.

Other fields in the Rocky Mountains region have produced oil in commercial amounts in crevices in shale.[1]   These include Big Muddy and Pilot Butte fields, Wyoming, the Rangely, Tow Creek, Iles, Fort Collins fields, Colorado.

Shales that yield oil also yield gas.   In some regions, gas only is obtained from the shale reservoirs.   In Cleveland, Ohio,[2] and in the surrounding country, wells have been sunk in the shale for domestic supply.   As a rule the pressure is low and the yield small, but the wells have long life, so that farmers find the fuel suitable for domestic use. Orton,[3] describing the differences between shale gas and "reservoir gas," notes that . . .

Shale-gas wells are generally of small volume compared to wells deriving their gas from sand reservoirs.   Moreover, they lack uniformity of rock pressure. Wells drilled in close proximity and to the same depth may have very different pressures.   In sand reservoirs, pressures are generally greater and more nearly uniform.   In the wells yielding shale gas there is no definite horizon from which their gas supply is derived.   Shale-gas wells are long lived.   Weak flows are maintained for long periods.

In eastern Kansas many shallow wells produce shale gas from thin shale beds that lie just above a limestone member of the Fort Scott formation.   The gas occurs in pores and fractures in the shale.[4]

In certain fields oil has accumulated in fissures and other openings in igneous rocks.   In Lytton Springs, Texas, the upper part of a body of serpentine is fractured and brecciated and at places vesicular, and large amounts of oil are derived from it (Fig. 89).   The oil-bearing mass is domed upward and occupies an area of about a square mile, the oil extending to depths about 200 feet below the top of the serpentine mass. The part that weathering has played in the formation of the reservoir is not certain, but, since the body is said to be in part vesicular and extrusive, it appears possible that it is also weathered.   At Dale, near Lytton Springs, some oil has been found in serpentine.   Oil is found in considerable amounts in an igneous rock, said to be basaltic, in the Totumo field, Venezuela.   Oil is found in igneous tuffs in the Thrall field, Texas, and in certain of the Japanese fields, but these rocks are fragmental stratified rocks.

[1] ESTABROOKE, E. L., and C. M. RADER, "Petroleum Development and Technology in 1925," p. 210, 1926.

[2] VAN HORN, F. R., Reservoir Gas and Oil in the Vicinity of Cleveland, Ohio, Am. Inst. Min. Eng. *Bull.* 121, pp. 75–86, 1917.

[3] ORTON, EDWARD, Geological Survey of the Iola Gas Field, Geol. Soc. Am. *Bull.*, vol. 10, p. 100, 1899.

[4] CHARLES, H. H., and J. H. PAGE, Shale-gas Industry of Eastern Kansas, Am. Assoc. Pet. Geol. *Bull.*, vol. 13, pp. 367–381, 1929.

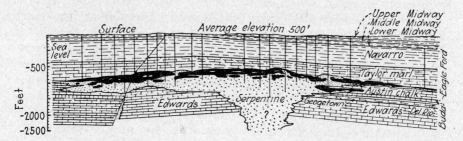

Fig. 89.—Cross section of Lytton Springs oil field, Texas. The oil (black) is concentrated in fractured and porous serpentine. (*After Collingswood and Rettger.*)

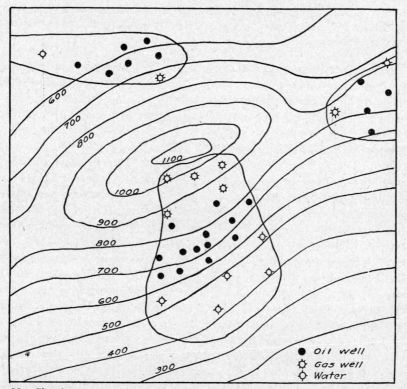

Fig. 90.—Sketch contour map showing accumulations of oil and gas in sands that are only locally porous.

ACCUMULATION IN SANDS OF IRREGULAR PORE SPACE

In many oil fields the oil-producing sands are irregular or "spotted." Borings that yield neither oil, gas, nor water may be sunk in a sand that contains oil or gas on all sides of it.   Examination of fragments of the oil stratum in the boring may discover a tight sand in which the pore space is filled by calcite, pyrite, or other secondary minerals, or one that is filled with clay.

On many domes and anticlines, as already noted, a belt that yields oil is found below a disk of gas-filled sand.   Some wells, however, that are sunk in the oil-producing belt may yield gas only.   Examination may reveal a sand that is coarser grained and contains larger pores than

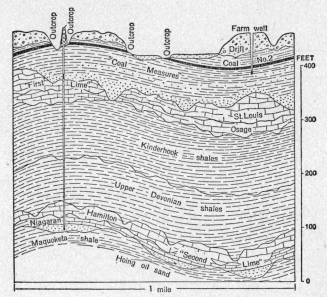

FIG. 91.—Diagram showing unconformities and spotted character of Hoing sand in Colmar field, Illinois.   (*After Morse and Kay.*)

the sands elsewhere in the oil-bearing area, for in some fields gas tends to accumulate in the larger openings.   In the areas of porous rock that are surrounded by impervious rocks at the same horizon, the oil, gas, and water that are contained in the porous rock are generally segregated in belts, the gas above the oil and the water below it, as is illustrated by Fig. 90.   In such a field where pools are not connected by open spaces in the petroliferous stratum, the lines of contact between gas and oil and between oil and water may be found at widely different elevations. Spotted sands are found in the Colmar field, Illinois (Fig. 91) and elsewhere.

SUCCESSIONS OF PETROLIFEROUS STRATA

Oil reservoirs are almost invariably related to geologic structure. There is no better proof of this relation than the accumulation of oil in different beds, one below the other, in the same field, and the absence of oil in commercial accumulations in the surrounding regions. In many pools oil is found in more than one stratum. In some it is found in five strata or more. Where the structure is anticlinal and there is an accumulation of petroleum in the upper sand at the crest, it is reasonable to suppose that lower strata, if conformable, lie in anticlines also, and that if they are porous they may contain additional reserves. In some districts the amplitude of folds increases with depth, and deeper accumulations, situated on the greater folds, are more productive than the shallow pools. Many fields have been revived again and again by deeper drilling.

Where petroliferous beds are steeply folded, as they are in the Grozny field, north of the Caucasus Range, Russia, in the Yenangyat-Singu field, Burma, and in other fields that contain accumulations of oil in Mesozoic and Tertiary rocks, where successive oil strata have been discovered, the planes that pass through the crests of folds or the "crest loci" are not vertical but dip at high angles. In general the crest locus will dip toward the gentle limb of an asymmetric fold, and accumulation on the gentle side of the fold as shown at or near the surface will be even more pronounced in depth. In a few fields, however, the crest moves with depth toward the steep limb (p. 99).

TOPOGRAPHIC EXPRESSION OF STRUCTURAL FEATURES

In many oil fields there is no obvious relation between the topography of the area and its geologic structure. Anticlines and domes are commonly found in the low areas and synclines may occupy the higher ones. This is likely to be true in areas that were deformed during a remote geologic period. In areas folded during a very late geological period the hills are likely to coincide with anticlines or domes as they do in certain Gulf Coast and in certain California oil fields. In the areas of older deformation this relation is less likely to exist, yet, as pointed out by Monnett,[1] even in the areas that have been eroded extensively, the streams, hills, and escarpments may have an evident relation to structure.

[1] MONNETT, V. E., Topographic criteria of oil field structure, Am. Assoc. Pet. Geol. *Bull.*, vol. 6, pp. 37–41, 1922.

CHAPTER IX

BEHAVIOR OF WELLS AND ROCK PRESSURE

BEHAVIOR OF WELLS

Oil, gas, and water are present in most oil reservoirs under considerable pressure. These three fluids affect each other and form a complicated system. If the pressure is high, it forces out the oil vigorously, the well becoming a "gusher," "fountain," or "spouter." If the pressure is low, the oil moves to the well and partially fills the hole but must be pumped to the surface. Nearly all of the highly productive wells flow naturally. The largest flow is often the first day's flow and after the first few days the production generally declines. In some wells, however, the production increases steadily at first and reaches a maximum a few days after completion of the well. Such a well may tap the oil sand where it is impure and shaly and the oil moves to the bottom of the well with difficulty. The moving oil establishes channels in the sand, however, which allow the oil to move to the well with greater freedom. Often sand is carried out with the oil, and both the number and size of the channels are increased. The well is said to "drill itself in." A considerable number of wells have been brought in with initial productions of 50,000 to 100,000 barrels per day. The Mid-Kansas Transcontinental Yates A30 well gaged for one hour at the rate of 204,681 barrels per day, which, according to Hennen and Metcalf, is the largest gaged production for any well. A well at Spindletop, Texas, had an initial production of 100,000 barrels, and several California wells have had large initial yields. In Oklahoma several wells have produced more than 25,000 barrels a day.[1] These wells are exceptional; many wells yield only 5 to 10 barrels per day. In 1929 the average production per day per well of New York and Pennsylvania was 0.36 barrel of oil. The total amount of oil from a single well ranges from a few score to millions of barrels. The Potrero No. 4 well of Tuxpam produced about 115,000,000 barrels before it began to yield water, which was about 8 years after it was brought in. A well in Persia has yielded 47,000,000 barrels in 15 years. On the other hand, many wells yield less than 5,000 barrels before exhaustion. Where many wells are drilled the yield per well is less.

The life of the average well is comparatively short. As a rule wells yield more oil the first year than any other, and each succeeding year the yield declines. Often in 10 or 12 years they are exhausted, although

[1] Several Oklahoma City wells have gauged much more than that.

there are wells that have produced small amounts of oil for 40 years or more.

Certain wells first yield gas and subsequently oil. If a body of gas, under high back pressure, is underlain by a deposit of oil, and if the gas is encountered in a well and drawn out, the oil may rise to take its place. Thus, in Fig. 92, well 1 will yield gas and later oil. A gas well on the flank of a fold near the gas-oil line will yield gas, and, as the pressure of the field declines, the oil may rise or be driven up by water pressure so that the gas well becomes an oil well. It is a common practice to allow gas wells to flow open with the hope that they will become oil wells. This practice reduces the pressure of a field and is prohibited by law in most states. Some wells yield oil, then water. Well 3 (Fig. 92) would first yield oil and later water. On the other hand, a well still lower on the flank will yield water, and, if the water were pumped long enough,

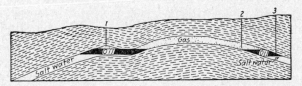

Fig. 92.—Sketch showing gas wells (1 and 2), that would become oil wells if, because of decrease of pressure of gas, the plane of contact of oil and gas were to rise. If the plane of contact between oil and water were elevated because of removal of gas or oil, well 3 would cease to flow oil and would flow water.

unless the back pressure of water were too high, the water well might yield oil.

Many wells yield two fluids simultaneously. Gas commonly contains oil and large amounts of gasoline are obtained from natural gas by compressing it, by refrigeration, or by passing the gas through mineral oil. A strong gas well near the oil level which later becomes an oil well (Fig. 92) will commonly pass through a stage when it sprays oil in large amounts. Salt-water spray also is commonly present in gas issuing from wells. The bore, with gas passing over liquid at the deep end, becomes a giant "atomizer."

Nearly all oil wells yield gas or water or both. Gas is absorbed by the oil and commonly a considerable amount of gas is present in the oil-bearing part of the reservoir, besides that absorbed. As a rule the amount of gas decreases toward the water-oil contact. The oil sands are not uniform bodies; they contain layers of shale and they feather out above and below. Thus, the oil-bearing part of a reservoir may contain pockets of gas or water trapped in parts of the sand. At many wells there are devices for dehydrating the oil by warming it or by other means. Many oil wells in the lower part of the oil-bearing portion of a reservoir yield large amounts of water. In many reservoirs this water is emulsified with oil and in certain fields, notably in Mexico and California, the appearance of a water-oil emulsion in a well, and, particularly, of warm emulsion, is regarded as evidence of rapidly approaching edge water which ends production.

Summarizing, it may be stated that an oil field on a dome may show the following horizons from the top down: gas, oil with much gas, oil with little gas, oil with increasing water and, in certain fields, oil and water emulsion, water with high salt content, water with low salt content. All of these zones may not be present in a single field, but, when present, they tend to lie in the order named. In many fields a gas zone without oil is lacking. That is essentially true in the Salt Creek field, Wyoming, in both the First and Second Wall Creek sands, although in this field there is considerable gas, the amount produced to 1924 being 1,620 cubic feet per barrel of oil. In this field nearly all of the oil carries gas; in the Second sand which is oil bearing over an area of 22,000 acres, the zone of "dead" oil, or oil with a little gas, does not extend more than 50 to 100 feet structurally above the oil-water contact. In the Urschell field, Kansas, according to Shea, there is practically no gas present except a little hydrogen sulphide. There is a strong water pressure in this field, and one of the early wells had an initial daily flow of 2,928 barrels.

The solids that issue from wells include (1) the fluids that, owing to changes of pressure and temperature, solidify as they reach the surface, and (2) the rock fragments and particles of sand and clay that are blown from the wells with gas or "sediment" that flows out with the oil and water.

Certain oils solidify at moderately low temperatures. Thus, the oil at Big Lake field, Montana, congeals at 66° F. A well was brought in, in subzero weather; the oil solidified and covered the area near the base of the derrick with congealed oil. A well at Newman, Hughes County, Oklahoma, produces an oil that solidifies when cold and has been called the "vaseline" well. Some of the oils of the Panhandle region, Texas, congeal at 50° F. and cause trouble in pipe lines and in waxing of sands. Paraffin wax is dissolved in oils of many fields. Cooling follows relief of pressure. In many wells the wax is deposited in quantities so great as to retard production. A deep well near Walden, Colorado, yielded large amounts of carbon dioxide gas under high pressure. The gas, on reaching the surface, expanded rapidly, and cooling, as a result of expansion, formed carbon dioxide "snow." Oil is associated with the gas, and on warming, the carbon dioxide passes off, leaving a light amber oil. This well produced about 500 barrels of oil per day in 1927.

Salt-water spray is often present in gas issuing from wells. When a reservoir containing gas is pierced by a boring, the pressure is decreased by the issue of gas. Expansion lowers the temperature of the gas, and the salt-water spray which is commonly present in the issuing gas will be cooled. Gas under low pressure will absorb more water than gas under high pressure, and evaporation results. As a result of the cooling and evaporation, much salt is deposited. The casings of wells and the interstices of sands may be filled with sodium chloride so that the well will cease to flow. Calcium carbonate, magnesium carbonate, iron carbonate, and calcium, barium, and strontium sulphates are deposited in casings and presumably also in interstices of sands in reservoirs. In certain wells rock fragments are blown out by gas, especially from wells where gas issues at high pressures in early stages of production. In fields where the oil sands are poorly consolidated, the oil commonly carries large amounts of loose sand. This is true in certain fields of California and Baku, Russia. The sand deposited in certain Russian wells is so great that derricks are half covered with it. A sediment is often carried by oil and special treatment is required for removing it.

Some flowing wells after being capped and reopened will cease to flow. In other wells if the flow of the oil is stopped, it may not be reestablished in its original force. As a result, many operators prefer not to shut off a well entirely, but to allow it to flow at a low rate during the period that preparations are made to dispose of the oil. In some cases the gas pressure has been reduced by other wells tapping the reservoir between the time of closing and reopening the well. Even consolidated sands often contain fine particles of clay. These commonly move with the oil and, lodging in openings between the sand grains, tend to seal up lines of drainage. Often they may be dislodged and drainage reestablished by "shooting" the well; that is, by exploding nitroglycerine in it. Wells in consolidated sands and limestones are often shot to provide channels for flow of oil to the well.

Flow by Heads.—Many oil wells spout periodically or flow by heads. At intervals, commonly from a half hour to an hour apart, the oil issues violently accompanied by gas. After an eruption the well ceases to flow, but the period of quiescence is followed by another head of oil. Flow by heads is characteristic of wells of moderate flow, many such wells yielding about 150 to 300 barrels per day. The behavior of the oil well is much like that of the geyser and is probably due in part to similar causes. The conditions necessary for flow by heads probably are (1) moderate supplies of oil and gas moving to the bottom of the bore, and (2) a porous reservoir near the bottom of the bore and, in part, higher than the bottom of the bore. Descriptions of experiments (Fig. 93) designed to illustrate the flow by heads, follow.[1]

[1] These experiments were made in my laboratory in 1923 by H. E. La Tendresse in connection with a study of geysers of Yellowstone Park, and in 1929 by Nathan Davies in connection with a study of behavior of oil wells. (W. H. E.)

A bent tube with a flask *A* to serve as a reservoir for gas was set up so that water under pressure and gas could be let into one end of the tube *B*. The other end of the tube *D* was fitted with a smaller tube *C* standing upright which represents the oil well. The water was let in first and flowed gently out of the small tube *C*. When the gas was let

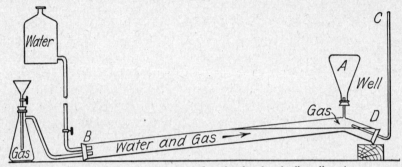

Fig. 93.—Apparatus used to illustrate flow by heads of oil well. *A*, gas reservoir flask; *B*, small tubes leading water and gas into large tube; *C*, small tube fitted into large tube at *D*.

in with the water, it would accumulate in the flask *A* until the gas pressure was sufficient to depress the water to the bottom of the small tube; then gas and water issued violently from the small tube *C*. After

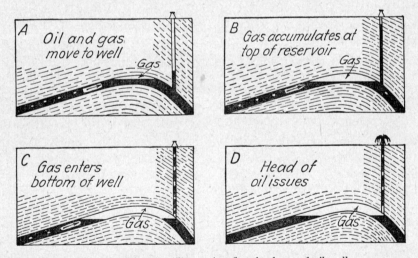

Fig. 94.—Diagrams illustrating flow by head of oil well.

the eruption, the pressure being relieved, water would seal off the gas at *D*, the small tube would fill with water, and some water would rise into the gas reservoir at *A*. Again gas would accumulate in the reservoir *A* until it became sufficient to depress the water at *D*, when another eruption would take place. The periods between eruptions could be varied by varying the rate at which water and gas were let into the system.

If a well taps a reservoir rock, as shown in Fig. 94a, oil and gas will rise together in the well, but some of the gas will accumulate in the high part of the fold, as shown in Fig. 94b. The gas pressure will balance the column of oil in the well. When the gas pressure has increased so that the gas accumulation extends to the bottom of the bore (Fig. 94c), gas will enter the well along with the oil. That will lighten the column of oil in the well, and the column of oil will no longer balance the gas pressure. The gas in the reservoir can then expand. More gas enters the well, decreasing further the weight of the oil column, so that the oil can be discharged violently (Fig. 94d). Subsequently, as soon as the oil flowing from the reservoir seals the bottom of the bore, the gas begins to accumulate again, and the process is repeated.

RESERVOIR PRESSURES

Oil, gas, and water exist in their reservoirs under pressure. It is this pressure[1] that causes the oil to move through the rocks to the wells and to be expelled from flowing wells. The study of reservoir pressures is useful, for, by such study, one may gain information that will aid in the development and operation of a field or in the estimation of its life. There is hardly a problem in the development of a field that is not closely related to the reservoir pressure. It is possible to reduce the study of reservoir pressures to mathematical terms and this is a valuable practice, although it is evident in many fields that some of the results arrived at are not precisely accurate. Comprehensive studies of pressures in any field at several stages of its development should prove of great value.

The pressure under which fluids are confined in rocks is termed "rock pressure." This pressure is rarely due to the pressure of the rock

[1] ORTON, E., Petroleum and Natural Gas in New York, N. Y. State Mus. *Bull.*, vol. 6, No. 30, p. 473, 1899.

WHITE, I. C., Petroleum and Natural Gas, W. Va. Geol. Survey, vol. A, pp. 48–64, 1885.

HEROY, W. R., Rock Pressure, Am. Assoc. Pet. Geol. *Bull.*, vol. 12, pp. 355–384, 1928.

BEAL, C. H., The Decline and Ultimate Production of Oil Wells with Notes on the Valuation of Oil Properties, U. S. Bur. Mines *Bull.* 177, pp. 1–215, 1919.

———, and J. O. LEWIS, Some Principles Governing the Production of Oil Wells, U. S. Bur. Mines *Bull.* 194, pp. 1–58, 1921.

LEWIS, J. O., Methods for Increasing the Recovery from Oil Wells, U. S. Bur. Mines *Bull.* 148, pp. 1–128, 1917.

DOW, D. B., and C. E. RISTLE, Absorption of Natural Gas and Air in Crude Petroleum, *Mining Met.*, pp. 336–337, 1924.

HEROLD, S., "Analytical Principles of the Production of Oil, Gas, and Water from Wells," pp. 1–659, Stanford Univ., Calif., 1928.

but to the fluids in the voids of the rocks.   Heroy proposes to substitute the term "reservoir pressure" for "rock pressure" and gives it a clearer definition.

If the pressure of an oil field is due to the weight of the rocks, one would suppose that the rocks above the oil would commonly subside as the oil is driven from the reservoir.   This, however, is almost never the case, although in the Goose Creek, Texas field, subsidence of a few feet has been noted during the exploitation of the field.[1]

The measurements of the pressures in fluids in an oil field are generally made by the gage at the surface of the ground.   In measuring gas pressure the well is closed.   The pressure increases gradually to a maximum which is the full pressure at the casing head.   If oil or water rise to the top of the well, their pressure also may be measured by the gage, or if the well overflows under low pressure at the casing head, their pressure may be measured in a tube carried upward from the surface to a point where the liquid will just overflow.   When the liquids do not rise to the surface, their elevations are usually determined by a tape and float.   Another method of measuring the pressure at the bottom of a well in which liquids rise is to pump gas into the casing, pressing down the fluids in the well until they have been forced completely out of the well into the reservoir rock.   As the fluid is being forced out of the well, the reading of the pressure gage shows increasing pressure, and, when no further increase of pressure is recorded, the reading will indicate the reservoir pressure. A "pressure bomb" built on the principle of the aneroid barometer is constructed to record the maximum pressure when let down into a well, but this device is not in general use.

The term "head" or "static head" is the vertical distance of the fluid from a plane of reference, such as sea level.   The "hydrostatic head" indicates that the fluid measured is water.   The "rise" of a liquid in a well is the vertical distance measured from the reservoir stratum, from which it flows, to the top of the liquid.   If a reservoir yields only gas, the pressure at the casing head will be the same as that in the sand at the bottom of the well, disregarding the relatively light weight of the gas column (Fig. 95).

If the reservoir yields only oil or water, the reservoir pressure is the weight in pounds of the column of liquid with a cross-section of 1 square inch extending from the reservoir to the surface of the liquid.   If the height in feet is measured, the reservoir pressure in pounds is the product of the height in feet, the specific gravity of the liquid, and 0.434 (the weight in pounds of a column of pure water 1 foot high and 1 square inch in cross-section).   When the bore contains both water and oil, the contact is determined by trial bailing.   The reservoir pressure is the

[1] PRATT, W. E., and D. W. JOHNSON, *Jour. Geol.*, vol. 34, pp. 577–590, 1926.

sum of the weights of the column of water and the column of oil. These weights are determined by measuring the specific gravities of the two liquids and by soundings to determine the heights of the columns of water and oil. When a well contains gas above a liquid, the reservoir pressure is the pressure of the gas, as determined at the casing head, plus the

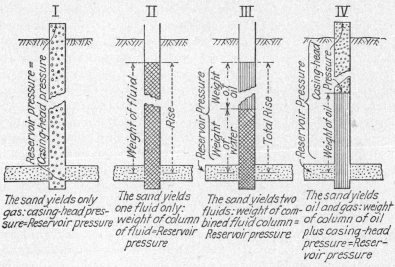

The sand yields only gas: casing-head pressure=Reservoir pressure

The sand yields one fluid only: weight of column of fluid=Reservoir pressure

The sand yields two fluids: weight of combined fluid column = Reservoir pressure

The sand yields oil and gas: weight of column of oil plus casing-head pressure=Reservoir pressure

Fig. 95.—Diagrams illustrating pressure relations of oil, gas and water in reservoirs. "Weight" means weight of column of fluid having a cross section of one square inch. (*After Heroy.*)

weight of the column of liquid. These four sets of conditions are illustrated by Fig. 95.

In many oil fields it is supposed that the gas and oil are in equilibrium with a column of water. If the gas pressure in pounds equals the column of water measured in feet times 0.434, this supposition is warranted. This relation is illustrated by Fig. 96. If the column of water represented

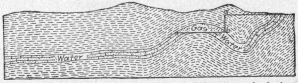

Fig. 96.—Sketch illustrating a gas pool with underlying water body in sand connected freely with surface. The level of ground water is assumed to be at the surface. Theoretically the pressure should equal the weight of a column of water as high as *ab*.

by *ab* is 1,000 feet high, the pressure would be 434 pounds, and if it is 2,000 feet high, the pressure would be 868 pounds. In a moist flat country where the ground-water level is high, the depth of a well in feet times 0.434 is often approximately the same as the gas pressure per square inch as measured by gage at the top of the well. In the Lima-Indiana field, in many of the shallower sands in the oil fields of Oklahoma and

Kansas, and in many other fields, the recorded pressure is very near the
weight of a column of water equal to the depth of the well.

Gas exerts pressure equally in all directions. If, as is illustrated by
Fig. 97, well 1 should tap a gas reservoir near its base, its pressure would
be the same as that of well 2 which taps the reservoir near the top. If
the oil sand were so coarse that friction were inconsiderable, then, when
closed, the gages on the wells would show 217 pounds per square inch in
both wells, if the balancing water column were 500 feet high.

The reservoir pressure, as already stated, is the pressure under which
the fluids exist in the reservoir. All parts of a gas deposit, as already
noted, have the same reservoir pressure. The reservoir pressures
existing in the oil and water bodies are different at different places. This
is illustrated by Fig. 98, which shows a reservoir connected with the
surface by a water column which is in equilibrium with oil. Assuming
that the water has a specific gravity of 1 and disregarding friction, the
pressure exerted at B, which is 1,000 feet deep, is 434 pounds per square
inch. At C, which is 1,625 feet deep, the pressure is 705.25 pounds,
and at D it is 509.95 pounds per square inch. The pressure at E is the
same as at D, minus the weight of the column of oil 175 feet high. If the
oil has a specific gravity of 0.800, the column 175 feet high will weigh
60.76 pounds per square inch, and the reservoir pressure at E will be
509.95 − 60.76, or 449.19 pounds per square inch. The reservoir
pressure at E is more than the reservoir pressure at B, because the water,
being heavier than oil, will balance a longer column of oil.

Considering a system with oil, gas, and water, it is evident that
the reservoir pressure at any point in the reservoir will be the algebraic
sum of the pressures of the fluids above the point. The "equivalent
hydrostatic level," as defined by Heroy, is the level to which the amount
of reservoir pressure existing in the oil and gas areas would cause a column
of pure water to rise. This is illustrated by Fig. 99. Assuming an
undeveloped oil and gas pool of anticlinal structure in which the oil and
gas are retained in the upper part of the structure by artesian pressure
of the surrounding water and disregarding varying porosity and friction,
a static profile may be drawn showing the equivalent hydrostatic level.
If the specific gravity of the water is assumed to be 1 and the specific
gravity of oil is assumed to be 0.875, or 30° Bé., then,

Reservoir pressure at bottom of A = 2,200 × 0.434 = 954.8 lb. per sq. in.

Reservoir pressure at oil-water contact = 2,000 × 0.434 = 868 lb. per sq. in.

Reservoir pressure at oil-gas contact = 868 − (217 × 0.875) = 868 − 189.875 or
678.125 lb. per sq. in. 100 feet of oil weigh 37.975 lb. per sq. in. of cross-section.

Reservoir pressure at bottom of B = 868 − (300 × 0.37975) = 754.075 lb.
754.075 (pounds of water) ÷ 0.434 = 1,737.5 ft., height of column of water
weighing 754.075 lb.

1,737.5 ÷ 0.875 = 1,985.7 ft., height of column of oil weighing 754.075 lb.

The oil well penetrates the sand 800 feet above sea and the oil will rise to an elevation 800 + 1,985.7 or 2,785.7 ft. above sea.

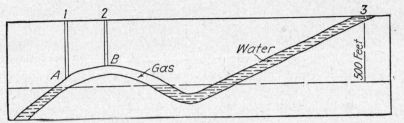

FIG. 97.—Diagram showing a gas reservoir in anticline with wells at 1 and 2 and out-crop of sand at 3, which is 500 feet higher than the gas-water contact. Pressure of gas is 217 pounds per square inch whether measured in well 1 or well 2.

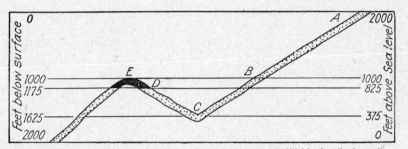

FIG. 98.—Diagram showing pressures in an ideal reservoir. Solid black, oil; dotted, water.

Reservoir pressure at B, 1,000 feet deep, 434   pounds per square inch.
Reservoir pressure at C, 1,625 feet deep, 705.25 pounds per square inch.
Reservoir pressure at D, 1,175 feet deep, 509.95 pounds per square inch.
Reservoir pressure at E, $509.95 - (175 \times .434 \times .8) = 509.95 - 60.76$ or 449.19 pounds per square inch.

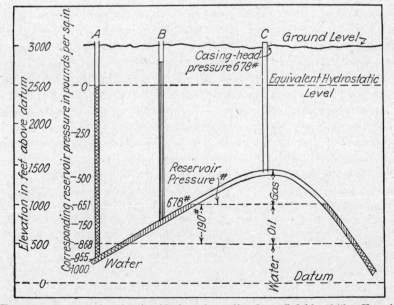

FIG. 99.—Cross section showing ideal static profile of an oil field. (*After Heroy.*)

It is not possible to make calculations of this character for all fields, but often they may be rudely made, and such calculations may supply data that will show whether or not the oil or gas is balanced by water columns connected with the surface.   The calculation may aid also in the identification and correlation of sands, for the fluids in a single sand should show consonant pressure relations.   As a field approaches exhaustion, the relations of reservoir pressure in various parts of the field should throw light on the problem of water encroachment, which commonly is related to the life of the field.

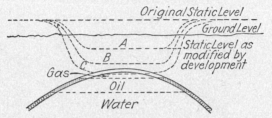

Fig. 100.—Sketch showing depression of static level of an oil field during development due to decline of pressure.   Water, which is assumed to extend from the oil to the surface, rises in the reservoir but not rapidly enough to restore pressure.   (*After Heroy.*)

Decline of Pressure.—Ideal cases in fields at the early stages of development have thus far been considered.   As oil and gas are produced the pressure rapidly declines, and if the oil and gas were in equilibrium with water, the domeward movement of water is so slow that the original static level is rapidly depressed.   Figure 100 shows the original static level far above the surface of the ground.   The pressure would be great enough to cause the oil to flow from wells.   As the development proceeds the gas is drawn off or escapes, the oil is pumped out, and the static level moves rapidly downward, being depressed most over the part of the field that yields gas.   It is evident that if enough gas is withdrawn, pressure rapidly declines.   In the absence of pressure much of the oil will remain in the rocks.   The steep pressure gradient at the edges of the gas area is noteworthy.   Water, which is under high pressure around the field, will move toward the gas area and, the balancing back pressure of the gas against water having been removed, an unbalanced condition is established.   Water tends to occupy the zone of low pressure, either forcing the oil before it or passing by the oil, leaving a large part of it adhering to the sands.   Water encroachment increases rapidly, particularly in the late stages of development.   Encroachment of water in Salt Creek, Wyoming, is shown by Fig. 101.

In many fields gas and oil are found together on the tops of the anticlines.   A part of the gas is absorbed by the oil.   The amount absorbed varies directly as the pressure, and it varies also with the kinds of gases present.   As pressure increases more gas is absorbed.[1]   A table

[1] The solubility of gas in oil depends on the character of the gas, the oil, the temperature, and the pressure.   Curves and tables are stated by H. C. Miller, "The Function of Natural Gas in the Production of Oil," pp. 1–267, New York, 1929.   Heroy states that a barrel of oil at 1,000 lb. pressure absorbs about 200 cu. ft. of gas.

showing the boiling points of paraffin gases is given on page 33. From these figures it is evident that methane, ethane, and propane exist in reservoirs mainly in the gaseous state, but pentane and hexane may

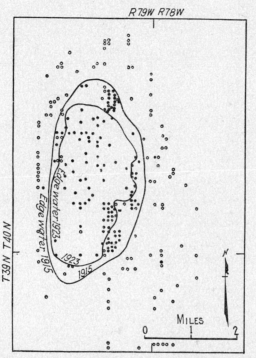

FIG. 101.—Sketch of Salt Creek oil field showing movement of edgewater in the First Wall Creek sand. Outer line shows edgewater in 1915; inner line in 1923. Dots show oil wells in First Wall Creek sand and circles show wells in Second Wall Creek sand in which a larger area is productive than in First Wall Creek sand. (*Data from Wegemann and from Nowels.*)

exist in part or altogether as liquids. When a well penetrates a sand containing oil charged with gas under high pressure, the oil with its absorbed gas passes into the bottom part of the well. Pressure is decreased and part of the absorbed gases will be released. The gas expanding will form bubbles which decrease the weight of the oil, move upward, and carry the oil with them. The gas is thus absorbed in the oil and associated as gas with the oil. The proportion of gas produced with a barrel of oil is the gas-oil ratio. The maximum production of a field is probably obtained when this ratio is maintained uniformly. The gas-oil ratio of the Salt Creek field has been calculated by Estabrook and Reader. To 1924 Salt Creek produced 1,620 cubic feet of gas per barrel of oil. In the Old Grozny field, Russia, according to Lindtrop and Nikolaeff, the gas-oil ratio is 95 to 140 cubic feet of gas per barrel of oil.

INITIAL GAS PRESSURES AT DIFFERENT DEPTHS IN SEVERAL GAS FIELDS
(*Prepared by Mills and Wells*)

Name of bed	Locality	Depth, feet	Initial gas pressure, lb. per sq. in.	Average pressure per 100 ft. depth, lb. per sq. in.	Authority
Salt sand.............	Woodsfield, Ohio	1,295	280	22	Mills and Wells
Big Lime sand.........	Southwest corner of Wayne Township, Belmont County, Ohio	1,310	365	28	Mills and Wells
	Southeast corner of Malaga Township, Monroe County, Ohio	1,412	400	28	Mills and Wells
	Wayne Township, Belmont County, Ohio	1,465	440	30	Mills and Wells
Keener sand..........	Woodsfield, Ohio	1,515	475	31	Mills and Wells
Big Injun sand........	Woodsfield, Ohio	1,468	500	34	Mills and Wells
Berea sand............	Woodsfield, Ohio	2,090	710	34	Mills and Wells
	Summerfield, Ohio	1,698	565	33	Mills and Wells
	Sunsbury Township, Monroe County, Ohio	2,060	735	36	Mills and Wells
Butler gas sand........	Summit Township, Butler County, Pennsylvania	1,200	380	32	Mills and Wells
Hundred-foot sand.....	Butler, Pennsylvania	1,400	780	56	Mills and Wells
Third sand............	Butler, Pennsylvania	1,700	785	46	Mills and Wells
	Butler, Pennsylvania	1,452	600	41	Mills and Wells
Fourth sand..........	Butler, Pennsylvania	1,800	870	48	Mills and Wells
	Butler, Pennsylvania	1,568	225	14	Mills and Wells
Fifth sand............	Butler, Pennsylvania	1,950	870	45	Mills and Wells
"Clinton" sand........	Harrison Township, Knox County, Ohio	2,700	810	30	Mills and Wells
	Cleveland, Ohio	{ 2,500 / 2,900	800 / 1,100	} 32–38	Rogers[1]
	Newberg, Ohio	3,000	425	14	Van Horn[2]
Trenton limestone......	Findlay, Ohio	950	400–450	42–47	Orton[3]
	Kokomo, Indiana	650	328	50	Orton[3]
	Cleveland, Ohio	4,500	37	0.82	Van Horn[2]
Benson sand..........	Barbour County, West Virginia	4,090	1,800	44	I. C. White[4]
(?)....................	West Virginia	2,989	1,420	47	I. C. White[4]
(?)....................	Havre, Montana	947	490	52	Stebinger[5]
(?)....................	Havre, Montana	1,370	540	39	Stebinger[5]
(?)....................	Louisiana	1,650	650	39	Knapp[6]
Unconsolidated sand....	Louisiana	1,800	600	33	Knapp[7]
(?)....................	Loco, Oklahoma	750	310	41	McMurray and Lewis[8]

[1] ROGERS, G. S., The Cleveland Gas Field, Cuyahoga County, Ohio, U. S. Geol. Survey *Bull.* 661, p. 37, 1917.

[2] VAN HORN, F. R., Reservoir Gas and Oil in the Vicinity of Cleveland, Ohio, Am. Inst. Min. Eng. *Trans.*, vol. 56, p. 839, 1917.

[3] ORTON, EDWARD, The Trenton Limestone as a Source of Petroleum and Natural Gas in Ohio and Indiana, U. S. Geol. Survey *Eighth Ann. Rept.*, p. 645, 1889.

[4] Personal communication.

[5] STEBINGER, EUGENE, Possibilities of Oil and Gas in North-central Montana, U. S. Geol. Survey *Bull.* 641, p. 73, 1916.

[6] KNAPP, I. N., Discussion of Paper by R. W. Johnson, The Role and Fate of Connate Water in Oil and Gas Sands, Am. Inst. Min. Eng. *Trans.*, vol. 51, p. 593, 1915.

[7] KNAPP, I. N., Discussion of Paper by W. H. Kobbe, The Recovery of Petroleum from Unconsolidated Sands, Am. Inst. Min. Eng. *Trans.*, vol. 56, p. 825, 1917.

[8] McMURRAY, W. F., and J. O. LEWIS, Underground Wastes in Oil and Gas Fields and Methods of Prevention, U. S. Bur. Mines *Tech. Paper* 130, p. 13, 1916.

Pressures in Closed Lenses.—Certain oil reservoirs are clearly not connected with the surface of the earth by a column of water under artesian pressure. That is known to be true because the gas pressure of the field is either considerably more or considerably less than the pressure calculated for a column of water extending from the nearest outcrop of the sand to the depth of the gas reservoir. The oil and gas exist in a sand that does not extend to the surface or becomes impervious up dip. Oil fields on monoclines and very deep oil fields are likely to show pressures that are inconsistent with depth.

In reservoirs that are completely sealed from the surface, the oil, gas, and water tend to segregate by gravity, but there is no column of water continually replenished to supply pressure as the oil and gas are removed from the field. The amount of fluid which the sand contains is essentially fixed. As the gas is removed the pressure is correspondingly decreased, and there may be little or no water encroachment.

Proportion of Oil Recovered.—There are few determinations of the amount of oil remaining in rocks after they have ceased to yield oil,

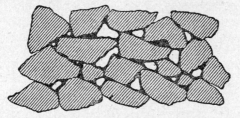

Fig. 102.—Sketch illustrating a pile of sand grains, and showing how oil is retained by adhesion. (*After Lewis.*)

although certain reservoirs are believed to retain more than half of the oil originally present (Fig. 102). For other fields this estimate is probably too high. In the Grozny field, Russia, the oil sands are believed to have a porosity of 25 per cent, and it is estimated that they yield oil equal to 12.5 per cent of their volume. According to Lindtrop and Nikolaeff,[1] the liquid remaining in the sand consists of the connate water that occupied the pores of the sand before the oil entered it and oil that remains adhering to the sand grains. These two liquids are present in the sand that has ceased to yield oil approximately in equal amounts. If these estimates are correct, about 75 per cent of the oil in the Grozny sands is recoverable. For American fields estimates of oil recovered made from examination of cores and chunks range from 8 to 60 per cent.

ESTIMATION OF RESERVES

The estimation of the reserves of oil in a field presents obvious difficulties. The oil deposit can not be examined and sampled

[1] LINDTROP, N. T., and V. M. NIKOLAEFF, Am. Assoc. Pet. Geol. *Bull.*, vol. 13, p. 820, 1929.

like ore in the ground, and the reservoir rock generally varies in thickness
and porosity.   In certain fields it is a practice to assume that the future

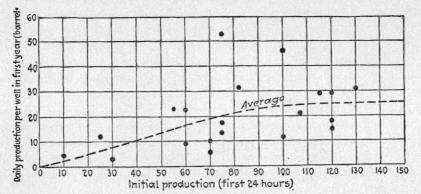

Fig. 103.—Curve showing relation of initial production to average daily production per
     well during the first year in the Lawrence County field, Illinois.   (*After Beal.*)

yield of a group of producing wells will be a thousand times the present
daily yield.   The results are generally in error.   In the early history of
a field the estimate may be too low; in the late stages of development

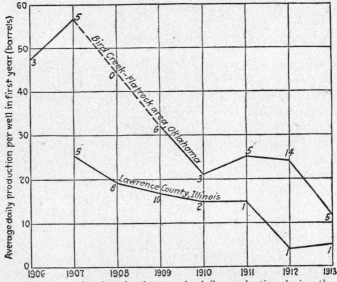

Fig. 104.—Curves showing the decrease in daily production during the first year on
several properties in the Bird Creek-Flatrock field, Oklahoma, and in the Lawrence County,
Illinois, pool.   The numbers on the curves show the number of wells used to obtain the
data.   (*After Beal.*)

the estimate generally would be much too high.   A method in common
use is to estimate the volume, porosity, and degree of saturation of the

reservoir rock and to assume that a certain percentage of the oil is recoverable.   Thus, if the producing area is estimated to be 20,000,000 square feet, the sand 25 feet thick, the pore space $\frac{1}{5}$ of the reservoir rock, the saturation with oil $\frac{1}{2}$, and the recoverable oil $\frac{1}{2}$, the total yield would be 20,000,000 $\times$ 25 $\times$ $\frac{1}{5}$ $\times$ $\frac{1}{2}$ $\times$ $\frac{1}{2}$, or 25,000,000 cubic feet of oil.   If more than one sand produces, estimates are made for each sand.

When the records of producing wells in the area are available, production curves[1] are constructed for the area and for the district.   The

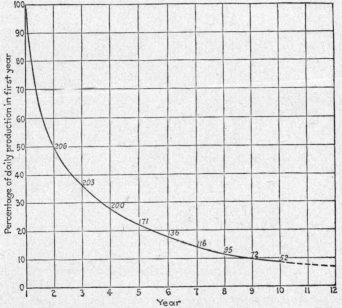

Fig. 105.—Composite decline curve for the Bartlesville field, Oklahoma.   (*After Beal.*)

curve is a convenient device for summarizing the history of production of a well or a district, and it is the method in general use.   Figure 103 shows the production in the first year of 20 wells in Lawrence County, Illinois.   A well with an initial production of 100 barrels might have been

[1] RUEDEMANN, P., Some Graphical Methods for Appraising Oil Wells, Am. Assoc. Pet. Geol. *Bull.*, vol. 6, pp. 533–546, 1922.

———, and I. GARDESCU, Estimation of Reserves of Natural Gas Wells by Relationship of Production to Closed Pressure, Am. Assoc. Pet. Geol. *Bull.*, vol. 6, pp. 444–463, 1922.

BEAL, C. H., U. S. Bur. Mines *Bull.* 177, pp. 1–215, 1919.

CUTLER, W. W., JR., Predictions of the Future of Oil Pools by Early Wells, Am. Assoc. Pet. Geol. *Bull.*, vol. 10, pp. 747–752, 1926.

LEWIS, J. O., Methods for Increasing the Recovery from Oil Sands, U. S. Bur. Mines *Bull.* 148, pp. 1–128, 1917.

GAYLORD, E. E., and J. A. TAFF, Geological Organization of an Oil Company, Am. Assoc. Pet. Geol. *Bull.*, vol. 8, pp. 651–661, 1924.

expected to yield an average of 24 barrels of oil per day during the first year.   The rapid decline of daily production during the first year in the Bird Creek-Flatrock field, Oklahoma, and in Lawrence County, Illinois, is shown by Fig. 104.   As these fields were developed the wells that were drilled yielded less during their first year's production.   Figure 105 is a decline curve for wells in the Bartlesville field, Oklahoma.   The numbers on the curve show the numbers of properties used in determining averages for each year.   Figure 106 shows the relation of rock pressure to production of oil in a well in the Midway field, California.   The use of such curves is obvious, and with sufficient data available one may make an

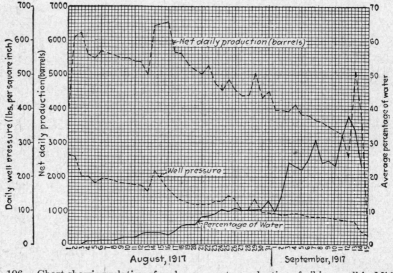
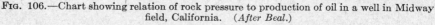

Fig. 106.—Chart showing relation of rock pressure to production of oil in a well in Midway field, California.   (*After Beal.*)

estimate of future performance.   Precise accuracy is not expected, but the method is the best available.

In the estimation of gas reserves the problem differs somewhat, because the amount of gas in a reservoir varies approximately as the pressure of the gas.   Thus, if a tank holds 10,000,000 cubic feet of gas with a pressure of 100 pounds per square inch, it will hold 20,000,000 cubic feet with a pressure of 200 pounds per square inch.   A thousand cubic feet of gas means the amount of gas that would expand to a thousand cubic feet at the pressure at which the gas is sold, which is approximately atmospheric pressure.   Thus, the amount of gas in a reservoir rock is generally calculated at atmospheric pressure, and the figures given in the estimates mean that the free gas would expand to the amount stated. In estimating the amount of gas in a natural reservoir, the methods used include (1) the volume-pressure method, (2) the pressure-loss method, and (3) the decline-curve method. To illustrate the first method, let it be assumed that the pore space of a reservoir is 1,000,000,000 cubic feet and that the gas is under a pressure of 30 atmospheres, or about 450 pounds per square inch. The amount of gas in the reservoir would be about 30,000,000,000 cubic feet at atmospheric pressure. The method does not take into account the gas that is absorbed in water below the gas deposit. This is probably considerable in certain fields. According to Winkler,[1] a liter of water at a temperature of 20° C. at 1 atmosphere will absorb about $\frac{1}{30}$ liter of methane. This amount is small but probably increases directly with pressure, so that at 30 atmospheres the amount absorbed would be equal to 1 liter of gas at atmospheric pressure. In domes, where the volume of the water column increases downward below the gas deposit, the absorbed gas is doubtless considerable. Some of this gas would be released when the pressure declines and be added to the gas held in the gas reservoir. In estimating the amount of gas present in the great Panhandle gas field of Texas, Bauer[2] assumed that the field covers 949,120 acres and stated that the initial pressure was about 430 pounds per square inch. He used an estimate of Roth that the reservoir averages 36.2 feet of pay. He assumed a porosity of 20 per cent and estimated the amount of the gas reserve when the field was opened to be equivalent to 4,436,000,000,000 cubic feet of gas at 1 atmosphere of pressure, if the recovery is equal to 50 per cent of the gas present.

Pressure-loss Method of Estimating Gas Reserves.—The amount of gas in a reservoir varies directly as the pressure. In calculating the amount of gas remaining in a reservoir, it is common practice to calculate the amount of gas withdrawn and to assume that this is directly proportional to the loss of pressure that has taken place during the time of withdrawal. Thus, if a reservoir has lost 100,000,000,000 cubic feet of gas and its pressure has declined from 400 to 300 pounds per square inch, it is calculated that 300,000,000,000 cubic feet of gas remain in the reservoir.

This method was used by Broughton to calculate the amount of gas of the Elk City field, Kansas. The Elk City[3] gas field is located on two low connecting domes. Gas is found in the Bartlesville sand at a depth of 1,350 feet. The original pressure was 520 pounds per square inch, which is the weight of a column of water only a little less than the depth of the well. Allowing for a water level 152 feet lower than the surface of the field, the gas and water would be in equilibrium. If the movement of water during development is disregarded, an estimate may be made of

[1] Landolt-Boernstein Physikalische-Chemische Tabellen, p. 145d, Berlin, 1912.

[2] BAUER, C. M., Gas a Big Factor in the Texas Panhandle, Am. Assoc. Pet. *Geol. Bull.*, vol. 12, pp. 165–176, 1928.

[3] BROUGHTON, C. W., Elk City Gas Field, Kan. Geol. Survey *Bull.* 5, pp. 1–31, 1921.

the amount of gas in the field.   The gas was first marketed in December, 1918, when the rock pressure was 520 pounds.   In February, 1920, about 7,500,000,000 cubic feet had been marketed, and the pressure had fallen to 320 pounds.   Assuming 40 pounds pressure to be the minimum working pressure, Broughton calculated that the amount of gas available in the pool was 18,000,000,000 cubic feet.

$$\frac{\text{original pressure} - 40}{\text{decline in pressure}} \times \text{amount of gas produced} = \text{total gas}$$

$$\frac{520 - 40}{200} \times 7,500,000,000 = 18,000,000,000 \text{ cu. ft. originally available.}$$

In the Eldorado field, Kansas, according to Fath, the original rock pressure was 393 pounds per square inch and the average pressure March, 1918, was estimated to be 108 pounds.   The total production to that date was about 8,880,356,000 cubic feet.   The total production to that date is to the amount of gas originally in the fields as the decrease in pressure at that date (285 pounds) is to the original pressure (393 pounds).   Solving the equation, the gas originally present is found to be about 12,245,000,000 cubic feet, of which the production to March, 1918, represents about 73 per cent.

In the Monroe field, Louisiana, in 1925 when 638,000,000,000 cubic feet of gas had left the reservoir, the pressure, according to H. W. Bell, was reduced one-sixth.   It is estimated that the field originally contained six times that amount, or 3,828,000,000,000 cubic feet.

The method[1] of utilizing the decline in pressure and total production during the period of decline is useful, for it suggests hypotheses that may be tested, but it is subject to limitations.   Water encroachment tends to keep up the pressure.   One may imagine a field, supplying gas from a coarse gravel that extends to the surface, filled with water, moving freely.   A well might supply gas until the reservoir is exhausted, with very little decline of pressure.   It would be possible to show large reserves by calculation, when practically all of the gas had been drawn from the reservoir.   On the other hand, a correction could be made if the amount of encroachment of water were known from wells near the edge of the field.

There is also a lag in the pressure due to friction of gas in passing through the gas sand to the well where it is measured.   This tends to make the calculations of reserves too small.   The method, moreover, is based on Boyle's law which is not precisely true when applied to methane, which is the chief constituent of natural gas.   Finally, water

[1] JOHNSON, R. H. and L. C. MORGAN, A Critical Examination of the Equal Pound Loss Method of Estimating Gas Reserves, Am. Assoc. Pet. Geol. Bull., vol. 10, pp. 901–914, 1926.

VERSLUYS, J., An Investigation of the Problem of the Estimation of Gas Reserves, Am. Assoc. Pet. Geol. Bull., vol. 12, pp. 1095–1106, 1928.

absorbs gas. The amount is small under atmospheric pressure, but probably increases directly with the pressure. It is probably released approximately as the pressure of the gas deposit declines and would not affect the calculation made by pressure-loss method as much as calculations made by pressure-volume method. A more accurate method for calculating the gas reserve is one utilizing pressure determinations in a number of wells taken over a considerable period, with corrections made for water encroachment. These data are expressed by curves which supply a basis for estimating the actual reserve.

CHAPTER X

DEFORMATION OF PETROLIFEROUS STRATA

Deformation in Unconsolidated Materials.—In many districts the petroliferous beds are covered by strata that include considerable thicknesses of unconsolidated clay, marl, or clayey sand. In such districts, even after extensive folding and faulting, the reservoir rocks may retain large accumulations of oil and gas. Some of the most productive oil fields are in areas of rocks that are largely unconsolidated where the beds lie in overturned folds or are greatly disturbed by complicated faults. In unconsolidated materials openings due to faulting and folding tend to close promptly, so that the oil remains in the reservoir. In such materials there is generally some leakage, however, and oil seeps, asphalt, gas seeps, and other surface associates of oil or gas are commonly found above the reservoirs. Many of the Tertiary oil fields are in highly deformed rocks. In consolidated rocks that had undergone so much deformation the gas pressure generally would have driven the bulk of the available oil from its reservoirs.

Influence of Faulting on Reservoirs.—The shales that supply the so-called "impervious" covers to keep the petroleum confined within the sandstones are not absolutely impervious to fluids, otherwise the oil and gas could not pass from them to the porous beds in which they are found. Fracturing doubtless facilitates the passage, however, by supplying more readily available openings. In the Santa Clara, Summerland, Puente Hills, Los Angeles, and in certain other California districts the fracturing appears to have aided accumulation by permitting the oil to move from lower to higher levels, where it is more readily accessible. Asphalt and ozokerite deposits in fissures have been mentioned. It is clear that some faults have served as channels through which petroleum has moved.

As is well known by students of ore deposits, the fissures which serve as channels of metalliferous waters and the openings filled by metalliferous ores are, in general, the fissures and faults of small throw rather than the great faults. Except in limestone a comparatively small number of veins are formed in faults of considerable tangential movement. Without doubt the clay gouge developed along the greater faults provides an impermeable barrier and prevents circulation. It is obvious that this principle will apply also in many districts that yield petroleum. The smaller faults may serve as channels for migration and escape of oil, whereas the greater faults may seal the reservoirs. Turner Valley, Canada, is an example of a highly faulted field with much gas in Paleozoic beds.

METAMORPHISM OF PETROLEUM BY DYNAMIC AGENCIES

Petroleum and the materials of which it is formed are changed by heat and pressure that attend dynamic metamorphism. At many places petroleum and gas are found in areas that contain coals, and the degree of alteration of the coals affords a kind of index which shows the intensity of the metamorphic processes. In such regions the coals are altered progressively more toward the areas of intense deformation. The heat and pressure drive the gases from the coals and the residue becomes richer in fixed carbon, higher in ash, lower in volatile hydrocarbons and moisture. Not only does the fixed carbon in a single bed increase with the intensity of metamorphism, but also the degree of carbonation of a series of coals generally increases with stratigraphic depth.[1] In certain areas the degree of carbonation is greater on the crests of anticlines than in synclines. That probably is because the anticlines are areas of deformation by fracturing as well as by folding, and fracturing of overlying beds facilitates the escape of volatile materials, thus increasing the percentage of fixed carbon in the coal. In other areas, however, the percentage of carbon increases somewhat down dip where the load of strata above the coal increases.

In testing coals to ascertain their ranks and value, it is customary to make proximate analyses. The coal is weighed and heated to about 107° C. to drive off moisture. The coal is weighed again and roasted in absence of air to drive off gas. The residue is coke which is burned in air to remove fixed carbon. The remainder is ash. The amount of carbon divided by the carbon plus gas, or volatile hydrocarbons, gives the proportion of carbon to total combustible material expressed as a percentage which is called the "carbon ratio." Thousands of proximate analyses of coals[2] have been made and reported for various fields in the United States, and the carbon ratios express the ranks of these coals as percentages.

Isocarbs are lines drawn to connect places where coals are found to have the same carbon ratios, and all of the coals found along such lines are assumed to have the carbon ratio indicated by the line. David

[1] HILT, C., Die Beziehungen zwischen der Zusammensetzung und der technischen Eigenschaften der Steinkohlen, *Z. Deut. Eng.*, Band 17, Heft 4, pp. 194–202, 1873.

[2] PARKER, E. W., J. A. HOLMES, and M. R. CAMPBELL, Report on the Operation of the Coal-testing Plant of the U. S. Geological Survey at the Louisiana Purchase Exposition, St. Louis, 1904, U. S. Geol. Survey *Prof. Paper* 48, pp. 1–1492, 1906.

WHITE, D., Some Relations in Origin between Coals and Petroleum, Wash Acad. Sci. *Jour.*, vol. 5, pp. 189–212, 1915.

White[1] first noted that there is a relation between the carbon ratio of coal and the distribution of oil and gas. As a result of the work of White and other investigators, there was proposed the "carbon-ratio theory" which holds that as coals decrease in volatile constituents the oils of the coal-bearing areas increase in the lighter and more volatile constituents, so that low-grade heavy oils are associated with low-rank coals or with the coals that have low carbon ratios. The higher grade oils are associated with the higher rank coals. In areas containing coals that have reached the stage of devolatilization at which the fixed carbon is between 65 and 70 per cent of total combustibles, the oils will have been converted to gas. In areas in which the carbon ratio of coal is above 70 or 80, gas generally will have escaped from the reservoirs.

The carbon-ratio theory has been accepted as a working hypothesis by many investigators. It has recently been reviewed by Reeves[2] and others who question its validity. Most of the coals used to establish isocarb lines are taken from near the surface, and, according to Reeves, the coals that lie deeper would show much higher carbon ratios in accordance with Hilt's law, which holds that the degree of carbonation of a series of coals increases with stratigraphic depth.

In certain areas it has been found difficult to apply the carbon-ratio theory also because cannel coals and canneloid layers in coal differ greatly in carbon ratios from ordinary bituminous coals. The ordinary bituminous coals are formed mainly in swamps and are the product chiefly of woody fiber. The cannel coals are composed chiefly of the remains of spores, pollen, and similar material, and Russell states that the ordinary bituminous coals of Kentucky contain about 10 per cent more fixed carbon than the cannel coals that are closely associated with them, but that the differences are irregular, so that the cannels can not be used for indexes of the amounts of metamorphism of strata associated with the cannel coals.[3]

In certain coal fields of the Midlands region, England, the carbon ratios decrease with depth. Near the Hardstoft oil well, Derbyshire, the Deep Hard coal seam has a carbon ration of 64.7 per cent; the Low

[1] WHITE, D., Progressive Regional Carbonation of Coals, Am. Inst. Min. Eng. Trans., vol. 71, pp. 253–281, 1925.

FULLER, M. L., Appalachian Oil Fields, Geol. Soc. Am. Bull., vol. 28, p. 643, 1917.

REEVES, F., The Carbon-ratio Theory in the Light of Hilt's Law, Am. Assoc. Pet. Geol. Bull., vol. 12, pp. 795–824, 1928.

DORSEY, G. E., The Present Status of the Carbon-ratio Theory, Am. Assoc. Pet. Geol. Bull., vol. 11, pp. 455–465, 1927.

TARR, R. S., Oil Gas Jour., No. 30, p. 15, Dec. 17, 1925.

BRIGGS, H. B., Vertical and Lateral Variation in the Composition of Bituminous Coal Seams, Colliery Guardian, vol. 125, No. 3259, pp. 1507–1508, 1923.

[2] REEVES, FRANK, The Carbon-ratio Theory in the Light of Hilt's Law, Am. Asso. Pet. Geol. Bull., vol. 12, pp. 795–825, 1928.

[3] RUSSELL, W. L., Econ. Geol., vol. 20 pp. 250–260, 1925.

Main bed, 250 feet deeper, has a ratio of 62.7 per cent; and the Black Shale coal at the base of the productive coal measure 450 feet below the Deep Hard coal has a ratio of 59.1 per cent.[1]

Since the moisture content of coals decreases with the metamorphism of associated strata, it has been proposed to use the water content of coals to compare the state of metamorphism of the coal-bearing areas. Lines joining areas of equal moisture content of coals are called "isohumes." Moulton[2] prepared an isohume map of the Illinois coal fields. It was found, however, that methods of sampling and of caring for samples are not likely to be uniform, so that the isohume map is not likely to show the state of metamorphism of strata as accurately as the isocarb map. Although coal or lignite is found in many oil fields, there are relatively few such areas in which part of the field has carbon ratios above 62 per cent and part of it below 62 per cent. Consequently, the opportunities for testing the carbon-ratio theory are limited. Isocarb maps have been prepared for the areas treated below.

Appalachian Field.—The first isocarb map of an oil field was that of the Appalachian field prepared by White.[3] Later contributions[4] to this subject were made by Fuller, Reger, Eby, and Reeves. Large deposits of oil and gas are found in the Appalachian[5] field where carbon ratios are below 60, and gas with some oil is found within the area where carbon ratios are between 60 and 65. Some gas is found in the area in which the carbon ratios are between 65 and 70, but little oil is found within that area (Fig. 107). Where carbon ratios are above 70, gas is practically wanting. Fuller's interpretation of these relations is shown by Fig. 108. In Fig. 109 Reeves shows both oil and gas below the 70 isocarb. The position of this isocarb, however, is inferred from the degree of alteration of sediments. It is not based on alteration of coals.

[1] ICKES, E. L., Am. Inst. Min. Eng. *Trans.*, vol. 70, p. 1071, 1924.

[2] MOULTON, G. F., Carbon Ratios and Petroleum in Illinois, Ill. Geol. Survey *Rept. of Investigations* 4, p. 15, 1925.

[3] WHITE, D., Some Relations in Origin between Coals and Petroleum, Wash. Acad. Sci. *Jour.*, vol. 5, pp. 189–212, 1915.

[4] FULLER, M. L., Carbon Ratios in Carboniferous Coals of Oklahoma and Their Relations to Petroleum, *Econ. Geol.*, vol. 15, p. 232, 1920.

REGER, D. B., Carbon Ratios of Coal in West Virginia Oil Fields, Am. Inst. Min. Eng. *Trans.*, vol. 65, p. 523, 1923.

EBY, J. B., The Possibilities of Oil and Gas in Southwest Virginia as Inferred from Isocarbs, Assoc. Pet. Geol. *Bull.*, vol. 7, p. 423, 1923.

REEVES, FRANK, *op. cit.*, p. 816.

[5] WHITE, D., Late Theories Regarding the Origin of Oil, Geol. Soc. Am. *Bull.*, vol. 28, pp. 727–734, 1917.

———, Genetic Problems Affecting the Search for Oil in New Regions, Am. Inst. Min. Eng. *Trans.*, vol. 65, pp. 176–198, 1921.

———, Progressive Regional Carbonation of Coals, Am. Inst. Min. Eng. *Trans.*, vol. 71, pp. 253–281, 1925.

Reeves believes that the conditions in the barren areas east of the oil fields, as to source materials, reservoir rocks, and favorable structure, are probably similar to the conditions in the oil-bearing area; he attributes the absence of oil to water flushing at the east edge of the field, where the oil sands crop out.　If the degree of alternation of the sands is the chief controlling factor in the distribution of oil on the east margin of the field, and if alteration increases with stratigraphic depth, one would suppose that the upper sands would produce oil farther east than the

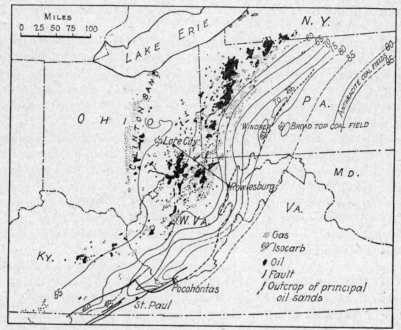

Fig. 107.—Isocarb map of the Appalachian oil fields.　(*Data from Reeves, White, Reger, and Eby.*)　For section Lore City to Rowlesburg see Fig. 109.

lower sands; yet, as pointed out by Reeves, oil is found farther east in the deeper sands than in the shallow sands.　This relation would be expected if the upper sands have lost their oil by water flushing, for, at a given place, the upper sands lie nearest the outcrops.

Kentucky.—In Kentucky there are two areas of coal-bearing rocks, and, in each of these, deposits of oil and gas are found.　One of these areas is east of the Cincinnati arch and is part of the Appalachian oil fields province.　The other is west of the Cincinnati arch and is the southern extension of the Eastern Interior coal field.　The carbon ratios vary considerably within narrow limits, owing to the presence of cannel coals and of canneloid layers in bituminous coals.　Russell,[1] by throwing out analyses of cannel coals and averaging groups of analyses, has made

---

[1] Russell, W. L., The Proofs of the Carbon-ratio Theory, *Econ. Geol.*, vol. 20, pp. 249 260, 1925.

an isocarb map of Kentucky.   Nearly all of the oil and gas production
from sandstone and most of that from limestone is from areas in which

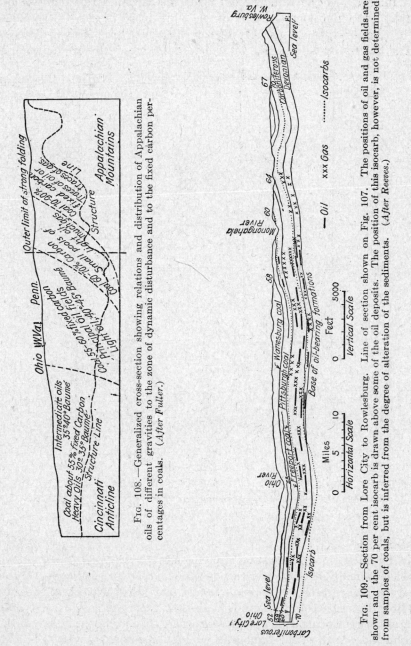

FIG. 108.—Generalized cross-section showing relations and distribution of Appalachian oils of different gravities to the zone of dynamic disturbance and to the fixed carbon percentages in coals. (*After Fuller.*)

FIG. 109.—Section from Lore City to Rowlesburg.   Line of section shown on Fig. 107.   The positions of oil and gas fields are shown and the 70 per cent isocarb is drawn above some of the oil deposits.   The position of this isocarb, however, is not determined from samples of coals, but is inferred from the degree of alteration of the sediments.   (*After Reeves.*)

the carbon ratio is 60 or less.   The gas fields are mainly between the 60
and 65 isocarbs.   In Kentucky, as noted by Russell, the oil fields in

limestone occur in older rocks than oil fields in sandstone, and also in
rocks associated with higher carbon coals.

Illinois.—In the Illinois[1] coal fields the carbon ratios increase from
about 48 in the northern part of the state to 60 in the southern part.
The carbon ratios are notably higher along anticlines than in synclines,
as is illustrated by Fig. 110 on which the carbon ratios are shown, using

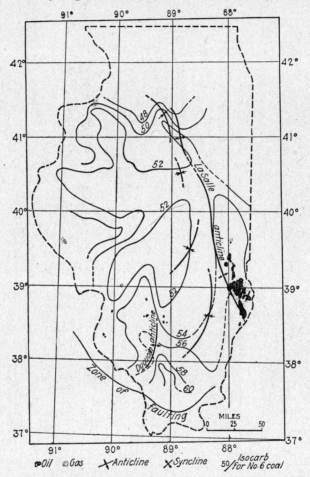

Fig. 110.—Isocarb map of Illinois.   (*Drawn by Reeves from maps by Moulton.*)

No. 6 coal as the standard and applying corrections for coals above No. 6
which normally have a lower carbon ratio and for coals below No. 6 which
have a higher ratio.   The coals above and below No. 6 are separated
from it by unconformities, and, in Illinois, there are considerable differences between coals of any given area where they are separated by unconformities.   Most of the Illinois oil production comes from areas in which

[1] MOULTON, G. F., Ill. Geol. Survey *Rept. of Investigations* 4, pp. 1–18, 1925.

the carbon ratio lies between 54 and 57 for No. 6 coal. None of the coal-bearing area seems to be so highly metamorphosed as to preclude the occurrence of oil.

Oklahoma.—In Oklahoma[1] the carbon ratios show an increase to the southeast. In this area, also, the older coals crop out to the southeast in the direction of the increase of the carbon ratio. Very little oil is

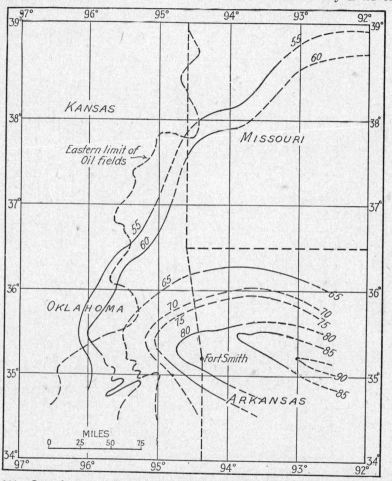

Fig. 111.—Isocarb map of Eastern Oklahoma and Western Arkansas. (*After Croneis.*)

found east of the 65 isocarb, although gas is found near Fort Smith and in the Poteau field near the east side of Oklahoma (p. 297). The occurrences

[1] Croneis, C., Oil and Gas Possibilities in the Arkansan Ozarks, Am. Assoc. Pet. Geol. *Bull.*, vol. 11, pp. 279–297, 1927.

Fuller, M. L., Carbon Ratios in Carboniferous Coals of Oklahoma and Their Relations to Petroleum, *Econ. Geol.*, vol. 15, pp. 225–235, 1920.

Gardner, J. H., The Mid-Continent Oil Field, Geol. Soc. Am. *Bull.*, vol. 28, pp. 685–720, 1917.

of gas fields in the areas between the 80 and 85 isocarbs are noteworthy. In this area the line separating oil- and gas-bearing areas from others yielding gas alone does not parallel an isocarb (Fig. 111).

North-central Texas.—In north-central Texas[1] the coals near the surface are higher in fixed carbon toward the east. Figure 112 shows

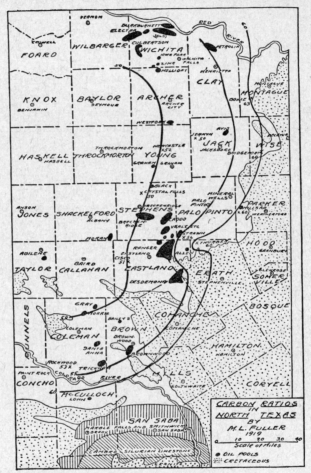

Fig. 112.—Sketch map showing isocarbs and relation of oil pools to carbon ratios of coals in Northern Texas. (*After Fuller.*)

that most of the oil fields lie west of the 55 isocarb. The isocarbs are drawn on the outcrops of the coals. The coals used are two beds located stratigraphically far apart and they are probably more highly altered in depth than at the surface. Reeves states that the coals in a single bed probably would be altered so much more down dip than at the

---

[1] FULLER, M. L., Relation of Oil to the Carbon Ratios of Pennsylvanian Coals in North Texas, *Econ. Geol.*, vol. 14, pp. 536–542, 1919.

surface that the increase in carbon may actually lie to the west. Thus, although there is an increase in the number and size of gas fields to the east and south, and a relatively smaller amount of oil, it is possible that this relation may be due to water flushing.

Western Canada.—The carbon ratios of coals of western Canada have been studied by Jones,[1] who shows that the carbon ratios are very erratic in the areas east of the Rocky Mountains front. He states that the carbon ratios of coals are not accurate indices to the amount of metamorphism of the associated strata, and that they do not serve as an index to the character and accumulation of oil and gas.

Summary.—Because practically all important oil fields that are associated with coal beds are in areas where coals that lie near the surface have carbon ratios of 62 or less and because no important commercial oil field is found in an area where carbon ratios of shallow coals exceed 70, the carbon-ratio theory has been accepted by many geologists. The development of important oil fields at great depths where no coal is present but where the pressures due to the overlying rock have been considerable have led many to question the value of the theory as a working hypothesis. It is possible that a prejudice that exists in the minds of many investigators who accept the theory has restricted exploration in areas of high carbon ratios but a cautious policy with regard to drilling of such areas seems to be justified. As already noted, commercial gas fields are found in areas where the carbon ratios lie between 80 and 85 and where the coals are good semianthracites. Attempts have been made to utilize the carbon ratios of cannel coals and carbonaceous shales and associated oil to test the theory, but the results are inconclusive.

---

[1] JONES, L. W., Carbon Ratios as an Index of Oil and Gas in Western Canada, *Econ. Geol.*, vol. 23, pp. 353–380, 1928.

CHAPTER XI

EASTERN UNITED STATES

The United States is divided into physiographic provinces which embrace the principal mountain ranges, plateaus, and plains (Fig. 113). The principal oil fields are in the Appalachian Plateau and Interior Plains, the Gulf Coastal Plain, the Rocky Mountains, and the California Valley and Coast Range. The Appalachian Plateau lies west of and is parallel to the Appalachian Mountains and with the Interior Plains

Fig. 113.—Sketch showing physiographic provinces of the United States. (*After Black-welder.*)

constitutes the interior lowlands orographic element.[1] This element, which lies between the Appalachian and Rocky Mountains, contains many of the largest oil fields in the United States. Among them are the Appalachian field, the Lima-Indiana field of Ohio and Indiana, the Illinois-Indiana field, and the larger portion of the Mid-Continent field. The Rocky Mountains element includes the main fields of Montana, Wyoming and Colorado. Some of these fields perhaps should be included

[1] "An orographic element is a region which is characterized by certain distinctive geologic features, particularly by a certain type of structure and a more or less unified geologic history . . . The orographic elements tend to coincide with the physiographic provinces."—BLACKWELDER, ELLIOTT, United States of North America, *Handbuch der Regionalen Geologie*, Band 8, Abt. 2, (Heft 11), p. 69, 1912.

in the interior lowlands, for they lie on foothill folds of the Rockies much as the fields of the Appalachian geosyncline lie with respect to the Appalachian Mountains. In accordance with the practice of the U. S. Geological Survey, these are described with other fields in the Rocky Mountains division.

Petroleum is found in the United States in rocks that range in age from Ordovician to Recent. Considerable oil is obtained from Paleozoic, Mesozoic, and Tertiary rocks. The general distribution of the strata is shown by Fig. 114.

The interior lowlands segment of the United States lies south of the Canadian Shield and slopes gently southward to the Gulf of Mexico. It is underlain almost everywhere by Paleozoic rocks, although the latter at places are covered by Mesozoic and Tertiary beds. The rocks in general dip at low angles, although locally they are highly deformed. This area, including the foothills regions of the bordering mountains, produces more than one-third of the world's oil.

The larger structural features of part of this area are shown by the contour map drawn on the top of the Ordovician (Fig. 115). The Appalachian Mountains extend from Newfoundland to Alabama. They are characterized by strong folds and thrust faults that were formed near the close of the Paleozoic era. The system of folds was deeply eroded before Cretaceous time and was covered at the southwest end by Cretaceous rocks. There is little evidence that the range bends to strike west at its south end, but the Ouachita Mountains of Arkansas strike east and, if continued, would join the Appalachian Mountains. The

CRUDE PETROLEUM PRODUCED IN THE UNITED STATES, 1928 AND 1929

(From U. S. Bureau of Mines)

Field	1928		1929	
	Barrels	Value at wells	Barrels	Value at wells (estimate)
Appalachian............	31,059,000	$82,320,000	33,757,000	$104,100,000
Lima-Indiana...........	1,670,000	2,630,000	1,549,000	2,500,000
Illinois and southwestern Indiana..............	7,425,000	11,450,000	7,216,000	11,800,000
Michigan..............	594,000	920,000	4,354,000	6,400,000
Mid-Continent..........	553,125,000	634,550,000	584,751,000	720,900,000
Gulf coast.............	46,591,000	55,150,000	55,574,000	69,500,000
Rocky Mountain and Alaska..............	29,199,000	37,860,000	26,360,000	35,800,000
California.............	231,811,000	230,000,000	292,037,000	289,000,000
	901,474,000	1,054,880,000	1,005,598,000	1,240,000,000

SYMBOLS AND COLORS ASSIGNED TO ROCK SYSTEMS IN THE UNITED STATES[1]

Era	System	Series	Symbol	Color for sedimentary rocks
Cenozoic.........	Quaternary	Recent / Pleistocene / Pliocene	Q	Brownish yellow
	Tertiary	Miocene / Oligocene / Eocene	T	Yellow ocher
Mesozoic.........	Cretaceous	Upper / Lower	K	Olive green
	Jurassic	Upper / Middle / Lower	J	Blue green
	Triassic	Upper / Middle / Lower	Ʀ	Peacock blue
Paleozoic.........	Carboniferous	Permian / Pennsylvanian / Mississippian	C	Blue
	Devonian	Upper / Middle / Lower	D	Blue gray
	Silurian		S	Blue purple
	Ordovician	Cincinnatian / Mohawkian / Lower	O	Red purple
	Cambrian	Saratogan / Acadian / Georgian	Є	Brick red
Proterozoic.......	Algonkian		A	Brownish red
	Archean		Ʀ	Gray brown

[1] U. S. Geol. Survey.

Ouachita system also is characterized by strong folds and thrust faults similar to those of the Appalachian Mountains. The main folding took place in middle and late Pennsylvanian time. The two mountain systems are of about the same age and may be a single system, although this is uncertain, since the area between them is covered by the Mesozoic and later rocks of the Mississippi River embayment.

West of the Ouachita Mountains belt of deformation are the Arbuckle and Wichita mountain ranges which extend to the Panhandle of Texas, where they are represented by the buried Amarillo Hills. In this region a granite range lies below gently folded Permian rocks. The axis of the range is parallel to and on the strike of the Wichita Mountains. The Amarillo buried hills extend nearly to the foothills of the Rocky Mountains.

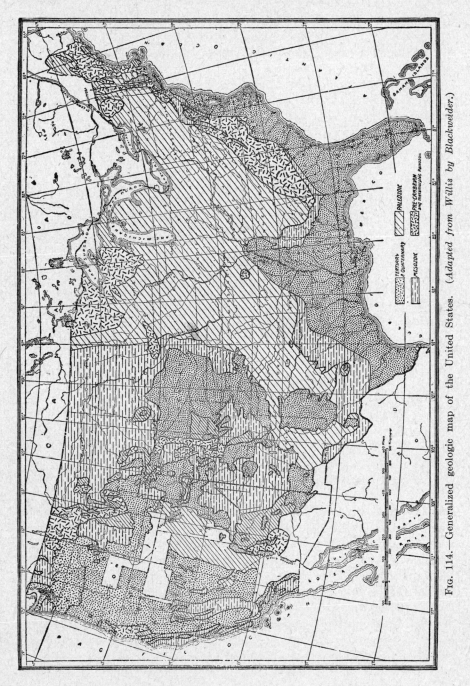

Fig. 114.—Generalized geologic map of the United States. (Adapted from Willis by Blackwelder.)

In the Ouachita and Arbuckle Mountains[1] strong folding followed the deposition of early Pennsylvanian sedimentary rocks. In this region the Permian is much less highly folded. In the Ouachita Mountains region very close folds and thrust faults prevail, and the Comanchean and Cretaceous rocks, where present, are essentially flat lying. In the Arbuckle and Wichita Mountains there is less thrust faulting. The folds and faults strike northwest rather than east-west, which is the prevailing direction in the Ouachita Mountains. The folds, moreover,

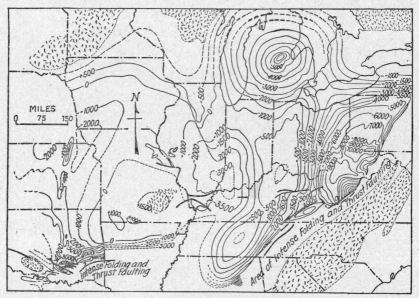

FIG. 115.—Map showing structure of Ordovician system in part of the United States. Contours on sea level datum: St. Peter sandstone in Ohio, Indiana, Illinois and Missouri; Ellenburger and Arbuckle limestone in Kansas, part of Oklahoma and Texas; Viola limestone in Oklahoma and Arkansas. (*After Ruedemann and Levorsen.*) Certain state lines were omitted in copying.

are shown in Comanchean rocks, particularly on the Preston anticline, although these rocks are much less closely folded than are the pre-Permian rocks. The major deformation of the Arbuckle and Wichita Mountains, however, is about the same age as that of the Ouachita Mountains; that is, of Middle and Late Pennsylvanian age. Certain uplifts and geosynclines of the interior lowlands are shown by Fig. 116. The major uplifts, some of the minor ones, and certain faults are shown by Fig. 117. The geosynclines include the Appalachian geosyncline,

[1] POWERS, S., Age of the Folding of the Oklahoma Mountains, Geol. Soc. Am. *Bull.*, vol. 39, pp. 1031–1071, with maps and numerous references, 1928.

MISER, H. D., Structure of the Ouachita Mountains of Oklahoma and Arkansas, Okla. Geol. Survey *Bull.* 50, pp. 1–30, 1929.

TOMLINSON, C. W., Buried Hills near Mannsville, Oklahoma, Am. Assoc. Pet. Geol. *Bull.*, vol. 10, pp. 138 143, 1926.

the synclinal basin of the Lower Peninsula of Michigan, the southern Illinois geosyncline, and the great broad syncline of Nebraska, Kansas, Oklahoma, and Texas, which lies east of the Rocky Mountains. In this area, at least in western Kansas, the Upper Pennsylvanian and Permian rocks rest directly upon pre-Cambrian rocks. Thus, a part of this great geosyncline seems to overlie an older anticline.

One of the most persistent zones of deformation in the intermontane region is the great belt of folding and faulting known as the Chestnut

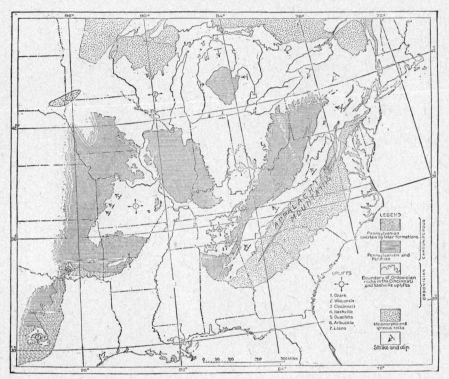

Fig. 116.—Map of part of eastern United States, showing position of principal uplifts. (*Based on map by Siebenthal.*)

Ridge-Rough Creek uplift, which extends southwest from Pennsylvania to the Ozark Mountains (Fig. 117). The zone includes the Chestnut Ridge anticline in Pennsylvania and West Virginia, the Warfield anticline in West Virginia, the Campton-Irvine fault in Kentucky, which lies east of the Cincinnati arch, the Rough Creek uplift in Kentucky, west of the Cincinnati arch, the Hick's dome and Bald Hill uplift, in southeastern Illinois. It extends to the Ozark Mountains uplift of Missouri (Fig. 118). This zone of faulting and folding is nearly 1,000 miles long. At certain places it is a fault or the axis of a fold. At other places it is a broad zone of deformation. At such places it is 50 miles wide or more.

Displacements along the faults of this great zone of deformation are at places known to be several hundred feet.   In Perry County, Missouri, a great fault zone crosses the Mississippi River near Wittenburg.   This fault has been mapped by Weller, Flint, Ekblaw, and others.   It extends southeast in Illinois about 30 miles; to the northwest in Missouri the fault zone is followed about 100 miles.   It is a great group of faults rather than a single slip.[1]   On some of the faults the beds are overturned

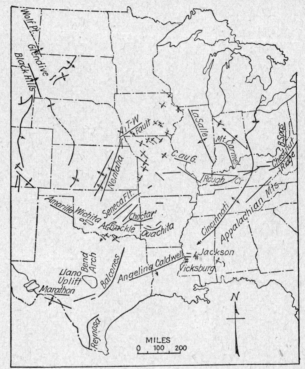

Fig. 117.—Map showing major and a few minor anticlines and faults in Interior Lowlands of the United States.

and there is a maximum vertical displacement of 1,000 feet.   In Missouri the faults of the zone are in part thrust faults.   In Illinois the main fault is probably a tension fault.   This zone of deformation is crossed by the Cincinnati anticline and the Mount Carmel fault, and the La Salle anticline extends northward from it.   The Cap au Gres fault,[2] which has a large displacement, extends northwest from near Alton, Illinois.   The Cincinnati anticline extends northward from Cincinnati.   One branch

[1] Weller, S., advance copy of Geology of Ste. Genevieve County, supplied through the courtesy of Dr. H. A. Buehler, Mo. Geol. Survey.

Flint, R. F., Thrust Faults in Southeastern Missouri, *Am. Jour. Sci.*, ser. 5, vol. 12, pp. 37–40, 1926.

[2] Krey, F., Ill. Geol. Survey *Bull.* 45, pp. 1–86, 1924.

is followed through Findlay, Ohio, to Windsor, Ontario, and another branch extends toward Chicago. Southwest of Cincinnati the anticline passes into Tennessee, where it is called the Nashville arch. It is followed southward into northeast Mississippi where the Paleozoic rocks are covered by Cretaceous strata. Its course is uncertain in Mississippi in the Tertiary beds, but slight movements along it may have continued into Tertiary time, for the Angelina-Caldwell flexure of Louisiana and Texas, which is a belt of very gentle Tertiary folding, is almost in line with the Cincinnati anticline.

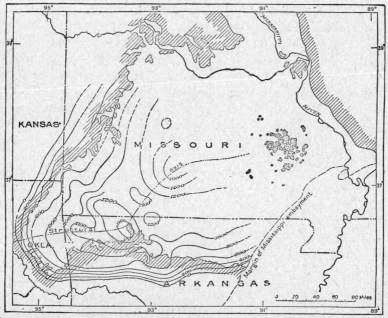

Fig. 118.—Map showing deformation of part of Ozark uplift. Figures on contours represent approximate elevation of base of Mississippian limestone above sea level; parts shaded with diagonal lines represent areas in which Pennsylvania shale is at the surface; areas with strokes and dots represent exposures of crystalline rocks. (*After Siebenthal.*)

The La Salle anticline is traced almost to the northern boundary of Illinois. It is not identified in Wisconsin or Minnesota. Faulting at Dresbach, Hastings, and in northeastern Washington County, Minnesota, suggests that a zone of deformation continues northwest on the strike of the La Salle anticline, but the faults at the places noted in Minnesota do not strike in the direction of the projection of the La Salle anticline. At Hastings and in northeastern Washington County, the deformed areas are fault mosaics. North of these areas there is a great fault that extends south from near Superior, Wisconsin, to Pine City, Minnesota, and brings the Keweenawan lavas against the Hinkley sandstone. Movement on this fault is in part of post-Cambrian age, and it is probably part of the zone of deformation that passes through Washington County and Dresbach and is aligned approximately with the LaSalle anticline.

In Missouri there are many gentle anticlines that strike northwest and plunge northwest. This northwest strike prevails also in low anticlines in northeastern Iowa.

In Kansas a great buried ridge called the Nemaha[1] Ridge extends across the east-central part of the state. This ridge is covered by Pennsylvanian rocks and at many places its summit is marked at the present surface by a series of gentle anticlines. This ridge is probably due to pre-Pennsylvanian faulting and folding. The granite does not crop out but rises to within 500 feet of the surface. The anticline which marks the ridge in southern Kansas extends southward into Oklahoma and is traced to near Oklahoma City. In southeastern Nebraska the granite is found 557 feet deep at DuBois,[2] and the northward extension of the granite ridge is marked by the Table Rock anticline which is traced northward 45 miles to a point west of Nebraska City. Here, if it continued, it would meet the Thurman-Wilson fault. The Nehawka anticline lies north of this fault and extends north 25 miles to near Omaha. The Nemaha system of deformation is not known north of Omaha. The Thurman-Wilson fault strikes northeastward from the buried ridge and is followed more than 100 miles to near central Iowa.[3] In Nebraska it is mainly a flexure, and the Redfield anticline is found about a mile north of it. Tilton states that the fault probably extends farther to the northeast, although it has not been traced beyond the place indicated in Fig. 117. West of the Nemaha buried ridge are found the Bluff City and Abilene anticlines, and many smaller folds which lie approximately parallel to it.

In western Kansas a low anticline is traced northwest toward the Black Hills. This anticline, however, is of post-Cretaceous age, since the Cretaceous rocks are folded on it. The folding of the Nemaha anticline is post-Pennsylvanian in part and probably post-Permian, since Permian beds are gently folded above it.

The Paleozoic strata of the lowlands are consolidated, but they are not much metamorphosed by pressure. They consist principally of shales, sandstones, and limestones. Muds, sands, and marls are generally lacking. Nowhere, except near the mountain uplifts, are pronounced secondary structural features developed in the shales. They are rarely

[1] MOORE, R. C., and W. P. HAYNES, Oil and Gas Resources of Kansas, Kan. Geol. Survey *Bull*. 3, pp. 140–173, 1917.

[2] CONDRA, G. E., The Stratigraphy of the Pennsylvanian System in Nebraska, Neb. Geol. Survey *Bull*. 1, ser. 2, pp. 1–291, 1927.

[3] TODD, J. E., Iowa Acad. Sci. *Proc.*, vol. 1, p. 61, 1889; vol. 13, p. 184, 1906.
SMITH, G. L., Iowa Geol. Survey, vol. 19, p. 612, 1909.
TILTON, J. L., *Jour. Geol.*, vol. 27, pp. 383–390, 1919.

slates or schists. The sandstones may be locally altered to quartzite through infiltration and cementation. The limestones are generally recrystallized somewhat, but away from the mountains they show very little evidence of deformation by pressure.

APPALACHIAN OIL FIELD

General Features.—The Appalachian field includes all the oil- and gas-producing districts in the United States east of central Ohio and northeast of central Alabama. These districts are in New York, Pennsylvania, West Virginia, southeastern Ohio, eastern Kentucky, Tennessee, and northern Alabama. This field, which was the first great oil field in the world to be extensively developed, still produces about 33,000,000 barrels annually.

PRODUCTION OF OIL, GAS AND NATURAL GASOLINE, APPALACHIAN STATES

State	1929		1928		1929	
	Oil, barrels	Value at wells	Natural gas, M cu. ft.	Value	Natural gasoline, gallons	Value
New York	3,346,000	$13,200,000	7,224,000	$ 4,827,000	400,000	$ 46,000
Pennsylvania	11,805,000	45,700,000	99,466,000	48,432,000	19,100,000	1,700,000
West Virginia	5,587,000	20,170,000	163,018,000	72,265,000	70,700,000	5,970,000
Ohio	6,708,000	14,100,000	56,341,000	32,090,000	11,400,000	940,000
Kentucky	7,776,000	13,300,000	15,383,000	5,349,000	6,800,000	550,000
Tennessee	19,000	30,000				

Surface indications of oil are not numerous, although they are present at several places. Noteworthy among them are Oil Spring, Allegany County, New York; Oil Creek, Venango County, Pennsylvania; the gas seep at Burning Springs, Wirt County, West Virginia; and the grahamite dike in Ritchie County, West Virginia. The oil from seeps was gathered by Indians and by early settlers and used for medicinal purposes. In the early days oil was encountered in small amounts in many wells sunk for brine, but it was not generally regarded with favor because there was little use for it.

The Appalachian field is a great geosyncline that lies west of the Appalachian Mountains front and extends from southwestern New York to northern Alabama. On the west the strata rise to the Cincinnati geanticline in Ohio, Kentucky, and Tennessee. The field is somewhat larger than the Appalachian coal basin, although some of the most productive parts of it are below the area occupied by that basin.

The strata that yield oil or gas in the Appalachian field (Fig. 119) include those of the Cambrian, Ordovician, Silurian, Devonian, and Carboniferous systems. The pools occur generally on axes and flanks of

FIG. 119.—Sketch showing the areal geology of part of the Appalachian geosyncline; 11, Permian; 12, Pennsylvanian; 13, Mississippian; 14, Devonian; 15, Silurian; 16, Ordovician. (*After Willis.*)

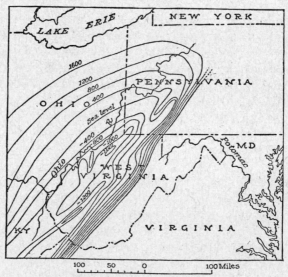

FIG. 120.—Structure contour map of part of the Appalachian geosyncline, showing contours on the Big Injun sand. (*After Reeves.*)

anticlines, parallel with the strike of the Appalachian Mountains, on minor terraces or other structural features associated with them, and in water-free synclines. The reservoir rocks are mainly sandstones or conglomerate layers.

The Paleozoic rocks of the region are mainly shales, sandstones, and limestones. The general structure is shown by Fig. 120. The contour interval on this map is not small enough to show the details of folding. The map does show, however, the great Burning Springs Volcano anticline in western West Virginia. Unlike the other minor folds of the geosyncline, which strike northeast, the Volcano fold strikes nearly north across the regional strike of the country. A section from eastern Ontario southward to West Virginia is shown as Fig. 121. The strata vary in character so that a section taken at one place differs considerably from other sections. There are, however, certain persistent and fairly constant strata that can be correlated. The Pittsburgh coal lies near the surface over much of this area. It is a persistent member, and, because of its value, its position has been determined with great accuracy. It therefore serves as a horizon marker and a key rock to the structure. Below the Pittsburgh coal are other coals, which also serve as keys to the structure. The section containing the coals is made up principally of sandstones, shales, and limestones. Another horizon marker is the Salt sand, at about the top of the Pottsville formation. Below the Salt sand is the Big Lime. The Big Injun sand lies below the Big Lime, and below it are the Gordon, Elizabeth, Bradford, and other sands. Sections of the rocks are shown in Fig. 122 and the generalized West Virginia section by Fig. 123. Axes of folds and sections are shown on Figs. 124 and 125.

NEW YORK, PENNSYLVANIA, AND WEST VIRGINIA

The great Appalachian synclinorium is about 800 miles long. It is over 200 miles wide at the northeast end and 50 miles or less at the southwest end. The synclinorium embraces many minor anticlines and synclines, which are of considerable amplitude in the eastern part of the field, near the mountains, but gradually die out or become flatter toward the northwest. Noteworthy folds are the Burning Springs-Volcano-Eureka

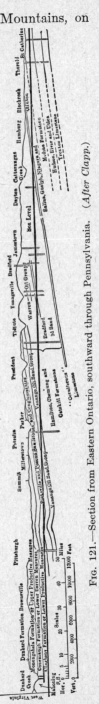

Fig. 121.—Section from Eastern Ontario, southward through Pennsylvania. (*After Clapp.*)

anticline (Figs. 124, 125), the Wick, Arches Fork, Chestnut Ridge and Laurel Ridge anticlines. In southern West Virginia the subordinate folds become less pronounced toward the northwest, the beds rising gradually toward the west, where they are exposed at the Cincinnati anticline in Ohio, eastern Kentucky, and eastern Tennessee. As a rule the dips are gentle, commonly less than 3 degrees. Locally, the strata dip

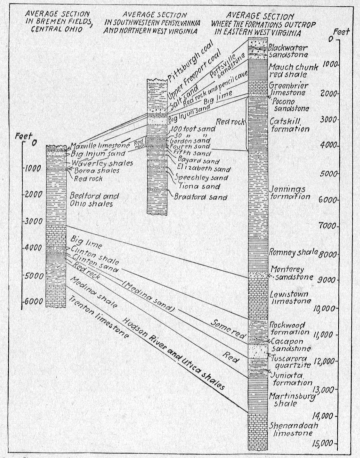

Fig. 122.—Comparative stratigraphic columns for Ohio, Pennsylvania and West Virginia. (*After Clapp.*)

at higher angles, and, exceptionally, as on the flanks of the Burning Springs-Volcano anticline, the dips rise to 10 degrees or more. In New York, Pennsylvania, West Virginia, and Ohio there is very little faulting in the oil fields. In eastern Kentucky and Tennessee faults of considerable magnitude are present.

Where the rocks are saturated with salt water, as a general rule the oil and gas occupy the anticlines, or the domes, and the gas rises

	Series	Columnar section	Thickness (feet)	Total (feet)	Description
Permo-Carboniferous	Dunkard		1150	1150	Variegated shales and gray sandstones with a few thin coal beds
Carboniferous / Pennsylvanian	Monongahela (Pittsburgh coal at base)		400	1550	Gray sandstones, gray shales, limestones, and coal beds
	Conemaugh		600	2150	Gray or brown sandstones, gray and red shales, and coal beds
	Allegheny		250	2400	Gray sandstones, gray shales, and coal beds
	Pottsville (Salt sands of West Virginia)		300	2700	Gray sandstones, and shales, with a few coal beds
Miss-issippian	Mauch Chunk (Contains Maxton sand of West Virginia)		250	2950	Red shales with a few thin sandstones
	Greenbrier (Big lime of West Virginia)		100	3050	Limestone
	Pocono (Big Injun at top; Berea sand at base)		500	3550	Gray sandstones and gray shales
Devonian	Catskill (Gordon group of oil sands)		800	4350	Brown sandstones and red shales
	Chemung (No productive sands in West Virginia)		1500(?)	5850	Olive-brown, shales with sandstones lentils
	Portage (No productive sands in West Virginia)		800(?)	6650	Gray shales with sandstones lentils
	Hamilton (No productive sands in West Virginia)		700(?)	7350	Brown, shales with sandstone lentils
	Marcellus or Romney (Gas in Ohio and Kentucky)		300(?)	7650	Brown, or black bituminous shales with sandstone lentils
	"Onondaga" limestone (Ragland sand of Kentucky)		50(?)	7700	Dark flinty limestone
	Oriskany		150(?)	7850	Gray sandstone
Silurian	Helderberg Salina, and Niagara (Big lime of Ohio)		800(?)	8650	Limestone
	Clinton		200(?)	8850	Variegated shales
	Medina white sandstone (Clinton oil sand of southern Ohio)		50(?)	8900	White sandstone
	Medina shales		500(?)	9400	Red shales and thin sandstones
Ordovician	Martinsburg or Cincinnati shale (Contains Hudson sand of Kentucky)		500(?)	9900	Gray shales with sandstone lentils
	Utica		300(?)	10200	Black shales with sandstone lentils
	Trenton and other limestones (Oil and gas horizon of northern Ohio)		1200(?)	11400	Limestones

FIG. 123.—Columnar section for central part of West Virginia oil fields, Marion and surrounding Counties. (*After Reger.*)

State Teachers College Library
Willimantic, Conn.

above the oil.   According to Griswold and Munn,[1] this is true of deposits
in the Salt sand and in the Big Injun sand below it, which belongs to
the Pocono of the Mississippian.   At places the Berea sand at the base
of the Mississippian is dry.

The still lower Catskill sands are not fully saturated, and some of
them are dry.   The oil apparently has been let down from the higher
structural positions and in some places is held up on the flanks of syn-

Fig. 124.—Map showing axes of folds in part of Appalachian geosyncline.   For sections
along lines A-A', etc., see Fig. 125.   (Based on map by Reger.)

clines by water that remains in the beds.   If no water remains the oil
will be at the bottoms of the folds.

Many wells in this field produce both oil and gas, and some produce
both from the same stratum.   In many wells the gas carries considerable
gasoline.   Many of the folds yield gas only, and in general such folds lie
east of the petroleum-bearing folds and nearer to the Appalachian
Mountains.   Where dynamo-chemical alteration has been sufficient

---

[1] Griswold, W. T., and W. J. Munn, Geology of Oil and Gas Fields in Steubens-
ville, Burgettstown, and Claysville Quadrangles, Ohio, West Virginia, and Pennsylvania, U. S. Geol. Survey Bull. 318, 1907.

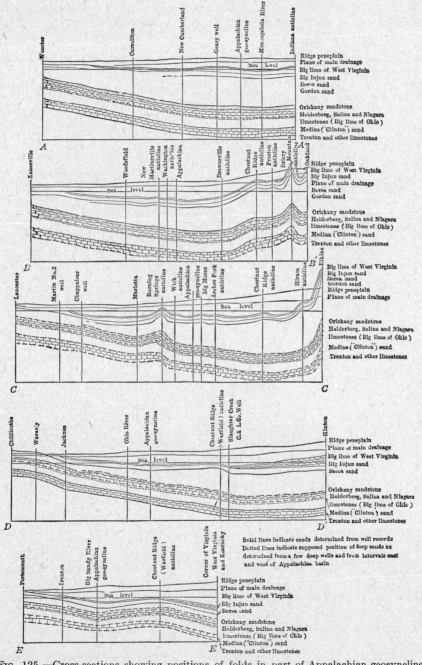

FIG. 125.—Cross-sections showing positions of folds in part of Appalachian geosyncline. For lines of sections, see Fig. 124. (*After Reger.*)

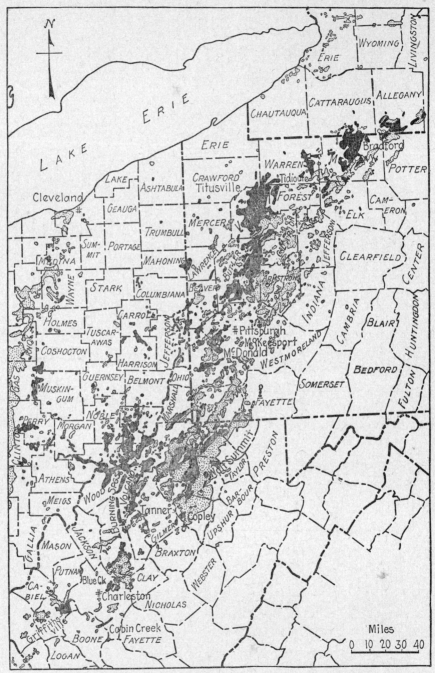

FIG. 126.—Map showing main oil and gas producing areas of Appalachian region.

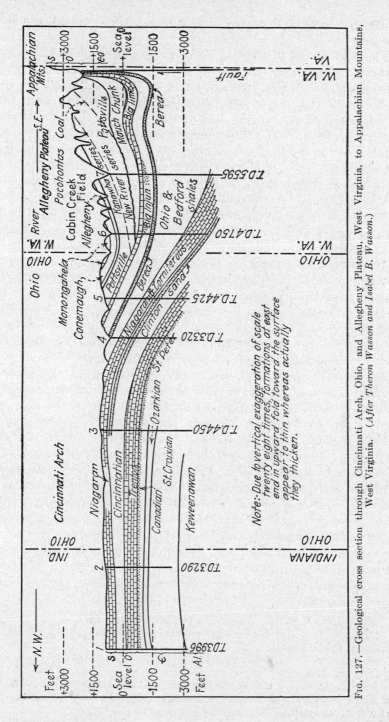

FIG. 127.—Geological cross section through Cincinnati Arch, Ohio, and Allegheny Plateau, West Virginia, to Appalachian Mountains, West Virginia. (After Theron Wasson and Isabel B. Wasson.)

to alter the coals so that they have a high carbon content, gas only is produced.

The first serious attempt to develop the petroleum industry in the northern Appalachian region resulted from the drilling of a well at Titusville, Pennsylvania, by E. L. Drake in 1859. Although it was not a large well, there was a sale for the oil and other wells were drilled, opening many oil pools. The first flowing well or gusher was one sunk near Rouseville in 1860, and several others yielding from 3,000 to 4,000 barrels a day were brought in during 1861. Development in this region thereafter was rapid, reaching a maximum in 1891. The oil is of high grade, rich in lighter derivatives, has a paraffin base, and is essentially free from sulphur. It yields lubricants of excellent quality.

The most productive portion of the Appalachian field lies in New York, Pennsylvania, and West Virginia. A map of the oil-bearing area is shown by Fig. 126 and a cross-section by Fig. 127.

In western New York[1] gas is produced from lower Paleozoic strata, particularly from the Corniferous limestone of the Devonian, from Niagara limestone and Medina sandstone of the Silurian, and from the Trenton limestone and Loraine shale of the Ordovician. The oil production of New York is from the Chemung formation (Devonian) and is found in Steuben, Allegany, and Cattaraugus counties (Fig. 128). New York produced about 79,000,000 barrels of oil to 1929. The oil is high grade, 42° Bé., and wells yielding only ⅓ barrel a day are profitably operated. A small amount of gasoline is obtained from natural gas.

The oil fields of New York lie on the east side of the axis of the Appalachian geosyncline. The axis plunges gently to the southwest and the regional dip of the rocks of the oil-bearing area is southwest. Very gentle anticlines and synclines are developed. In some of the pools no salt water is present; the oil is found in the bottoms of the synclines; and gas is present above the oil (Fig. 128). In one or two pools the sands contain salt water beyond the oil-producing territory, but in general there is no edge water outlining the pools. Commonly, the oil sand pinches out below the oil as in a lens reservoir.

According to Hartnagel and Russell the Chemung sediments carry marine fossils. The oil-bearing sands have a porosity of 5 to 17 per cent. The source of the oil is believed to be the dark shales of the Portage and underlying strata.

[1] Lewis, J. O., U. S. Bur. Mines *Bull.* 148, pp. 108–120, 1917.

BASSLER, R. B., Oil Fields Rejuvenated, Pa. Geol. Survey *Bull.* 56, pp. 1–14, 1922 (mimeograph sheets).

NUTTING, P. G., Chemical Problems in Water Driving, *Oil Gas Jour.*, vol. 24, No. 19, p. 76, 1925.

HARTNAGEL, C. A., and W. L. RUSSELL, The Oil Fields of New York State, Am. Assoc. Pet. Geol. *Bull.*, vol. 9, pp. 798–802, 1925; New York Oil Fields, "Structure of Typical American Oil Fields," vol. 2, pp. 269–289, 1929.

GENERAL COLUMNAR SECTION, NEW YORK OIL FIELDS

(*After Hartnagel and Russell*)

System	Series	Description	Thickness, feet
Carboniferous — Pennsylvanian (Pottsville)	Olean	Conglomerate, with well-rounded pebbles mostly vein quartz and coarse sandstone	60–70
	Unconformity	Absence of the Mauch Chunk and associated formations. 4,000 + feet	
Mississippian (Bradford)	Oswayo	Olive-green and rusty colored limonitic shales. Few thin beds of sandstone (limestone near base)	160–250
	Cattaraugus	Bright-red shales with interbedded green or bluish shales and fine-grained micaceous sandstones. Local beds of conglomerate; jasper pebbles	300–350
Devonian	Chemung	Gray, olive, and bluish shales, some dark purple or chocolate color. Many thin beds of argillaceous sandstone. Lower half contains all oil-producing sands of state	1,200–1,500
	Portage	Sandstones, flags, black carbonaceous shales. Gas bearing	1,200–1,700
	Hamilton and Marcellus	Blue, gray, and olive shales. Basal portion, the Marcellus black shale, which is gas bearing	600–700
	Onondaga	Also called "Corniferous." A heavy-bedded limestone. Gas bearing	130
	Unconformity	Absence of Helderbergian formations	
Silurian	Salina	Waterlimes, gypseous shales, anhydrite, gypsum, rock salt. Red shales at base. Upper part gas bearing	700–800
	Niagara	At top Lockport and Guelph dolomites. Rochester shale at base. Gas	200
	Clinton	Limestones, shales, thin hematite bed	80
	Medina	Upper 150 feet white and red sandstones. Main mass red shale with white Oswego sandstone at base. Prolific gas horizon	1,100–1,200
Ordovician	"Hudson River"	Sandstone and shales. At base is Utica black shale	600
	Trenton	Dark limestone, nearly everywhere containing a little gas, but few long-lived wells	700–900
	Beekmantown	Heavy-bedded limestone known as "Calciferous" formation	137
Cambrian	Potsdam	Sandstone where present directly overlying the pre-Cambrian	?

The most productive field is the Richburg field in Allegany County, (Fig. 128) which produces from the Richburg sand. West of that in Cattaraugus County is the north end of the Bradford pool which produces from the Bradford sand which lies at a horizon a little lower than the Richburg. The Bradford sand is commonly from 30 to 60 feet thick, including shale partings, and lies about 1,000 feet deep in New York. It is from 1,100 to 1,700 feet deep or more in Pennsylvania.

The larger part of the Bradford pool[1] lies in Pennsylvania. The sands present from the surface downward include the First, Chipmunk

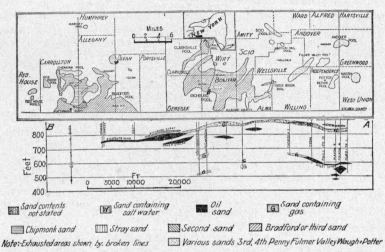

Fig. 128.—Map and section showing oil fields of New York. (*After Hartnagel and Russell.*)

sand, Second, Bradford, Fourth or Lewis Run, Kane, and Haskell. These sands are probably all marine. The Kane and Haskell sands are commonly gas sands. In the Pennsylvania part of the field the Big Shady syncline strikes northeast. On the southeast side of it is the Simpson anticline and on the northwest side the Bradford anticline. In general the sands are thicker on the anticlines and more productive. On the east side of the field the Bradford sand thins out. Water is found below the oil and, according to Torrey,[2] the Bradford sand was once completely saturated with water.

[1] NEWBY, J., P. D. TORREY, C. R. FETTKE, and L. S. PANYITY, Bradford Oil Field, McKean County, Pennsylvania and Cattaraugus County, New York, "Structure of Typical American Oil Fields," vol. 2, pp. 407–442, 1929.

[2] TORREY, P. D., Oil-field Waters of the Bradford Pool, Am. Inst. Min. Eng. *Tech. Pub.* 38, pp. 1–15, 1927; *Tech. Pub.* 39, pp. 1–24, 1927.

STEPHENSON, E. A., and I. G. GRETTUM, Valuation of Flood Oil Properties, Am. Inst. Min. Eng. *Tech. Pub.* 323, pp. 1–20, 1930.

UMPLEBY, J. B., Increasing the extraction of oil by water flooding, Amer. Inst. Min. Eng. Petr. Div., pp. 112–129, 1926.

The Bradford field is the first field in which flooding or water driving was practiced on a large scale. This practice was begun about 1892 and has been carried on ever since. There is a water sand 800 feet above the oil sand, and it is said that the rusting of a casing at this sand led to the practice of flooding.

In the circular flooding method a well is sunk about 1,000 feet deep to the oil sand. The well is filled with water and allowed to stand. Wells are drilled around the first well about 150 feet from it, and the oil driven into them is pumped until the water drive reaches them. These wells are then filled with water and other wells are sunk around the first circle of wells. Another method is the "line flood," in which wells are sunk 150 feet apart along a line and are filled with water, other wells are drilled on lines each side of this, the lines being 150 feet apart and the wells staggered so that a well in one line is opposite the middle point between two wells in a neighboring line of wells. The two lines of wells are pumped until they cease to yield oil. Subsequently, they are filled with water and wells are drilled further out. The advance of the water is about 60 to 200 feet a year, depending on the pressure or depth of the well and the porosity of the sandstone. Other methods of flooding include the introduction of soda ash, of air or gas under pressure, or of air under pressure along with water. It is estimated that the Bradford field in New York and Pennsylvania had yielded 257,000,000 barrels of oil to 1927. Present production is 4,000,000 barrels per year and about 2,500,000 barrels a year may be attributed to flooding.

In western Pennsylvania the Paleozoic strata dip away from the Canadian Shield and toward the trough of the Appalachian geosyncline. The major structure is simple (Fig. 121). Because the oil is found largely in anticlines in rocks above the Devonian strata and in synclines in the Devonian and lower beds, a large part of the area is productive. The oil fields were among the first drilled in North America and long ago passed their zenith of production, yet in 1927 Pennsylvania produced 9,596,000 barrels of oil, the daily average production of New York and Pennsylvania together being 0.36 barrel per well. Because of the high quality of the oil and the ready sale for gas in the region, it is still found profitable to operate the wells notwithstanding the low yield. Some of the oil fields are being drilled to greater depths, and in recent years a few new fields or extensions of old ones have been opened.

The Tidioute[1] field southwestern Warren County, Pennsylvania (Fig. 126), has been revived in recent years by drilling to the Queen sand, where small flowing wells were obtained. The rocks exposed near Tidioute include the section from the lower part of the Pottsville conglomerate to the second sand of the Venango group. The rocks dip

[1] JOHNSON, M. E., Tidioute Oil Pool, Warren County, Pennsylvania, Pa. Geol. Survey *Bull.* 79, pp. 1–17, 1923 (mimeographed sheets with maps).

OIL HORIZONS OF PENNSYLVANIA-WEST VIRGINIA DISTRICT

Distance above (+) or below (−) the Pittsburgh Coal

(*After Robinson*)

	Feet
Carboniferous.	
Pennsylvanian:	
Monongahela formation (Upper Productive measures):	
Carroll sand (Uniontown sandstone), productive in West Virginia only	+ 300
Pittsburgh coal horizon	0
Conemaugh formation (Lower Barren measures):	
Murphy, Shallow, Little Dunkard, or First Cow Run sand (Saltsburg sandstone)	− 200
Big Dunkard or Cow Run sand (Mahoning sandstone)	− 500
Allegheny formation (Lower Productive measures):	
Second Cow Run sand (Freeport sandstone)	− 600
Gas sand	− 800
Pottsville formation (Salt sand):	
Johnson Run sand (Homewood sandstone)	− 900
Upper Salt sand (Lower Conoquenessing sandstone)	− 950
Middle Salt sand (Lower Conoquenessing sandstone)	−1,050
Lower salt (Sharon conglomerate)	−1,150
Maxton sand (Maxon sand)	−1,230
Mississippian:	
Mauch Chunk formation (Green County, Pa.):	
Little Lime	−1,195
Pencil Cave	−1,200
Big Lime	−1,205
Pocono:	
Big Injun	−1,255
Squaw	−1,590
Wier	
Berea (Murrysville)	−1,840
Devonian:	
Gantz	−1,930
Fifty Foot	−1,968
Thirty Foot	+2,035
Catskill:	
Snee	
Gordon Stray	−2,100
Gordon	−2,175
Fourth	−2,225
Fifth	−2,290
Chemung (Clarion County, Pa.):	
Bayard	−1,550
Elizabeth sand	−1,640
First Warren sand	−1,890
Second Warren	−1,950
Third Warren	−2,030
Speechley Stray	−2,120

OIL HORIZON OF PENNSYLVANIA-WEST VIRGINA DISTRICT.—(*Continued*)

Feet

Chemung (Clarion) County, Pa:

Speechley	−2,190
Tiona	−2,300
First Balltown	−2,420
Second Balltown	−2,500
Sheffield sand	−2,570
Chipmunk sand	
First Bradford sand	−2,680
Second Bradford sand	−2,770
Third Bradford sand	−2,855

Portage:

First Kane sand	−2,940
Second Kane sand	−2,980
Third Kane sand	3,085
First Elk sand	−3,420
Second Elk sand	−3,465
Third Elk sand	−3,520

Oriskany:

Corniferous limestone	−5,625
Oriskany sand	−5,700

Silurian.

Salina group	−6,050
Niagaran limestone	−6,570
Clinton sand	−6,800
Medina sand	−7,200

Ordovician.[1]

[1] The section from the top of the Mississippian to the bottom of the Catskill is in Green County, Pennsylvania; from Catskill to Medina sand is in Clarion County, Pennsylvania. Both parts named are from J. F. Robinson, *Oil Gas Jour.*, vol. 26, p. 18, June 16, 1927.

gently southward, and there is an unconformity at the base of the Pottsville conglomerate. The underlying beds were tilted from north to south and eroded, and the Pottsville conglomerate was deposited on successively younger beds from north to south. Consequently, there is a convergence to the north. The Venango group of oil sands is correlated with the Catskill group. At Tidioute it is not red as is the Catskill at most places.

The Venango group includes three sands at Tidioute. Below the Venango group are 350 feet of brown or purplish shale of the Chemung formation. The lower part of the Chemung is sandy and includes the Queen sand recently developed. The Queen sand is found at depths of about 1,000 to 1,500 feet. The productive pool is on a small structural nose that plunges southwest. Two domes near by are barren.

In 1919 a well just south of McKeesport[1] was drilled in, yielding 4,000,000 cubic feet per day and soon increased production to 62,000.000

[1] ASHLEY, G. H., Pa. Geol. Survey *Bull.* 3, pp. 1–3, 1919.

cubic feet. The field, which has been producing gas since 1883, is on an anticline. The gas brought in in 1919 comes from a depth of about 2,900 feet from the Speechley sand. The Foster well produced about 5,000,000,000 cubic feet of gas in 100 days. It met a place in the sand that was exceptionally porous and blew out channels for itself, increasing production. The initial rock pressure was about 1,400 pounds per square inch, but quickly declined to half that amount. Other wells were drilled to the sand and the production speedily declined.

In Westmoreland[1] County, a mile west of West Newton, gas was found in the Big Injun sand in 1920 in several wells, the rock pressure being about 500 pounds. A well in the latter part of May flowed 7,750,000 cubic feet per day and a month later it flowed only 100,000 cubic feet.

In the Scenery Hill[2] gas field 25 miles southwest of McKeesport, gas was discovered in 1927. The main production is from the Fifth sand at the base of the Catskill formation.

The oil-bearing area of West Virginia is the southwestern extension of that of Pennsylvania. The same sands are productive in the main, although the Chemung group of the Devonian, which yields oil from several sands in Pennsylvania, produces little oil in West Virginia.

In southwestern Pennsylvania and northwestern West Virginia the sands in the Upper Devonian contain much oil and gas. These sands constitute the Venango oil-sand group, which is an important oil-bearing series in southwestern Pennsylvania. Below the Catskill the Corniferous limestone is found at great depths in this field. A well near McDonald, Pennsylvania,[3] penetrated the Lower Devonian limestone. At a depth of 6,260 feet a sandstone, possibly the Oriskany, was encountered which contained concentrated brine.

In many of the oil sands the oil and gas occur in pockets, where the sands are coarser (p. 82). In the Carboniferous rocks, which are generally saturated with water, the oil at many places is on high parts of the folds. A well-known example is the Volcano dome of the Burning Springs-Volcano-Eureka anticline in West Virginia.

The oil deposits near the base of the Mississippian system and in the upper Devonian strata are generally located near the axes of synclines. Examples are the Copley[4] and Cabin Creek fields. The Copley oil field is in north-central West Virginia in Lewis and Gilmer counties near the trough of the Grassland syncline which lies east of the Chestnut Ridge

[1] ROBINSON, J. F., Gas Wells on Pollock Vein, Westmoreland County, Pennsylvania, Pa. Geol. Survey *Bull.* 12, pp. 1–3, 1920.

[2] ROBINSON, J. F., Scenery Hill Gas Field, Washington County, Pennsylvania, "Structure of Typical American Oil Fields," vol. 2, pp. 443–450, 1929.

[3] WHITE, I. C., Note on a Very Deep Well Near McDonald, Pennsylvania, Geol. Soc. Am. *Bull.*, vol. 24, pp. 275–282, 1913.

[4] REGER, D. B., Copley Oil Pool of West Virginia, Am. Assoc. Pet. Geol. *Bull.*, vol. 11, pp. 581–599, 1927.

anticline. The oil is found at depths of about 2,500 feet in the Gordon Stray, Gordon, and Fifth sand of the Catskill group of the Upper Devonian system. The first well was drilled in 1900 and had an initial production of 5,000 barrels a day. The gas pressure of the field was about 550 pounds per square inch when the field was brought in. The oil has a gravity of 43° Bé. and like other Appalachian oils is essentially free from sulphur. The axis of the syncline plunges southwest and gas is found above the oil on both flanks of the syncline and on the northeast side. Southwest, the oil deposit lies against poor sand.

The Cabin Creek[1] field is located 20 miles southeast of Charleston near the bottom of a syncline that lies southeast of the Warfield-Chestnut Ridge anticline. Oil is found near the bottom of the syncline in a lens of the Berea sand at depths of about 3,000 feet, where the Berea sandstone dips southeast 85 feet per mile. The field is 12 miles long and 1 mile or less wide. It was opened in 1914 and has produced steadily an oil with a gravity of 47° Bé., high in gasoline, and yielding excellent lubricating oil. The 58 per cent isocarb passes through the middle of the field. The sand lens contains oil and gas but no water (Fig. 63). The Berea sand is about 35 feet thick and includes a hard quartzite bed 15 feet thick that lies above the oil sand and forms the cap rock. The oil sand is about 20 feet thick. The oil accumulated at the bottom of the lens and gas above the oil. The initial rock pressure was 300 pounds or more per square inch. The sand is a marine sand, probably an offshore deposit, and the absence of water in it is noteworthy. It is suggested that the oil entered the sand largely as a gas during the Appalachian revolution and liquefied subsequently at lower temperatures.

Oil is found in a syncline[2] in the Wolf Summitt field northeast of Copley. In the Tanner Creek field west of Copley, oil and gas are found in a syncline. The main production is from the Big Injun, Berea, and Maxon sands. In the Griffithsville field southwest of Charleston, oil is found in the Berea sandstone in a syncline.

Because of its great gas production in Ohio, the east extension of the "Clinton" sand has aroused much interest. The sand dips east from central Ohio and rises again toward the west front of the Appalachian Mountains. As stated by Bownocker, the small pools found in the sand contain no water, and he suggests that they may occur in small shallow basins rather than on anticlines. It is believed by some, that large deposits of oil will be found below the gas in the deeper part of the basin.

[1] WASSON, T., and ISABEL B. WASSON, Cabin Creek Field, West Virginia, Am. Assoc. Pet. Geol. *Bull.*, vol. 11, pp. 705–719, 1927.

[2] DAVIS, R. E., and E. A. STEPHENSON, Synclinal Oil Fields in Southern West Virginia, "Structure of Typical American Oil Fields," vol. 2, pp. 571–576, 1929.

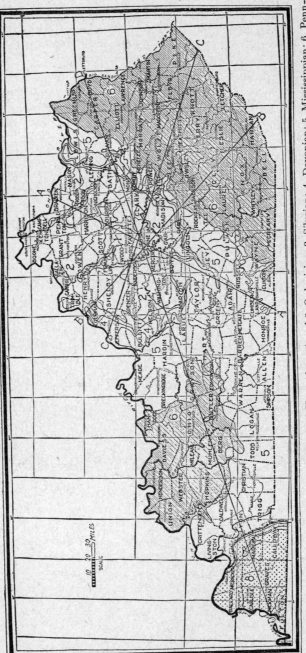
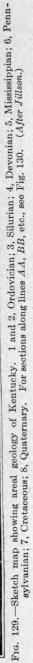
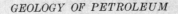

Fig. 129.—Sketch map showing areal geology of Kentucky. 1 and 2, Ordovician; 3, Silurian; 4, Devonian; 5, Mississippian; 6, Pennsylvanian; 7, Cretaceous; 8, Quaternary. For sections along lines *AA*, *BB*, etc., see Fig. 130. (*After Jillson.*)

KENTUCKY

The rocks exposed in Kentucky[1] are Paleozoic, Cretaceous, and Quaternary (Figs. 129, 130). The most prominent structural feature of this state is the Cincinnati anticline, which in Ohio and Indiana is termed the Cincinnati arch (p. 190). This anticline extends southward from Cincinnati through east-central Kentucky and passes out of the state in the eastern part of Monroe County. In Tennessee it expands into a great dome in the region of Nashville. From Tennessee it passes southward into Alabama.

A zone of deformation known in West Virginia as the Warfield anticline extends into Kentucky, where it is known as the Campton anticline (Fig. 117). This zone practically crosses Kentucky from east to west and intersects the Cincinnati arch near the north border of Lincoln County.

The oldest formation in the state, the Mohawkian (Ordovician), is exposed at the crest of this arch in Jessamine County. This portion has been termed the Jessamine dome. Around the Mohawkian is a great area of Cincinnatian rocks (Ordovician). Silurian, Devonian, Mississippian, and Pennsylvanian rocks occur in succession stratigraphically above the Ordovician central mass. The dip of the beds is essentially eastward to the West Virginia border; the Pennsylvanian coal measures in eastern Kentucky lie on the west limb of the great Appalachian coal basin. In the coal region the rocks are thrown into gentle folds like those in West Virginia. West of the Cincinnati anticline the beds dip westward below the western coal basin and rise again near the Cumberland River.

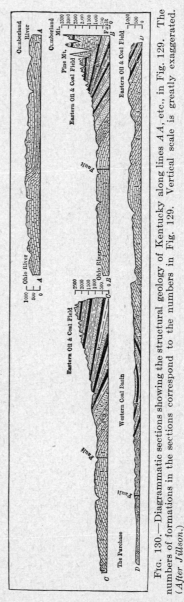

Fig. 130.—Diagrammatic sections showing the structural geology of Kentucky along lines *A A*, etc., in Fig. 129. The numbers of formations in the sections correspond to the numbers in Fig. 129. Vertical scale is greatly exaggerated. (*After Jillson.*)

[1] HOEING, J. B., Oil and Gas Sands of Kentucky, Ky. Geol. Survey *Bull.* 1, 1904.

FOHS, F. J., Oil and Gas Possibilities of Kentucky, Am. Inst. Min. Eng. *Bull.* 99, pp. 621–628, 1915.

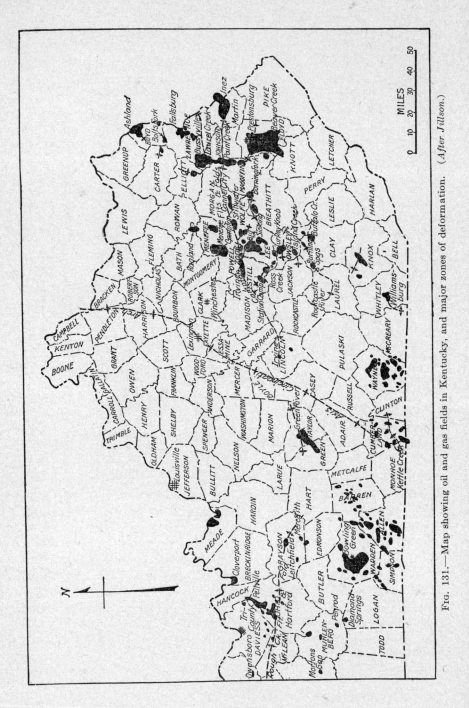

Fig. 131.—Map showing oil and gas fields in Kentucky, and major zones of deformation.   (After Jillson.)

Most of the oil and gas[1] produced in Kentucky (Figs. 131, 132) is derived from Devonian limestone, but some is obtained also from Ordovician, Silurian, Mississippian, and Pennsylvanian rocks. Any porous limestone, where covered with shales, may serve as a reservoir. The reservoir limestones are not uniformly porous, and the production is therefore spotted.

Both east and west of the Cincinnati arch, at places not far from the coal measures, are areas of bituminous sandstones. These are shown on a map by Eldridge. They appear not to be closely connected with the oil pools.

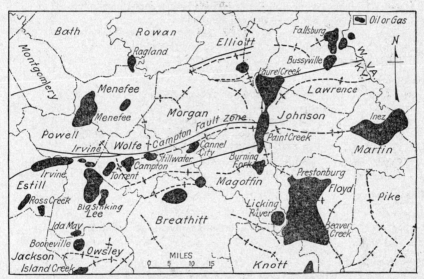

Fig. 132.—Map showing oil and gas fields in eastern Kentucky. (*After Jillson.*)

The maximum yield of oil in Kentucky was reached in 1919 when the state yielded 9,226,473 barrels valued at $24,459,017. The Corniferous sand produces about 60 per cent of the oil and the Mississippian sands most of the remainder.

Eastern Kentucky.—The zone of deformation known in West Virginia as the Warfield anticline extends southwest into eastern Kentucky where, as stated, it is known as the Campton anticline and also as the "Irvine-Paint Creek-Warfield fault and fold." From Irvine west it is called the Kentucky River fault and fold. From Leitchfield to Shawneetown on the Ohio River there is a great fault zone called the Rough Creek fault. The chief production of oil and much of the gas of Kentucky has come from fields located on and near these zones of deformation. East of the Cincinnati arch these fields include Irvine, Campton, Cannel City,

---

[1] Jilson, W. R., The Oil and Gas Resources of Kentucky, Ky. Dept. Geol. and Forestry, ser. 5, vol. 1, pp. 1–630, 1919.

General Section for Kentucky Fields
(Based on sections by Hoeing, Matson, and Jillson)

	Feet
Pennsylvanian:	
Allegheny sandstone, "Sebree" sand, western Kentucky..........	40– 60
Pottsville conglomerate; alternating sands, shales, and coals, conglomerate at base; contains Beaver, Horton, and Pike sands in Floyd, Knott, and Pike Counties, and Wages, Jones, and Epperson sands in Knox County; Williamsburg in Whitley County.......	60–1,000
Unconformity.	
Mississippian:	
Mauch Chunk or Pennington shales and sandstone, some limestone; contains Maxon sand. In eastern Kentucky..................	30– 275
Chester group in western Kentucky. Tar Springs, Hardinsburg, and Cypress sands; Ste. Genevieve; oolitic white limestone (Big Lime)...	300– 800
	20– 400
Unconformity.	
St. Louis; fine white-gray limestone, cherty "Big Lime." Thickness in western Kentucky......................................	300– 650
Waverly sandstone and shales. In eastern Kentucky 400 to 600 feet thick; contains Keener, Big Injun, Squaw, Wier, and Berea sands. St. Louis-Warsaw in western Kentucky calcareous shales and limestone; contains amber oil of Barren, Warren, and Simpson Counties. Thickness in western Kentucky..................	400
Unconformity.	
Devonian:[1]	
Ohio shale; in shallow wells yields an abundance of highly mineralized water..	150
Unconformity.	
"Corniferous limestone," usually a cherty magnesian limestone with some shale beds. Oil sand in Irvine region..............	0– 45
Unconformity.	
Silurian:	
Niagaran; blue shales and yellow limestones, in places containing chert; locally includes some sandstone. Oil in Allen County....	50– 250
Unconformity.	
Ordovician:	
Upper; limestones, blue shales, sandstones; includes Caney, upper Sunnybrook, Barren County deep and Cumberland County shallow sands...	450– 700
Unconformity.	
Middle; limestone, gray granular to crystalline; "Trenton.".......	870
Unconformity.	
Lower; hard limestone, sandy limestone, dolomitic limestone, "calciferous"...	500 ±

[1] The section of the Devonian and older rocks represents the central Blue Grass region, after G. C. Matson, U. S. Geol. Survey *Water Supply Paper* 233, 1909.

Paint Creek, and Inez fields. West of the Cincinnati arch they include the Hartford and Leitchfield fields.

The Irvine pool is at the southwest edge of the Appalachian coal basin, a few miles east of the eastern border of the broad area of Ordovician limestones. A southeastward dip carries the Ordovician beneath successively younger rocks of Silurian and Devonian age, which crop out not far west of Irvine. To the east these rocks are overlain by rocks of Carboniferous age. As a general rule the formations thicken toward the east. This gradual eastward thickening of the Maxville (?) and Corniferous limestones is illustrated in Fig. 133. A fault zone borders the crest of the Irvine anticline on the northwest. The effect of the faulting is to drop a block of strata from ½ to 2 miles wide and probably more than 20 miles long 25 to 200 feet. The Irvine fault zone is nearly parallel to the axis of the Irvine anticline.

Fig. 133.—Cross-section from Irvine to Campton, Kentucky, showing the dip and thickening of formations to the east, the structural features on which oil and gas are found and the general attitude of the surface. (*After Shaw.*)

The oil sand in the Irvine pool is Corniferous limestone. The oil-bearing portion of the sand differs from the remainder of the limestone or dolomite in having larger pores and in being softer. In places it is cavernous. After penetrating the clay shale that overlies the oil sand, the drill commonly enters a hard limestone, which, here and there, yields water and ranges from a few inches to several feet in thickness. Below this rock is the soft brown sandy-textured magnesian limestone that constitutes the oil reservoir. In the eastern part of the field, where the whole sand is thicker, oil-bearing strata are found at more than one horizon. The oil is accumulated on domes and anticlines, particularly where the limestone is porous. Most of the wells in the Irvine field yield little gas. Salt water is probably present in the lower part of the oil sand throughout much of the field, particularly the southern half, and many wells bordering the field have yielded considerable quantities of water. Along the northern border, however, wells that fail to produce oil are commonly reported altogether dry. The oil of the Irvine sand has a gravity of about 38° Bé. At places in the Irvine field the Niagara limestone produces oil.

The Big Sinking field which is the southeast extension of the Irvine field is one of the most productive oil fields in Kentucky. The oil is found in the Onondaga (Corniferous) limestone and also in the Niagara

COMBINED SECTION IN ESTILL COUNTY, KENTUCKY

(*After Shaw*. The column showing depth has been recalculated to conform with other sections)

	Thickness, feet	Depth, feet	Geologic formation
Heavy sandstone...................	196	196	
Shales and shaly sandstone...........	50	246	
Black slate.......................	4	250	Conglomerate
Coal.............................	1	251	measures
Gray shales......................	4	255	
Coal.............................	1	256	
Shales............................	15	271	
Buff earthy limestones..............	8	279	
Archimedes limestone...............	2	281	Chester, 33 feet
Gray limestone....................	13	294	
Calcareous shales..................	10	304	
Oolitic limestone..................	10	314	
Buff limestone.....................	11	325	
Semioolitic limestone...............	22	347	
Gray limestones...................	12	359	St. Louis, 150 feet
Earthy buff limestone...............	5	364	
Thin gray cherty limestones..........	24	388	
Massive limestone..................	22	410	
Blue limestone and shale.............	38	448	
Earthy yellow limestone.............	6	454	
Sandstones and shales...............	490	944	Waverly, 490 feet
Black shale.......................	125	1,069	Devonian shales, 125 feet
Estill County oil sand...............	25	1,094	Corniferous, 25 feet
Blue and gray shales................	145	1,239	Niagara, 150 feet
Gray lime.........................	5	1,244	
Gray lime.........................	25	1,269	
Gray shale........................	10	1,279	Clinton, 53 feet
Gray lime.........................	8	1,287	
Red lime..........................	10	1,297	
Gray lime.........................	17	1,314	
Brown lime........................	40	1,354	Lower Silurian (Ordovician), Hudson and Trenton groups, 1,476 feet
Gray lime.........................	839	2,193	
Greenish-white friable shaly sandstone.	10	2,203	
Hard fine-grained limestone, dark dove color, with occasional bands of dark-blue hard limestone................	425	2,628	
Hard gray limestone.................	145	2,773	
White fine-grained sand and lime.......	15	2,788	Calciferous (St. Peter?)
Bottom of Whiteoak well			

limestone of the Silurian and is accumulated on small low anticlines. Both producing limestones are below unconformities. The oil sands lie in the main within 1,000 feet of the surface. Ross Creek, 10 miles southwest of Irvine, produces oil from the Corniferous limestone. The Campton[1] field lies a few miles east of the Irvine field on the south side of the Campton fault zone. The rocks at the surface are the lower part of the Pottsville group. The oil is found in the Corniferous limestone and is concentrated in an anticline on the south side of the fault and also on the south side of a dome at a place where the limestone is porous. The Cannel City pool east of Campton also produces oil from a Corniferous limestone on an anticline south of the fault. The Paint Creek field, east of Cannel City, is on an anticline that crosses the Campton fold and forms a dome. It produces from the Wier sand of the Waverly formation which is found at from 1,300 to 1,500 feet deep. Gas is found on the dome and oil on the flanks.

The Inez gas field is in Martin County about 25 miles east of Paint Creek. The rocks in general dip east from Irvine to Martin county and in the Inez field the "Big Lime" and "Big Injun" beds of the Mississippian system are found at depths from 1,000 to 1,500 feet; both of these horizons yield gas. Gas from the Inez fields is piped west to Louisville and north to Ashland. A third pipe line carries gas to Pittsburgh, Pennsylvania.

The Menifee gas field[2] is in Menifee County, about 20 miles northeast of the Irvine pool. The rocks are of Pennsylvanian, Mississippian, and Devonian age. The Devonian rocks, however, do not crop out. The gas is found in the Onondaga or Corniferous (Devonian) limestone just below the Ohio shale.

The Ragland oil field is about 15 miles northeast of the Menifee gas field. The surface rock is of Mississippian age, the beds being essentially the same as in the Menifee field. The Corniferous limestone carries the oil. This formation varies greatly in thickness and at places is absent.

The Olympia field a few miles northwest of Ragland obtains oil from the Corniferous limestone at shallow depths. The Laurel Creek oil field lies 5 miles north of the Paint Creek field. The oil is in the Berea and Wier sands and is concentrated on a dome. Gas lies above the oil. At Busseyville northeast of Lawrence Creek field, oil is produced from the Berea sand which lies on a monocline.

At Fallsburg, northeast of Busseyville, oil is found in the Berea sand. The Ashland gas field in Boyd County, northeastern Kentucky

[1] MUNN, M. J., U. S. Geol. Survey *Bull*. 471, pp. 9–17, 1912.

FISKE, L. E., Am. Assoc. Pet. Geol. *Bull*., vol. 11, pp. 477–492, 1927.

[2] MUNN, M. J., The Menifee Gas Field and the Ragland Oil Field, Kentucky, U. S. Geol. Survey *Bull*. 531, p. 9, 1913.

(Fig. 131), is on a gently warped monocline, the rocks dipping southeast about 35 feet per mile. Gas has been found in sands of the Pennsylvanian series and in Devonian strata, but the chief production is from the Berea sand 700 feet below the top of the Mississippian and from the sandy layers in the Ohio shales. Gas and some oil are found in the Corniferous limestone. The Clinton sand has been encountered but has not proved productive.

Ivyton or Burning Fork field is near the southwest end of the Paint Creek field. A dark heavy oil is found in the Pottsville formation and a light oil in the Wier sand. The area occupies a dome.

The Prestonburg field, southeast of Paint Creek, lies on an anticline; production is found in the Beaver, Horton, and Pike sands of the Pottsville; in the Maxon (Maxton) Big Lime and Big Injun of the Mississippian and from the Devonian black shale. Production is found as deep as 2,000 feet below the surface.

South of Irvine field in Laurel, Clay, and Owsley counties, there are several small gas and oil fields located on or near the Rockcastle River uplift that strikes northeast. The rocks exposed are of Pennsylvanian age. In the Burning Springs gas field, Clay County, gas issuing at the surface was known to the Indians and early pioneers who dried wild meat at the springs. Gas is developed in this field in the Devonian limestone and in higher strata.

At Buffalo Creek[1] in Clay County, on the east slope of a low anticline 15 miles west of Chavies, oil is found in the "Big Lime" or Gasper sand of the Chester at a depth of 1,111 feet.

In the Island Creek pool west of Buffalo Creek, oil is found in the "Big Lime" at 740 feet. The Corniferous limestone at 1,200 feet yields gas. About 5 miles southwest of Booneville, in Turkey Knob field, a large flow of gas with a pressure of from 225 to 360 pounds per square inch was found in the Corniferous limestone.

The Williamsburg[2] district is in Whitley County, southeastern Kentucky, about 90 miles south of Lexington. The field produced oil and gas from several shallow sands in the Pottsville series and lately has developed considerable gas at depths of about 1,155 to 1,550 feet. The gas is found in the "Big Lime" of the Chester group (Mississippian system) and occurs near the axis of a plunging anticline where the latter flattens locally. The gas occurs in crevices and joints in the limestone.

Wayne County is near the south border of Kentucky east of the Cincinnati arch. The rocks dip southeast and the surface rocks of the oil fields are of Mississippian and Pennsylvanian age. The oil is found

[1] JILLSON, W. R., op. cit., pp. 257–259.
   FISKE, L. E., op. cit. p. 486.
[2] JILLSON, W. R., New Oil Pools in Kentucky, Ky. Geol. Survey, ser. 6, vol. 12, pp. 33–38, 1926.

in the Mississippian and Ordovician systems. The Devonian is probably cut out. In west McCreary County east of Wayne County, oil is found in several small pools. In this county, along the south fork of Cumberland River, oil was discovered in 1819 in the Beatty well which was drilled for salt water. This was the first oil discovered in Kentucky.

In Cumberland County just east of the axis of the Cincinnati arch, oil is found in the Ordovician limestone (Trenton) in shallow wells.

From the Cincinnati arch the rocks dip northwest into Allen, Simpson, and Barren counties. Local anticlines and domes are developed on the monocline. Production in the main is shallow and comes from the Corniferous and Devonian limestones and subordinately from sands in the Mississippian. In Allen County there are over 2,000 wells and the oil fields developed are Gainsville, Bays Fork, Scottsville, Rodemer, Petroleum, Adolphus, Rough Creek, East Rodemer, Motley, Jewell Bend and others. The Bowling Green field is in Warren County, northwest of Allen and Barren counties. The oil of these fields is high gravity in the main.

At Diamond Springs, 30 miles west of Bowling Green, gas and oil are found on a monocline in the Waverly and Cypress sand of the Mississippian system.

Morton's Gap field is in western Kentucky about 45 miles southwest of Owensboro. The Pennsylvanian rocks are exposed at the surface and a fault zone strikes east just south of the field. The chief producing sand is the Finnie sand, Pottsville group, which is found at a depth of 500 feet. A well 2,057 feet deep produces oil from a limestone of the Chester group (Mississippian).

In the Hartford field, northwest of Bowling Green field, oil is found probably in the Devonian sand on a small anticline located on the Rough Creek uplift. In the Leitchfield field, 30 miles east of the Hartford field also on the Rough Creek uplift, oil is found in the Waverly formation of the Mississippian system.

The Pellville[1] oil pool 19 miles east of Owensboro was discovered in 1920 and by September, 1925, had produced 306,431 barrels of oil. The field is located on and near the crest of an anticline that plunges southwest. The oil is found in four sands in the Chester series of the Mississippian. The wells yield 7 to 10 barrels of oil per day. The region near Pellville, called the Tri-County field is being rapidly developed. The oil is associated with gas and salt water and ranges in gravity from 29 to 36° Bé. At Cloverport on the Ohio River, northeast of Pellville, gas is developed on a dome in the Warsaw formation of the Mississippian. In the Rock Haven field, Mead County, gas is developed in a thin sand included in the Devonian black shale.

[1] JILLSON, W. R., New Oil Pools in Kentucky, Ky. Geol. Survey, ser. 6, vol. 12, pp. 1–31, 1926.

TENNESSEE

Tennessee[1] is divided into three geologic provinces (Fig. 134). In the eastern part of the state there is a broad belt of closely folded rocks ranging from Cambrian or older to Carboniferous. These rocks are extensively faulted and as far as known contain no oil or gas. The western part of the state is occupied by Cretaceous, Tertiary, and Quaternary rocks, which are flat or dip at low angles. The central part of the state is lower than the eastern and western parts and is known as the central basin. The oldest rocks in this basin are of Ordovician age and consist of limestones and calcareous shales. Surrounding the Ordovician is a great belt of Devonian and Mississippian rocks. East of the Mississippian is a broad belt of Pennsylvanian conglomerate, sandstones, shales, and coal. The Pennsylvanian belt is only about 35 to 50 miles wide, and at some places the coal beds are eroded.

The Sumner County field, near the Kentucky line and about 45 miles north-northeast of Nashville, is a south continuation of the Allen field in Kentucky. The Corniferous limestone of the Devonian is wanting and below the Chattanooga shales there are 125 feet of Silurian strata in which the oil is found at two horizons.[2] The regional dip is northwest and is modified by small local flexures in which the oil is found. In 1920 several wells were producing from 4 to 25 barrels of oil per day.

Tinsley's Bottom field (Figs. 134, 135) is on the Clay and Jackson county line, 75 miles northeast of Nashville. The strata dip north away from the great Nashville dome and the oldest rocks exposed are beds of the Leipers formation (Ordovician). The oil is found in the Lebanon limestone (Ordovician) and is accumulated on a small dome. The oil probably occurs in caverns in the limestone. The field produced 15,500 barrels of oil in 1925 and 1926. Near Celina, northeast of Tinsley's Bottom field, oil is found on small domes in strata of the upper part of the Ordovician chiefly above the Lebanon formation.

The Spurrier-Riverton field in Pickett County, 20 miles east of Celina, was discovered in 1892, produced 90,000 barrels of oil, and was abandoned in 1906. The Bob's Bar well ran wild several months and considerable

[1] Munn, M. J., Preliminary Report on the Oil and Gas Developments in Tennessee, Tenn. Geol. Survey *Bull.* 2E, pp. 9–10, 1911.

Lusk, R. G., The Significance of Structure in the Accumulation of Oil in Tennessee, Am. Assoc. Pet. Geol. *Bull.*, vol. 11, pp. 905–917, 1927.

Nelson, W. A., The Oil Horizons of Kentucky, Northeastern Mississippi, and Tennessee, Am. Assoc. Pet. Geol. *Bull.* 8, pp. 621–631, 1924.

Miser, H. D., Structure of the Waynesboro Quadrangle with Special Reference to Oil and Gas, Tenn. Geol. Survey, Resources of Tenn., vol. 7, No. 4, pp. 199–219, 1917.

[2] Mather, F. K., Oil and Gas Resources of the Northeastern Part of Sumner County, Tennessee, Tenn. Geol. Survey *Bull.* 24, pt. 2B, pp. 1–39, 1920.

Lusk, R. G., *loc. cit.*

oil was lost.   The rocks cropping out are the Fort Payne strata (Mississippian), and the regional dip is to the southeast.[1]   The oil is from the upper part of the Ordovician system and is found chiefly on small, low, elongated domes.   The main productive horizons are 107 and 267 feet below the Chattanooga shale.   In the Holbert Creek field, in eastern Pickett County, a well drilled in 1921 found oil and gas probably in the Wells Creek formation (Ordovician).

In the Spring Creek field 20 miles southwest of Spurrier, the Fort Payne strata crop out dipping gently to the east.   A well drilled near an

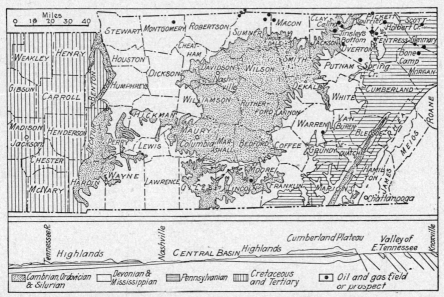

Fig. 134.—Map and cross section of part of Tennessee, showing chief oil fields.   (*After Munn, Lusk, Nelson, Miser and others.*)

oil seep in 1866 at a depth of 52 feet encountered a considerable flow of oil and ran wild for several months.   The oil occurred in crevices in the Fort Payne formation.   About 7,000 barrels of oil were marketed.

The Bone Camp and Glenmary districts are about 30 miles southeast of the Spurrier-Riverton field.   The regional dip is east and the rocks are folded and faulted.   In the Glenmary[2] field oil is found on a faulted anticline near the top of the St. Louis limestone.   In the Bone Camp field 4 miles southwest of Glenmary, oil is found on a structural terrace at a depth of 1,400 feet in a porous limestone about the middle of the Fort Payne chert.   The field was discovered in 1924 and in 1926 it shipped 25,400 barrels of oil.

[1] BUTTS, C., Geology and Oil Possibilities of the Northern Part of Overton County, Tennessee, Tenn. Geol. Survey *Bull.* 24, pt. 2A, pp. 1–45, 1919.

[2] GLENN, L. C., The Glenmary Oil Field, Tenn. Geol. Survey Resources of **Tenn.**, vol. 8, No. 3, pp. 211–219, 1918.

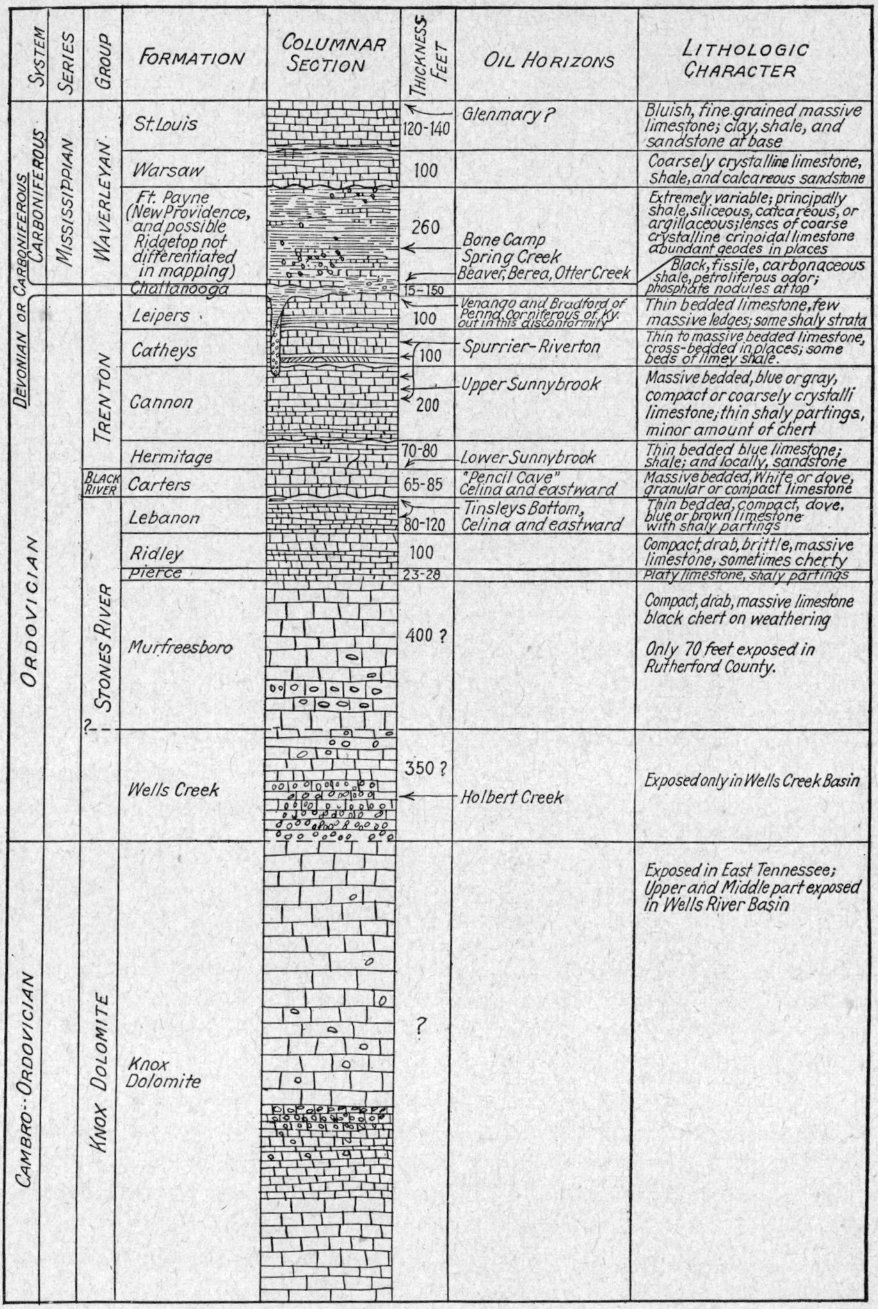

System	Series	Group	Formation	Columnar Section	Thickness Feet	Oil Horizons	Lithologic Character
Devonian or Carboniferous	Mississippian Carboniferous	Waverleyan	St.Louis		120-140	Glenmary?	Bluish, fine grained massive limestone; clay, shale, and sandstone at base
			Warsaw		100		Coarsely crystalline limestone, shale, and calcareous sandstone
			Ft. Payne (New Providence, and possible Ridgetop not differentiated in mapping)		260	Bone Camp Spring Creek Beaver, Berea, Otter Creek	Extremely variable; principally shale, siliceous, calcareous, or argillaceous; lenses of coarse crystalline crinoidal limestone abundant geodes in places
			Chattanooga		15-150		Black, fissile, carbonaceous shale, petroliferous odor; phosphate nodules at top
Ordovician		Trenton	Leipers		100	Venango and Bradford of Penna. Corniferous of Ky. out in this disconformity	Thin bedded limestone, few massive ledges; some shaly strata
			Catheys		100	Spurrier–Riverton	Thin to massive bedded limestone, cross-bedded in places; some beds of limey shale
			Cannon		200	Upper Sunnybrook	Massive bedded, blue or gray, compact or coarsely crystalli limestone; thin shaly partings, minor amount of chert
			Hermitage		70-80	Lower Sunnybrook	Thin bedded blue limestone; shale; and locally, sandstone
		Black River	Carters		65-85	"Pencil Cave" Celina and eastward	Massive bedded, White or dove, granular or compact limestone
			Lebanon		80-120	Tinsleys Bottom, Celina and eastward	Thin bedded, compact, dove, blue or brown limestone with shaly partings
		Stones River	Ridley		100		Compact, drab, brittle, massive limestone, sometimes cherty
			Pierce		23-28		Platy limestone, shaly partings
			Murfreesboro		400 ?		Compact, drab, massive limestone black chert on weathering. Only 70 feet exposed in Rutherford County.
			Wells Creek		350 ?	Holbert Creek	Exposed only in Wells Creek Basin
Cambro-Ordovician		Knox Dolomite	Knox Dolomite		?		Exposed in East Tennessee; Upper and Middle part exposed in Wells River Basin

FIG. 135.—Generalized columnar section for northeast middle Tennessee. (*After Lusk.*)

NORTHEAST MISSISSIPPI

In October, 1926, a gas well with a daily flush production of 4,500,000 feet was brought in 6 miles east of Amory, and the following year a large gas well was drilled 15 miles southeast of Amory. The Amory[1] well is on the southwest extension of the Cincinnati arch which in this region strikes about southwest and plunges southwest (Fig. 117). The surface rocks are Tularosa sands, gravels, and clays. The Mesozoic rocks are 600 to 700 feet thick below which, the Pottsville Pennsylvanian sands are found to a depth of 1,468 feet. Below the Pennsylvanian is a thick series of Mississippian shale, sandstone, and some limestone. The gas is found at a depth of 2,470 feet and, according to Jillson, is in the Hardinsburg sand which he correlates with the Hartsell (Chester), which crops out in northwest Alabama[2] as highly petroliferous beds and with the Jett sand which yields large amounts of oil in Ohio County, Kentucky.

OHIO

Eastern Ohio.—In eastern Ohio[3] the rocks dip east into the Appalachian geosyncline away from the Cincinnati arch. The beds exposed range from the strata of the Ordovician system, which occupies the top of the arch, to the Permian beds which crop out in southeastern Ohio (Fig. 136). There are three groups of oil and gas fields: (1) the eastern Ohio fields, (2) the Clinton gas fields, (3) the Trenton fields (Fig. 137).

The southeastern Ohio fields are in the west extension of the Appalachian oil-bearing region. The production is less than in Pennsylvania

[1] JILLSON, W. R., Geology of Amory, Mississippi, Gas Field, *Oil Gas Jour.*, vol. 26, p. 58, Jan. 26, 1928.

[2] Geology of Alabama, Ala. Geol. Survey *Special Rept.* 14, p. 195, 1926.

[3] GRISWOLD, W. T., The Berea Grit Oil Sand in the Cadiz Quadrangle, Ohio, U. S. Geol. Survey *Bull.* 198, pp. 1–43, 1902; Structure of the Berea Oil Sand in the Flushing Quadrangle, U. S. Geol. Survey *Bull.* 346, pp. 1–30, 1908.

CONDIT, D. D., Oil and Gas in the Northern Part of the Cadiz Quadrangle, Ohio, U. S. Geol. Survey *Bull.* 541, pp. 9–17, 1913.

———, Structure of the Berea Oil Sand in the Woodsfield Quadrangle, Ohio, U. S. Geol. Survey *Bull.* 621, pp. 233–249, 1915.

———, Structure of the Berea Oil Sand in the Summerfield Quadrangle, Ohio, U. S. Geol. Survey *Bull.* 621, pp. 217–231, 1916.

BOWNOCKER, J. A., Petroleum in Ohio and Indiana, Geol. Soc. Am. *Bull.*, vol. 28, pp. 667–676, 1917.

———, The Clinton Sand in Ohio, *Econ. Geol.*, vol. 6, pp. 37–50, 1911.

BONINE, C. A., Anticlines in the Clinton Sand Near Wooster, Wayne County, Ohio, U. S. Geol. Survey *Bull.* 621, pp. 87–98, 1915.

COTTINGHAM, K., Structural Conditions in Portions of Eastern Ohio, Am. Assoc. Pet. Geol. *Bull.*, vol. 11, pp. 945–958, 1927.

LOCKETT, J. R., General Structure of the Producing Sands in Eastern Ohio, Am. Assoc. Pet. Geol. *Bull.*, vol. 11, pp. 1023–1033, 1927.

PANYITY, L. S., Lithology of the Berea Sand in Southeastern Ohio, Am. Inst. Min. Eng. *Bull.* 140, pp. 1317–1320, 1918.

and West Virginia fields, but in the main the oil is from the same strata
and is of similar high grade. The average initial production of oil
per well in 1927 was 22 barrels per day. Gas constitutes a valuable
product. The oil is obtained chiefly from the Pennsylvanian, Mississippian, and Devonian strata. The sands are farther from their sources
and are generally finer and more lenticular than in areas farther east.

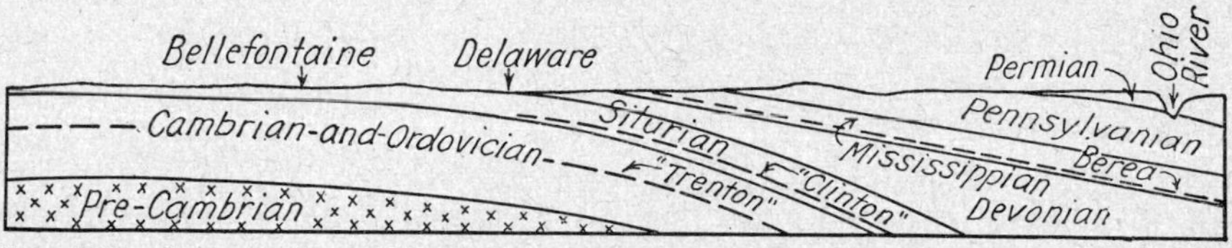

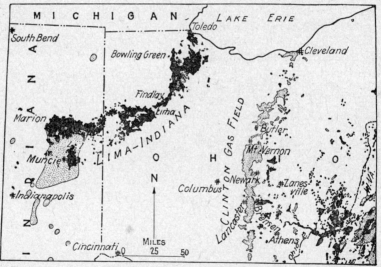

Fig. 136.—Cross section through Bellefontaine and Delaware to Ohio River. (*After
Westgate*). Devonian outlier at Bellefontaine is not shown.

The Pittsburgh coal affords a datum plane for mapping structures.
The Pennsylvanian oil sands, youngest named first, with depths in feet
below the Pittsburgh coal, are as follows: First Cow Run 300, Buell Run
350, Peeker 525, Macksburg 650, Second Cow Run 700, Salt 750, Maxton

Fig. 137.—Sketch showing oil and gas fields of parts of Ohio and Indiana.

950. The Mississippian sands are Big Lime (Maxville) 975, Keener
1,060, Big Injun 1,100, Squaw 1,200, Berea 1,600. Of these the main
production is from the Salt, Keener, Big Injun, and Berea sands. Below
the Berea formation the Devonian strata contain several sands of
restricted extent which thin out or disappear westward. In northeastern
Ohio these sands are enclosed in shale and produce "shale gas." In

western Guernsey County on a large anticline there is a gas field developed in a sand near the base of the Devonian system. Many of the oil and gas fields of eastern Ohio are neither on anticlines nor in troughs, although in general their long axes are parallel to the strikes of the rocks. Some are located where the rocks have high porosity and others are not closely related to any known structural feature. Below the Berea

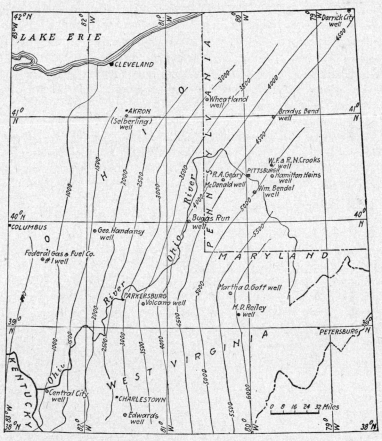

FIG. 138.—Map showing approximate thickness of the upper Devonian strata in parts of Ohio, Pennsylvania and West Virginia. (*Redrawn from a map by I. C. White.*)

sand the thickening of the Devonian (Fig. 138) and Silurian toward the east is so great that the structure below the Berea sand is difficult to interpret from beds that crop out. Along the Ohio River in Washington County, extending west into Athens County, there is a "shoestring" pool in the First Cow Run sand. The oil in this pool is in a coarse conglomerate sand which, according to Cottingham, represents a buried stream channel.

Clinton Gas Field.—The Clinton gas field (Fig. 57) which extends from Lake Erie to near the Ohio River is one of the greatest gas fields in the United States east of the Mississippi River. The beds dip east toward the Appalachian geosyncline. The gas is found in the "Clinton" sand which is from 0 to 100 feet thick. This sand is in the Medina formation which lies below the true Clinton formation. By an error the name was applied to the gas sand at an early date and is still generally used to designate the sand. The Clinton gas sand was deposited from the southeast as a heavy sand which becomes lenticular and plays out up dip before it reaches the surface. Producing parts of the sand are found at depths between 1,500 and 5,000 feet. The lenses of the sand seem to be independent, since oil is found in different lenses below the gas and since the gas pressures are different at different places. Locally, the sand, where present, is tight and barren.

The initial pressure in the field was everywhere high and increases with the depth. In the southern part of the field it was about 700 pounds to the square inch; between Newark and Mount Vernon, 750 pounds; in Ashland County, 1,200 pounds; and in Cuyahoga County 1,050 pounds. The greatest pressure near Butler, Richland County, was 1,260 pounds.

The first large well in the "Clinton" was the Mithoff, at Lancaster, which yielded initially at the rate of 12,000,000 cubic feet a day. From Newark to Mount Vernon the largest wells yielded about 12,000,000 cubic feet, and in Ashland County 13,000,000 cubic feet. A well drilled in Congress Township, Wayne County, early in September, 1915, started flowing at the rate of 22,000,000 cubic feet a day. Many wells flow from 3,000,000 to 5,000,000 cubic feet. Wells in the "Clinton" are long lived, for gas wells, as a result of the porous nature of the rocks and the high pressure of the gas.

RECORD OF A "CLINTON" OIL WELL NEAR BREMEN, FAIRFIELD COUNTY, OHIO
(After Bownocker)

	Thickness, feet	Depth, feet
Mantle rock..	49	49
Cuyahoga and Sunbury sandstone and shales...........	626	675
Berea sandstone....................................	35	710
Bedford and Ohio shales............................	975	1,685
Devonian limestone................................	50	1,735
Silurian { Monroe limestone.........................	275	2,010
Niagara limestone.........................	360	2,370
Clinton limestone.........................	95	2,465
Shales..	120	2,585
"Clinton" sand....................................	34	2,619
Bottom of well....................................	...	2,620

In the Clinton[1] sand oil is rarely present in large amounts, although a number of wells were drilled in 1927 averaging 57 barrels of oil per day initial production. One of the earlier oil fields to be developed in the Clinton sand is the Bremen field in the south end of the Clinton belt. It contains the Pleasantville, Rushville, Bremen, Junction City, and Straitsville pools. The field was discovered in 1907 when the Clinton sand was penetrated by a well 2 miles northeast of Bremen that flowed 140 barrels of oil a day. The production of the field soon rose to over a million barrels of oil annually. The oil is of light gravity and similar to that of Pennsylvania fields.

The wells at Bremen encounter the Berea sand at a depth of 675 feet, pass through the sand at 710 feet, below which are 975 feet of Bedford and Ohio shales. Below the shales is the "Big Lime" 780 feet thick. The Clinton sandstone is 120 feet below the base of the "Big Lime" and is separated from it by shales. The Clinton sandstone is 34 feet thick. The structure is a shallow basin tipped to the southeast on the broad monocline that dips southeast.

Trenton.—The Trenton[2] oil and gas field of Ohio and Indiana occupies a large crescentic area that extends from Lake Erie southwest to Marion, Ohio. Its width varies from less than 1 mile to 20 miles, and altogether more than 60,000 wells have been drilled in it. Although small amounts of oil and gas were known in this area as early as 1860, the first systematic drilling was undertaken in 1884 at Findlay, Ohio, where gas had been found in shallow wells. The output from the field reached its maximum in Ohio in 1896 when it was 20,757,138 barrels and in Indiana in 1904 when the production was about 11,300,000 barrels. The production of the field has declined greatly in recent years.

The oil field is located on and near the crest of the Cincinnati arch. This arch branches in western Ohio, one branch extending northeast to Lake Erie and the other northwest to near Chicago (Figs. 139, 140, 141). Gas accumulates on the crest and on the north side of the arch, and oil is found below the gas mainly on the north side of the arch. The oil is found in the Trenton limestone of Ordovician age. In general this limestone lies at depths between 950 and 1,500 feet. The Niagara limestone crops out over much of the field, and below it are found Niagara shale and Clinton limestone about 110 feet thick and below that Medina shale 45 feet thick; below the Medina shale are found the Hudson River shale and limestone 460 feet thick and the Utica shale 300 feet thick. A map of this field, by Orton, was issued in 1888. It shows that the

---

[1] BOWNOCKER, J. A., The Bremen Oil Field, Ohio Geol. Survey *Bull.* 12, ser. 4, pp. 7–31, 1910. Contains also a treatment of Clinton sand north and south of Bremen.

[2] ORTON, E., The Trenton Limestone as a Source of Petroleum and Inflammable Gas in Ohio and Indiana, U. S. Geol. Survey *Eighth Ann. Rept.*, pt. 2, pp. 475–662, 1889; also Ohio Geol. Survey, vol. 6, 1888.

accumulations of oil and gas are mainly along and north of the crest of the two branches of the arch. On the cross-sections (Fig. 140) the Utica shale is shown about 300 feet thick. This group of shaly strata is in part probably younger than the true Utica shale in New York. There was a period of erosion of the Trenton limestone in parts of Ohio before the overlying shales were laid down.[1]

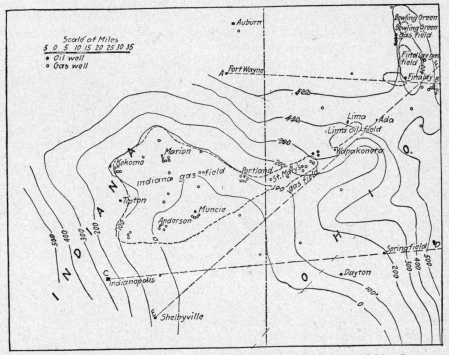

Fig. 139.—Map showing structure of Lima-Indiana or Trenton oil and gas field. Contours on top of Trenton limestone. Cross sections shown by Fig. 140. (*After Orton.*)

The oil and gas are found in the porous and fractured parts of the Trenton limestone, mainly in the upper 50 feet, but locally at greater depths. The producing part of the limestone, according to Orton, is the part made porous by dolomitization. According to Bownocker,[2] the magnesium content of the limestone decreases rapidly with depth, and it is lower also outside of the oil field. The relation of oil accumulation to dolomitization and of dolomitization to an ancient plane of erosion is noted elsewhere. It appears probable that both dolomitiza-

[1] Prosser, C. S., Revised Nomenclature of the Ohio Geologic Formations, Ohio Geol. Survey *Bull.* 7, pp. 4, 35, 1905.

Ulrich, E. O., Revision of the Paleozoic System, Geol. Soc. Am. *Bull.*, vol. 22, pp. 287–680 (particularly pp. 416–420), 1911.

[2] Bownocker, J. A., Petroleum and Natural Gas in Ohio, Ohio Geol. Survey *Bull.* 1, ser. 4, pp. 1–320 (see p. 18), 1903.

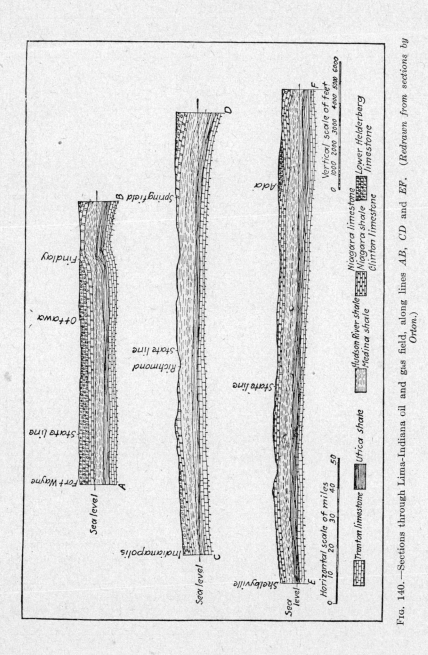

FIG. 140.—Sections through Lima-Indiana oil and gas field, along lines *AB, CD* and *EF*. (*Redrawn from sections by Orton.*)

GENERALIZED SECTION OF OLDER PALEOZOIC FORMATIONS IN EASTERN OHIO
(*After Rogers*)

System	Group or formation		Thickness, feet	Character	Driller's description
Devonian or Carboniferous	Bedford shale		20–40?	Mottled gray, reddish, and brownish shale	
Devonian	Ohio shale group	Cleveland shale	50–120	Massive hard black bituminous, with a few bluish layers in lower portion	Ohio shale, 1,100–3,000 feet, usually treated as a unit in southern Ohio
		Chagrin shale	850–1,200	Soft bluish-gray clay shale, with some concretionary layers	
		Huron shale		Black and bluish shale in upper and lower portions, with a band of gray shale near middle	
	Olentangy (?) shale		80	Gray calcareous shale	
Unconformity	Delaware limestone		500–700	Blue and gray limestone, becoming dolomitic in lower part. Contains a 30- to 50-foot bed of white quartz sandstone, 350 to 450 feet below top	Big Lime; includes Newburg sand and some "stray" sands in lower 300 feet, 490–1,825 feet
	Columbus limestone				
	Monroe formation				
	Salina formation		400–600	Shale, dolomite, anhydrite or gypsum, and rock salt	
	Niagara limestone		400–600	Dolomite and limestone	
Silurian	"Clinton" formation		150–250	Crystalline limestone of various light colors; calcareous shale and thin-bedded limestone, with sandstone layer in lower part	Includes Little Lime, 75–150 feet
					"Clinton" sand, 0–60 feet
					25–75 feet
	Medina shale		300–400	Red clay shale, with thin layers of sandstone	Medina red rock
Ordovician	Shale and limestone of Cincinnatian age		750–1,250	Dark shale, with thin layers of limestone, especially in upper part	Slate and shells
	Trenton (?) limestone		(?)	Limestone	Trenton lime

GENERALIZED SECTION OF CARBONIFEROUS FORMATIONS IN EASTERN OHIO
(*After Mills and Wells*)

System	Series	Group or formation	Thickness, feet	Character	Driller's description
Carboniferous	Permian	Washington formation[1]	400	Non-persistent sandstone members with shale and clay of reddish-brown color. A few thin beds of coal and limestone in lower portion	
	Pennsylvanian	Monongahela formation	255–275	Limestone, shale, and a little sandstone. Contains the Pittsburgh, Pomeroy, Meigs Creek, Uniontown, and Waynesburg coal beds, all of more or less value in the Woodsfield quadrangle	
		Conemaugh formation	460–475	Irregular members grading into shales, commonly of reddish-brown or variegated colors. Upper and lower Pittsburgh limestone members near top; Ames and Cambridge limestone members a little below middle. Mahoning sandstone member at the base, locally productive of oil	Includes First Cow Run, Buell Run, and Mahoning sands
		Allegheny formation	250–265	Sandstone, shale, and important clay and coal beds, including the Lower Kittanning, Middle Kittanning, and Lower and Upper Freeport	Includes Peeker, Macksburg 500-foot, and Second Cow Run oil sands named in descending order
		Pottsville formation	155–170	Consists largely of sandstone and conglomerate, which rest with uneven contact on the eroded surface of the Mississippian beds. The sandstone is generally divided into several parts by beds of clay shale, and coals also are locally present	Includes Maxton sand
	Mississippian	Unconformity Maxville limestone	0–100	Dark-gray and bluish to light-gray limestone with interbedded shale and fine-grained sandstone	Big Lime; includes Big Lime sand
		Unconformity Logan formation	25–100	Consists of sandstone, the Keener sand, interbedded with shale; a valuable source of oil and gas	Includes Keener oil sand
		Black Hand formation	75–175	Coarse sandstone interbedded with and grading laterally into sandy shale	Probably includes Big Injun and Squaw oil sands
		Cuyahoga formation	350–450(?)	Mostly sandy shale in lower part with a few beds of shaly sandstone	Includes Welsh oil sand
		Sunbury shale	25–40	Dark carbonaceous shale	Black shale
		Berea sandstone	0–40	Berea sand, consisting of coarse to fine-grained gray to white sandstone. Lenticular in the Woodsfield and Summerfield quadrangles. Unconformity at base	Berea oil and gas sand

[1] At places in eastern Ohio the Greene formation of the Permian overlies the Washington.

tion and porosity are related to an ancient surface that was exposed to weathering.

Although the Trenton is porous on both sides of the arch over northern and central Indiana, in the southeastern part of the state it is more compact. The main body of the arch may be regarded, then, as a long inverted bifurcating trough having its south end closed and its north end immersed in the salt water, which is forced up into and around it by the hydrostatic pressure of the water. The Cincinnati arch is a dome surrounded by a larger basin. The water descends the slopes of the basin and rises in the arch, pushing oil and gas ahead of it. Equilibrium is established by the back pressure of gas when it equals the water pressure. It appears highly probable that the reservoir is connected with the surface at places, for the original gas pressure of the wells was equal, approximately, to the weight of a column of water as high as the wells are deep.

INDIANA

The rocks of Indiana[1] in general dip west from the Cincinnati arch into the coal basin of Illinois. As stated, the axis of the Cincinnati anticline branches in Ohio, one branch extending northeast toward Toledo and another northwest toward Chicago. In northern Indiana the rocks dip north into the coal basin of Michigan. The consolidated rocks cropping out in Indiana are all of Paleozoic age. The Ordovician rocks crop out in the southeast part of the state; the coal measures of the Pennsylvanian are in the southwest part and the Silurian, Devonian, and Mississippian rocks in the northern part of the state. Most of Indiana is covered with drift, except in a relatively small area in the south part of the state near Ohio River.

Aside from the Cincinnati anticline and its northwest branch, there are minor structural features that are noteworthy, particularly the Mount Carmel fault which extends north from the Ohio River to Putnam County, then northwestward into Illinois. This fault is probably 150 miles long in Indiana and its total length is not known. At places it is a fault zone a mile or more wide including two or more nearly parallel

[1] LOGAN, W. N., Economic Geology of Indiana, "Handbook of Indiana Geology," Ind. Dept. Conservation *Pub.* 21, pp. 571–1058, 1922.

CUMMINGS, E. R., Description of Geologic Formations, "Handbook of Indiana Geology," Ind. Dept. Conservation *Pub.* 21, pp. 403–570, 1922.

PHINNEY, A. J., The Natural Gas Fields of Indiana, U. S. Geol. Survey *Eleventh Ann. Rept.*, pt. 1, pp. 617–742, 1890.

GORBY, S. S., Natural Gas and Petroleum, Ind. Dept. Geol. and Nat. Resources, *Sixteenth Ann. Rept.*, pp. 189–301, 1889.

BLATCHLEY, W. S., Petroleum Industry in Indiana, Ind. Dept. Geol. and Nat. Resources, *Ann. Rept.*, pp. 27–96, 1896; pp. 70–210, 1903; pp. 429–558, 1906.

Fig. 141.—Map of Indiana showing oil and gas fields.   (*After Logan, Esarey, Moulton, and others.*)

faults. The amount of throw is probably 200 to 300 feet. It was probably formed near the close of the Paleozoic era.

The oil fields of Indiana are shown on Fig. 141, which also shows, approximately, the axis of the northwest branch of the Cincinnati arch and the Mount Carmel fault. The geologic section is shown on a following page. In 1889 soon after the discovery of oil in Indiana, the production was 33,375 barrels. The production rose gradually until 1904 when Indiana produced 11,339,124 barrels valued at $12,235,574. The zenith of gas production was reached in 1900 when the value of the gas produced was $7,254,539. In 1929 Indiana produced 977,000 barrels of oil valued at $1,600,000 and in 1928 about 1,290,000 thousand cubic feet of gas valued at $639,000. The Trenton oil is sulphurous and has a paraffin base; the gas is about 92 per cent methane. The oil in southwestern Indiana is generally lighter than the Trenton oil.

The Trenton oil field has been treated briefly in the section on Ohio. The locations of the main oil fields are shown on Fig. 141. In this field the structure is relatively simple. The northwest branch of the Cincinnati arch strikes across the state toward Chicago. Gas is found along the crest of the arch and on its northeast side and oil on its northeast side below the gas. Many of the wells are about 1,000 to 1,500 feet deep. A typical one in the shallow part of the field passes through 153 feet of "Niagara" limestone, 451 feet of "Hudson River" formation, 300 feet "Utica" shale, and finds the Trenton at 954 feet. The Hudson River and Utica shale are both largely shale in Indiana; although both contain limestone, the Hudson River contains thicker beds. These two formation names are widely used by drillers and are equivalent to the Richmond, Maysville, and Eden, as shown on the generalized geologic section. The porosity of the Trenton limestone is more pronounced in the upper than in the lower part of the formation. At many places the Trenton limestone yields salt water and no oil.

South of the main oil field small oil and gas fields are developed in the Trenton limestone at many places. In DeKalb County, in northeast Indiana, gas is found in the Trenton limestone. In the northwest part of the state oil is found in the Trenton limestone in small amounts. In Jasper County, however, it is in the Devonian limestone.

West of the Mount Carmel fault the oil is mainly in beds above the Trenton. Surface indications of oil are few, although near Princeton[1] a bed of asphalt several feet thick was found in a coal mine at a depth somewhat over 100 feet below the surface. In another coal mine, near Princeton, 450 feet deep, "liquid asphalt" in large amounts seeps into the workings along a "break" so that some of the rooms have been abandoned.

[1] FULLER, M. L., Asphalt, Oil, and Gas in Southwestern Indiana, U. S. Geol. Survey *Bull.* 213, pp. 333–334, 1903.

In the Tricounty[1] field, southwest Indiana, at the junction of Pike, Gibson, and Warrick counties, a well completed in 1924 found gas, and wells drilled soon afterward found oil, one of them having initial production of 75 barrels a day. The outcropping rocks are of the Pennsylvanian system and dip south-west 35 feet to the mile. The oil has accumulated in sand lenses on small domes and is found in the Oakland City sandstone which is part of the Mooretown sandstone of the Chester group (Mississippian). The structure near the surface, contoured on Indiana No. 5 coal, is nearly similar to that of the beds associated with the oil sand, although there is an unconformity between the Mississippian and Penn-sylvanian (Fig. 142) series and a slight convergence of rocks that lie between the surface and the oil sand. The main accumulation of oil is on the southwest side of the dome in the direction of the regional dip. The oil has a gravity of 34° Bé. and is asso-ciated with relatively little gas and water. Near Somerville, a few miles west of the Tricounty field, gas is accumulated on an anticline.

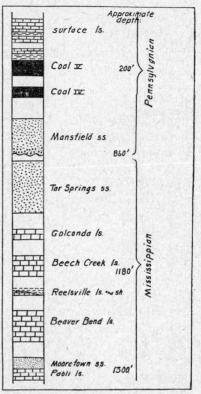

FIG. 142.—Geologic section of Tri-county oil field, Indiana. The oil is in the Mooretown sandstone. (*After Esarey.*)

At Terra Haute, Vigo County, western Indiana, the Prox well has produced oil for many years from Devonian limestone. A short dis-tance east of Wabash River on the Vigo-Sullivan[2] county line, oil is found at the top of the Devonian limestone at a depth of 2,185 feet. This horizon produces oil in the Martinsville pool, Illinois, 25 miles west. The Vigo-Sullivan oil has a gravity of 47° Bé. and yields 56 per cent gasoline on straight distillation.

In the west-central part of Sullivan County, 30 miles south of Terre Haute, several fields[3] were opened in 1913, and in 1915 the production

[1] ESAREY, R. E., The Tricounty Oil Field in Southwestern Indiana, Am. Assoc. Pet. Geol. *Bull.*, vol. 11, pp. 601–610, 1927.

WANNEMACKER and CREALEY, Am. Assoc. Pet. Geol. *Bull.* (in press), 1930.

[2] MOULTON, G. F., Important Developments in Southwestern Indiana, Am. Assoc. Pet. Geol. *Bull.*, vol. 11, pp. 991–992, 1927.

[3] VISHER, S. S., Sullivan County, "Handbook of Indiana Geology," Ind. Dept. Conservation *Pub.* 21, pp. 984–995, 1922.

GENERALIZED GEOLOGIC SECTION FOR INDIANA

Series and formation	Thick-ness, feet	Description
Quaternary:		
Recent...............		Clay, sand, loam
Pleistocene:		
Glacial drift........	0–400	
Tertiary:		
Gravels, Lafayette (?)		
Pennsylvanian:		
Merom...............	40–60	Sand
Shelburn.............	200 ±	Shale, sandstone, limestone
Allegheny:		
Petersburg.........	300 ±	Sandstone, shale, thin limestone, lean oil and gas sands
Staunton...........	200 ±	Sandstone, shale, thin limestone, lean oil and gas sands
Unconformity.		
Pottsville:		
Brazil..............	100–200	Sandstone, shale, coal, block coal, thin limestone
Mansfield.........	0–280	Sandstone, shale, conglomerate, coal, Mansfield oil sand
Unconformity.		
Mississippian:		
Chester..............	500 ±	Sandstone, limestone, oolitic limestone, shales Sandstones carry oil in southwest Indiana; sandstones finer grained than Mansfield
Mitchell..............	200–300	Limestone and shale approximately St. Louis and Ste. Genevieve
Salem................	0–100	Oolitic limestone (Bedford)
Harrodsburg..........	60–90	Limestone with quartz geodes, thin bedded, shales equivalent to Warsaw
Knobstone...........	530–650	Shale, sandstone with limestone lenses, sandstone contains gas
Rockford.............	1–3	Limestone, greenish, weathers brown
Unconformity.		
Devonian:		
New Albany..........	80–124	Black bituminous shale
"Corniferous"........	90	Limestone, porous limestone, some oil and gas
Unconformity.		
Silurian...............	95–140	Limestone and thin calcareous shale, "Niagara limestone"
Unconformity.		
Ordovician:		
Richmond............	250 ±	Shale interbedded with limestone, some massive limestone
Maysville............	250	Shale, limestone, shales, and thin limestone
Eden................	200–240	Shale, green marly, some thin limestone
Trenton.............	247–586	Limestone, upper part dolomitic and porous, main oil and gas horizon in Indiana
St. Peter.............	150–300	Sandstone
Lower Magnesian.....	300	Limestone
Cambrian:		
Potsdam.............	300+	Sandstone

reached 3,500 barrels per day. The oil is derived from four sands which lie at depths between 615 and 810 feet. Several small pools are developed, most of them yielding oil from two or more sands. The oil is of good quality and is generally accompanied by gas. The region slopes southwest and the rocks dip southwest at about the angle of the slope. The highest oil is derived from an unconformity between the Allegheny and Pottsville divisions of the Pennsylvanian which lies just below No. 3 coal. The second and third sands are in the Mansfield sandstone of the Pottsville formation and the fourth sand also is probably in the Mansfield. The pools are not known to be related to folds or domes, but, according to Visher, the oil sands probably occupy channels of ancient streams.

Near Francisco, 6 miles east of Princeton in Gibson[1] County, production has been obtained recently from a sand in the Chester formation, probably the Sample sand, at a depth of 1,400 feet. One well produced 150 barrels a day for 2 months. The oil is heavy and has a gravity of about 27° A.P.I. The field is located on a low dome with a long axis trending north.[1]

ILLINOIS

Petroleum and natural gas were known in Illinois at an early date as a result of seepages, but commercial quantities of oil were not discovered until 1905. The maximum yield was reached 3 years later when the total production of Illinois was 33,686,238 barrels. In 1917 the state yielded 15,776,860 barrels, and in 1929 it yielded 6,304,000 barrels of oil valued at $10,300,000. The oil is of high gravity and relatively free from sulphur. The chief production comes from Clark, Cumberland, Jasper, Crawford, Lawrence, and Wabash counties in the southeast part of the state[2] (Figs. 143, 144).

Most of Illinois is covered with glacial drift, and surface indications of oil or gas are meager. In the first producing field the evidences were obtained by deep drilling for coal and by chance prospecting. In the Sandoval dome, in Marion County, oil seeps along a fault into a coal mine. The principal oil-bearing strata are in the Mississippian and Pennsylvanian series. These series consist of sandstones, shales, and limestones. The sands are variable, some of them attaining a thickness of more than 100 feet in places; the producing part is generally but a small percentage of the total thickness. The different lenses of the Robinson sand in Crawford County average 25 feet in thickness, whereas the pay is only about 7 feet. In two pools the sand ranges from 25 to 40 feet and is saturated with oil throughout, but this condition is unusual.

[1] Moulton, G. F., "Structure of Typical American Oil Fields," vol. 2, pp. 138–141, 1929.

[2] Kay, F. H., Oil Fields of Illinois, Geol. Soc. Am. *Bull.*, vol. 28, pp. 655–666, 1917.

Structurally the oil fields of Illinois lie in part of a great synclinal basin which lies between the pre-Cambrian uplift of Wisconsin, the Cincinnati arch, the Rough Creek uplift of Kentucky, and the Ozark Mountains. This basin is like the bowl of a spoon, and the axis trends

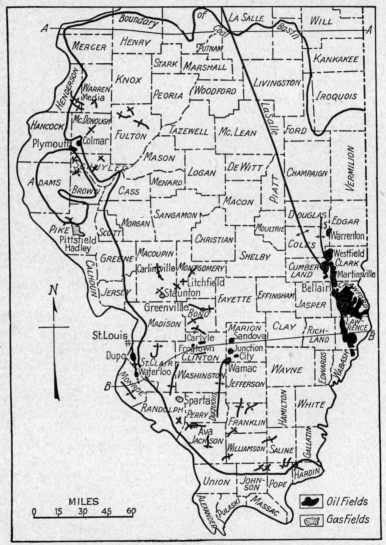

Fig. 143.—Map of Illinois showing anticlines and oil fields. (*Data from Kay, Moulton, DeWolf, Leighton and others.*)

northwestward parallel to the trend of the main oil fields. In western and central Illinois the dip toward the axis of the basin commonly is as low as 10 feet to the mile. In the south part of the state the rocks dip north 100 feet or more to the mile, and in the eastern part they rise

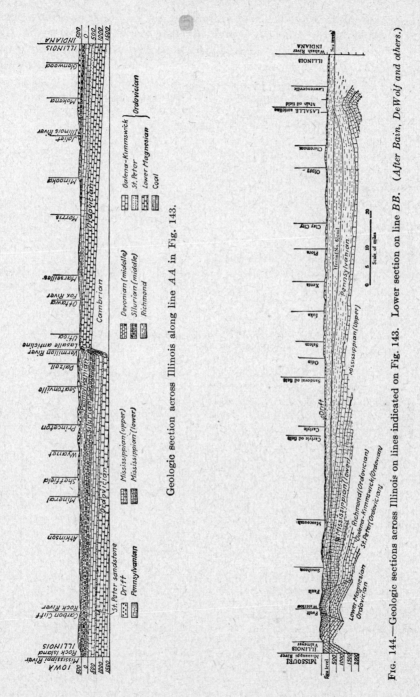

Geologic section across Illinois along line AA in Fig. 143.

Fig. 144.—Geologic sections across Illinois on lines indicated on Fig. 143. Lower section on line BB. (After Bain, DeWolf and others.)

SECTION FOR THE AREA LYING SOUTH OF A LINE DRAWN EASTWARD FROM THE MOUTH OF THE MISSOURI RIVER TO MARSHALL, ILLINOIS, AND THE STATE LINE

(After Bain, Mylius, Moulton, and others)

Quaternary:

　　Glacial till, sand, and gravel; loess and alluvium.　Present as surface rocks everywhere except in northwest and extreme south.　Thickness 30 to 225+ feet.

Unconformity.

Tertiary:

　　Lafayette, LaGrange, and Porters Creek.　Clays, sands, gravel, and ferruginous conglomerate.　Occurs only in extreme south.　Thickness 250 feet.

Unconformity.

Cretaceous:

　　Ripley.　Clay and sand.　Occurs only in extreme south.　Thickness 20 to 40 feet.

Unconformity.

Pennsylvanian:

　　McLeansboro formation.　Shales, sandstones, thin limestone, and coal.　Rocks above top of Herrin (No. 6) coal, thickness 500 to 900 feet.　Contains upper Siggins sands, gas sands, Kickapoo, and stray sands in Clark County.

Unconformity.

　　Carbondale formation.　Shales, sandstones, and coals.　Rocks below top of the Herrin coal and base of Murpheysboro (No. 2) coal.　Thickness 300 to 350 feet. Includes Casey, Claypool, lower Siggins, Bellair; 500-foot sands in Clark County, some Robinson and Bridgeport sands in Crawford and Lawrence counties. Dykstra sand of Centralia.

　　Pottsville.　Sandstone, thin shales, and coals.　Thickness 300 to 800 feet.　Some Robinson sands of Crawford County.　Some Bridgeport and rarely Little Buchanan and Ridgely sands of Lawrence County.　Sand at Litchfield, western Illinois.

Unconformity.

Upper Mississippian:

　　Chester.　Sand, shale (blue, green, dark, red), sandy limestone, and oolitic limestone.　Thickness at places 300 to 700 feet, porosity due in part to weathering. Includes Bellair 800- to 900-foot sands.　Some Little Buchanan, some Ridgewood, Buchanan, Kirkwood, Tracey, some McClosky, St. Francisville and strays (Lawrence County), Biehl (Wabash County), Klein and Benoist (Marion County) Carlyle (Clinton County).

　　Cypress.　Sandstone, irregular, usually thin in southeast Illinois and generally wanting in many oil fields.

Unconformity.

Lower Mississippian:

　　Ste. Genevieve.　Limestone, mainly oolitic, cross-bedded, some sandstone porosity due to weathering.　Thickness 80 to 100 feet.　McClosky sand.

　　St. Louis.　Limestone thickness 150 to 300 feet.　Porosity due to weathering. Martinville sand, some Westfield sand.

　　Spergen (Salem).　Thickness 300 feet.　Limestone, dolomitic, oolitic, porosity due to weathering.　Westfield lime, Westfield, Clark County.

Osage (Burlington, Keokuk, Warsaw). Limestone, shaly in upper part. Thickness 425 feet ±.

Upper Kinderhook. Shale, shaly sands. Thickness 75 to 200 feet. Carper sands of Martinville.

Sweetland Creek. Shale; brown, chocolate, green. Thickness 60 feet.

Unconformity.

Devonian:

Upper Devonian. Limestone Thickness 200 feet ±.

Hamilton. Limestone, chiefly dolomitic. Thickness 100 feet ±. Porosity due to weathering. Gas at Siggins.

Onondaga (Corniferous). Limestone, dolomitic. Thickness 165 feet. Porosity due to weathering. Martinsville, probably Marshall. Marked at base by white sandy limestone in area north of southeast Illinois oil fields.

Unconformity (?).

Silurian:

Niagaran. Dolomite, siliceous. Thickness 300 feet. Porosity due to weathering. Oil in Macon County, shows in western Illinois.

Alexandrian. Limestone and shale, red in part. Thickness 100 to 300 feet.

Hoing. Sand lenses above Maquoketa 0 to 25 feet thick produces oil at Plymouth-Colmar Field.

Ordovician:

Maquoketa. Shale, shaly limestone. Thickness 100 to 165 feet. Local oil shows.

Kimmswick. Limestone, yellow to drab, soft, sandy. Thickness 160 feet. "Trenton" oil sands of Clark and Monroe counties. Produces oil at Dupo field near St. Louis; shows of gas in St. Louis.

Plattin. Limestone, bituminous impure. Thickness 350 feet ±.

gently to the Cincinnati arch in Indiana. The structural basin includes or is crossed by long gentle anticlines chief of which are the LaSalle and Duquoin. There are also many smaller folds, some of which are shown on Fig. 143. Nearly all of the oil is associated with these folds.

In most of the oil fields of Illinois the petroliferous rocks are covered by workable coals of the Pennsylvanian system. These coals have been opened in many mines, and by mapping the coal beds the structures at the surface may be ascertained. Soon after the oil was discovered in the southeastern part of the state, the Illinois Geological Survey undertook the mapping of the coals in many regions, and as a result of this work the anticlines were drilled and several oil fields brought in. The Mississippian and older rocks are unconformable with the coal measures, but generally the folds in the latter in western Illinois are found to be present and accentuated in the Mississippian and older rocks, for areas that had been folded upward to form anticlines and domes in pre-Pennsylvanian times were folded again in post-Pennsylvanian time.

Edgar, Coles, Clark, and Cumberland Counties.—The main oil-bearing area of Illinois lies near the La Salle anticline. Part of this anticline lies near the west border of an area called the Champaign-

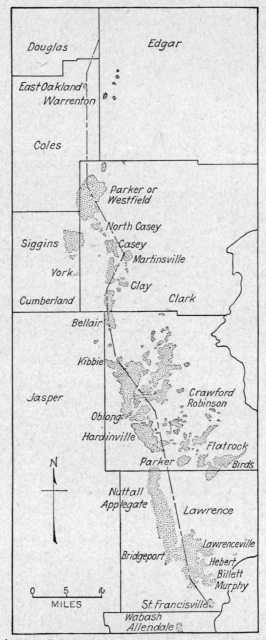

Fig. 145.—Map showing oil fields (stippled areas) in southeastern Illinois.   (*After Mylius, Blatchley, Moulton and others.*)

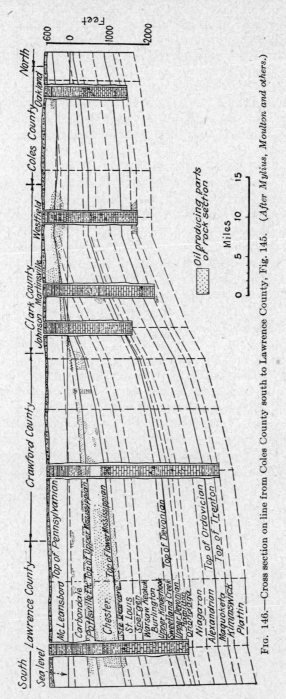

Fig. 146.—Cross section on line from Coles County south to Lawrence County, Fig. 145. (*After Mylius, Moulton and others.*)

Bellair uplift. This uplift was a topographic "high area" and structural uplift in early Pennsylvanian time. South of Bellair no similar uplift is known. Near the east part of the uplift are found the East Oakland, Warrenton, Westfield, South Parker, Martinsville, Clay, and Johnson fields. These fields are in part on a discontinuous zone of folding called the Oakland anticline.[1] On the La Salle anticline are located the Siggins and York fields. The oil fields between Bellair and Allendale are in line with the La Salle anticline and lie south of its junction with the Oakland zone of folding.

A map of the main Illinois field is shown as Fig. 145, and a section drawn from north to south as Fig. 146. The Ordovician, Silurian, and Devonian systems underlie the entire area, but they are most deeply buried in Lawrence County. North of Lawrence County they lie progressively nearer the surface. The Mississippian and Pennsylvanian formations also rise toward the north, and several of them are cut out to the north. The Champaign-Bellair uplift which lies between and also includes the La Salle and Oakland anticlinal areas, during Pennsylvanian time constituted a land mass that was progressively sinking, but this sinking was interrupted by periods of slight emergence so that successive shore lines moved northward but at places crossed. During this time, after the Carbondale formation was deposited, the McLeansboro formation was deposited on Carbondale, Pottsville, Chester, and older formations. As a result of these movements the structure of the McLeansboro does not show the structure of the older rocks, for the latter converge to the north.

At the close of Mississippian time the Champaign-Bellair uplift was raised by gentle folding, and eroded and the later Mississippian and older strata formed belts around the uplift. The limestones exposed were weathered, forming more porous oil reservoir rocks. Off shore the Pennsylvanian beds were formed, and near shore sand beaches and bars were formed. These, later, became oil reservoirs. As the land subsided shore conditions moved northward, so that the sand reservoirs of the earlier Pennsylvanian rocks lie farther south than the sand reservoirs of the later Pennsylvanian rocks. From north to south the sands play out or become shaly, and below them deeper and older sands are found. Not only were the limestones that were exposed on the Champaign-Bellair uplift weathered and made more porous hosts for oil, but certain limestones were exposed to weathering before the uplift was formed, and these also were made more porous. In this region, as in many other regions, the unconformities are favorable places for the accumulation of oil and gas

[1] MYLIUS, L. A., Oil and Gas Development and Possibilities in East-central Illinois, Geol. Survey *Bull.* 54, pp. 1 205, 1927.

The Oakland pool at the north end of the belt is located on a dome that has a gentle west dip and a steeper dip to the east. The Pennsylvanian rocks are thin and contain a little oil. The Chester formation is wanting on the top of the dome. In the Warrenton pool, southeast of Oakland, some oil is found in the Pennsylvanian strata. In the Westfield or Parker district, northwest Clark County, the McLeansboro formation of the Pennsylvanian series rests directly on the St. Louis limestone and the Spergen-Salem limestone. The Chester series was eroded before the Pennsylvanian was laid down. The rocks are folded to form a dome which is well defined in both the Pennsylvanian and older rocks. The producing sands are the "gas sand" of the McLeansboro formation which is found about 250 feet deep; the Westfield limestone which is about 325 feet deep and is the chief producing sand of the district; and the Trenton limestone. In 1920, about 1,600 wells were operating the average daily production being between 0.1 and 4.0 barrels per day. The oils have a paraffin base and the Trenton is slightly lighter than the oil derived from the Pennsylvanian sands. The gravity of the "gas sand" oil is 28.8° Bé. at 15° C. That of the upper part of the Mississippian limestone has a gravity of 33.7 and that of the lower part of the same limestone a gravity of 32.4° Bé. The Trenton oil has a gravity of 36.8° Bé. The Trenton oil has a tendency to wax up the rods. Adding oil from higher sands removes the wax.

The "gas sand" is a zone of shaly sand lenses in the shale of the McLeansboro. It produces both oil and gas which are associated with relatively little salt water. The "Westfield lime" includes the Spergen-Salem formation and probably also remnants of the St. Louis limestone which overlie the Spergen formation and also probably the top of the Keokuk-Warsaw limestone which is found below the Spergen limestone. The oil is found in about 200 feet of the limestone at depths of about 300 to 500 feet, generally in dolomitized oolitic limestone ($MgO = 9$ to 18 per cent). The Trenton (Kimmswick) limestone is found about 2,270 feet deep and the base is about 2,400 feet deep. The oil is found chiefly in a porous zone of the dolomite, 125 feet thick, near the base of the formation and is associated with salt water which is called "blue lick."

The North Casey pool, a mile or two south of the Westfield pool is on an anticlinal nose that plunges southeast. The main production is from the lower sands of the McLeansboro formation which overlap the Mississippian limestone, the eroded surface of the latter rising to the north so that the reservoirs in the lower sands of the McLeansboro are probably sealed to the north at an unconformity. The pay sands of the McLeansboro formation in the North Casey pool have an average thickness of 21 feet. The Casey field, 2 miles southeast of the North Casey pool and 2 miles west of Martinsville, is located on a dome with a

closure of about 60 feet.   The sands of the Carbondale formation are
the chief producing sands.   Most of the wells are between 350 and 500
feet deep.   Production in the St. Louis limestone is unimportant.

The oil fields of Johnson and Orange townships lie south of the
Casey field.   The chief production is in the Claypool, Casey, and Partlow
sands of the Pennsylvanian system.   The North Johnson pool is the
south extension of the Casey pool.   The field is on a low dome, and the
oil is found in the Claypool sand of the Carbondale formation (Pennsylvanian) at depths of about 499 to 500 feet.   The Johnson pool to the
south is on the same zone of folding.   The Partlow sands, which lie
about 500 to 600 feet deep, are below the Claypool and Casey sands
and are also in the Carbondale formation.   They are the chief producing
sands.   The Casey and Claypool sands thin southward and disappear
at the south end of the Johnson pool.

The Martinsville[1] pool, about 2 miles east of the Casey pool, is
located on a well-defined dome elongated to the northeast.   Oil is found
in the base of the Pennsylvanian, in the weathered surface at the top
of the Mississippian limestone, in the Kinderhook (Carper sands) near
the base of the Mississippian system at depths of 1,350 feet, and in the
limestone in the weathered zone near the top of the Devonian limestone
which lies about 1,500 feet deep, just below the Kinderhook formation.
The Carper sands, which have produced considerable oil since 1922,
include two or more sand beds separated by shales.

In the Martinsville field the salt content of water of the Devonian
limestone is only about half that in the productive Mississippian limestone
above.   Assuming that these waters once had approximately equal salt
content, the water flowage through the Devonian must have been much
greater than in the Mississippian limestone.   This is due to the greater
permeability of the Devonian limestone.   According to Moulton, limestone more open than the Devonian would have accumulation of oil only
on an exceptionally sharp structure.   The waters of the Devonian limestone at Martinsville carry about 20,000 parts per million of sodium
chloride; a field containing a more dilute water would probably be
unfavorable for oil accumulation in the Devonian limestone, since it would
indicate dilution or excessive water flushing.   On the other hand, a field
with 20,000 to 30,000 parts per million would indicate favorable conditions
of permeability, while waters with higher salt content would be interpreted as indicating too low a degree of permeability to favor
accumulation.[2]

[1] MOULTON, G. F., Ill. Geol. Survey Petroleum *Press Bull.* 4, pp. 1–5, Aug. 28,
1926.

————, and A. H. BELL, "Structure of Typical American Oil Fields," vol. 2,
pp. 132–137, 1929.

[2] MOULTON, G. F., Illinois Petroleum, Ill. Geol. Survey *Bull.* 14, p. 11, March 17,
1928.

The Siggins field west of Casey is on a well-defined dome that lies on the axis of the LaSalle anticline. The chief production is from the McLeansboro and Carbondale formations of the Pennsylvanian system. The latter is about 250 feet thick and contains many lenses of sand, as many as six pay streaks being found in one well. The York pool is south of the Siggins field and shows a dome in the Pennsylvanian strata. The chief production is from the Carbondale formation. Some of the wells produce considerable gas.

.**Crawford and Lawrence Counties.**—The LaSalle anticlinal belt extends southeastward through Crawford and Lawrence counties and crosses the Wabash River near Allendale, Wabash County. These counties contain the most productive oil fields in Illinois. The districts

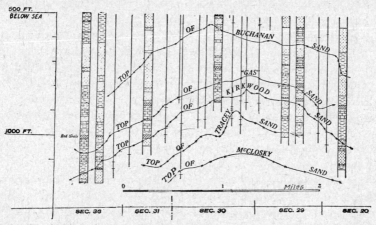

Fig. 147.—Section across dome in oil field in Petty township, Lawrence County, Illinois. The surface of the ground is about 1,000 feet above the top of the section. (*After Blatchley.*)

on the west side of the group from north to south are Bellair, Kibbie, Oblong, Hardinville, Parker, Nuttall, Applegate, Bridgeport, St. Francisville, and Allendale. On the east side of the pool are Robinson, Flatrock, Birds, Lawrenceville, Hebert, Billett, and Murphy. The oil in this area was discovered in 1905 and, as oil-bearing strata at places lie very near the surface, the field was developed rapidly, reaching its maximum production 3 years after discovery. In the northern part of the area producing sands are found about 300 feet deep. The rocks that crop out are of the Pennsylvanian series, and the oil is derived[1] from the Pennsylvanian and Mississippian rocks (Fig. 147).

Broadly considered, accumulation has taken place at the southeast end of the plunging LaSalle anticline. The dip of the beds to the southeast along the axis of the anticline is comparatively high. The most

[1] BLATCHLEY, R. S., Oil in Crawford and Lawrence Counties, Ill. Geol. Survey *Bull.* 22, 1913.

productive stratum, the McClosky "sand" of the Ste. Genevieve limestone, lies within 350 feet of the surface at the northwest end of the Clark
County field, whereas in the Lawrence County district it ranges in depth
from 1,700 to about 1,860 feet. Minor warpings extend from the La
Salle anticline both east and west. There are seven productive sands,
and the contour maps for each sand present noteworthy differences.
The rocks as a general rule are saturated with salt water, and the oil
and gas accumulate on anticlines and terraces. The gas is rich in
gasoline, but the gas production is comparatively small.

The crest of the La Salle anticline in Crawford, Lawrence, and
adjoining counties is very irregular. The part of the arch containing
oil is 2 to 8 miles wide or more and 50 miles long. On the flanks of the
fold the field is marked off by lines of salt water. Some of the wells,
particularly those in the McClosky "sand," were gushers. The Bellair
pool in Crawford County is the south continuation of the Johnson pool.
A low dome is superimposed on the top of the anticline. The main
production is from depths of from 500 to 900 feet and is derived from
sands of the Carbondale formation of the Pennsylvanian and from limestones of the Chester formation of the Upper Mississippian series.

The Robinson pool in Crawford County is about 7 miles wide, but
narrows southwest of Robinson. The Crawford County pools possess
one general oil-producing zone, the Robinson sand, which is of Pennsylvanian age, lying at the top of the Pottsville. This sand is very
irregular in distribution and ranges in thickness between 2 and 50 feet,
the average being 25 feet. At some places the Robinson sand is a series
of lenses with many streaks, tongues, and detached portions. The arch
on which the oil is found is very irregular, with an undulating top and a
mapped closure of about 100 feet. According to Blatchley, of 2,370
wells mapped in this area all but 206 yielded oil or gas. The initial
daily production was between 1 and 1,600 barrels.

The field extends southward into Lawrence County, which contains
its most productive portion. Oil or gas occurs in the Bridgeport and
Buchanan sands of the Pennsylvanian and in the Gas, Kirkwood, Tracey,
and McClosky sands of the Mississippian. Blatchley has contoured each
of these sands over the most productive portion of the Lawrence field.
The McClosky sand does not produce oil throughout the length of the
field, because of local irregularities in structure and the variable nature
of the producing stratum. It is variable in thickness and averages not
more than 10 feet over the entire field. Instead of being a single bed,
it is probably a zone in the upper part of the Ste. Genevieve formation,
the position of the oil being controlled by the porosity of the rocks.
Within the zone, which has a maximum thickness of 80 feet, one to three
oil horizons are reported. Toward the north the sands play out or
become thin and unproductive. At the south end of the oil field the

structure of the McClosky, Tracey, and Kirkwood sands is different from that of the Buchanan and Bridgeport (Fig. 147). The thickness of the beds between the sands varies from place to place, and there is probably an unconformity near the base of the Buchanan.

In the Lawrenceville field, which adjoins Lawrenceville on the southwest, the productive horizons are the "Shallow," Bridgeport, and Buchanan sands of the Pennsylvanian series and the Kirkwood, Tracey, and McClosky sands of the Mississippian. The field[1] is a low, irregular, anticlinal area the long axis striking west of north. In the Billett pool, southeast of Lawrenceville, oil is found on a small dome in approximately the same sands. The Hebert pool on a small dome 4 miles southeast of Lawrenceville produced oil chiefly from the McClosky sand. The Murphy pool south of Billett is also located on a low dome and produces from the Kirkwood and McClosky sands.

The Flatrock, Birds, and Parker fields are in Crawford County south of the Robinson field. These fields[2] yield oil from the Robinson sand or from the Flatrock sand which is equivalent to it. The sand is thicker where it is productive than elsewhere, and folding appears to have played little or no part in concentration of the oil. According to Rich, the productive areas represent ancient deltas, barriers, and bars which are separated by barren places, where the sand is thin or absent. At places the oil-bearing sand is underlain by salt-water sand which requires careful drilling and management to prevent flooding.[3]

Wabash County.—Wabash County lies south of Lawrence County and west of the Wabash River. The structure is that of a westward-dipping monocline on which are located several low domes and structural noses and terraces in which most of the oil is accumulated. The producing sands of Wabash[4] County are the Bridgeport of Pennsylvanian age, the Biehl-Jordon, 1,600 foot, and McClosky of Mississippian age. The chief production is from the Biehl-Jordon sands, but recently the McClosky sand has proved productive in an area near Linn, northwest of Allendale.

The Allendale[5] oil field is in the eastern part of Wabash County which lies south of Lawrence County. The field is located just north of the

---

[1] RICH, J. L., Oil and Gas in the Vincennes Quadrangle, Ill. Geol. Survey *Bull.* 33, pp. 147–175, 1915.

[2] RICH, J. L., Oil and Gas in Birds Quadrangle, Ill. Geol. Survey *Bull.* 33, pp. 105–146, 1916.

[3] TOUGH, F. H., S. H. WILLISTON, and T. E. SAVAGE, Experiments in Water Control in the Flatrock Pool, Crawford County, Ill. Geol. Survey *Bull.* 40, pp. 99–140, 1919.

[4] MOULTON, G. F., Illinois Petroleum No. 10, Ill. Geol. Survey, p. 12, 1926.

[5] MOULTON, G. F., Further Contributions to the Allendale Oil Field, Ill. Geol. Survey *Rept. of Investigations* 7, pp. 1–27 (rev. map), 1925.

———, Deeper Production in the Allendale Oil Field, Ill. Geol. Survey *Press Bull.* 12, pp. 1–19, 1927.

RICH, J. L., Ill. Geol. Surv. *Bull.* 31, pp. 57–68, 1914; *Bull.* 33, pp. 164–166, 1916.

place where the LaSalle zone of deformation crosses the Wabash River. The first solid rocks penetrated are the Pennsylvanian, which consist of a series of shales alternating with sandstones and thin lenses of limestone. At the base of the Pennsylvanian is the Pottsville sandstone. The Chester group, of Mississippian age, consists of a series of thin limestones and shales with a few thin beds of sandstone, which increase in thickness toward the base of the section penetrated by the wells. The chief producing sand in the Allendale field, commonly known as the Biehl sand, has been correlated with the Buchanan sand.

Central and Western Illinois.—The Carlyle field is in Clinton County 40 miles east of East St. Louis. This field[1] was discovered in 1911 and in 1927, according to Moulton, had produced 3,500,000 barrels of oil. The producing sand is the Carlyle, which is a soft porous sandstone of irregular thickness that belongs to the Chester group of the Mississippian series. Around the edges of the pool it is harder than in the center and locally it pinches out. Above the sand are about 30 feet of blue shale which locally contains red shale. Above the Chester is the Pottsville formation which carries salt water and gas; this is overlain by Pennsylvanian sandstone, shale, limestone, and coal. The oil sand is practically horizontal. Outside the field the sand dips in all directions except north, and apparently it also pinches out in all directions except to the north.

The Sandoval-Centralia[2] group includes the Sandoval, Junction City, and Wamac oil fields. The Sandoval field, 15 miles east of the Carlyle field, was the first opened. It was discovered from a seep of oil that came into a coal mine along a fault. An oil well was completed in 1908, and in 1926 the field had produced 2,500,000 barrels of oil. In this region the rocks from the surface down are glacial drift, McLeansboro, Carbondale, Pottsville, and Chester formations.

The oil field is a little west of the center of the Illinois structural basin, and the regional dip is eastward. The Duquoin anticline, which is a long low fold that strikes north, lies between the Ozark Mountains and the LaSalle anticline. This zone of faulting and relatively sharp folding strikes north to the Sandoval field. The structure of this region was worked out by Bell of the Illinois Geological Survey from underground workings of coal mines. The Sandoval field is on a dome that lies on the strike of the Duquoin zone of folding and also an east-west anticline.

[1] SHAW, E. W., Carlyle Oil Field and Surrounding Territory, Ill. Geol. Survey *Bull.* 20, pp. 43–80, 1915.
[2] BELL, A. H., Structures of Centralia and Sandoval Oil Fields, Ill. Geol. Survey, Illinois Petroleum No. 10, pp. 1–11, 1927; *idem* No. 4, pp. 6–12, 1927; *idem* No. 5, pp. 1–10, 1926.

BLATCHLEY, R. S., Illinois Oil Resources, Ill. Geol. Survey *Bull.* 16, pp. 130–146, 1910.

The Junction City field, south of Sandoval, and the Wamac field, south of Junction City, are on domes that are developed along the Duquoin zone of folding and faulting. Langewisch-Kuester and Brown fields are east of this zone and lie on the flanks of low anticlines.[1]

The oil sands of this region are shown in Fig. 148. The five sands shown are not all present in each field. The greatest production is in the Sandoval field, where most of the oil has come from the Benoist sand, although a small amount has come from the Stein sand above the Benoist. In the Junction City pool the Dykstra and Wilson sands carry oil, the chief production being in the Wilson sands. In the Wamac pool the Petro sand is the chief producing sand.

At Carlinville,[2] 45 miles northeast of St. Louis, oil and gas are found near the crest of a dome in sands of the Pottsville formation near the base of the Pennsylvanian. Gas is found at the top of the dome, oil below the gas, and salt water below the oil. Over much of this area the Pennsylvanian rests on limestone of the Ste. Genevieve or St. Louis formations, and the Chester is believed to be cut out along an unconformity. At Litchfield, 16 miles southeast of Carlinville, oil was found in a coal mine in 1879. The hole was drilled from the bottom of a shaft to explore for a lower coal bed. Salt water rose through the hole and threatened to flood the mine, but the hole was plugged, though oil leaked into the mine for several years. The structure is domatic,[3] but the production is small. At Staunton, 15 miles south of Carlinville, a small gas field is developed on an anticline. Near Greenville on the Ayers[4] anticline, 20 miles southeast of Litchfield, gas is found in the Chester formation at a depth of about 800

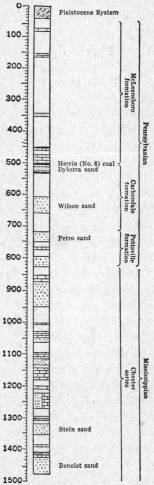

FIG. 148.—Generalized columnar section of Centralia-Sandoval area, Illinois. Depths in feet. (*After Bell.*)

[1] BELL, A. H.,' 'Structure of Typical American Oil Fields," vol. 2, pp. 120–130, 1929.

[2] KAY, F. H., Carlinville Oil and Gas Field, Ill. Geol. Survey *Bull.* 20, pp. 81–95, 1917.

[3] LEE, WALLACE, Oil and Gas in the Gillespie and Mount Olive Quadrangles Illinois, Ill. Geol. Survey *Bull.* 31, pp. 71–107, 1915.

[4] BELL, A. H., Oil Possibilities of the Ayers Anticline, Ill. Geol. Survey, Illinois Petroleum No. 5, pp. 15–18, 1926.

feet.   The Waterloo[1] field is in Monroe County 20 miles south of East
St. Louis.   Oil is found in the Trenton limestone on an elongated
anticline.

The Dupo[2] oil field is in St. Clair County, about 10 miles south of
East St. Louis.   An anticline strikes north a few degrees west from
Waterloo and is followed about 25 miles across the Mississippi River
to St. Louis.   This anticline has a relief of 800 feet or more, and the
structure may easily be seen where the St. Louis limestone is exposed in
a cliff that once marked the bank of the Mississippi River.   The dip at
Sugar Loaf is 20 degrees west.   East of that point the east dip is lower.
At Dupo the oil is found on the crest of a dome that lies on the anticline
and is accumulated in the Kimmswick limestone which is found at depths
of about 400 to 600 feet near the top of the dome.   On the north extension
of this anticline in the city of St. Louis, small amounts of gas are encountered in the Kimmswick limestone.   Other anticlines[3] are mapped in
east St. Clair and in Monroe Counties.   In the Sparta[4] field in Randolph
County, 40 miles southwest of Carlyle, gas was discovered about 1886.
Pennsylvanian rocks are found below the drift and below the Pennsylvanian is the Chester group consisting of shales, sandstone, and thin limestone.   This group contains the gas.   The Chester lies in several small
domes.   It was folded before the Pennsylvanian rocks were deposited,
and the domes are not all shown on the overlying coal-bearing group of
the Pennsylvanian.

The Ava-Campbell Hill[5] field is in Jackson County about 16 miles
southeast of Sparta field.   Oil and gas were known to be present in
the field before 1916, and in 1921 gas was first marketed.   Since then
the gas production has been maintained at about 500,000 cubic feet per
day.   The total oil production to 1925 was about 25,000 barrels.   The

[1] MOULTON, G. F., Oil-field Water Investigations, Waterloo Field, Ill. Geol.
Survey, Illinois Petroleum No. 5, pp. 11–15, 1926.

[2] BELI, A. H., The Dupo Oil Field, Ill. Geol. Survey, Illinois Petroleum, vol. 17,
pp. 1–14, 1929.

[3] BELL, A. H., The Darmstadt Anticline, St. Clair County, Ill. Geol. Survey,
Illinois Petroleum, vol. 18, pp. 1–13, 1929.

MOULTON, G. F., Anticlinal Areas near Renault, Monroe County, pp. 14–16,
1929.

FENNEMAN, N. M., Geology and Mineral Resources of the St. Louis Quadrangle,
U. S. Geol. Survey Bull. 438, p. 36, 1911.

[4] MOULTON, G. F., Ill. Geol. Survey Bull. 1, pp. 2–6, 1926.

[5] ROOT, T. B., The Oil and Gas Resources of the Ava-Campbell Hill Area, Ill. Geol.
Survey, Rept. of Investigations 16, pp. 1–27, 1928.

ST. CLAIR, S., Oil Possibilities of the Ava Region, Ill. Geol. Survey Bull. 35, pp.
57–65, 1917.

SHAW, E. W., and T. E. SAVAGE, Murphysboro Quadrangle, U. S. Geol. Survey
Folio 185, 1912.

SAVAGE, T. E., Geology and Mineral Resources of the Ava and Canton Quadrangles, Ill. Geol. Survey Bull. 38, pp. 209–271, 1921.

rocks of the region include the McLeansboro, Carbondale, and Chester formations. The gas is found in the Tar Springs sandstone about 600 feet deep and in the Cypress sandstone 900 feet deep, both sands being in the Chester series. The gas is accumulated near the crest of an anticline that strikes northeast and east. Some of the pools are on domes on the top of the anticline and others on the flanks of the anticline.

GENERALIZED SECTION OF ROCKS IN COLMAR OIL FIELD AND SURROUNDING TERRITORY
(After Morse and Kay)

System	Series	Driller's interpretation	Formation	Character	Thickness, feet
Quaternary		Surface		Alluvium; confined to valleys	Variable 0–75
				Loess; most conspicuous along bluffs of Illinois River	Average, 25
				Drift; mixed clay, sand, gravel, and boulders	In filled valleys, 100+
Carboniferous	Pennsylvanian	Coal-Bearing formations	Carbondale	Principal coal-bearing formation of Illinois. Shales, sandstones, thin beds of limestone, clay and coal	0–140+
			Pottsville	Includes beds from base of coal No. 2 to Mississippian. Sandstone and shale, and some limestone, clay, and thin coal	0–140
			Unconformity		
	Mississippian	"First lime"	St. Louis	Limestone, brecciated, blue, weathers yellow in places; contains scattered corals	0–30+
			Unconformity		
			Salem	Impure limestones of yellow tint, difficult to distinguish from limy sandstone; at places shale increases and the formation consists of limy shales, limy sandstone, and impure limestone	30±
			Unconformity		
			Warsaw	Thin-bedded impure limestone and shales, fossiliferous. Considerable blue clay shale is locally present	30±
			Keokuk	Gray crystalline limestone, fossiliferous, shaly toward top	30+
			Burlington	Limestone, generally cherty; not exposed	?
			Kinderhook	Shale, bluish gray, limy	100±
			Unconformity		
Devonian	Upper Devonian			Shale, light to dark; many spores of Sporangites, a minute reddish fossil	100±
		"Second lime"	Unconformity		
			Hamilton	Limestone, gray, small amount of sand, and some pyrite. Usually not magnesian	15–30
			Unconformity		
Silurian			Niagaran	Limestone, gray, crystalline, magnesian. Exists in separate lenticular masses; where it is not present, Hamilton rests on Maquoketa shale. Show of oil in places near base	0–20
		Hoing oil sand		Sandstone, quartzitic; grains well rounded. In lenses with no connection. Probably accumulated in depressions on Maquoketa surface. Producing bed of Colmar field	0–25 (Average in Colmar field 14)
Ordovician			Unconformity Richmond (Maquoketa)	Shales, bluish green	180–200
			Unconformity Kimmswick-Plattin. (Trenton)	Limestone, gray, white, or brown. Crystalline in places. Odor of oil not unusual. Not magnesian in Colmar field	300–400
			St. Peter	Sandstone; generally saturated with mineral water	145–225 recorded

232   *GEOLOGY OF PETROLEUM*

The Colmar[1] oil field in McDonough County is 35 miles east of Warsaw. It was discovered in 1914 as a result of studies of coal No. 2 made by Henry Hinds. The oil was found in the Hoing sandstone at the base of the Niagaran which was deposited in depressions on the Ordovician surface. A geologic section of the rocks of the region is shown on page 130. The Hoing sand is erratic its lenses being surrounded by impervious beds. Several small domes are found in the field, but the lack of continuity of the Hoing sand has made development difficult. There is an unconformity below the Pennsylvanian and the Niagaran is more highly folded than the coal beds, although the axis of the dome in the two series is superimposed.[2]

On the Media anticline in Henderson County, 30 miles north of Colmar, shows of oil were found in the top of the Devonian limestone.[3]

The Pittsfield-Hadley gas field in Pike County, 35 miles southeast of Quincy and 45 miles south of the Colmar oil field, was discovered by drilling wells for water. The field[4] is located on an anticline with an axis striking northwest. The gas is found in a porous dolomite bed of the Niagara limestone which is covered by the Kinderhook shale; 39 wells were productive in 1918. The Hoing sand, which is the chief oil-producing stratum in the Colmar field, is found below the limestone.

Small amounts of oil and gas are found about 6 miles east of Jacksonville.[5] The unconsolidated rocks of the Pleistocene are 30 to 100 feet thick and below these are some 200 feet of Pennsylvanian beds consisting of shale, limestone, sandstone, and coal. These rest on eroded Mississippian limestone and shale. Gas is found in a sand in the Pennsylvanian and in the limestone of the Mississippian on which the Pennsylvanian rests unconformably. The Mississippian limestone includes the Salem

[1] MORSE, W. C., and F. H. KAY, The Colmar Oil Field, a Restudy, Ill. Geol. Survey *Bull.* 31, pp. 37–55, 1915.

MORSE, W. C., and F. H. KAY, Area South of the Colmar Oil Field, Ill. Geol. Survey *Bull.* 31, pp. 10–35, 1915.

CURRIER, L. W., Geology of Northeastern Adams County, Ill. Geol. Survey *Bull.* 43, pp. 305–323, 1922.

[2] MOULTON, G. F., Ill. Geol. Survey, Illinois Petroleum No. 3, p. 3, 1926.

[3] BELL, A. H., and L. E. WORKMAN, The Media Anticline, Henderson County, Illinois, Illinois Petroleum No. 13, Ill. Geol. Survey pp. 1–12, 1928.

[4] CORYELL, H. N., Parts of Pike and Adams Counties, Ill. Geol. Survey *Bull.* 40, pp. 69–95, 1919.

KREY, F., Structural Reconnaissance of the Mississippi Valley Area from Old Monroe, Missouri, to Nauvoo, Illinois, Ill. Geol. Survey *Bull.* 45, pp. 1–86, 1924.

BELL, A. H., Oil Prospects in Central Pike County, Illinois Petroleum No. 3, Ill. Geol. Survey, pp. 7–10, July 24, 1926.

SAVAGE, T. E., The Pike County Gas Field, Ill. Geol. Survey *Bull.* 2, pp. 77–87, 1908.

[5] BELL, A. H., Recent Development in the Vicinity of Jacksonville, Ill. Geol. Survey, Illinois Petroleum No. 11, pp. 1–12, 1927.

limestone and probably the St. Louis. The limestones are porous at a pre-Pennsylvanian erosion surface.

An anticline is mapped at the northwest edge of Decatur[1] and drilling has discovered shows of oil.

MICHIGAN

The southern peninsula of Michigan is structurally a great basin.[2] The country is nearly everywhere deeply covered with glacial drift, and information pertaining to the underlying strata is obtained chiefly from well drilling. The area was a seat of deposition through nearly all of the Paleozoic era, and strata from the Ordovician to Pennsylvanian crop out or are discovered in drill holes. Shales are abundant in the section, limestones are numerous, and a few beds of sand are present. In the eastern part of the peninsula small folds are probably developed on the westward-dipping beds (Figs. 149, 150). At Port Huron oil has been produced from the Dundee formation (Onondaga or "Corniferous"), which is chiefly limestone. This formation is also the source of oil in Lambton County, Ontario, east of Port Huron. The Port Huron wells have produced oil since 1900, but the yield is small. Gas and salt water are associated with the oil.

In 1929 Michigan produced 4,354,000 barrels of oil valued at $6,400,000.

The Saginaw[3] oil field is at the city of Saginaw about 90 miles northwest of Detroit. A little oil was found in wells drilled in 1913, and in 1925 a well was drilled yielding 20 barrels a day after being shot. Other wells were drilled and many of them yield 15 barrels of oil a day. These wells are located on a dome (Fig. 151) that has an axis striking southeast which passes through the city of Saginaw.

Most of the oil is from the Berea grit (Fig. 152) about 1,900 feet deep, but certain wells derive oil from the top of the limestone of the Traverse formation, 2,300 feet deep, and a little oil comes from the Dundee limestone which is about 3,000 feet deep.

In the Muskegon field, western Michigan,[4] oil was discovered in 1927 in the Traverse formation at a depth of 1,641 feet, the well having an initial daily flow of 300 barrels. The field has steadily developed and has become one of the most productive oil fields in the United States east of the Mississippi River. The surface is covered with drift. Wells

[1] COLLINGWOOD, D. M., Further Considerations of Prospects for Oil in the Decatur Area, Ill. Geol. Survey *Rept. of Investigations* 1, pp. 1–44, 1924.

[2] SMITH, R. A., The Occurrence of Oil and Gas in Michigan, Mich. Geol. and Biol. Survey *Pub.* 14, geol. ser. 11, pp. 1–281, 1914.

[3] CARLSON, C. G., Geology of the Saginaw Oil Field, Michigan, and Discussion of Michigan Oil Prospects, Am. Assoc. Pet. Geol. *Bull.*, vol. 11, pp. 959–965, 1927.

[4] NEWCOMBE, R. B., Oil and Gas Development in Michigan, Mich. Geol. Survey *Pub.* 37, ser. 31, pp. 142–314, 1928.

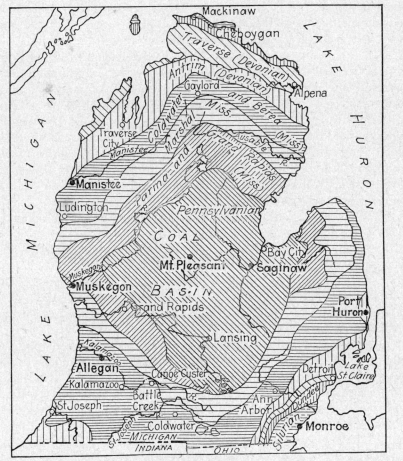

Fig. 149.—Outline map of southern peninsula of Michigan.   Dots show oil fields.   (*After Smith.*)

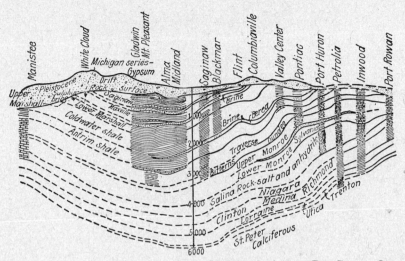

Fig. 150.—Diagrammatic cross section of the Michigan basin from Port Rowan, Ontario through Port Huron to Manistee, Michigan. (*After Smith.*)

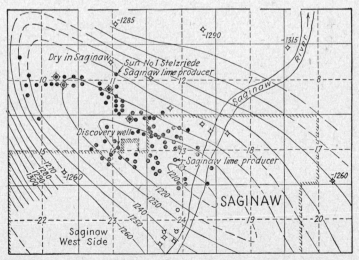

Fig. 151.—Map of Saginaw oil field, Michigan. (*After Carlson.*)

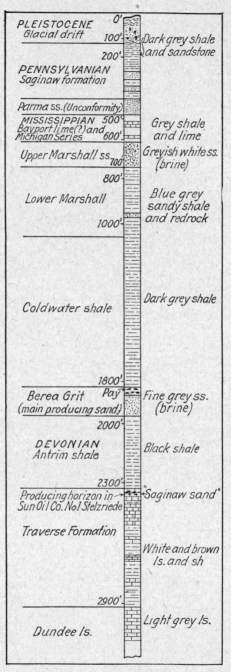

FIG. 152.—Log of Saginaw oil field, Michigan. (*After Carlson.*)

encounter a little gas at about 550 feet, shows of oil at 1.200 feet, and the main oil-producing formation at about 1,640 feet. The wells enter the Lower Marshall formation below the drift and pass into the shaly limestones of the Coldwater formation, which, about 260 feet below the limestone, contains a red limestone which is the best horizon marker in the field. The field is located on a low structural dome (Fig. 153). The oil is found in the porous limestone of the Traverse formation about 40 feet below the top of the formation. There is no sharp

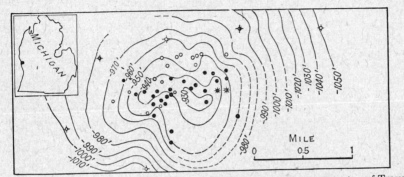

Fig. 153.—Structure map of Muskegon oil field, Michigan. Contours on top of Traverse formation. Sea level datum. (*After Newcombe.*)

division plane between the Traverse and Dundee limestones, the two together being 300 feet thick. Some of the wells produce oil from the Dundee limestone. The gravity of the oil of the Muskegon field is about 35° Bé. and it contains about 0.38 per cent sulphur.

At Manistee, north of Muskegon, a well found oil and gas at a depth of 1905 feet. At Allegan, south of Muskegon, a small production was obtained from the Dundee limestone. At Mount Pleasant, near the center of the basin, oil is found in a sand, probably the Berea sand. This field is now being successfully developed. A little oil and gas were found in the Trenton limestone in Monroe County, southeast Michigan.

GENERALIZED GEOLOGIC SECTION OF LOWER MICHIGAN

(After Lane, Smith, Newcombe, and others)

System and formation	Thickness, feet	Description
Pleistocene:		
Drift, etc.......	0–1,000	Sand, gravel, clay, etc.
Pennsylvanian:		
Woodville......	0–95	Light red sandstone, sandy shale
Saginaw........	0–535	Sandstone, shale, limestone, coal
Parma.........	0–223	White and gray sandstone, conglomerate, some shale
Mississippian:		
Bayport........	0–100	Limestone locally cherty, white sandstone
Michigan......	0–460	Limestone, some shale, gypsum, red shale and sandstone
Marshall.......	0–485	Sandstone, shale, gypsum, conglomerate, salt water
Coldwater......	800–1,090	Shale, sandstone, ironstone, limestone, red shale beds
Sunbury.......	0–103	Shale, brown to black; pyrite
Berea.........	0–273	Sandstone, white to gray; salt water, oil at Saginaw
Bedford........	0–520	Shale, red, gray, blue
Devonian:		
Antrim........	140–466	Shale, black with blue beds, ironstone balls
Traverse.......	60–681	Limestone and shale; oil at Muskegon
Bell..........	0–80	Shale with thin limestone (Marcellus shale)
Dundee........	65–225	Limestone, some chert, bitumens, salt water; oil at Muskegon, Saginaw, and Port Huron
Detroit River..	0–435	Dolomite and limestone; mineral water (Upper Monroe)
Sylvania.......	0–310	Sandstone, sandy dolomite, mineral water
Silurian:		
Bass Island	400–522	Gray dolomite and shale, mineral water (Lower Monroe)
Salina.........	0–1,575	Dolomite, salt, gypsum, red, blue, and dark shale
Niagara........	270–790	Dolomite and limestone, red and blue shale at base
Cataract.......	0–355	Red and blue shale, gray dolomite
Ordovician:		
Richmond ⎱ ... Lorraine ⎰ ...	215–595	Red and blue shale, locally sandy
Utica.........	50–300	Shale; black, weathers gray
Trenton........	100–875	Limestone and dolomite at places shaly, salt water
St. Peter.......	0–75	White sandstone, loosely cemented
Beekmantown..	0–250	Sandstone, white, buff to red dolomite
Cambrian:		
Lake Superior	0–1,500	Sandstone, red and white

CHAPTER XII

MID-CONTINENT REGION

The Mid-Continent fields include the oil- and gas-producing areas of Kansas, Oklahoma, Arkansas, Missouri, and those of Texas and Louisiana except the Gulf Coast region. This group includes a number of fields that are not naturally classed together. As the Mid-Continent fields developed, the U. S. Geological Survey issued statistics of production of the group as a whole, and this classification was continued for many years as the production increased, until the practice of considering the area as a unit became firmly established. In this area the oil is found in the Ordovician, Siluro-Devonian, Mississippian, Pennsylvanian, Permian, and Lower and Upper Cretaceous systems. Most of these systems contain large amounts of oil.

The Mid-Continent fields are divided as follows:

1. Kansas, northern Oklahoma, Missouri, and western Arkansas.
2. Southern Oklahoma and Texas Panhandle.
3. North-central Texas.
4. West Texas.
5. Balcones fault region.
6. Southern Arkansas and northern Louisiana.

KANSAS, OKLAHOMA, MISSOURI, AND WESTERN ARKANSAS

The oil fields of Kansas, northern Oklahoma, western Missouri, and western Arkansas form a natural subdivision of the Mid-Continent field. This unit, however, is not sharply set off from the southern Oklahoma fields, for the development of the Seminole region in Oklahoma has extended it southward almost to the north flank of the Arbuckle Mountains. The rocks exposed in this region (Fig. 154) are chiefly Pennsylvanian and Permian shales, sandstones, and limestones. These rocks generally dip westward at low angles away from the line of the Ozark Mountains and Llano uplift. The first field to be developed in this region was probably the Paola field, Kansas (Fig. 155), about 35 miles southwest of Kansas City, where gas seeps noted as early as 1860 led to the drilling of the field. The Chelsea field, Rogers County, Oklahoma, was drilled in 1889. The oil and gas in both of these fields are in beds that lie near the base of the Pennsylvanian series, and both fields are on the east border of the region where the oil sands lie at shallow depths. The oil-bearing region was gradually extended westward and

239

southward, and oil was found in many different sands in the Pennsylvanian series. Later, it was developed in Mississippian, Devonian, Silurian, and Ordovician strata. The Ordovician in most of the fields lies deep, but at places it yields large amounts of oil, so that its development is profitable. The oils of Kansas and northern Oklahoma are of

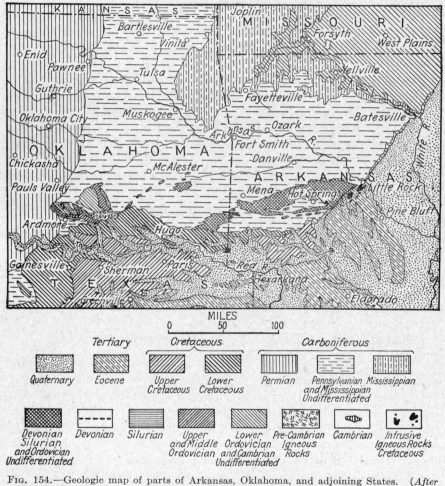

Fig. 154.—Geologic map of parts of Arkansas, Oklahoma, and adjoining States. (*After Miser.*)

high grade, low in sulphur, and generally have high gasoline content. Most of the oil derived from the Ordovician strata is very light, about 40° Bé. gravity or lighter.

The oil-bearing region, as already stated, extends southward to near the Arbuckle Mountains. Southeast of the oil-bearing area in Oklahoma, there is a region containing gas in which no oil has been found. It is

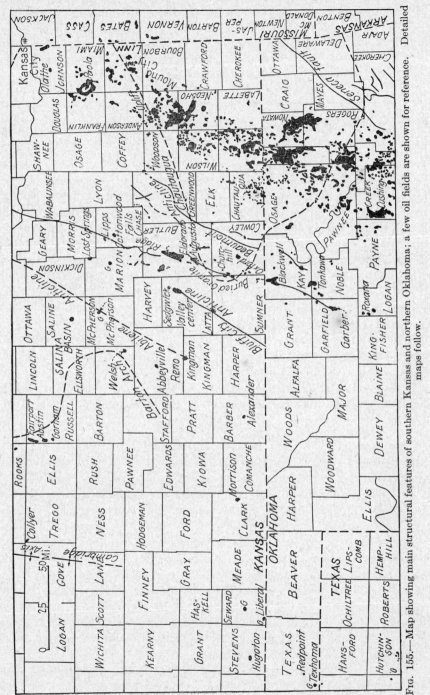

Fig. 155.—Map showing main structural features of southern Kansas and northern Oklahoma; a few oil fields are shown for reference. Detailed maps follow.

PRODUCTION OF OIL, GAS AND NATURAL GASOLINE, MID-CONTINENT STATES

State	1929		1928		1929	
	Oil, barrels	Value of wells	Natural gas, M cu. ft.	Value	Natural gasoline, gallons	Value
Kansas............	42,875,000	$ 63,500,000	45,644,000	$14,144,000	33,800,000	$ 2,060,000
Oklahoma..........	253,704,000	354,200,000	320,861,000	47,476,000	676,500,000	42,960,000
Texas..............	298,441,000	324,900,000	301,990,000	51,316,000	422,300,000	25,930,000
Louisiana..........	20,229,000	25,200,000	227,821,000	20,279,000	63,400,000	3,902,000
Arkansas..........	25,076,000	22,600,000	20,235,000	3,562,000	32,300,000	2,301,000

stated that any oil in this region has been vaporized by metamorphism and converted into gas (p. 159). East of the oil-bearing region, on the Ozark uplift, the Pennsylvanian rocks have generally been removed by erosion. Large areas of Ordovician strata are known, but no oil has been found in them. The oil-bearing rocks extend northward into northern Kansas and into Nebraska and Iowa, far beyond the known oil fields, but thus far drilling in this region has not been profitable. The westward extension of the Kansas and Oklahoma field is now under development. In this region the Pennsylvanian rocks are covered by Permian rocks. Oil is found as far west as Trego County, Kansas, and at Oklahoma City, Oklahoma, and, probably in Pennsylvanian rocks, in the Sayre field, western Oklahoma near the Texas Panhandle. Gas and some oil are found in the Ramsay district, northwestern Oklahoma. These fields are of great interest as indicating the trend of development.

MISSOURI

Pennsylvanian strata cover approximately the northwest third of the state.[1] The beds dip northwest and are thrown into gentle folds that strike northwest and pitch northwest at low angles. Some of these folds are shown on Fig. 117. Asphaltic sandstones and limestones are found in beds of the Mississippian and Pennsylvanian systems and are exposed at many places. These are described by Wilson in the paper cited. Wells have found shows or small amounts of oil but no district has been exploited on a commercial scale, except the region south of Kansas City in Cass and Jackson counties (Fig. 155). Ordovician strata are present under most of the state, and this system contains valuable deposits of oil in Indiana and in Oklahoma. In Missouri some gas and a little oil have been found in Ordovician beds on an anticline at St. Louis.[2] Numerous wells sunk to the Ordovician for water in Missouri have found no oil or gas.

[1] WILSON, M. E., The Occurrence of Oil and Gas in Missouri, Mo. Bur. Geol., ser. 2, vol. 16, pp. 1–284, 1922.
[2] FENNEMAN, N. M., Geology and Mineral Resources of the St. Louis Quadrangle, U. S. Geol. Survey *Bull.* 438, p. 58, 1911.

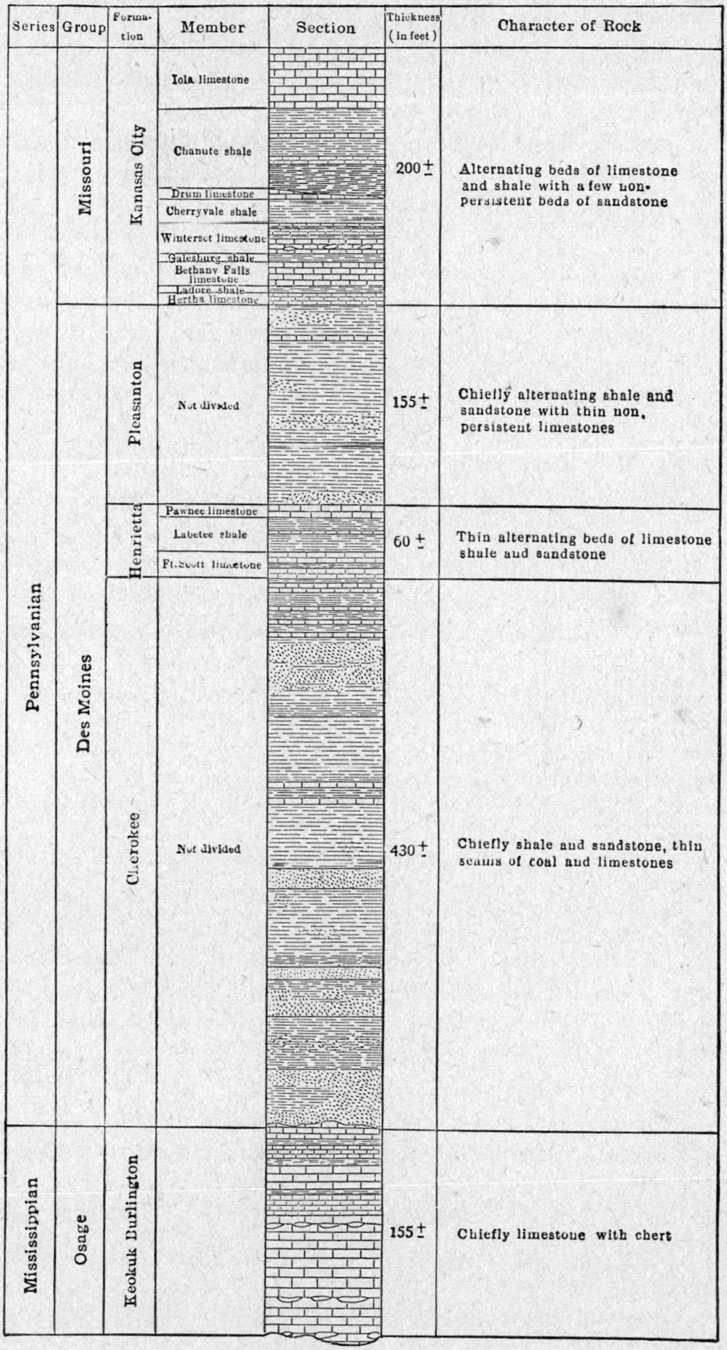

Series	Group	Formation	Member	Section	Thickness (in feet)	Character of Rock
Pennsylvanian	Missouri	Kansas City	Iola limestone Chanute shale Drum limestone Cherryvale shale Winterset limestone Galesburg shale Bethany Falls limestone Ladore shale Hertha limestone		200 ±	Alternating beds of limestone and shale with a few non-persistent beds of sandstone
	Des Moines	Pleasanton	Not divided		155 ±	Chiefly alternating shale and sandstone with thin non-persistent limestones
		Henrietta	Pawnee limestone Labette shale Ft. Scott limestone		60 ±	Thin alternating beds of limestone shale and sandstone
		Cherokee	Not divided		430 ±	Chiefly shale and sandstone, thin seams of coal and limestones
Mississippian	Osage	Keokuk Burlington			155 ±	Chiefly limestone with chert

Fig. 156.—Generalized geologic section of region near Belton, Missouri. (*After Wilson.*)

Near Kansas City in Cass and Jackson Counties, the outcropping rocks are of Pennsylvanian age and extend to depths of 650 to 875 feet or more. The series is divided into two groups classified as the upper or Missouri group and the lower or Des Moines group. The exposed strata belong chiefly to the upper group, but only its lowest formation, the Kansas City, is present. The limestone members of this formation crop out conspicuously over nearly all of the area; they dip northwest about 10 feet per mile.

In the region near Belton and Hickman Mills there are a number of low anticlines, domes, monoclines, terraces, and synclines. Southwest of Belton there is a small area of complicated faulting. In wells sunk to depths of about 400 feet oil or gas or both have been encountered. A section of the rocks is shown in Fig. 156.

KANSAS

General Features.—Kansas[1] is part of the Great Plains region of the interior lowlands segment of North America. The surface slopes gently from the Rocky Mountains of Colorado eastward about 10 feet to the mile. The west part of the state is 3,500 to 4,000 feet and the eastern boundary 750 to 1,000 feet above sea. The rocks exposed range in age from Mississippian to Tertiary. The rocks crop out in broad belts that strike east of north, the oldest rocks appearing in the eastern part

[1] HAWORTH, E., and others, Special Report on Oil and Gas, Kan. Geol. Survey, vol. 9, pp. 1–586, 1908.

MOORE, R. C., and W. P. HAYNES, Oil and Gas Resources of Kansas, Kan. Geol. Survey *Bull.* 3, pp. 1–391, 1917.

———, Geology of Kansas, Oil and Gas Resources of Kansas, Kan. Geol. Survey *Bull.* 6, pp. 1–98, 1926.

———, Petroleum Resources of Kansas, Am. Inst. Min. Eng. *Trans.*, vol. 65, pp. 97–107, 1921.

SCHRADER, F. C., and E. HAWORTH, Economic Geology of the Independence Quadrangle, Kansas, U. S. Geol. Survey *Bull.* 296, pp. 1–74, 1906.

ADAMS, G. I., E. HAWORTH, and W. R. CRANE, Economic Geology of the Iola Quadrangle, Kansas, U. S. Geol. Survey *Bull.* 238, pp. 1–83, 1904.

———, Oil and Gas Fields of the Western Interior and North Texas Coal Measures, U. S. Geol. Survey *Bull.* 184, pp. 1–64, 1901.

BERGER, W. R., The Relation of the Fort Scott Formation to the Boone Chert in Southeastern Kansas and Northwestern Oklahoma, *Jour. Geol.*, vol. 26, pp. 618–621, 1918.

BEEDE, J. W., and E. H. SELLARDS, Stratigraphy of the Eastern Outcrop of the Kansan Permian, *Amer. Geol.*, vol. 34, pp. 83–111, 1905.

BLACKWELDER, E., The Origin of the Central Kansas Oil Domes, Am. Assoc. Pet. Geol. *Bull.*, vol. 4, pp. 89–94, 1920.

LEY, H. A., Subsurface Observations in Southwest Kansas, Am. Assoc. Pet. Geol. *Bull.*, vol. 8, pp. 445–453, 1924.

GOULD, C. N., The Correlation of the Permian of Kansas, Oklahoma, and Northern Texas, Am. Assoc. Pet. Geol. *Bull.*, vol. 10, pp. 144–153, 1926.

of the state, where in general they dip west to northwest about 25 feet to the mile.

The oil-producing strata are Ordovician, Mississippian and Pennsylvanian. At places the Pennsylvanian strata lie horizontal. Locally they dip east at low angles, forming very gentle domes and anticlines which in general are the controlling features in the accumulation of the oil and gas. The closures of nearly all of the domes are low at the surface although the Eldorado field has a closure of 160 feet. Many of the producing wells are located on sand lenses and sand strings. The oil of Kansas ranges from 20 to 40° Bé. or more. The bulk of the production is high-gravity oil of good grade. The eastern part of the field produces much gas.

Wells drilled in eastern Kansas have revealed prominent structures that are buried below the Pennsylvanian rocks. The Nemaha granite ridge[1] extends across the state. This ridge is flanked by Mississippian and older rocks and is buried by the Pennsylvanian beds in which low anticlines are developed above the ridge. These folds are believed by certain investigators to be due to differential settling of beds above the ridge. In southeast Kansas there is a broad arch below the Mississippian rocks which represents an uplift of pre-Mississippian age. This arch is called by Barwick[2] the Chautauqua arch. It is the buried west extension of the Ozark Mountains. West of the granite ridge is the Barton arch of pre-Pennsylvanian age and probably in part of pre-Mississippian age.[2] These ancient upfolds which are concealed at the surface by overlying Pennsylvanian rocks are probably of approximately the same age as certain pre-Mississippian buried arches in Oklahoma.

The oil first developed in Kansas was found in the Pennsylvanian system which includes shale, limestone, sandstone, and coal beds, in all about 3,500 feet thick. Early discoveries were made near Paola, Miami County, about 35 miles southwest of Kansas City.[3] The rocks exposed at the surface include the Kansas City, Lansing, and Douglas formations. In Miami County and in Franklin County, which adjoins Miami County to the west, the producing sands lie at depths between 178 and 920 feet. Gas seeps were noted in this region about 1860, and, as a result of these,

[1] TAYLOR, C. H., The Granites of Kansas, Am. Assoc. Pet. Geol. *Bull.*, vol. 1, pp. 111–126; 1917.

MOORE, R. C., Geological History of the Crystalline Rocks of Kansas, Am. Assoc. Pet. Geol. *Bull.*, vol. 2, pp. 98–112, 1918.

POWERS, S., Granite in Kansas, *Am. Jour. Sci.*, ser. 4, vol. 44, pp. 146–150, 1917.

[2] BARWICK, J. S., The Salina Basin of North-central Kansas, Am. Assoc. Pet. Geol. *Bull.*, vol. 12, pp. 177–200, 1928.

[3] MOORE, R. C., and W. P. HAYNES, Oil and Gas Resources of Kansas, Kan. Geol. Survey *Bull.* 3, p. 307, 1917.

MOORE, R. C. and K. K. LANDES, Underground resources of Kansas, *idem*, Bull. 13, pp. 1–147, 1927.

the first oil and gas wells were drilled in Miami County.   Near Mound
City (Fig. 155), 30 miles south of Paola, some oil and gas have been found
in the Cherokee formation at depths of 328 and 625 feet.

Southeastern Counties.—In Anderson[1] County (Fig. 157), about 70
miles southwest of Kansas City, the Pennsylvanian rocks dip about 20

GENERALIZED SECTION OF PERMIAN SYSTEM IN KANSAS
(After Moore)

Group	Formation	Member	Thickness, feet
Cimarron	Greer	Big Basin sandstone	12
		Big Basin shale	20
	Woodward	Day Creek dolomite	1–5
		Whitehorse sandstone	175–200
		Dog Creek shale	30
	Cave Creek	Shimer gypsum	4–25
		Jenkins shale	5–50
		Medicine Lodge gypsum	2–30
	Enid	Flowerpot shale	150
		Cedar Hills sandstone	50–60
		Salt Plain shale	155
		Harper sandstone	350
Big Blue	Wellington	Undifferentiated	500–800
	Marion	Abilene limestone	4–8
		Pearl shale	70
		Herington limestone	12–15
		Enterprise shale	35–44
		Luta limestone	30
	Chase	Winfield limestone	20–25
		Doyle shale	60
		Fort Riley limestone	40–45
		Florence flint	20
		Matfield shale	60–70
		Wreford limestone	35–50
	Council Grove	Garrison shale and limestone	135–150
		Cottonwood limestone	6

[1] CHARLES, H. H., Anderson County, Oil and Gas Resources of Kansas, Kan. Geol.
Survey *Bull.* 6, part 7, pp. 1–95, 1927.

RICH, J. L., Further Observations on Shoestring Sands of Eastern Kansas, Am.
Assoc. Pet. Geol. *Bull.*, vol. 10, pp. 568–580, 1926.

WILLIAMS, D. W., Correlation of Producing Sands in Southeastern Kansas:
Am. Assoc. Pet. Geol. *Bull.*, vol. 5, pp. 293–297, 1921.

GENERALIZED SECTION OF PENNSYLVANIAN ROCKS OF KANSAS

(*After Moore*)

Group	Formation	Member	Thickness, feet
Missouri	Wabaunsee	Eskridge shale	30–40
		Neva limestone	3–5
		Elmdale shale	120–140
		Americus limestone	6–10
		Admire shale	275–325
		Emporia limestone	5–10
		Willard shale	45–55
		Burlingame limestone	7–12
	Shawnee	Scranton shale	160–200
		Howard limestone	3 7
		Severy shale	40–60
		Topeka limestone	20–25
		Calhoun shale	0–50
		Deer Creek limestone	20–30
		Tecumseh shale	40–70
		Lecompton limestone	15–30
		Kanwaka shale	50–100
	Douglas	Oread limestone	50–70
		Lawrence shale	150–300
		Iatan limestone	3–15
		Weston shale	60–100
	Lansing	Stanton limestone	20–40
		Vilas shale	5–125
		Plattsburg limestone	5–80
		Lane shale	50–150
	Kansas City	Iola limestone	2–40
		Chanute shale	25–100
		Drum limestone	0–80
		Cherryvale shale	25–125
		Winterset limestone	30–40
		Galesburg shale	10–60
		Bethany Falls limestone	4–25
		Ladore shale	3–50
		Hertha limestone	10–20
Des Moines	Marmaton	Pleasanton shale	100–150
		Coffeyville limestone	8–10
		Coffeyville shale	60–80
		Altamont limestone	3–10
		Bandera shale	60–120
		Pawnee limestone	40–50
		Labette shale	0–60
		Fort Scott limestone	20–40
	Cherokee shale	Undifferentiated	400–500

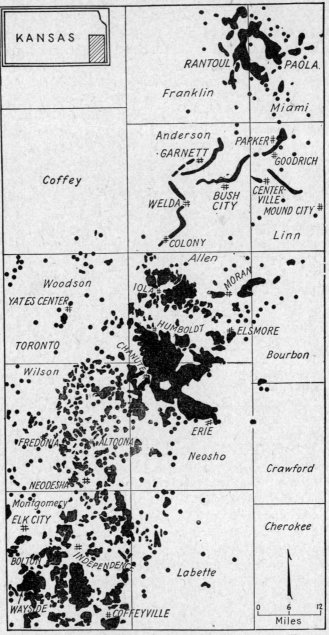

FIG. 157.—Map showing oil and gas fields of southeastern Kansas.

feet per mile. On this gentle monocline are low anticlines and domes which are due to thickening and thinning of the Pennsylvanian rocks and also to readjustments of beds by movements involving the Mississippian rocks. Oil and gas are found near the base of the Marmaton and in the Cherokee formation in the 300-, 600-, 800-, and 900-foot sands. These sands are long narrow bodies called "shoestrings." The 800-foot sand, near the horizon of the Squirrel sand of Oklahoma and 25 to 50 feet below the top of the Cherokee formation, is the chief oil sand of the county, and the 900-foot sand, sometimes called the Bartlesville sand, which supplies most of the gas, is 75 to 100 feet below the top of the Cherokee. The Burgess sand on top of the Mississippian is barren. A little gas and oil are found at the top of the Mississippian limestone, where the latter is weathered and porous. The top of the Arbuckle limestone also showed some oil together with large amounts of sulphur water.

The distribution of the shoestring sands is shown by Fig. 157. These sands are chiefly the filling of ancient river channels, but some are probably ancient bars and beaches. The sands are essentially without water, and the oil commonly is found in low places in the sands with the gas above it. According to Rich, the main oil deposits of Anderson and Linn counties are filled channels of an ancient delta drainage system. The reservoirs were formerly filled with water, oil, and gas, and parts of them were subsequently drained of water which gave the oil an opportunity to spread into parts of the reservoirs formerly occupied by water. The regional dip of the beds is northwest. The Bush City string curves 60 degrees in such a way that the convex part of the curve is higher than either end, forming a central reservoir (Fig. 73). The high part of the reservoir is more productive than the parts of the string on either side. About 2 miles northeast of Bush City in 1927 a well 710 feet deep drilled to the Colony sand ("Bartlesville") encountered a light oil; this sand previously had produced gas but little oil in this area.[1] The Centerville Shoestring[2] in Linn County is an area 5 miles long in which the oil lies 15 feet below the top of the Cherokee shale.

In Allen and Neosho[3] counties which are south of Anderson Countyl the chief producing fields are Iola, Humboldt, Chanute, and Erie. The Pennsylvanian rocks dip northwest about 25 feet to the mile. The structure is shown by numerous limestone beds which thin or play out to the south. Sections of wells are shown in Fig. 158.

[1] KESLER, L. W., "Petroleum Development and Technology in 1927," Am. Inst. Min. Eng., p. 581, 1928.

[2] RICH, J. L., Shoestring Sands of Eastern Kansas, Am. Assoc. Pet. Geol. *Bull.*, vol. 7, p. 104, 1923.

[3] MOORE, R. C., and E. R. ELLEDGE, Allen and Neosho Counties, Oil and Gas Resources of Kansas, Kan. Geol. Survey, *Bull.* 6, pt. 5, pp. 1–22, 1920.

ADAMS, G. I., E. HAWORTH, and W. R. CRANE, U. S. Geol. Survey *Bull.* 238, pp. 1–83, 1904.

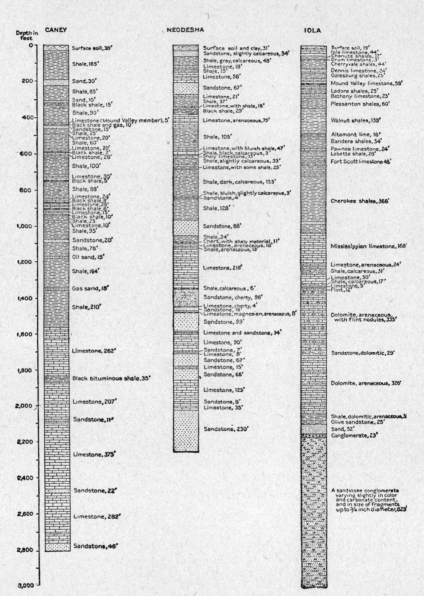

FIG. 158.—Records of deep wells at Caney, Neodesha and Iola, southeastern Kansas.
(*After Heald.*)

Oil is found in lenses of sand in the Cherokee shale at depths of 600 to 1,000 feet. The oil is mainly heavy oil, about 25° Bé., and in many of the fields it is associated with gas. Shoestring sands are found between Erie and Chanute and near Elsmore.[1]

In Wilson and Montgomery[2] counties the chief oil and gas fields are near Fredonia, Neodesha, Altoona, Independence, Wayside, and Coffeyville. The rocks dip north-west about 25 feet per mile, but locally lie in short anticlines and domes. On these the oil and gas are concentrated, although lenses between the folds also form reservoirs. The producing beds are in the Marmaton and Cherokee formations, and the chief sands lie at depths from 350 feet to 1,250 feet below the surface. The Bartlesville (Third) sand is found at depths between 1,150 and 1,250 feet and the Burgess sand, which is 100 feet or more below it, is at the top of the Mississippian limestone. The oil is of light gravity from 33 to 40° Bé.

The Elk City[3] gas field in northwestern Montgomery County and southeastern Elk County is one of the leading gas fields in Kansas. This field is located on two low domes exposed at the surface, each with a relief of 20 feet. The chief gas reservoir is the Bartlesville sand and is found at a depth of 1,350 feet.

The Coffeyville[4] field, Montgomery County, Kansas, and Nowata County, Oklahoma, is located on a dome mapped at the surface which moves southwest and increases the amount of closure with depth (Fig. 159). A heavy oil with a gravity of 24° Bé., rich in lubricants, is found at the top of the siliceous limestone which lies below the Chattanooga shale at a depth of about 1,200 feet. The field has produced about 265,000 barrels of oil.

In Chautauqua[5] County, west of Montgomery County, the rocks at the surface include the Lansing, Douglas, Shawnee, and Wabaunsee formations. The chief oil and gas centers are Peru and Sedan. The chief producing sands are the Bartlesville, 200 feet above the Missis-

[1] RICH, J. L., Shoestring Sands of Eastern Kansas, Am. Assoc. Pet. Geol. *Bull.*, vol. 7, p. 104, 1923.

[2] MOORE, R. C., and C. W. BOUGHTON, Wilson and Montgomery Counties, Kan. Geol. Survey *Bull.* 6, pt. 6, pp. 1–32, 1921.

———, Oil and Gas Resources of Kansas, *Bull.* 6, pt. 2, pp. 1–94, 1920.

SCHRADER, F. C., and E. HAWORTH, U. S. Geol. Survey *Bull.* 296, pp. 1–74; Independence Quadrangle *Folio* 159, 1908.

STRYKER, W. L., Subsurface Geology of Wilson County, Kansas, Am. Assoc. Pet. Geol. *Bull.*, vol. 9, pp. 1207–1214, 1925.

[3] BOUGHTON, C. W., Elk City Gas Field, Kan. Geol. Survey *Bull.* 5, pp. 1–31, 1921.

[4] FOSTER, W. H., Coffeyville Oil Field, Montgomery County, Kansas, "Structure of Typical American Oil Fields," vol. 1, pp. 48–51, 1929.

[5] MOORE, R. C., and W. P. HAYNES, Oil and Gas Resources of Kansas, Kan. Geol. Survey, *Bull.* 3, pp. 245–250, detailed map, 1917.

sippian, the Peru, 300 feet above the Bartlesville, and the Red, 125 to 200 feet above the Peru.

In Greenwood County (Fig. 160) a group of closely spaced oil fields extends southwest from Madison 40 miles to Sallyards. The oil in this region is found in three sands of the Cherokee formation: the Burgess

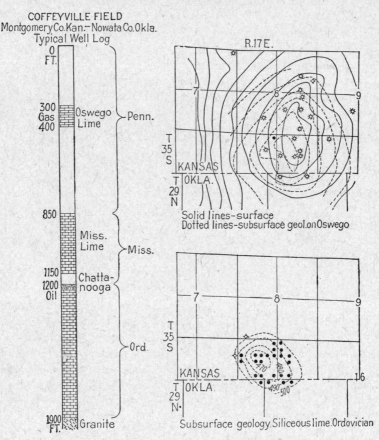

Fig. 159.—Well log and maps of Coffeyville field, Montgomery County, Kansas; contour intervals 10 feet. (*After Foster, Walker and Doub.*)

sand which rests on the base-leveled Mississippian; the "Bartlesville" sand, 135 feet above the Mississippi lime; and the Cattleman sand, 80 feet above the Bartlesville sand. In the Madison-Sallyards[1] group of oil fields practically all of the oil is in the "Bartlesville" sand. This group includes Madison, Fromm, Wick, Seeley, Burkett, Thrall, Agard,

[1] CADMAN, W. K., The Golden Lanes of Greenwood County, Kansas, Am. Assoc. Pet. Geol. *Bull.*, vol. 11, pp. 1151–1172, 1927.

LOOMIS, H., The Burkett-Seeley Pool, Greenwood County, Kansas, Am. Assoc. Pet. Geol. *Bull.*, vol., 7, pp. 482–487, 1923.

Polhamus, and Sallyards. The sands range in depth from 1,850 feet near Madison to 2,500 feet near Sallyards. The main bodies of sand are about ½ to 1½ miles wide and have an average thickness of 30 feet. According to Cadman, they represent a buried sand-filled channel and tributary channels of a stream that flowed southwest in early Cherokee time. The oil is light and high in gasoline. That of the Burkett-Seeley

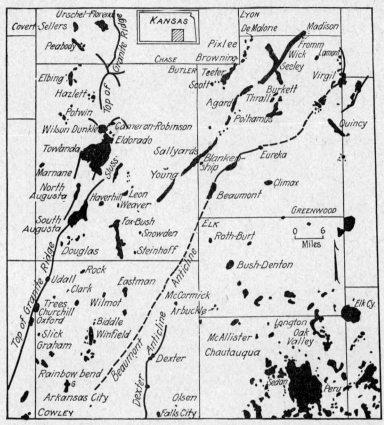

Fig. 160.—Map of Western part of main oil and gas producing area, Kansas.

pool has a gravity of 40° Bé. The average production of these pools is about 3,000 to 5,000 barrels per acre.

According to Cheyney[1] the Madison-Sallyards sands represent, in part, sand bars and tidal delta bars formed by waves and tides near an ancient shore line.

The Lamont pool, southeast of Madison, produces considerable high-grade oil from the Bartlesville sand at a depth of 1,600 feet. In

[1] CHEYNEY, A. E., Madison Shoestring Pool, Greenwood County, Kansas, "Structure of Typical American Oil Fields," vol. 2, pp. 150–159, 1929.

the Virgil[1] pool southeast of Lamont, 3 miles southwest of the town of Virgil, a sand approximately of Bartlesville horizon has produced a little oil, but the main production comes from the top of the Mississippian limestone which is found at a depth of about 1,700 feet. Structurally the field is on a dome elongated to the northeast which shows a closure of 60 feet at the surface. The gravity of the oil is 37 to 41° Bé.

The Quincy pool, near the east edge of the county, produces oil and gas from the Bartlesville sand at a depth of 1,450 feet. The Eureka pool is west of Quincy and near the crest of the Beaumont anticline;

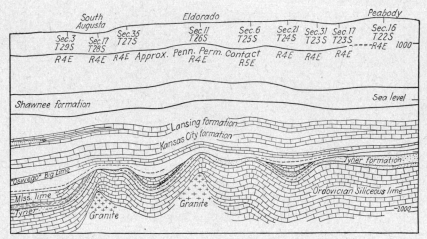

FIG. 161.—Cross section, South Augusta to Peabody, Kansas. (*After Aurin, Clark and Trager.*)

oil is found at the top of the Mississippi lime at a depth of 1,900 feet. At Climax southwest of Quincy, the same horizon produces oil.

Nemaha Ridge Region.—The Nemaha buried granite ridge strikes southward through Marion, Butler, and Cowley counties. The axis of the ridge, shown on Fig. 160, is at places irregular and ill defined, particularly where the ridge breaks up to form groups of irregular rounded scattered hills. On the south part of the ridge along its axis and at places over the buried hills (Fig. 161), oil fields are developed on low domes. The oil fields include Urschell, Covert-Sellers, Peabody, Elbing, Potwin, Eldorado, Augusta, Churchill, Oxford, and others. This is the most productive group of oil fields in Kansas. The oil was first developed in Pennsylvanian strata, but later large deposits were found in Mississippian and in Ordovician strata. The first large oil field of this group to be developed was the Eldorado field.

---

[1] BEEKLY, A. L., Virgil Pool Greenwood County, Kansas, "Structure of Typical American Oil Fields," vol. 2, pp. 142–149, 1929.

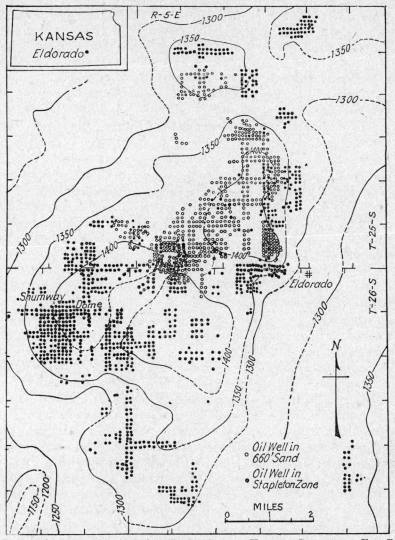

FIG. 162.—Map of Eldorado oil field, Butler County, Kansas. Contours on Fort Riley limestone, sea level datum. (*After Fath.*)

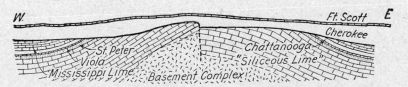

FIG. 163.—Ideal west-east cross section of Eldorado anticline from Sec. 7, T. 26 S., R. 4 E., to Sec. 12, T. 26 S., R. 5 E. Length, 12 miles; height, 1,200 feet. (*After Reeves.*)

The Eldorado[1] oil field, in Butler County, was discovered in 1915. It soon became the greatest oil field in Kansas, and in 1918 it produced 28,807,680 barrels of oil valued at $63,000,000. The oil has a specific gravity of 31 to 38° Bé. and that from the 660-foot sand is as light or perhaps a little lighter than that of the Stapleton zone which lies deeper. The altitude of the district is from 1,225 to 1,450 feet above sea level. The rocks exposed are near the base of the Permian, and the Fort Riley limestone of the Chase formation crops out over much of the area and affords a means of mapping the structure. The main productive area occupies a broad dome which, at the surface, has a closure of 150 feet (Fig. 162). Drilling has shown that this dome marks an eroded anticlinal hill that was folded and faulted in pre-Pennsylvanian time (Fig. 163) and subsequently eroded nearly to a peneplain, the erosion surface truncating the Siliceous lime, St. Peters, Viola, Chattanooga, and Mississippi lime formations. This eroded anticline was buried by the Pennsylvanian strata and with these beds was folded again in post-Permian time.

Of the productive sands nine have produced oil and six produced gas. The 550-foot sand in the Wabaunsee formation has had small production. The 660-foot sand or Second Admire, also in the Wabaunsee formation, has produced oil over a large area. The five gas sands in the Shawnee and Douglas formations are productive over a considerable area. These are the 900-, 1,125-, 1,200-, 1,275-, and 1,475-foot sands named according to their approximate stratigraphic distances below the top of the Fort Riley limestone. According to Fath, these "sands" are mainly porous limestones. The productive portions of the sands are chiefly at the tops of the small domes that are developed on the Eldorado anticline. The gas was used chiefly for the development of the field and the production is not determined. The gas carries methane and ethane and is high in nitrogen (29 to 41 per cent) and helium (0.9 to 1.2 per cent).

Oil occurs in sands in the Douglas formation at depths of 1,550 feet. The Boyer "sand" is a porous limestone in the lower part of the Douglas formation, 1,700 feet below the top of the Fort Riley limestone. It produces oil over the north part of the crest of the Shumway dome. The Stokes "sand" in the Kansas City formation, 2,000 feet below the top of the Fort Riley limestone, is also a porous limestone. It produces oil in only a few wells.

The Stapleton oil zone as stated lies below the pre-Cherokee peneplained erosion surface. This erosion surface bevels the Boone limestone,

---

[1] FATH, A. E., Geology of the Eldorado Oil and Gas Field, Kan. Geol. Survey *Bull.* 7, pp. 1–187, 1921.

MOORE, R. C., and W. P. HAYNES, Oil and Gas Resources of Kansas, Kan. Geol. Survey *Bull.*, 3, pp. 229–242, 1917.

REEVES, J. R., Eldorado Oil Field, Butler County, Kansas, "Structure of Typical American Oil Fields," vol. 2, pp. 160–167, 1929.

GENERALIZED GEOLOGIC SECTION OF ELDORADO FIELD

(*Rocks above Mississippian after Fath; Mississippian and lower after Aurin, Clark, and Trager*)

Formation	Thickness, feet	Description
Permian:		
Marion	65–80	Limestone and shale
Chase	280	Shale and limestone; includes Fort Riley limestone
Council Grove	130–140	Shale and limestone
Pennsylvanian:		
Wabaunsee	360–610	Shale and a few limestone lenses; some sandstone; contains the two shallow oil sands of the Augusta region, the 550- and the 650-foot sands
Shawnee	650–680	Limestone, shale and sandstone; contains 900-, 1,125-, 1,200-, and 1,275-foot gas sands
Douglas	300	Sandstone, shale, limestone; contains the 1,475-foot gas sand and Boyer sand
Lansing	210–410	Shale and limestone; upper part mainly limestone, lower part mainly shale
Kansas City	180–250	Limestone and shale; contains Stokes "sand"
Marmaton and Cherokee	250–650	Shale, some limestone and sandstone
Mississippian:		
Boone	0–420	Limestone and chert, sandstone, shale, at places removed.
Mississippian or Devonian:		
Chattanooga	0–100	Shale
Ordovician:		
Viola(?)	15–30	Cherty dolomitic limestone
St. Peter	65	Sand with green shale horizons, sand grains frosted
Cambro-Ordovician:		
"Siliceous Lime"	350–1,000	Porous limestone
Pre-Cambrian		Granite

the Chattanooga shale, the Viola(?) limestone, the St. Peter sandstone, and the Siliceous limestone. Erosion has removed much of the Siliceous limestone. According to Reeves, the Siliceous limestone in this region is generally about 1,000 feet thick, but on the crest of the dome only 350 feet of the limestone remain (Fig. 163) below which is granite.[1] Oil is found in the porous Boone limestone, in the Viola limestone, in the St. Peter (Wilcox) sandstone, and in the Siliceous limestone.

[1] AURIN, F. L., G. C. CLARK, and E. A. TRAGER, Notes on the Subsurface pre-Pennsylvanian Stratigraphy of the Northern Mid-Continent Field, Am. Assoc. Pet. Geol. *Bull.*, vol. 5, pp. 143–144, 1921.

The Augusta field, which is 10 miles south of Eldorado field, is also located on a dome near the top of the granite ridge. Oil is found in the Kramer sand 2,000 feet deep and in the Varner sand, which is included

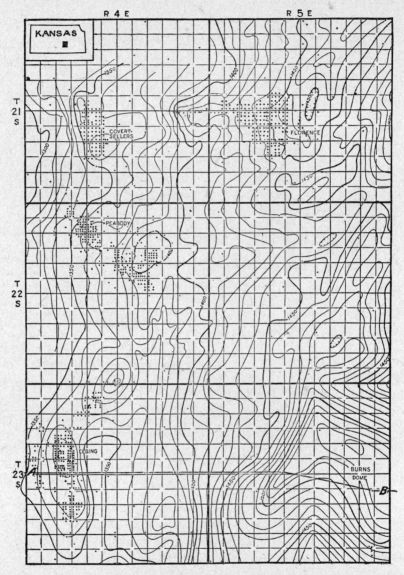

Fig. 164A.—Map of Elbing-Florence region, Kansas, showing structure of Herington lime-stone. (*After Thomas.*)

in the Stapleton oil zone, at a depth of 2,416 feet. The "Mississippi Lime" is eroded from the crest of the fold and the oil is in the Tyner sand and the "Siliceous Lime." Granite is found below the latter, about

2,850 feet deep.   The Haverhill field, east of Augusta, produces from the
Bartlesville sand, 2,700 feet deep.   At Leon, northeast of Haverhill,
oil is produced from the Leon limestone which is equivalent to the Urschel
limestone and to the Viola limestone of Oklahoma.

In the Elbing field (Figs. 164*A*, 164*B*), 18 miles northwest of Eldorado,
a structural dome is shown at the surface.   Oil is found at a horizon
between 2,000 and 2,500 feet deep which represents an ancient erosion
unconformity at the top of the Ordovician.   The oil-bearing zone
probably includes the Viola formation and part of the Siliceous Lime
of the Ordovician.   The oil has accumulated on a dome.   At Peabody, 8

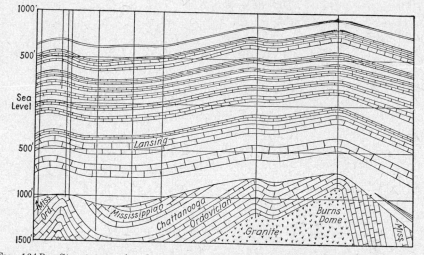

Fig. 164*B*.—Structure section through Elbing field, Kansas, drawn on line *AB* of Fig. 164*A*.
(*After Thomas.*)

miles north of Elbing, the producing "sand" is probably the Viola
formation and Siliceous Lime.   The main production is found at depths
of about 2,525 feet on a structural dome that is reflected at the surface.
In the Covert-Sellers and Urschel-Florence fields, both of which are
located on structural domes, the Viola or Urschel formation and possibly
the "Siliceous Lime" are productive.

The Urschel[1] field is located 3 miles southeast of Florence and about
6 miles northeast of the Peabody field.   The field was opened in 1920
and on August 1, 1922, had produced 10,300,000 barrels of oil.   The
productive area lies on a dome chiefly to the west of the axis.   It occupies

[1] Shea, E. F., Water Conditions in the Urschell Pool, Marion County, Kansas,
Am. Assoc. Pet. Geol. *Bull.*, vol. 6, pp. 426–443, 1922.

Thomas, C. R., Flank Production of the Nemaha Mountains (Granite Ridge),
Oklahoma, Am. Assoc. Pet. Geol. *Bull.*, vol. 11, pp. 919–931, 1927.

Barwick, J. S., The Salina Basin of North-central Kansas, Am. Assoc. Pet. Geol.
Bull., vol. 12, p. 185, 1928.

an area of about 1,500 acres.   The oil horizon lies about 2,318 feet below the surface.   According to Barwick, the main producing horizon is the Urschel limestone which is approximately equivalent to the Viola limestone.   The oil-bearing horizon is from a few inches to 12 feet thick. It carries salt water high in sodium chloride and practically no gas is present, except a small amount of hydrogen sulphide.   One of the early wells had an initial production daily of 2,928 barrels of oil.   The oil is under considerable water pressure and the wells flowed naturally at first, but most of the wells, soon after they are drilled, yield large amounts of water mixed with the oil and often also sediment.   This oil was treated with steam and lime to make it marketable.   As the yield of water increased, edge water also encroached on the field, and the productive area rapidly diminished.

The oil of the Elbing, Peabody, Covert-Sellers, and Florence-Urschel fields has an average gravity of about 32° Bé.   While the main oil-bearing zone (Ordovician) produces little or no gas, a little oil and gas are found in the Pennsylvanian rocks above the main oil zone.   Although most of the wells had to be pumped, a few flowed naturally.   The pressure appears to be essentially hydrostatic.

The Rock pool in northern Cowley[1] County produces oil (38° Bé.) from a sand lens about $\frac{1}{2}$ mile wide in the Cherokee shale.   The sand is 50 feet above the Mississippian limestone, which is found at about 2,775 feet.   The Eastman pool southeast of Rock pool produces oil (35° Bé.) and gas from the Bartlesville sand near the base of the Cherokee shale, 5 to 50 feet above the limestone.   Clark pool, southwest of Rock, produces oil from a sand in the shale 40 feet above the Mississippian limestone.

The Churchill and Oxford fields are located on the east edge of Sumner County on the crest of the Granite Ridge anticline.   These fields were discovered in 1926 and 1927 and are now among the foremost in Kansas.   Both produce high-gravity oil chiefly from the Stalnaker (Tonkawa) sand which lies about 1,880 feet deep at Churchill and 100 feet deeper at Oxford.   The Udall pool, north of Churchill, produces oil from the Stalnaker sand.   The Slick pool, which lies on a dome south of Churchill, produces oil from the Layton(?) sand, 2,600 feet deep, from a sand near the base of the Cherokee shale, 3,100 feet deep, and from the "Siliceous Lime," 3,425 feet deep, the latter being the chief producing horizon.   The oil has a gravity between 38 and 40° Bé. and the deepest oil is lightest.   The Graham pool, south of Slick, lies on a structural dome and produces oil from the Layton sand and from the "Siliceous Lime"; the latter is the more prolific horizon and lies 3,500 feet deep.   It produces oil with a gravity of 40° Bé., somewhat lighter than the oil of the Layton sand.

[1] Bass, N. W., The Geology of Cowley County, Kansas, Kan. Geol. Survey *Bull.* 12, pp. 1–203, 1929.

Kesler, L. W., "Petroleum Development and Technology in 1927," Am. Inst. Min. Eng., p. 589, 1928.

The Winfield field, east of Slick, is one of the most productive fields in Cowley County. It is situated on an elongated dome with a major axis about 6 miles long, and the main producing sand is about 3,000 feet deep. It lies near the base of the Cherokee formation and is correlated with the Bartlesville sand. Oil is obtained also from several higher sands of the Pennsylvanian system.

In the Hull Pool, which joins the town of Winfield on the north, wells sunk 2,300 feet deep produce oil from a sand of Pennsylvanian age, the wells having initial productions of about 250 barrels per day. Wells sunk 3,400 feet to the Siliceous lime of Ordovician age have initial production as high as 1,000 barrels. These wells find oil in a sharp structural dome over an area of $\frac{1}{2}$ square mile. The Pennsylvanian sands have low dips. The productive area in the Pennsylvanian sands is larger than that of the Ordovician strata.

The Rainbow Bend[1] field is southwest of Winfield near the west edge of the county. The rocks cropping out are of Permian age, and drilling has revealed an anticline that extends northeast to Graham. This anticline lies above a buried ridge of Ordovician limestone. The Mississippian limestone on the south and east sides of the field is 100 feet thicker than on the crest of the fold above the pre-Mississippian Ridge. The main production is from a sand lens at the base of the Cherokee sandstone resting on top of the Mississippian limestone and is found about 3,225 feet deep on the southeast side of the buried ridge. The "Siliceous Lime" of Ordovician age lies 3,500 feet deep and is productive in parts of the field. At the peak of its production, in June, 1926, the field yielded about 22,000 barrels of oil per day. The oil has a gravity of 40° Bé. The total yield is about 9,000,000 barrels.

The Dexter field in the southeast part of Cowley County is on a well-defined anticline and produces gas from shallow sands of Pennsylvanian age. The field is noteworthy since it is the first field in which helium was discovered in natural gas.[2] Oil and gas are recovered also from deeper horizons. The main oil-producing strata are the sandy streaks in the upper part of the Mississippian limestone. At Falls City,[3] south of Dexter, oil is found in sands in the upper part of the Kansas City group on a small dome.

Salina Basin and Barton Arch.—The Salina basin lies west of the buried granite ridge and east of the Barton arch (Figs. 155, 165). In this basin rocks older than the basal Pennsylvanian are folded downward in a broad low syncline and were eroded to a peneplain at the close of the Mississippian period. The Abilene anticline in the Salina basin

[1] Snow, D. R., and D. Dean, Rainbow Bend Field, Cowley County, Kansas, *Am. Assoc. Pet. Geol. Bull.*, vol. 9, pp. 974–982, 1925.

[2] Cady, H. P., and D. T. McFarland, Kan. Geol. Survey, vol. 9, pp. 228–302, 1908.

[3] Bass, N. W., Kan. Geol. Survey *Bull.* 12, pp. 174–180, 1929.

lies west of and strikes nearly parallel to the granite ridge. The Bluff City anticline lies east of the Abilene anticline and extends southwest to the border of the state. The Permian and Pennsylvanian sections are

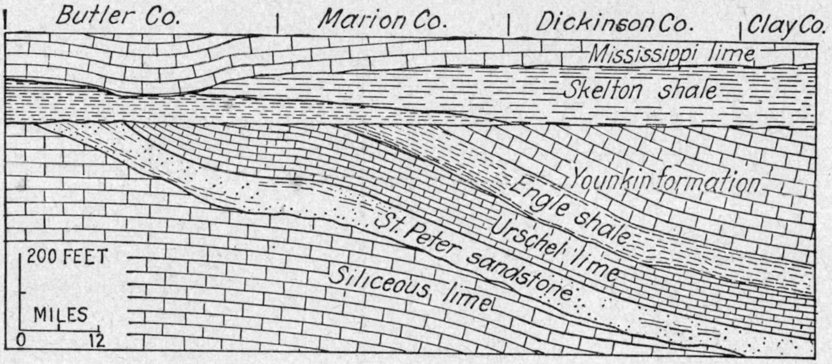

Fig. 165.—Generalized section south to north, looking west, of part of Salina basin, Kansas. (*After Barwick.*) The names of formations between St. Peter and Mississippi Lime are proposed by Barwick.

shown on pages 246 and 247. The strata below the Pennsylvanian, as described by Barwick, are as follows:

Formation	Thickness, feet	Description
Pennsylvanian:		
Welsh chert............	0–100	Residuary chert locally developed
Unconformity		
"Mississippian"........	0–300	Limestone, Boone or St. Louis
Unconformity		
Skelton..............	100–150	Shale, probably Kinderhook and Chattanooga
Unconformity		
Siluro-Devonian:		
Younkin..............	400	Gray dolomitic limestone with sand lenses
Engle................	60–100	Light-colored shale probably equivalent to Maquoketa and Sylvan
Ordovician		
Unconformity		
Urschel	0–135	Limestone probably equivalent to Viola. Main producing horizon at Florence-Urschel; produces oil at Eldorado, probably at Elbing, Peabody, Covert-Sellers
St. Peter..............	40–120	Equivalent to Wilcox sand of Oklahoma
Unconformity		
Cambro-Ordovician		
Siliceous Lime........		Upper part important source of oil in Augusta and Eldorado fields
Unconformity		
Pre-Cambrian		

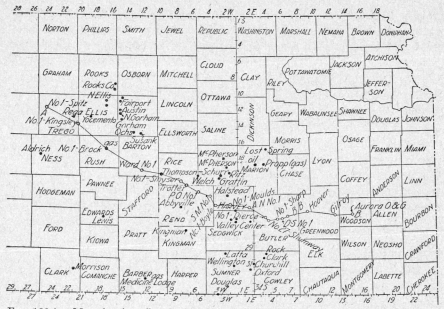

Fɪɢ. 166*A*.—Map showing oil and gas fields in central Kansas (dots) and position of cross section *AB* Fig. 166*B*. (*Data from McClellan and others.*)

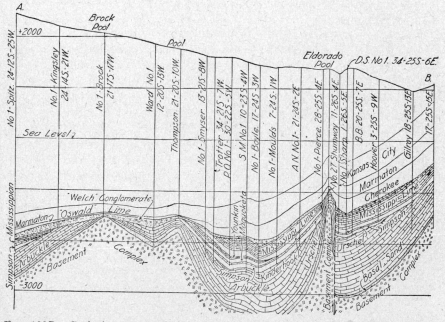

Fɪɢ. 166*B*.—Geologic cross section central Kansas; position of section shown on Fig. 166*A*. (*After McClellan.*)

The region west of the oil fields of the granite ridge is extensively prospected, and a discovery of an oil field in Russell County, 100 miles west of the granite ridge oil fields, has encouraged this development. The strata below the Pennsylvanian series in the Salina basin[1] west of the granite ridge become thicker to the west and north and the general relations as interpreted by Barwick are shown by Fig. 166.

At Valley Center, 6 miles north of Wichita, (Fig. 155) a low-pitching anticline was discovered by core drilling. In depth a structural dome was found in the Ordovician beds. Large wells were brought in producing oil, from the Simpson formation. The Misener and Mississippian beds also produce oil. At Greenwich 8 miles northeast of Wichita oil is obtained from the Simpson beds; east of Valley Center, a large well found oil at the top of the Mississippian limestone on a low fold. At Latta, northwest Sumner County, on the Bluff City anticline, oil is found in the Pennsylvanian series. To the northeast in Marion County in the Propp gas field, the flint or "chert" horizon at the top of the Mississippian series produces gas under a pressure of 845 pounds at a depth of 2,367 feet. In the Lost Springs field to the north, the same horizon produces oil.

On or near the Abilene anticline oil and gas are found in the McPherson field in the chert at the top of the Mississippi lime. In Kingman County, to the southwest, the same formation has produced oil. At Welch commercial oil is found in the chert at the top of the Mississippian limestone, and at Abbeyville some oil is found in the basal beds of the Kansas city formation.

On the Barton arch[2] the Mississippian, Silurian, and Devonian strata locally are wanting. The Ordovician beds dip southeast, and westward the Ordovician strata rise to the pre-Pennsylvanian surface, and the lower Pennsylvanian strata become thinner. Thus there is a great convergence of the Ordovician and Permian beds to the northwest.

In Russell[3] County (Fig. 155) a well drilled near Fairport (Fig. 167) in 1923 encountered oil at a depth of 2,998 feet. Several other wells drilled near by encountered oil, some of them yielding between 350 and 750 barrels a day, the oil having a gravity of 41° Bé. From Fairport the district was extended south and several fields were discovered including Austin, North Gorman, and Gorman. The Fairport field in 3 years has produced 3,500,000 barrels of oil with a gravity of about 40° Bé. Cretaceous rocks (Fig. 168) crop out and a dome striking north

[1] BARWICK, J. S., The Salina Basin of North-central Kansas, Am. Assoc. Pet. Geol. *Bull.*, vol. 12, p. 182, 1928.

[2] KESLER, L. W., "Petroleum Development and Technology in 1927," Am. Inst. Min. Eng., p. 593, 1928.

[3] RICHEY, W. W., N. W. BASS, M. N. BRAMLETTE, and R. C. MOORE, The Geology of Russell County, Kansas, Kan. Geol. Survey *Bull.* 10, pp. 1–104, 1925.

ALLAN, T. H., and M. M. VALERIUS, Fairport Oil Field, Russell County, Kansas, "Structure of Typical American Oil Fields," vol. 1, pp. 35–48, 1929.

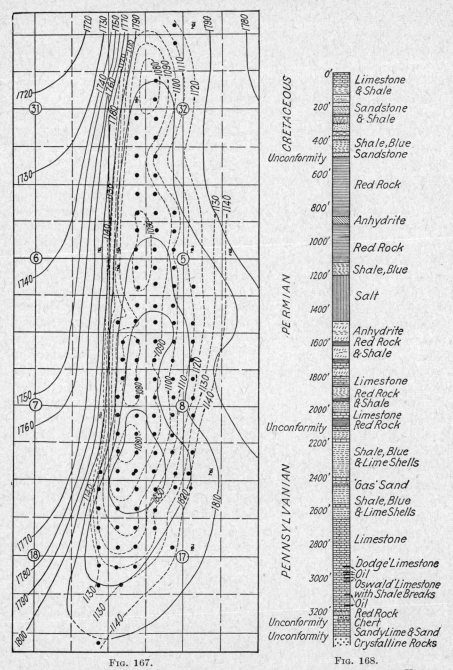

Fig. 167.

Fig. 168.

FIG. 167.—Map showing structure of the Fairport oil field, Russell County, Kansas. (*By T. H. Allen.*)   Datum sea level; Cretaceous Greenhorn limestone structure full lines; Pennsylvanian Oswald limestone structure (2900 feet deep) broken lines.

FIG 168.—Columnar section Fairport oil field, Russell County, Kansas, depth in feet. (*After Allen and Valerius.*)

is outlined on the Greenhorn limestone of the Benton formation. The Cretaceous rocks, in general, dip northeast and 500 feet deep lie on the Permian rocks that dip northwest. At a depth of 2,100 feet the Permian lies unconformably on the Pennsylvanian.

The Pennsylvanian rocks lie on sandy limestone and sand, probably of Ordovician or Cambrian age which rest on granite. These rocks are more steeply folded than the Pennsylvanian strata and probably overlie a buried hill of crystalline rock. Oil is found in the Dodge limestone horizon and below that in solution cavities in the Oswald limestone, which lies at the top of the Lansing formation and is the main producing zone. The porous part of the limestone is at the top and at various intervals to 220 feet below the top of the limestone. The structure shown in the Pennsylvanian rocks is much steeper than that of the Cretaceous, and its axis moves to the west with depth (Fig. 167) toward the steep side. The greatest accumulation of oil is on the east side, which is the side of low dip of the dome. Water five times as salt as sea water is found below the oil.

In western Kansas[1] Cretaceous rocks dip eastward at low angles. A broad low arch extends southeast from the Black Hills to Sheridan and Gove counties, Kansas. These rocks are locally thrown into folds of which several low domes have been drilled. In the Rega field Trego County (Fig. 166A), oil is found in Pennsylvanian strata. Near Liberal, Seward County, southwestern Kansas, 120 miles north of Amarillo, Texas, a large gas well was drilled in 1922 to a producing bed in the Permian system. At Hugoton, northwest of Liberal, gas is found in Permian beds.[2]

NEBRASKA

The Pennsylvanian rocks dip northwest from Missouri and Iowa into Nebraska and the Nemaha granite ridge passes from Kansas into the state. The granite is found 600 feet deep at Seneca, Kansas, 557 feet deep at DuBois, Nebraska, and 700 feet deep at Table Rock. The

[1] LUPTON, C., W. LEE, and L. R. VAN BURGH, Oil Possibilities of Western Kansas, Am. Assoc. Pet. Geol. *Bull.*, vol. 6, pp. 69–90, 1922.

DARTON, N. H., The Structure of Parts of the Central Great Plains, U. S. Geol. Survey *Bull.* 691a, pp. 1–26, 1919.

———, Preliminary Report on the Geology and Underground Water Resources of the Central Great Plains, U. S. Geol. Survey *Prof. Paper* 32, pp. 1–433, 1905.

TWENHOFEL, W. H., Significance of Some of the Surface Structures in Central and Western Kansas, Am. Assoc. Pet. Geol. *Bull.*, vol. 9, pp. 1061–1070, 1925.

PRATT, W. E., Oil and Gas in Texas Panhandle, Am. Assoc. Pet. Geol. *Bull.*, vol. 7, pp. 237–249, 1923.

[2] After this volume was set up an excellent paper on western Kansas by Charles E. Straub and Anthony Folger appeared in *Petroleum Development and Technology.* 1930 (pp. 437–465) and a map by Hugh McClellan appeared in *Oil and Gas Journal,* Oct. 23, 1930. Only a part of these data could be incorporated here.

Table Rock anticline represents the northern extension of the Nemaha granite ridge at the surface.[1] This anticline is followed 50 miles north to near Nebraska City. It is about 10 miles wide, has a low dipping western flank, and a steep dip to the east. The Humboldt fault is approximately parallel to the anticline and lies 5 miles east of it. The anticline, if continued, would join the Thurman-Wilson fault, which is chiefly a flexure in Nebraska, although it shows 300 feet of displacement in Iowa. The Redfield anticline lies about 1 mile north of the fault in Nebraska. The Nemaha anticline appears north of the fault and extends 25 miles north to near Omaha, having the same general strike as the Nemaha granite ridge. Several test wells have been drilled on or near this anticline but no oil deposits were found.

IOWA

Carboniferous strata are found over most of the state of Iowa,[2] except in the northeast corner, where older beds crop out, and in the northwest corner, where the Paleozoic rocks are covered by Cretaceous beds. Neither oil nor gas has been found in commercial amounts, although in Story County a small flow of gas was found at a depth of 90 feet, probably in Pennsylvanian strata. Inflammable gas is found in small amounts in shallow wells that penetrate a forest bed at the base of the Kansas drift.

The Thurman-Wilson[3] fault extends northeast from the southwest corner of the state about 120 miles. This fault (Fig. 117) probably branches off from the Nemaha granite ridge anticline. As shown by Tilton, the fault has a throw of about 300 feet.

OKLAHOMA AND WESTERN ARKANSAS

General Features.—In northern Oklahoma[4] the Pennsylvanian rocks dip west away from the Ozark uplift. The beds exposed are the continua-

[1] Condra, G. E., The Stratigraphy of the Pennsylvanian System in Nebraska, Neb. Geol. Survey *Bull.* 1, ser. 2, pp. 1–291, 1927.

[2] Howell, H. V., Petroleum and Natural Gas in Iowa, Iowa Geol. Survey, vol. 29, pp. 1–39, 1920.

[3] Tilton, J. L., Geology of Cass County, Iowa, Iowa Geol. Survey, vol. 27, pp. 173–276, 1916. ——., *Jour. Geol.*, vol. 27, pp. 383–390, 1919.

Bain, H. F., Iowa Geol. Survey, vol. 7, pp. 428–429, 1898.

Todd, J. E., On the Folding of Carboniferous Strata in Southwestern Iowa, Iowa Acad. Sci. *Proc.*, vol. 1, pt. 1, p. 61, 1889; also vol. 13, p. 184, 1906.

Beyer, S. W., Iowa Geol. Survey, vol. 9, pp. 155–237, 1899.

Dillé, G. S., Anticlines in the State of Iowa, Iowa Acad. Sci. *Proc.*, vol. 33, pp. 183–198, 1926.

[4] A bulletin on oil and gas in Oklahoma (No. 40) by the Oklahoma Geological Survey, edited by C. N. Gould, is in preparation and advance chapters treating groups of counties are referred to on subsequent pages. These chapters were kindly supplied

tions of those cropping out in southern Kansas, and the chief production has come from beds in the lower part of the Pennsylvanian and in the Ordovician system.   Some of the oil sands are widely recognized in both states.   There does not appear to be a very close relation between surface structure and production east of Range 11 in Osage County; west of that range the oil found is generally in domes that are recognized.   The early production of Oklahoma was almost entirely from the Pennsylvanian strata, the larger part of it coming from the Bartlesville sand.   Oil was discovered in the Ordovician strata as early as 1908, and in 1914 a well drilled in the Bixby field, by H. F. Wilcox, found oil in an Ordovician sand which was called the Wilcox sand.   The name soon came into general use in Oklahoma, although it was then the established name of a Tertiary formation of the Gulf Coast.   The production of oil from the Wilcox and other pre-Pennsylvanian strata was steadily increased and now exceeds that from the Pennsylvanian strata.

The rock formations exposed and discovered by drilling are listed in tables that follow and the relations are indicated in generalized cross-sections.   Near the close of the Cambrian time the area was submerged, and at places conglomerates and sandstones were laid down on the granitic rocks. These deposits are represented by the Reagan sandstone in the Arbuckle Mountains.   Above the sandstones the Arbuckle limestone was deposited in late Cambrian and early Ordovician time.   This formation was in places eroded, and above it were deposited, in Ordovician time, the various members of the Simpson group, including the Burgen, Tyner,

---

to the writer by Professor Gould.   No. 40Q, by Bess Mills-Bullard, gives notes on each oil field, together with a map showing the locations of the fields.   No. 40G, by Sidney Powers, is an account of the history of the exploration of the oil fields.   A map on a scale of 1:500,000, by G. B. Richardson, was issued by the U. S. Geological Survey in 1927.   The list of papers that follows is intended to include the more recent papers of general interest.   Other references are stated on following pages.

WHITE, L., Subsurface Distribution and Correlation of the pre-Chattanooga (Wilcox Sand) Series of Northeastern Oklahoma, Okla. Geol. Survey *Bull.* 40B, pp. 1–23, 1926.

LEVORSEN, A. I., Convergence Studies in the Mid-Continent Region, Am. Assoc. Pet. Geol., *Bull.*, vol. 11, pp. 657–682, 1927.

AURIN, F. L., G. C. CLARK, and E. A. TRAGER, Notes on the Subsurface pre-Pennsylvanian Stratigraphy of the Northern Mid-Continent Oil Fields, Am. Assoc. Pet. Geol. *Bull*, vol. 5, pp. 117–153, 1921.

FOLEY, L. L., The Origin of the Faults in Creek and Osage Counties, Oklahoma, Am. Assoc. Pet. Geol. *Bull*, vol. 10, pp. 293–300, 1926.

DOTT, R. H., Pennsylvanian Paleogeography with Special Reference to South Central Oklahoma, Okla.Geol. Survey *Bull.* 40J, pp. 1–22, 1927.

GOULD, C. N., Index to the Stratigraphy of Oklahoma, Okla. Geol. Survey *Bull.* 35, pp. 1–116, 1925.

MISER, H. D., Geologic Map of Oklahoma, U. S. Geol. Survey, 1926.

————, Structure of the Ouachita Mountains, Oklahoma and Arkansas, Okla. Geol. Surv. *Bull.* 50, pp. 1–30, 1929.

Section of Northeastern Oklahoma

(Above Mississippian after Gould; below Mississippian after White)

Group	Thickness, feet	Description
Permian:		
Enid..................	1,500	Red shales and clays, gypsum, sandstone
Wellington...........	225 —	Shales. blue, green, red; thin sandstone, limestone, some salt
Marion...............	150 —	Limestone and shale, includes Herrington limestone
Chase group..........	240–300	Includes, in Kansas, Wreford limestone, Melfield shale, Florence flint, Fort Riley limestone, Doyle shale, and Winfield limestone
Council Grove group...	150 —	Cottonwood limestone below; Garrison shale and limestone above
Pennsylvanian:		
Eskridge..............	40–60	Shale, brown, green, yellow; thin limestone
Neva.................	12–30	Limestone, thin bedded with shale, chert concretions
Elmdale..............	104	Shale, variegated, thin limestone, contains Cushing limestone
Sand Creek...........	200	Limestone at top and bottom, shale and sandstone between
Buck Creek...........	175	Limestone, shale, sandstone
Pawhuska.............	130–180	Limestone, shale, some sandstone to south
Elgin................	50–210	Sandstone, more shaly to north
Nelagoney............	500–600	Shales and sandstone, a 20-foot limestone near middle
Ochelata.............	400–480	Shale with sandstone and limestone members
Dewey................	3–20	Limestone usually shaly
Nellie Bly...........	15–200	Shale and sandstone (Bristow and Copan-Nelagoney to Nellie Bly)
Hogshooter...........	4–20	Limestone, massive; thin bedded to south
Coffeyville..........	225–435	Shale, blue or green; a 3-foot limestone (Checkerboard) at base
Lenapah..............	6–20	Limestone, dense, blue, partly crystalline
Nowata...............	50–600	Shale, some coal, a few sands; thickens to south
Altamont.............	30+	Limestone, blue, gray, cherty (equivalent to Oologah limestone)
Bandera..............	0–100	Shale, green or yellow, sandy
Pawnee...............	35–40	Limestone, cherty, white, gray or blue
Labette..............	20–80	Shale, sandy shale, shaly sandstone, brown and green
Fort Scott..........	34–200	Limestone, known as "Oswego lime" and Wheeler oil sand at Cushing
Cherokee.............	450–1,000	Shale, coal, oil sands, including Bartlesville
Unconformity.		
Morrow...............	100–120	Sandstone, limestone, shale

SECTION OF NORTHEASTERN OKLAHOMA.—(*Continued*)

(*Above Mississippian after Gould; below Mississippian after White*)

Group	Thickness, feet	Description
Mississippian.		
Unconformity.		
Pitkin..............	0–80	Limestone, at places earthy and shaly
Fayetteville..........	0–150	Shale, dark, bituminous, some limestone, and sandstone
Unconformity.		
Boone..............	0–450	"Mississippi Lime," limestone, chert, cherty limestone
Chattanooga.........	0–50	Shale commonly regarded as Devonian
Sylamore............	0–25+	Sand ("Misener") carries oil, commonly regarded as Devonian
Unconformity.		
Devonian-Silurian:		
Hunton..............	0–415±	White or gray limestone, carries oil 5 miles west of Stroud; 4 miles east of Seminole
Ordovician:		
Sylvan..............	0–125	Light blue shale somewhat calcareous. (Maquoketa age)
Viola...............	0–50	White limestone "buttermilk limestone," Fernvale age, gray near base. In Arbuckle area Viola is much thicker (500–600)
Unconformity.		
Post Wilcox (Simpson?)	0–140	Sandy dolomitic limestone, green shale, thin sandstone
Wilcox..............	0–300	White sand, more uniform, finer grained than Burgen but coarser at top of formation, grains angular, "frosted"
Tyner..............	0–150	Shale, green, sandy, red streaks, locally sandy dolomitic limestone
Burgen.............	0–100	Sand, various sizes, rounded grains, commonly cemented to form quartzite
Lower Simpson........	0–400	Sandy shales and sands
Unconformity.		
Cambro-Ordovician:		
Arbuckle............	50–5,000	"Siliceous Lime," "Turkey Mountain Sand," dolomitic limestone with highly porous phases at upper eroded surfaces
Reagan.............	0–	Sandstone
Pre-Cambrian:		Granite

Mainly from Luther White, *Oil Gas Jour.*, vol. 24, p. 60, Apr. 1, 1926.

CHIEF PRODUCING HORIZONS OF NORTHERN OKLAHOMA

(After Gould, Levorsen, Mills-Bullard, and others)

Permian:

Hoy (Garber field, 1,100 foot sand)
Kisner
Hotson (Garber field, 1,425 foot sand)

Pennsylvanian:

Blackwell
Newkirk
Hoover series: Upper Hoover, Middle Hoover, Lower Hoover
Elgin
Musselman
Carmichael
Endicott
Tonkawa (Stalnaker, Swaggert, Jones, Ponca)
Layton
Cleveland
Big Lime
Peru
Oswego (Wheeler, Fort Scott)
Prue (Bixler, Squirrel, Perryman)
Red Fork (Skinner)
Bartlesville (Salt, Glenn, Bluejacket, Burbank)
Tucker (Booch, Taneha)
Gilcrease (Dutcher, Youngstown, Boynton)
Wapanucka (Lyons)
Smith (Sykes, Cromwell, Papoose, Burgess)

Mississippian:

Mississippi Lime
Chattanooga
Misener sand (Sylamore sand)

Siluro-Devonian:

Hunton limestone

Ordovician:

Sylvan
Viola limestone
Simpson group
    Wilcox
    Tyner
    Burgen

Cambro-Ordovician:

"Siliceous Lime" (Arbuckle limestone, Turkey Mountain)

and "Wilcox" sand formations (Fig. 169). As shown by White, these
formations wedge out to the northeast, chiefly on account of pre-Chattanooga erosion, and the later formations overlap the older ones to the
northeast (Fig. 170). The Viola limestone of the Ordovician lies unconformably above the Simpson, and the Sylvan shale of the Ordovician
was laid down on the Viola limestone. The Hunton group of Silurian
and Devonian age were deposited on the Sylvan shale. In Seminole
County a broad arch was formed after the Hunton was laid down, and
the Hunton was eroded from a large area. This erosion surface is prob-

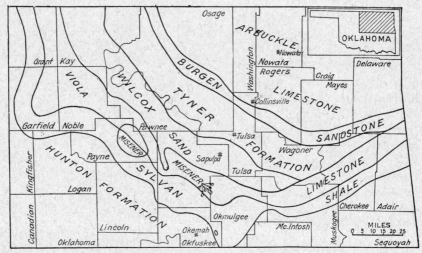

Fig. 169.—Map of northeastern Oklahoma, showing the distribution of rock formations as they would crop out if Chattanooga shale and later rocks were removed. (*After
Luther White.*)

ably of great extent for at most places the Mississippian rocks lie unconformably above the Hunton formation. The Devonian rocks which at
places are present above the Hunton were eroded over much of the area
before the Mississippian strata were laid down. The Misener sand at
the base of the Chattanooga shale (Mississippian) represents, in part,
the old residuary material that accumulated during this erosion interval.

On the Misener, or on older strata where the Misener was absent,
the Chattanooga shale and Mississippian limestone were deposited in
Mississippian time. In southern Oklahoma the Mayes and Caney
formations (Mississippian) were deposited on the Chattanooga shale.
Since the Mississippian strata were deposited on a gently folded and
eroded surface, at places the Mississippian rests on the Arbuckle limestone
and at other places on younger rocks. The Mississippian strata were at
places folded and faulted. Extensive erosion followed and the eroded
surface was tilted southeast. On it were deposited the Pennsylvanian
and Permian strata. The sea in which the Pennsylvanian beds were laid

down slowly expanded to the northwest, so that the Pennsylvanian formations wedge out to the northwest, the latter overlapping the younger members to the northwest (Fig. 171). The Pennsylvanian rocks increase in thickness about 15,000 feet between Okmulgee and the Ouachita Mountains.

In Pennsylvanian time, during the deposition of the Oswego, Calvin, and Palo Pinto limestones, there was a great southeast dipping monocline, probably extending from the Ozarks to the Llano uplift. After the Permian beds were deposited, the area was tilted downward to the west or northwest.

The folding of the Wichita-Arbuckle Mountains is mainly Pennsylvanian and older, but in part, post-Permian. In the Arbuckle Mountains the Permian red beds are much less folded than the Pennsylvanian strata. The tilting of the beds of the Great Plains monocline away from the Ozark-Llano line must have taken place largely after Permian time, because the Permian beds are tilted approximately the same amount as the Pennsylvanian beds.

Craig, Nowata, Rogers, and Washington Counties.—Craig County lies west of Ottawa County which contains the great zinc and lead deposits of Oklahoma. The Carboniferous rocks dip westward into Craig County and in the Vinita field along the

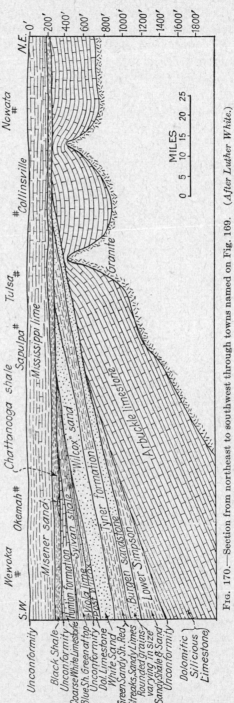

Fig. 170.—Section from northeast to southwest through towns named on Fig. 169. (*After Luther White.*)

Rogers-Craig county line (Figs. 172, 173) oil is found in the Burgess sand above the "Mississippi lime" at a depth of 400 feet. In the southern part of Nowata County there is an area of low folding on which are located the Delaware, Childers, Coody's Bluff, and Alluwe fields and the Chelsea[1]

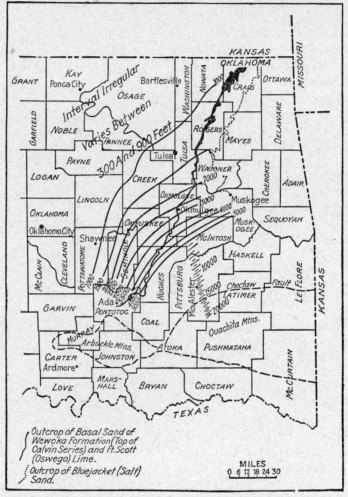

Fig. 171.—Isopach map of eastern Oklahoma showing the interval between the Calvin-Fort Scott horizon of the Pennsylvanian series and the Viola of the Ordovician. Contour Interval 500'. (*After Levorsen.*)

field in Rogers County. In this area oil or gas is found in the Big Lime, Oswego, Bartlesville, and Burgess horizons, the latter lying at about 1,000 feet deep or less. At Lenapah, north of Delaware in an area of minor folding, oil is found in the Bartlesville sand at a depth of 940 feet. In Califor-

[1] MILLS-BULLARD, BESS, Digest of Oklahoma Oil and Gas Fields, Okla. Geol. Survey *Bull.* 40Q, pp. 1–181, 1928.

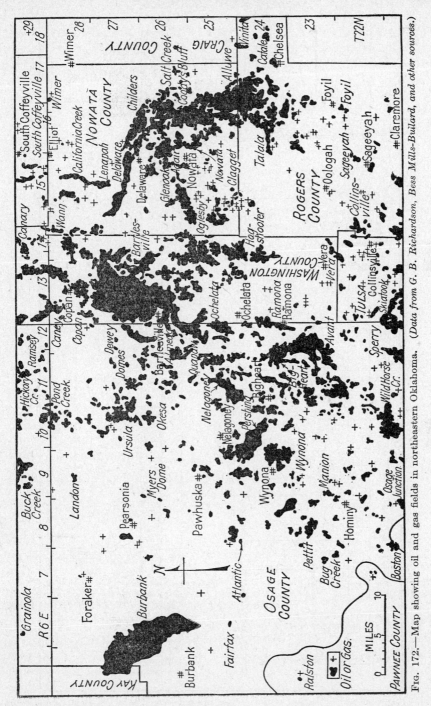

Fig. 172.—Map showing oil and gas fields in northeastern Oklahoma.   (Data from G. B. Richardson, Bess Mills-Bullard, and other sources.)

State Teachers College Library
Willimantic, Conn.

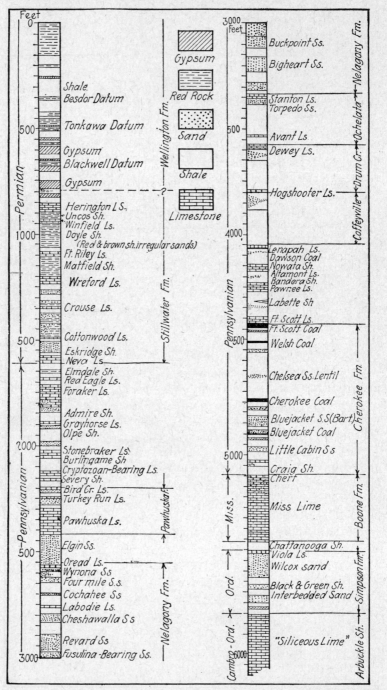

Fig. 173.—Generalized section of rocks cropping out in northern Oklahoma. (*Based on section by Clark and Cooper.*)

nia Creek north of Lenapah gas occurs in structural terraces in the Tucker sand at a depth of 1,020 feet and in the Mississippian limestone at 1,145 feet. At Elliot oil is found in the Bartlesville sand on low anticlines at a depth of 1,040 feet. This field was opened in 1909, and in 1924 the wells were put on air pumps which greatly increased production. At South Coffeyville oil is found chiefly in the Bartlesville sand which lies 920 feet deep. In the Wann pool west of Elliot oil is found on a monocline in the Bartlesville sand at a depth of 1,000 feet, and gas is found in the Burgess sand 1,200 feet deep. The Glenoak pool southwest of Delaware is a small gas field producing gas from the Oswego sand and Mississippi limestone, and small amounts of oil from the Peru, Bartlesville, and Burgess sands. The Adair field, south of Glenoak and 6 miles southwest of Nowata, produced oil from many small wells in the Bartlesville sand which lies 1,025 feet deep.

The Delaware Extension field extends northwest from Delaware about 8 miles. The oil is derived from the Bartlesville sand at a depth of 800 feet on the east and 1,200 feet on the west end of the field. According to Lewis,[1] the sand probably fills an ancient river channel similar to some of the shoestring sand channels of Kansas.

The Nowata-Claggett field south of Delaware produces from the Big Lime and Oswego formations and from the Bartlesville and Burgess sands, the latter lying 1,350 feet deep. At Collinsville these and the Redfork sands are productive.

In Washington[2] County, west of Nowata County, the Pennsylvanian rocks dip northwest 20 to 25 feet per mile. At the east edge of the county the Coffeyville formation crops out, and in the northwest part of the county the Nelagoney formation is exposed (p. 275). The chief oil sands

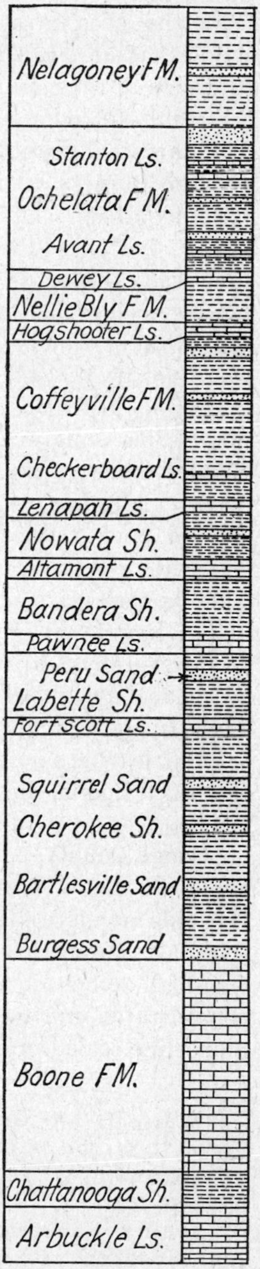

[1] LEWIS, J. O., Delaware Extension Pool, Nowata County, Oklahoma, "Structure of Typical American Oil Fields," vol. 2, pp. 362–364, 1929.

[2] CARPENTER, E., Geology of Washington County, Okla. Geol. Survey *Bull.* 40V, pp. 1–20, 1928.

FIG. 174.—Generalized geologic section, Washington County, Oklahoma. (*After Carpenter.*)

are the Peru, Bartlesville, and Burgess sands (Fig. 174).　In many of the
fields the oil is in sands on shallow domes; other pools are in lenticular
sands that are sealed up dip.　The fields are closely spaced and every
township in the country has produced oil.　The Dewey-Bartlesville field
is a gently folded area about 12 miles long and extends across the county.
The Bartlesville sand, which is the chief producer, is about 1,275 feet deep,
and the Burgess sand, which has produced considerable gas, is 1,400 to
1,500 feet deep.　Oil is found in the Big Lime, Peru, and Oswego formations.　In this field there were 4,816 producing wells in 1914.　The field is
practically drilled up.　The Canary pool, northeast Washington County,
produces oil from the Bartlesville and Tucker sands.　The Copan field
southwest of Canary produces oil from the Oswego and Siliceous limes and
gas from the Wayside and Burgess sands.　The Burgess sand occurs at a
depth of 1,800 feet and the gas had an initial pressure of 450 to 530
pounds per square inch.　In the Caney pool near the Kansas line the
Bartlesville sand lies 1,185 feet deep, is 50 feet thick, and produces both
oil and gas, while the Burgess sand 1,450 feet deep yields gas.　The Hog-
shooter pool southeast of Bartlesville was formerly a very productive
gas field, producing mainly from the Bartlesville, and Burgess sands.
The Bartlesville sand produces both oil and gas.　At Ochelata, south
of Bartlesville oil is produced from the Prue and the Bartlesville sand.
In the Oglesby field, southeast of Bartlesville, the Bartlesville sand, which
is 985 feet deep, produces oil and gas, and the Burgess sand produces
gas.　In the Ramona field south of Ochelata oil is produced chiefly from
the Bartlesville sand which lies 1,687 feet deep.　At the Vera pool southeast of Ramona the Bartlesville sand, which is the chief oil producer,
is 1,350 feet deep.

Osage County.—In the eastern part of Osage County[1] the structure is
similar to that of Washington County.　West of Range 11 East (Fig. 172)
the folds are more sharply defined.　There are numerous key beds and the
folds are mapped at the surface.　Many of the folds strike north and
the small domes tend to lie in broken lines.　The oil and gas are generally
concentrated in domes.　In the Burbank field, however, the reservoir is a
monocline sealed up dip.

[1] White, D., and others, Structure and Oil and Gas Resources of the Osage Reservation, U. S. Geol. Survey *Bull.* 686, pp. 1–427, 1922.

Beckwith, H. T., Geology of Osage County, Okla. Geol. Survey *Bull.* 40T,
pp. 1–63, 1928.

Fath, A. E., Geology of the Eldorado Oil and Gas Field, Kan. Geol. Survey *Bull.*
7, p. 150, 1922.

Heald, K. C., The Oil and Gas Geology of the Foraker Quadrangle, Osage
County, Oklahoma, U. S. Geol. Survey *Bull.* 641, pp. 17–47, 1917.

Foley, L. L., The Origin of the Faults in Creek and Osage Counties, Oklahoma,
Am. Assoc. Pet. Geol. *Bull.*, vol. 10, pp. 293–303, 1926.

In the Hickory Creek[1] district, northeastern Osage County, there is a series of anticlines that trend north. The oil is found chiefly in the Oswego formation at a depth of 900 feet and in the Bartlesville sand at 1,000 feet. Gas is found in the Mississippian limestone at 1,300 feet. At Pond Creek southwest of Hickory Creek, where also there are gentle anticlines striking north, the oil is found at depths of about 1,235 feet in the Peru sand and at 1,680 feet in the Burgess sand. At Ursula gas is found in an area of anticlinal folding in the Oswego and Burgess formations, but larger amounts are derived from the Mississippi lime. In the Domes district east of Ursula oil and gas are concentrated in domes and anticlines, the chief production coming from the Bartlesville sand and the Mississippian limestone. At Okesa southeast of Ursula the chief oil production is from the Bartlesville sand which lies 1,527 feet deep. At Almeda east of Okesa oil is found in the Bartlesville sand. At Myers dome southwest of Ursula the Burgess sand 2,400 feet deep yields oil, and at Pearsonia northwest of Myers dome anticlinal folds yield much oil from the Mississippian limestone which is found about 2,410 feet deep.

The Skiatook field is in southeast Osage County and extends into Tulsa County. It lies just north of the Bird Creek field. The main productive horizons are the Bartlesville and Burgess sands. The Bird Creek-Flat Rock field (Fig. 175) in southern Osage and northern Tulsa county was one of the first fields to be developed in Oklahoma and has yielded oil from more than 1,000 wells. The structure is not clearly defined, although structural terraces and open anticlines are identified in the field. The chief production is from the Bartlesville and Burgess sands, the latter lying at a depth of about 1,345 feet.

The Sand Springs, or Charles Page, field near Flat Rock, 6 miles west of Tulsa (Fig. 175, 176), produces oil from the Tucker sand, and recently large amounts have been found in the Siliceous limestone; the latter lies 2,177 feet deep.

In the Pawhuska[2] field (Fig. 172) southeast of Pearsonia, small domes developed on a monocline yield oil and gas. The section exposed is shown by Fig. 177. The chief production of oil is derived from Bartlesville and Burgess sands and from the "Siliceous lime" formation of the Ordovician. The Ordovician formation lies about 2,900 feet deep. About 12 miles southwest of Pawhuska,[3] oil is produced from four domes, the main production coming from the Layton and Burgess sands and from the underlying Ordovician formations which include the "Siliceous" limestone and probably the Tyner sand.

[1] MILLS-BULLARD, BESS, Digest of Oklahoma Oil and Gas Fields, Okla. Geol. Survey *Bull.* 40Q, p. 20, 1928.

[2] HEALD, K. C., Geologic Structure of the Northwestern Part of the Pawhuska Quadrangle, Oklahoma, U. S. Geol. Survey *Bull.* 691, pp. 57–100, 1919.

[3] STEPHENSON, C. D., An Oil Field in T. 25 N., R. 8 E., Osage County, Oklahoma, "Structure of Typical American Oil Fields," vol. 2, pp. 378–395, 1929.

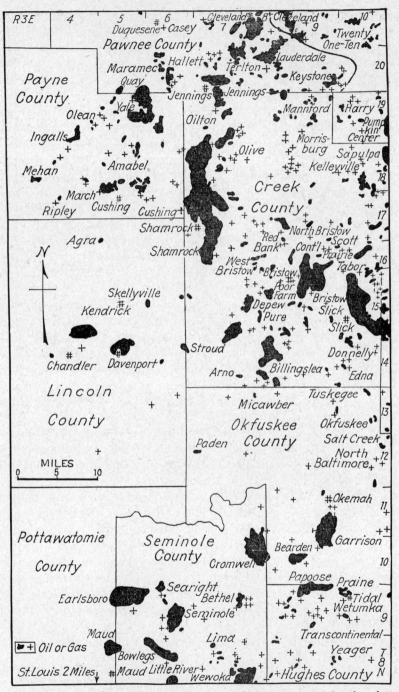

FIG. 175.—Map showing oil fields of northeastern Oklahoma. Area joins that shown by Fig. 176 on east. (*Data from Richardson, Mills-Bullard and others.*)

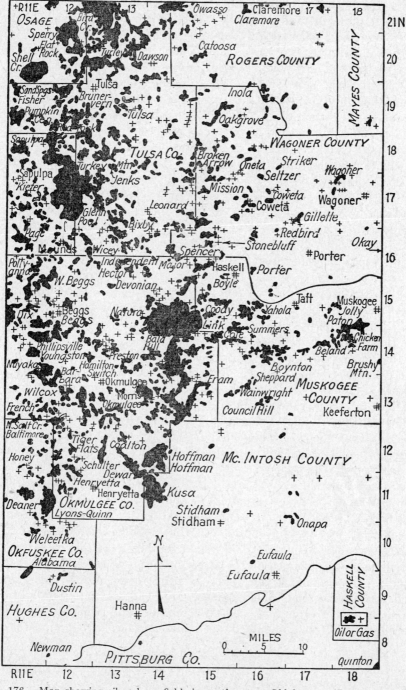

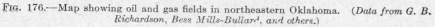

FIG. 176.—Map showing oil and gas fields in northeastern Oklahoma. (*Data from G. B. Richardson, Bess Mills-Bullard, and others.*)

In the Pershing[1] field 10 miles southeast of Pawhuska, oil is found in the Bartlesville sand in a belt that strikes northwest and is about 8 miles long and 2 miles wide. This belt includes two domes, and, except in the southeast portion, the oil field lies on these domes. In the southeast part of the field the oil deposit lies on a shallow syncline and rises up the regional monocline, which suggests that there is cementation of the sand up dip. Gas occupies the high parts of the domes at most places, but at certain parts of the field oil and gas are found near the tops of the domes in smaller amounts than lower on the flanks. Rubey suggests that this may be due to cementation of the sand by precipitation of calcite near the top of the structure. The Bartlesville sand is about 2,035 ft. deep.

The Wynona field southwest of Pershing is on an elongated dome that strikes northwest and has 30 feet of closure at the surface which increases with depth. Oil is found in the Peru sand, Oswego lime, and Bartlesville sand, 2,100 feet deep, and in the Burgen sand (Ordovician). The Quapaw pool northeast of Pershing is on an anticline. Most of the production comes from the Bartlesville sand from wells on the north and northwest flanks of the fold. The sand on the top of the fold is tight and dry. The Barnsdall or Bigheart field southwest of the Quapaw field produces oil from the Bartlesville and Peru sands.

In the Hominy field southwest of Wynona oil is found near the top of the Mississippian limestone, in the Hominy (Ordovician) sand and in the "Siliceous lime." In the Boston field southwest of Hominy two domes are located on an anticline. Wells on these domes encounter oil in the Bartlesville sand at about 2,300 feet and about 13 wells produce oil from the Arbuckle limestone about 400 feet deeper.[2] The field has produced about 11,500,000 barrels of oil. In the Pettit field southwest of Pawhuska and near Hominy a dome is located on an anticline that is exposed at the surface. Oil is found in a sand at a depth of 800 feet and below that in the Cleveland, Big Lime, Oswego, and Bartlesville formations. The largest production, however, is from a horizon called the Hominy sand, which is a pay zone at the top of the Arbuckle limestone about 2,600 feet deep, and from the Arbuckle (Siliceous) limestone 2,650 feet deep. The Wildhorse Creek field southeast of Hominy is on two adjoining domes mapped on the surface that are connected by a shallow saddle. Oil is found in the Cleveland sand, Oswego limestone, Skinner and Bartlesville sands and from the Mississippian limestone and also from the Tyner formation. The Bartlesville sand which is found at a depth of 1,800 feet is about 100 feet thick and has supplied most of the

[1] RUBEY, W. W., Progress Report on a Subsurface Study of the Pershing Oil and Gas Field, Osage County, Oklahoma, U. S. Geol. Survey *Bull.* 751B, pp. 23–70, 1925.

[2] BECKWITH, H. T., Geology of Osage County, Okla. Geol. Survey *Bull.* 40T, p. 49, 1928.

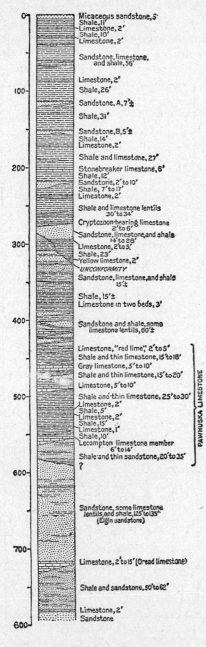

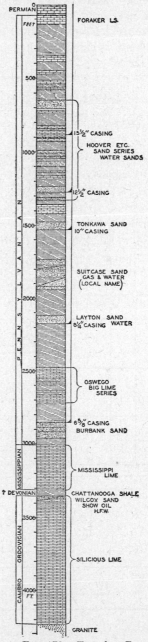

FIG. 177.—Section of rocks exposed in part of Pawhuska Quadrangle, Oklahoma. (*After Heald.*)

FIG. 178.—Type log, Burbank field, Osage and Kay counties, Oklahoma. (*After Sands.*)

oil of the district.   Wildhorse is one of the largest producers from the
Bartlesville sand in Osage County.

The Buck Creek area near the Kansas line produces oil chiefly from the
Peru sand.   The Landon field 6 miles south of Buck Creek produces

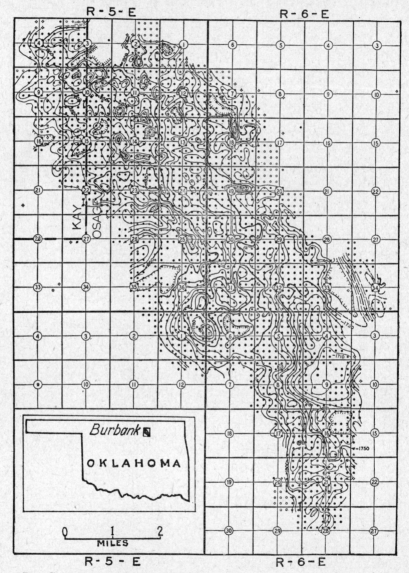

Fig. 179.—Contour map of Burbank district, Oklahoma.   Contoured on top of Burbank
sand; sea level datum.   (*After Sands.*)

oil from the Bartlesville sand, which is 2,890 feet deep and from higher
sands.   West of Buck Creek near Grainola (Frankfort) on a dome,
some oil is found in the Peru sand at a depth of about 2,040 feet, and

gas is found in the Mississippi lime at 2,905 feet. At Foraker southeast of Grainola and also on a dome, gas is found in the Burbank sand and oil in the Mississippian limestone at 2,750 feet.

The Burbank[1] field is in Osage and Kay counties, 40 miles west of Bartlesville. Oil was discovered in this field in 1920, and in 1927 over

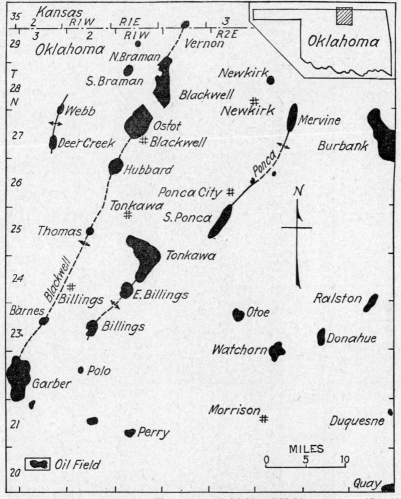

Fig. 180.—Outline map of parts of Kay, Grant, Garfield and Noble counties. (*Data from Clark, Cooper and from other sources.*)

130,000,000 barrels of oil had been produced from 2,000 wells. The rocks are of Pennsylvanian age (Figs. 178, 179) overlain in the west part of the field by the Permian. The production is from the Burbank sand

[1] SANDS, J. M., Burbank Field, Osage County, Oklahoma, Am. Soc. Pet. Geol. *Bull.*, vol. 11, pp. 1045–1054, 1927; vol. 8, pp. 584–592, 1924.

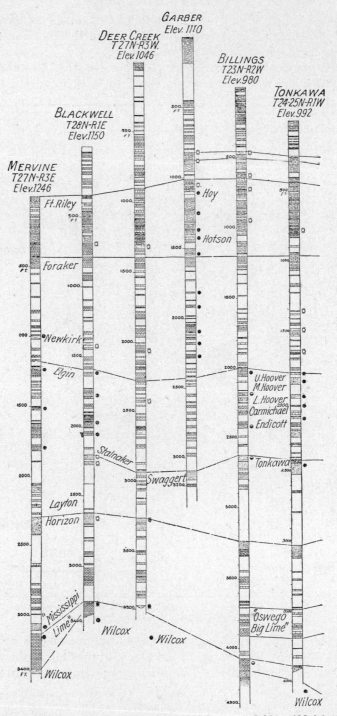

GARBER
Elev. 1110

DEER CREEK
T27N-R3W.
Elev. 1046

BILLINGS
T23N-R2W
Elev. 980

TONKAWA
T24-25N-R1W
Elev. 992

BLACKWELL
T28N-R1E
Elev. 1150

MERVINE
T27N-R3E
Elev. 1246

Ft. Riley

Hoy

Hotson

Foraker

Newkirk

Elgin

U. Hoover
M. Hoover
L. Hoover
Carmichael
Endicott

Stalnaker

Swaggert

Tonkawa

Layton
Horizon

"Mississippi Lime"

Wilcox

Wilcox

"Oswego Big Lime"

Wilcox

Wilcox

FIG. 181.—Correlation of well logs of northern Oklahoma oil fields. (*Mainly from G. C. Clark and F. L. Aurin.*)

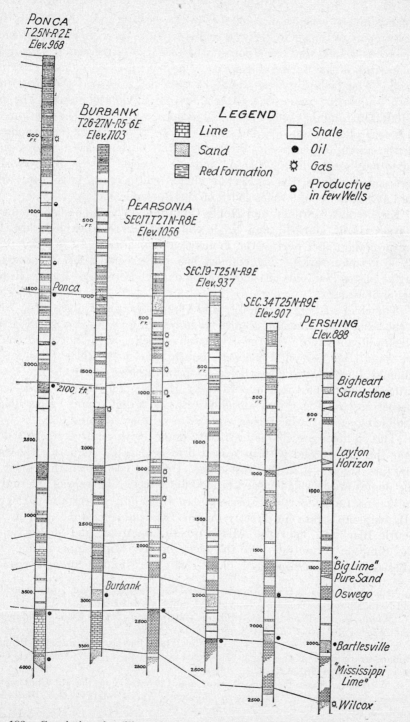

FIG. 182.—Correlation of well logs of northern Oklahoma. (*Mainly from G. C. Clark and F. L. Aurin.*)

which is met at a depth of 2,800 feet in the eastern and 3,200 feet in the western part of the field.   It is 50 to 80 feet thick, is a siliceous sand with calcareous cement and has a porosity of 13.7 to 32.7 per cent.   It is near the horizon of the Bartlesville sand.   The "Wilcox" contains a showing of oil.   The beds dip west about 35 feet per mile and the structure is an undulating monocline with a few small domes on it.   The oil is found in and between the small domes, and the concentration of oil is controlled by porosity and seems to have little relation to the domes. On the north and east sides of the field the Burbank sand grades into impervious sandy shale.   The oil and gas traveled up the dip from the west and stopped at the impervious shale.   Oil is found in the Burbank sand at Fairfax pool 6 miles south of the Burbank pool.

Kay, Grant, Garfield, and Noble Counties.—West of Osage County, in Kay, Grant, Garfield, and Noble counties[1] the rocks exposed are the strata of the upper part of the Pennsylvanian series and the lower part of the Permian series.   The country has a low regional dip to the west, but at places low folds are shown similar to those of the Granite Ridge region of Kansas.

The chief structure extending into Oklahoma from Kansas (Fig. 180) is the axis of the Nemaha granite ridge which in Oklahoma is called the Blackwell anticline.   On the Blackwell anticline from north to south are found the Vernon, Blackwell, South Blackwell, Retta (Hubbard), Thomas, Barnes, and Garber fields.   On an anticline east of the Blackwell anticline are found the Tonkawa, East Billings, and Billings fields, and farther east on the Ponca anticline are the Mervine and Ponca fields. Producing sands in this region are shown by Figs. 181 and 182.

The oil fields are characteristically domes with relatively gentle dips near the surface and with increased dips in depth.   As a rule the east dips are steeper than the west dips.   Drilling has shown that most of the domes are refolded buried eroded anticlines.   There was a period of uplift and erosion before Mississippian time, for, in certain fields the Mississippian strata lie directly on the Arbuckle limestone, and in the South Blackwell field the Mississippian limestone and shales lie on the Simpson formation.   At the close of the Mississippian time, the Mississippian limestone and older rocks were folded up and eroded,

---

[1] Clark, G. C., and L. C. Cooper, Oil and Gas Geology of Kay, Grant, Garfield, and Noble Counties, Okla. Geol. Survey *Bull.* 40H, pp. 1–44, 1927.

Aurin, F., Pre-Pennsylvanian Oil and Gas Horizons in Kay County, Oklahoma, Am. Assoc. Pet. Geol. *Bull.*, vol. 4, pp. 173–181, 1920.

————, G. C. Clark, and E. A. Trager, Notes on the Subsurface pre-Pennsylvanian Stratigraphy of the North Mid-Continent Oil Fields, Am. Assoc. Pet. Geol. *Bull.*, vol. 5, pp. 117–153, 1921.

White, L., Subsurface Distribution and Correlation of the Pre-Chattanooga (Wilcox sand) Series in Northeastern Oklahoma, Am. Assoc. Pet. Geol. *Bull.* 40B, pp. 1–23, 1926.

the whole series, including part of the Arbuckle limestone, being truncated. These anticlinal hills were not everywhere eroded to base level, for beds of fragmental chert, originally in the Mississippian limestone, accumulated on the sides of the hills before the Pennsylvanian rocks were laid down but did not extend over the tops of the hills. A third period of folding followed the deposition of Permian beds.

The Vernon field is on a small dome on the Blackwell anticline and produces gas from the Endicott horizon at 2,000 feet, oil from the Stalnaker sand at 2,300 feet, and from the chat or chert debris at the top of the Mississippi lime at 3,400 feet.

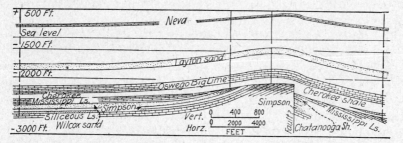

Fig. 183.—Cross section through Blackwell field, Kay County, Oklahoma. (*After S. K. Clark and J. I. Daniels.*)

The Blackwell[1] field is on a dome shown indistinctly at the surface. This dome is made up of two smaller domes separated by a low saddle. Gas is found at a depth of 700 feet above the north dome and oil is found in the Upper and Lower Hoover sands (Fig. 181) in the Endicott sand and gas is found in the Layton sand. The structure below the Cherokee shale is that of a very low buried hill or refolded anticline. The Siliceous limestone, Simpson formation, and Mississippian limestone were folded and nearly peneplained before the Cherokee shale was deposited. Oil is found in large amounts in the Simpson and "Siliceous Lime" formations at the unconformity below the Cherokee shale (Fig. 183).

The South Blackwell[2] field near the town of Blackwell is also a buried ridge, but the long axis of the dome extends northwest and southeast. On the west side of the field a fault which displaces Permian beds dips west about 45 degrees. Gas is found in the Neva limestone and oil in the Stalnaker and 3,100-foot sands of the Pennsylvanian. Below an arched unconformity (Fig. 184) which truncates the Mississippian limestone, oil and gas are found at the top of a subsurface dome in the Simpson ("Wilcox") sand.

[1] CLARK, S. K., and J. I. DANIELS, Relations between Structure and Production in the Mervine, Ponca, Blackwell, and South Blackwell Fields, Kay County, Oklahoma, "Structure of Typical American Oil Fields," vol. 1, pp. 158–175, 1926.

[2] CLARK, C. G., and C. L. COOPER, Oil and Gas Geology of Kay, Grant, Garfield, and Noble Counties. Okla. Geol. Survey *Bull.* 40H, p. 41, 1927.

The Retta[1] (Hubbard) field southwest of Blackwell is on a dome faulted along the longer axis by a fault which strikes N.10° E., dips 45 degrees west and is normal with 150 feet of displacement. The fault shows at the surface. Gas and oil are developed in the Stalnaker sand at a depth of 2,500 feet. The Layton sand at 2,950 feet produces oil, the wells yielding 100 to 200 barrels a day. Wells 3,600 feet deep to the "Wilcox" produce 300 to 1,300 barrels each per day. Certain wells have encountered Siliceous limestone (Arbuckle) at a depth of

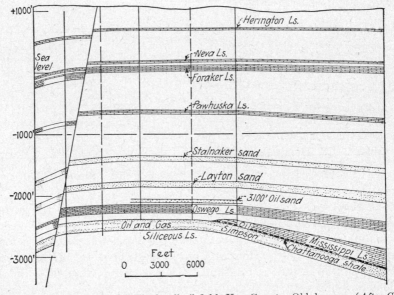

Fig. 184.—Cross section South Blackwell oil field, Kay County, Oklahoma. (*After Clark and Daniels.*)

3,700 feet and have produced oil from a horizon in that formation 150 feet below its top. Wells to the Arbuckle limestone cause trouble with water.

The Thomas[2] field is 8 miles southwest of Hubbard field and west of Tonkawa. The Rocks are closely similar to those of Blackwell. Two faults (Fig. 185) have raised a small block of pre-Pennsylvanian beds several hundred feet above the surrounding beds. The top of this elevated block was partly eroded before the Pennsylvanian beds were laid down, but a considerable hill remained, and, when the Pennsylvanian rocks were deposited, they were arched above the block, forming a dome which becomes flatter near the surface. The producing sands include

[1] Truex, A. F., *Oil Gas Jour.*, vol. 24, p. 15, Oct. 15, 1925.

[2] Clark, S. K., Thomas Oil Field, Kay County, Oklahoma, Am. Assoc. Pet. Geol. *Bull.*, vol. 10, pp. 643–655, 1926.

the 1,900-foot sand, the Thomas sand 100 feet lower, the Turk, the cherty accumulation at the top of the Mississippian limestone, and the "Wilcox" sand. The field had produced 3,000,000 barrels of oil July 1, 1926, most of it from the "Wilcox" sand. The oil is the green oil characteristic of the region, with a gravity of about 43° Bé. In Barnes[1] field south of Thomas, probably on the same fold, oil is found in the Barnes sand at a depth of 2,000 feet. The Sarah Whipple field southwest of Barnes produces oil from the Wilcox sand at a depth of about 5,300 feet. The structure is probably a faulted anticline.

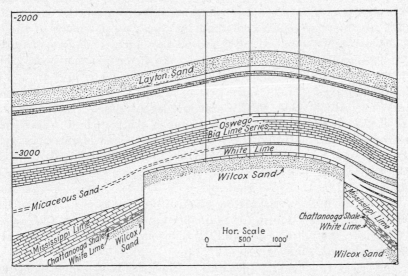

Fig. 185.—North-south section of Thomas field, Oklahoma. (*After S. K. Clark.*)

The Garber[2] field (pp. 120 and 285) is in Garfield County about 12 miles southwest of Billings. A structural dome on the Blackwell anticline occupies an area of about 10 square miles and was contoured on Permian beds. A well on the Hoy farm in 1917 was brought in yielding 90 barrels of oil per day. Later oil was found in other sands, and, in all, 20 horizons of Pennsylvanian and Permian age produced oil and gas. In 1925 wells sunk to the Ordovician strata found large amounts of high-grade oil at depths of about 4,300 feet, and on March 19, 1927, the field had produced 36,000,000 barrels of oil. The Hartley 27 well of the Sinclair Oil Company had an initial production of 25,000 barrels a day.

The closure of the Garber dome increased with depth, and, like most of the domes in this group, it presents a steeper side to the east than to

[1] MILLS-BULLARD, BESS, Digest of Oklahoma Oil and Gas Fields, Okla. Geol. Survey *Bull.* 40Q, p. 142, 1928.

[2] GISH, W. G., and R. M. CARR, Garber Field, Garfield County, Oklahoma, "Structure of Typical American Oil Fields," vol. 1, pp. 176–191, 1929.

CLARK, G. C., and C. L. COOPER, Okla. Geol. Survey *Bull.* 40H, pp. 1–44, 1927.

the west.   It is a buried refolded anticlinal hill.   The folding took place
in pre-Mississippian, post-Mississippian, and Permian time; as shown by
Clark's section (Fig. 81), there was strong folding in post-Mississippian
time.   Gish and Carr state that there was probably a great anticlinal hill
during the deposition of the Mississippian limestone and that the limestone
was not being greatly eroded during the post-Mississippian erosion interval,
because there are no great chert beds such as those found on the flanks
of the Tonkawa and Thomas buried hills.   The Arbuckle limestone is
very porous and is the reservoir rock of the major accumulation in pre-
Pennsylvanian sediments.   According to Gish and Carr, the Ordovician
strata are the chief source beds, and they believe that much of the oil
above the top of the buried hill migrated through the numerous fissures,
that are discovered in the district, into the Pennsylvanian beds.   The
temperature of the oil usually increases before salt water appears.

North Braman, 5 miles northwest of Blackwell field, is a flat-topped
buried hill, which slopes gently east and steeply west.   In the highest
part of the structure production is found in Siliceous lime where wells
yielding 2,500 barrels a day are drilled.   To the east of this area wells
yielding as much as 8,500 barrels a day are drilled to the "Wilcox" sand.
Shallow production is found in the Lower Hoover sand at a depth of
1,900 feet and in the Upper Endicott at 2,100 feet.

The South Braman[1] field is on a sharp fold that is probably faulted.
Production is obtained from the Stalnaker sand at 2,387 feet, the Layton
at 2,800 feet, the Wilcox sand, and the Siliceous lime, which is found at a
depth of about 3,350 feet.

The Deer Creek field 12 miles west of Blackwell is on a small elongated
dome with an axis striking north.   This dome is one of the most sharply
folded in this region, having 1,250 feet of structural relief on the Ordovician rocks.   It has produced oil from the Swaggert (Tonkawa) and
Wilcox sands and large amounts of gas from four sands, the deepest of
which is the Wilcox.   The Webb field north of Deer Creek produces oil
from the Tonkawa and Wilcox sands.

Tonkawa[2] field, Kay County, lies between the line of granite ridge
structures that include Blackwell, Thomas, and Garber and the line of
folding through Mervine and Ponca fields.   The producing sands include
six beds of the Pennsylvanian and the "Wilcox" sand of Ordovician age.
The Pennsylvanian had produced 49,258,000 barrels of oil to January 1,
1926.   The Wilcox sand at that date had produced 28,305,000 barrels.

[1] *Op. cit.*, p. 44.

[2] CLARK, G. C., Wilcox Sand Production, Tonkawa Field, Oklahoma, Am. Assoc.
Pet. Geol. *Bull.*, vol. 10, pp. 885–891, 1926.

————, and F. L. AURIN, The Tonkawa Field, Oklahoma, Am. Assoc. Pet. Geol.
Bull., vol. 8, pp. 269–283, 1924.

HOSTERMAN, J. F., The Tonkawa Oil and Gas Field, Oklahoma, Am. Assoc. Pet.
Geol. *Bull.*, vol. 8, pp. 284–300, 1924.

The wells are sunk through 950 feet of Permian beds, then 900 feet of Pennsylvanian, then through 750 feet also Pennsylvanian containing five productive sands, including the Tonkawa at a depth of about 2,500 feet.

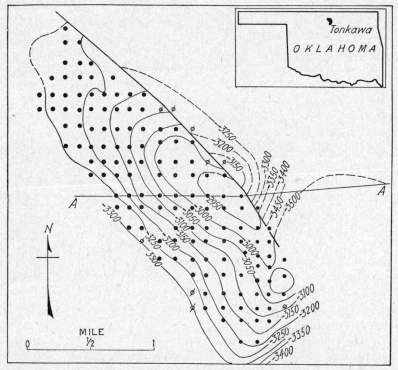

Fig. 186.—Contour map showing position of Wilcox sand Tonkawa field Oklahoma. (*After G. C. Clark.*)

Below the productive zone is one 1,550 feet thick which carries little pay. Below the Pennsylvanian beds are the Mississippian limestone, Chattanooga shale, Viola limestone, and the Wilcox sand. The oil field is on a

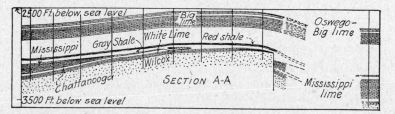

Fig. 187.—Cross section of Tonkawa field, Oklahoma, along line *AA*, Fig. 186. (*After G. C. Clark.*)

dome of which the major axis strikes northwest and a minor axis southwest. The Mississippian rocks were folded and faulted along the northeast side of the dome before the Pennsylvanian rocks were deposited, and at the top of the dome the Mississippi lime and at places also the Viola are eroded (Figs. 186, 187). A red shale 50 feet above the ancient eroded surface is an easily recognized horizon. The structure of the Pennsylvanian rocks is possibly in part a reflection of the topography of the buried hills. The amplitude of the folds increases with depth. The dips on the southeast side of the dome are steeper than those on the northwest side, and the axis of the dome shifts east with depth. The Wilcox, which is found at a depth of about 4,000 feet, is 280 feet thick and rests on the "Siliceous lime." The top 40 feet of the Wilcox is productive; below that is a non-productive zone 20 to 30 feet thick and below that a 60-foot productive zone. Below the latter are dark shales alternating with sandstone.

The East Billings[1] field, 7 miles east of Billings, is on the southwestern extension of one of the axes of the Tonkawa field. It was drilled on the axis on an anticline mapped by Fath,[1] and the oil was developed in the Upper Hoover sands which lie about 2,000 feet deep. A show of oil is found in the Mississippi lime.

The Billings field is 6 miles southeast of Billings. Drilling has revealed a dome with 500 feet of closure, covering 10 square miles and a producing area of one square mile. The dome is in line with East Billings and Tonkawa, but it does not show elongation on the line. Oil is found at many horizons, including the Upper Hoover, Tonkawa, and Mississippi lime.[2] Many of the wells have had large initial production but they decline rapidly.

The Mervine field 6 miles southeast of Newkirk was drilled on a structure discovered by Gould,[3] of which maps were published in 1913. The field is located on a strong well-defined dome with a long axis striking northeast. Oil is found in several sands on top of the dome. The productive horizons include the Newkirk (Mervine), Hoover, Endicott, Stalnaker and Burbank sands, and the Mississippian limestone. A promising field was opened about 10 miles northeast of Perry in 1930.

The South Ponca field, also called Ponca field, is 16 miles southwest of the Mervine field and 2 miles south of Ponca City. It was the first field drilled in Oklahoma west of Osage County. A gas well was drilled in 1910 and oil was developed in the 1,500-foot sand in 1917. The field is on a pronounced dome. Gas is found in the basal Permian,

[1] FATH, A. E., An Anticlinal Fold Near Billings, Noble County, Oklahoma, U. S. Geol. Survey *Bull.* 641, pp. 121–138, 1917.

[2] CLARK, G. C., and C. L. COOPER, Okla. Geol. Survey *Bull.* 40H, p. 28, 1927.

[3] OHERN, D. W., and R. E. GARRETT, The Ponca City Oil and Gas Field, Okla. Geol. Survey *Bull.* 16, p. 161, pl. 2, 1912.
CLARK, G. C., and C. L. COOPER, *op. cit.*, p. 23.
OHERN, D. W., and R. E. GARRETT, The Ponca City Oil and Gas Field, Okla. Geol. Survey *Bull.* 16, pp. 1–30, 1915.
CLARK, S. K., and DANIELS, J. T. *op. cit.*, pp. 163–164, 1929.

gas or oil in six sands in the Pennsylvanian, and oil in the Mississippian limestone and the Wilcox sand. The later rocks rest unconformably on the Mississippian limestone and Ordovician rocks, and the dome is more steeply folded below the unconformity suggesting two periods of folding, one before, the other after the erosion interval represented by the unconformity. The Mississippian limestone was removed from the top of the anticlinal hill during the erosion interval, and chert from the Mississippian was deposited on its flanks. Oil is found in chert horizons on the flanks of the ancient dome but not on its summit.

The Morrison[1] field (Watchorn), Pawnee County, is 20 miles south of Ponca City. A large gas well in the Tonkawa sand was brought in in 1915, and the field soon became an important producer of gas. In 1922 an oil well was completed in the Layton sand at 2,752 feet. This well was deepened to the Wilcox sand in 1923 and had an initial production of 650 barrels. The Mississippian limestone which is found 3,750 feet deep also produces oil. The producing area is 320 acres and the field to the close of 1926 produced 4,566,800 barrels of oil. Permian rocks crop out and a small dome is contoured on the surface, using the Fort Riley limestone as a datum. This shows 40 feet or more of closure, and the closure increases with depth. The Wilcox sand, which is found at a depth of about 3,800 feet, has produced 90 per cent of the oil of the district. The Wilcox sand shows 150 feet of closure.

Wagoner County.—The Carboniferous rocks dip west into Wagoner[2] County (Fig. 176) and the Mississippian rocks lie at the surface just east of the east edge of the county. The Lower Pennsylvanian rocks crop out at its east edge. The Carboniferous and older rocks are faulted by northeast faults, one of which is the Seneca that is followed 80 miles into Missouri. This fault has a throw of 300 feet at places, and the rocks are thrown into folds that lie parallel to the faults.

In the Oakgrove district in the northwest part of the county oil is produced from the Pitkin sand at a depth of 785 feet; gas from the Chattanooga shale at 900 feet; from the Tyner sand at 1,000 feet; and oil from the Burgen sand at 1,190 feet. The pre-Pennsylvanian beds lie in a dome which does not show at the surface. The Oneta field south of Oakgrove field produces oil from the Dutcher sand which lies in domes at depths of about 1,200 feet. The Striker field, 5 miles east of Oneta, lies in a faulted area and produces oil chiefly from the Morrow-Pitkin sand which is about 915 feet deep. The Wagoner field, northwest of the town of Wagoner, is also in a faulted area. The oil is derived from the Dutcher sand and from Ordovician formations. In the Seltzer

[1] CARPENTER, E., The Morrison Field, Pawnee County, Oklahoma, Am. Assoc. Pet. Geol. *Bull.*, vol. 11, pp. 1087–1096, 1927.

[2] BOYLE, J. P., Geology of Wagoner County, Okla. Geol. Survey *Bull.*, 40L, pp. 1–18, 1927.

field 3 miles southwest of Striker, oil is found in the Dutcher sand. The Coweta district is 12 miles west of Wagoner and 3 miles northeast of Coweta. A fault of the Seneca system strikes northeast, and the beds rise on both sides of the fault to form a sharp anticline. Oil is produced from a sand at a depth of 791 feet. A gas field at the east edge of Coweta lies on a low dome located on a fault of the same system and produces gas from a sand of the Dutcher series. The same sand produces oil in a series of small anticlines parallel to the Seneca fault in the field 2 miles east of Coweta. In a field near Redbird, 6 miles southeast of Coweta, oil is found on an anticline located along the footwall of a small normal fault.

At Gillette, 8 miles southwest of Wagoner, oil is found in the Tyner formation at a depth of 1,320 feet. In the Stone Bluff district, 5 miles south of Coweta in a faulted region, oil is produced from the Misener sand about 1,800 feet deep. At Webster in an area of local folds oil is found in the Burgen sand at a depth of 1,160 feet. In the Mission field, 6 miles northwest of Webster field in an area of faulting, oil is found in the Tyner sand at a depth of 1,495 feet and in the Burgen sand at 1,840 feet. In the Porter field in the southwest part of the county gas is found in the Dutcher and Burgen sands. At Okay field in the southeast part of the county a little oil is found at a depth of about 550 feet in the Dutcher sand which lies in domes.

Muskogee County.—The strata exposed in Wagoner County extend southward into Muskogee County, and the lower Pennsylvanian rocks crop out at the east border of the county. The Jolly-Paton or Bradley field is on the southwest border of Muskogee city. Pennsylvanian rocks crop out. Oil is produced from sands at depths of 512, 675, and 707 feet. The Chicken Farm field joins the Jolly-Patton field on the southwest. Oil is produced from lenticular sands which include the Oswego sand at a depth of 400 feet, the Tucker sand at 700 feet, the Boynton at 1,200 feet and the Taneha at 1,350 feet. The Beland field southwest of the Chicken Farm produced oil from Pennsylvanian sands and gas from the Wilcox sand, which is 2,250 feet deep. The Timber Ridge field lies between Chicken Farm and Beland fields. The Boynton field, which lies west of Beland, is located in an area of anticlinal folding. Oil or gas is produced from the Salt, Booch, Mounds, Leidecker, and Boynton sands and from the Mississippi lime, which is 1,800 feet deep. The Cole field northwest of Boynton produces gas from a sand 1,475 feet deep and oil from a sand 1,610 feet deep. The Booch Sand field, 2 miles south of Coody, produces from the Booch sand at a depth of 1,075 feet, and the Link field east of the Booch Sand field produces oil from a sand at 2,044 feet. The Haskell field, which is 5 miles southwest of the town of Haskell, produces oil from a sand 1,360 feet deep, gas from a sand 1,850 feet deep, and oil from a sand 1,900 feet deep. The Yahola field

5 miles south of Haskell has produced much gas from the Salt (Bartlesville) sand which is found at a depth of about 670 feet.   Oil and gas are produced from the Booch sand 1,220 feet deep and from the Boynton sand 1,320 feet deep.   The Butler field near Summers produces oil from a sand about 1,250 feet deep.

McIntosh County and Area South and East.—The rocks that are exposed in Muskogee County strike south into McIntosh[1] County. Gas is developed in several districts in McIntosh County and also in the area to the south and east of the county.   The carbon ratio of coals increases to the south and east of Muskogee County, and it is commonly believed that oil in the reservoirs in these directions may have been

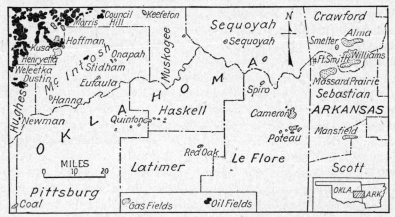

Fig. 188.—Map showing oil and gas fields in east central Oklahoma and west central Arkansas.

converted to gas.[2]   This theory has been questioned, yet it is a fact that drilling in the region south and east of Muskogee County has discovered only small amounts of oil (Fig. 188).

The productive horizons in the eastern part of McIntosh County, in descending order, are Salt, Booch, Morris, Glenn of Morris, and Fields sands, the three last named being in the Dutcher group of Pennsylvanian age.   The Lyons-Quinn sand near the base of the Pennsylvanian also is productive.   In the northwest part of the county the Glenn sand, which lies 1,250 feet deep, produces gas, and the Booch sand, 1,550 feet deep, produces gas and some oil.   In the Kusa field these sands produce gas, and the Dutcher sand, which is 1,800 feet deep, produces oil.   In the

[1] CLARK, R. W., Geology of McIntosh County, Okla. Geol. Survey *Bull.* 40W, pp. 1–14, 1928.

CRAM, I. B., Cherokee and Adair Counties, Okla. Geol. Survey *Bull.* 40QQ, pp. 1–59, 1930.

[2] FULLER, M. L., Carbon Ratios in Carboniferous Coals of Oklahoma, *Econ. Geol.*, vol. 15, p. 232, 1920.

Stidham field 8 miles southeast of Kusa, a little oil is encountered at a depth of 1,170 feet.

In the Onapa field 10 miles east of Stidham gas is found in sands of the Pennsylvanian series. In the Eufaula district 8 miles southeast of the Stidham field, considerable gas is found in the Booch sand. In the Hanna field, southwest McIntosh County, gas is found in several sands. In the Quinton district, Pittsburg County, gas is produced from five sands that lie between 1,470 and 2,729 feet deep. Red Oak field is southeast of Quinton. Gas is found on an anticline at a depth of 2,500 feet. In the Poteau field east of Red Oak gas is found on an anticline at depths of 1,300, 1,500, 1,830, and 2,000 feet. In the Cameron field it is found in anticlines at 1,575 and 1,900 feet. In the Spiro field northwest of Cameron gas is found at a depth of about 1,600 feet. In the Sequoyah field northwest of Spiro it is found in several sands on the Vian anticline. In the Coal district in Coal County gas is found on the Savanna anticline at a depth of 1,400 feet.

Western Arkansas.—Natural gas is found at Massard Prairie, 5 miles southeast of Fort Smith, Arkansas; at Mansfield, 25 miles southeast of Fort Smith; at Williams and Alma, east of Fort Smith (Fig. 188). The gas[1] is found mainly in the Atoka formation (Pennsylvanian), which consists of shale and sandstone and is about 7,000 feet thick. The sandstones are about 100 feet thick and lie between thick zones of shale. Gas is found also in the Hartshorne formation which lies above the Atoka and consists mainly of sandstone 100 to 200 feet thick. The rocks are thrown into sharp folds and the gas fields are located on the anticlines. The Clarksville gas field is on the Clarksville anticline about 50 miles east of Fort Smith and 5 miles northwest of Clarksville. Eight gas wells have been drilled. The gas is found at depths between 2,000 and 2,400 feet in several sands of the Atoka formation. The wells have initial flows as high as 8,000,000 cubic feet per day.

Okmulgee County.—The Pennsylvanian strata dip westward from Wagoner into Okmulgee[2] County. The strike of the beds changes to about N. 25° E. and the beds dip west 50 to 90 feet per mile. A fault parallel to the faults of the Seneca fault system strikes southwest to near Morris. Two main anticlines are identified, one striking southwest from Schulter toward Henryetta and another north-northeast from Hoffman. Oil and gas are found in the Pennsylvanian and in the "Wilcox" group of strata below the Pennsylvanian. The structures[3]

---

[1] SMITH, C. D., Structure of the Fort Smith-Poteau Gas Field, Arkansas and Oklahoma, U. S. Geol. Survey *Bull.* 541, p. 23, 1914.

COLLIER, A. J., The Arkansas Coal Field, U. S. Geol. Survey *Bull.* 326, 1907.

[2] CLARK, R. W., Geology of Oil and Gas Development in Okmulgee County, Oklahoma, Okla. Geol. Survey *Bull.* 40F, pp. 1–28, 1926.

[3] LEVORSEN, A. I., Convergence Studies in the Mid-Continent Region, Am. Assoc. Pet. Geol. *Bull.*, vol. 11, pp. 657–682, 1927.

below the Pennsylvanian are difficult to interpret at the surface, because of the great thickening to the southeast of Pennsylvanian beds.

A generalized section of south-central Oklahoma, compiled from Gould's summary,[1] is shown on page 300. At many places certain

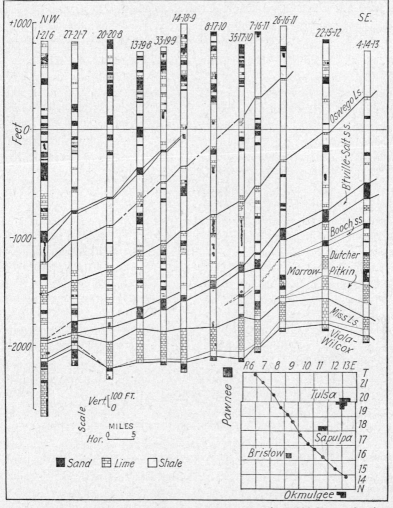

FIG. 189.—Cross section between Okmulgee and Pawnee areas Oklahoma, showing converging of strata to northwest. (*After Levorsen.*)

formations are wanting. The southeast divergence of the strata of the Carboniferous system is shown by Fig. 189. Oil is found in several sands of the Pennsylvanian system, in the Misener and "Wilcox" sands. In

[1] GOULD, C. N., Index to the Stratigraphy of Oklahoma, Okla. Geol. Survey *Bull.* 35, pp. 1–115, 1925.

GENERALIZED SECTION OF SOUTH-CENTRAL OKLAHOMA NORTH OF ARBUCKLE
MOUNTAINS

(Mainly after Gould)

Formation	Thickness, feet	Description
Pennsylvanian:		
Pontotoc...............	1,000–1,500	Conglomerate, sandstone, shale, limestone, red beds, may be in part Permian
Ada....................	100	Shales, sandstone, limestone conglomerate
Vamoosa...............	250	Conglomerate, sandstone, shale
Belle City.............	30	Limestone and shale
Coffeyville............	400	Shales and sandstone, checkerboard limestone (3 feet) near base (Francis)
Seminole..............	15–355	Sandstone and conglomerate
Holdenville...........	180–260	Shale, some sandstone and limestone
Wewoka...............	50–700	Sandstone, shale, upper part cross-bedded, more shale than lower part
Wetumka..............	80–120	Shale with thin sandy shale beds
Calvin................	145–240	Sandstone, becomes shaly at base
Senora................	50–500	Sandstone and shale, Henryetta sand, becomes shale to north
Stuart................	90–280	Shale
Thurman..............	80–250	Sandstone, massive, shaly in east part Okmulgee County
Unconformity		
Boggy................	1,200–2,600	Shales, some sandstone in upper part, some limestone
Savanna..............	1,150±	Interbedded brown sandstone and shale
McAlester............	2,000	Shale, sandstone and coal, includes Salt sand 50 to 200 feet thick, oil and gas, correlated with Glenn of Glenn pool and Bartlesville sand
Hartshorne...........	100–200	Sandstone with some shale (Booch)
Atoka................	2,000–7,800	Shale with sandstone lenses, some limestone (Dutcher and Gilcrease sands)
Unconformity		
Wapanucka............	0–800±	White to brown limestone, chert, sandstone, shale; equivalent to Morrow
Unconformity		
Pennsylvanian-Mississippian:		
Caney Creek...........	800–1,600	Dark shale with thin limestone and sandstone in upper parts
Unconformity		
Mississippian:		
Sycamore.............	0–200	Limestone
Woodford.............	600–650	Chert, correlated with Chattanooga shale
Devonian:		
Bois d'Arc............	0–90	Limestone, white to gray, crystalline
Harragan.............	0–166	Shale, soft, marly, some limestone
Silurian:		
Henryhouse...........	0–223	Shale, soft gray, some marly limestone
Unconformity		
Chimney Hill..........	0–53	Limestone, oolitic, glauconitic, crinoid
Unconformity		
Ordovician:		
Sylvan................	50–300	Shale, greenish or greenish blue
Viola.................	500–800	Limestone, heavy bedded, massive
Unconformity		
Simpson..............	1,200–2,000	Sandstone, thin limestone, greenish shale
Unconformity		
Arbuckle..............	4,000–8,000	Limestone, massive, thin bedded at top and bottom

the latter the oil is found at depths between 2,200 feet in the east part of the county and 3,300 feet in the west part. There are 18 pools in the Wilcox sand in the county, which, in general, cover less than 80 acres each but are very rich in oil. These are found chiefly on small domes where at the surface small structural noses plunge northwest. These noses, with terraces up dip, commonly indicate small domes at depths below the Pennsylvanian rocks, because of the great divergence of the Pennsylvanian strata to the southeast (page 66). The oil of the Pennsylvanian sands has a gravity of about 35° Bé. and that of the Wilcox about 40 to 44° Bé.

In eastern Okmulgee County there is a large area known as the Bald Hill field, which includes the subdistricts Mose-Carr, Jolly Ogg, Pine Pool, and Booch fields. In this region the Salt sand (Bartlesville) lies within 750 feet of the surface and is the shallowest producing sand. The Booch which is about 1,200 feet deep, the Red Fork 1,300 feet deep, Morris 1,575 feet, Glenn of Morris 1,700 feet, Fields 1,850 feet, Lyons-Quinn 1,950 feet and Wilcox 2,250 feet are productive. The oil of this field is light with a gravity of about 42° Bé. The Eram field south of Bald Hill field produces oil from the Dutcher sand 1,900 feet deep and from the Wilcox sand at 2,700 feet. The field is located on a subsurface dome.

The Morris field west of Eram is an area of anticlinal folding. Oil (36° Bé.) is found in nine sands and in most of them in large amounts. The sands lie at depths between 450 and 2,580 feet and include a stray sand, the Salt sand (Glenn 700 feet deep), first Booch, second Booch, Morris, Glenn of Morris, Fields, Lyons-Quinn, and Wilcox. In the Okmulgee field west of Morris, oil and gas are found in the Bartlesville sand at a depth of 1,240 feet, in the Booch at 2,000 feet, in the Dutcher at 2,400 feet, and gas is found in the Wilcox sand at 2,750 feet. Brinton field, 3 miles west of Okmulgee, produces oil from the Pennsylvanian and from the Wilcox. In the Schulter field 8 miles south of Okmulgee, the productive sands are the Red Fork, Glenn 1,963 feet, Booch, Deaner, and Lyons-Quinn 2,390 feet deep. In Tiger Flats west of Schulter the Glenn, Booch, Deaner, and Lyons sands yield oil. In the Coalton field east of Schulter, oil is produced from the Booch, second Dutcher, and Wilcox sands. The Hoffman field 12 miles southeast of Okmulgee has produced much gas from Pennsylvanian sands. The Wilcox sand recently opened has produced oil from a subsurface dome. The Henryetta field, 10 miles south of Schulter, produces gas from several Carboniferous sands and oil from the Lyons-Quinn sand which lies 2,630 feet deep. The Wilcox and "Siliceous" formations also produce gas. The Lyons-Quinn field west of Henryetta produces oil from the Deaner and Lyons sands, the latter lying 2,600 feet deep. Deeper sands, including the Wilcox, produce gas. French field lies 3 miles north of Lyons-Quinn field and produces oil from the Salt and Booch sands and gas from other sands.

The Spencer district near the north line of Okmulgee County produces oil from the Red Fork and Dutcher sands. The Independent or Sheridan district west of Spencer is an extension of the Mounds field of Creek County. The oil is produced from the Dutcher and Wilcox sands. The Hector district in northeastern Okmulgee County produces oil from the Salt sand at 800 feet, from the Glenn, Booch, and Dutcher sands of the Pennsylvanian and also from the Mississippian limestone and Wilcox sand. Natura produces gas from numerous sands and oil from the Glenn of Morris and Wilcox sands. The Devonian field north of Natura produces oil from the Glenn and Wilcox sands and gas from several sands. The Pollyanna pool, west of Independent, produces oil from the Glenn sand which is 1,840 feet deep and from the Taneha 2,285 feet deep. A little oil is found in the Wilcox sand. The Hamilton Switch field near Okmulgee has produced considerable oil from the Glenn sand 1,385 feet deep and the Dutcher sand 2,020 feet deep. Youngstown, which is west of Hamilton Switch, produces oil from the same sands, and also from the Youngstown sand which lies between them at a depth of 2,250 feet. Phillipsville, west of Youngstown, produces oil chiefly from the Wilcox sand, which lies in a dome about 2,750 feet deep.

The Preston district is about 6 miles northeast of Okmulgee in an area of local folding. Oil is obtained from the Glenn sand 1,400 feet deep, from the Booch 1,700 feet deep, and from the Dutcher 2,000 feet deep. The Beggs field is about 10 miles northwest of Okmulgee. Oil is derived chiefly from the Taneha sand about 1,700 feet deep, from the Dutcher 2,090 feet deep, and the Wilcox sand. The Mississippi formation also produces some oil. Dix or Oklahoma-Central district is west of Beggs and produces oil from the same formations.

Okfuskee County.—The Pennsylvanian rocks dip westward from Okmulgee and McIntosh Counties into Okfuskee County (Figs. 175, 176). The Okfuskee district in northeastern Okfuskee County produces oil from the Dutcher sand, which is 2,660 feet deep. North Baltimore district 8 miles southeast of Okfuskee produces from the Deaner sand 2,470 feet deep and also from the Lyons and Hunton sands. In the Okemah field oil is found in the Deaner sand at a depth of 2,970 feet. Midwest district south of Okemah produces from the Deaner and Lyons sands. In the Deaner field the Deaner sand 2,800 feet deep produces oil. The Lyons produces at 3,150 feet and the Wilcox sand at 3,650 feet. The Lyons-Quinn field, which is partly in Okfuskee County, has been mentioned under Okmulgee County.

The Weleetka field, 5 miles south of Lyons-Quinn field, produces oil from the Gilcrease sand at about 2,600 feet deep. Bearden, north of Papoose, produces gas from the same sands. Garrison field east of

Bearden and south of Okemah produces oil from the Gilcrease and the Cromwell sands (Figs. 25, 26).

The Micawber field in northwest Okfuskee County produces oil from the Wheeler sand 2,430 feet deep and from the Dutcher sand 3,470 feet deep. The Paden field south of Micawber produces oil from the Prue, Bartlesville, and Dutcher sands, the latter lying 3,796 feet deep.

Hughes County.—In Hughes County south of Okfuskee County, in the Alabama field, gas is found in the Glenn sand and oil in the Deaner and Lyons sands. The Dustin pool in the northeast part of the county (Figs. 175, 176) produces oil from the Lyons sand. In the Papoose field in the northwest part of the county drilling has developed a sub-surface dome where some oil is produced from the Gilcrease sand 3,070 feet deep and larger amounts from the Papoose sand 3,350 feet deep.

Wetumka is in an area of faulting and about 3 miles east of the Papoose field. It produces oil from the Dutcher and Papoose sands. Transcontinental or Fuhrman, 5 miles south of Papoose, produces from a dome fold in Papoose sand which is 3,350 feet deep. Yeager, 6 miles south of Transcontinental, produces oil and gas from several Pennsylvanian sands, oil from the Papoose sand, and gas from the Hunton limestone and the Wilcox sand. At Newman, 12 miles east of Yeager, one well produces oil from the Lyons sand. This well yields an oil which solidifies when cold and has been called the "vaseline" well. The Sesakwa field some 8 miles north of Allen and 8 miles south of Wewoka produces considerable oil from Simpson beds.

Tulsa County.—The early production of Tulsa County was derived from the Bartlesville, Burgess, and other sands of the Pennsylvanian. Later, considerable oil was found in the Ordovician strata which include the "Turkey Mountain sand." The Turkey Mountain sand is a porous dolomite about 60 feet thick or less, which lies upon and generally is included in the Arbuckle limestone. It produced oil in several fields in Tulsa and Osage Counties.[1] As a rule the fields are small but have produced considerable oil. The top of the limestone is an old eroded surface. The best production comes from the porous gray member of the limestone below the unconformity, especially where the plane of the unconformity is arched up. The fields producing from the Turkey Mountain sand include Turkey Mountain, Country Club, Bruner, Inscho, Oakhurst, Fisher, Bowden, and Glidden.

The Collinsville, Owasso, Bird Creek-Flat Rock fields which are partly in Tulsa County have been mentioned. Sperry, west of Collinsville (Fig. 172), produces oil and gas from the Bartlesville, Taneha, and Burgess sands, the latter at 1,335 feet deep, and oil from the Mississippi lime. The Tyner produces oil and gas and is encountered at 1,760 feet.

[1] RUEDEMANN, P. and H. E. REDMON, Turkey Mountain Lime Pool, Oklahoma, Am. Assoc. Pet. Geol. *Bull.*, vol. 11, pp. 933–944, 1927.

The Dawson field northeast of Tulsa (Fig. 175) produces oil from the Bartlesville sand which is 850 feet deep and much gas from the Burgess sand and Mississippian limestone.   At Turley field, near Dawson, oil and gas are produced from the Pennsylvanian formations and also from the "Siliceous" or Arbuckle limestone.   In the Tulsa field, southeast of Tulsa, a large number of formations between the Perryman and Wilcox inclusive yield oil.   Approximately the same formations produced oil at Turkey Mountain, 8 mile south of Tulsa.   In this field the Turkey Mountain limestone, which produces oil and gas, is 2,145 feet deep.   The Bruner-Vern field, southwest of Tulsa, produces gas from the Burgess sand and considerable oil from the Tyner and Turkey Mountain formations.   The Country Club field northwest of Tulsa, 2 miles west of the country club, produces oil chiefly from the Wilcox and Turkey Mountain formations.   The Red Fork field is 5 miles southwest of Tulsa.   Wells in the Pennsylvanian with small yields and long lives were among the first to be developed in Oklahoma.   Recently, oil and gas were encountered in the Turkey Mountain limestone at depths of about 2,160 feet. The Fisher district, 6 miles northwest of Red Fork, produces chiefly from the Turkey Mountain formation, which is 2,400 feet deep.   At the Broken Arrow field, 15 miles southeast of Tulsa, the chief production is from the Bartlesville sand, which lies 1,350 feet deep, although gas and some oil are found in deeper formations.   In the Jenks field, west of Broken Arrow, oil is found in the Red Fork, Bartlesville, Dutcher, and Mississippi formations.   In the Leonard field south of Broken Arrow, oil is derived from the Layton, Red Fork, and Bartlesville formations, the latter lying 1,500 feet deep.   The Bixby field, west of Leonard and 4 miles southwest of Bixby, is a small but highly productive field deriving oil from the Glenn, Taneha, Dutcher, and Wilcox sands.   Wicey, on the south border of the county, produces oil from the Glenn, Taneha, and Dutcher sands.

Creek County.—In Creek County[1] the surface rocks at most places dip westward at low angles.   Locally, low folds are developed on the westward-dipping monocline.   The oil-bearing sands in order of increasing age are Musselman, Layton, Cleveland, Wheeler (Oswego lime), Prue, Skinner, Red Fork, Bartlesville, Taneha (Tucker, Booch), Dutcher, Mississippi lime, Misener, Wilcox, and Turkey Mountain (Siliceous lime).

[1] MERITT, J. W., and O. G. McDONALD, Oil and Gas in Creek County, Okla. Geol. Survey *Bull.* 40C, pp. 1–47, 1926.

AURIN, F. L., G. C. CLARK, and E. A. TRAGER, Notes on the Subsurface pre-Pennsylvanian Stratigraphy of the North Mid-Continent Oil Fields, Am. Assoc. Pet. Geol. *Bull.* 5, pp. 121–153, 1921.

FATH, E. A., Geology of the Bristow Quadrangle, U. S. Geol. Survey *Bull.* 759, pp. 1–63, 1925; also *Prof. Paper* 128, pp. 75–84, 1921.

FOLEY, L. L., Origin of the Faults in Creek and Osage Counties, Oklahoma, Am. Assoc. Pet. Geol. *Bull.*, vol. 10, pp. 293–303, 1926.

The Misener sand, as already noted, is laid down on an erosion surface of Devonian age and, with the Chattanooga shale, is included by White in the Mississippian. The "Wilcox" sand of Ordovician age produces a light gravity oil at several places in the southern part of the county. It shows more folding than beds above it and generally produces prolifically from small and relatively steep domes. The "Siliceous Lime" produces oil in the northeastern part of the county.

The chief oil fields in Creek County are the Cushing and Glenn fields, in which the Bartlesville sand has produced most of the oil; the Bristow or Continental field, in which the Bartlesville and Dutcher sands are productive; and the Slick field in the southeastern part of the county, in which the Cherokee and Wilcox sands are productive.

The Glenn field is on a monocline sealed up dip by the lensing out of the oil sand. The Cushing field is on a strong closed anticline. The fields near Bristow as a rule do not show closed structures at the surface, but are crossed by closely spaced faults that strike northwest. In certain of these fields, however, subsurface mapping has shown that some of the producing structures show low domes and closed anticlines

SECTION OF GLENN POOL AND AREA TO THE EAST
(After Smith, Wilson)

	Feet
Carboniferous:	
Pennsylvanian:	
Limestone, blue gray, locally called Lost City limestone.............	1–40
Shale and sandstone...	350
Limestone, bluish, hard, locally called Checkerboard................	$2\frac{1}{2}$
Shales with beds of sandstone....................................	215
Coal, Dawson..	$1\frac{1}{2}$–$2\frac{1}{2}$
Shale with irregular beds of sandstone...........................	210–350
Limestone, massive gray, "Big Lime".............................	35
Shale with irregular beds of sandstone...........................	150
Limestone, Fort Scott or "Oswego," 4-foot shale near middle........	20
Cherokee shale, contains Red Fork, Bartlesville, Taneha and Dutcher	
sands...	1,000 ±
Unconformity.	
Mississippian:	
Mississippi limestone..	230
Chattanooga shale, black..	60
Unconformity.	
Ordovician:	
Simpson:	
Mounds or "Wilcox" sandstone...................................	20–50
Tyner formation...	60
Burgen sandstone...	20
Arbuckle limestone[1]...	500 ±

[1] About 8 miles northwest of the pool a well passed through 600 feet of Arbuckle limestone into granite.

where contoured on the oil sands. The Depew field,[1] southwest of Bristow, is on a low anticline with a long axis that strikes nearly north.

The Glenn pool[2] southwest of Tulsa and 30 miles east of Cushing pool is one of the most productive of the Mid-Continent field. In 1907 it yielded oil at the rate of 120,000 barrels a day, and in 1927 it yielded about 10,500 barrels daily from 4,000 wells. The rocks dip west about 50 feet to the mile but show gentle terraces where they are nearly flat. There is broad fluting down dip.

The Glenn pool produces from the Big Lime, Oswego, Glenn (Bartlesville), and Taneha formations of the Pennsylvanian series. The chief production is from the Bartlesville sand. The surface shows little or no structure except the fluting on the monoclinal dip. The Bartlesville sand shows small domes and troughs, but these are about equally productive. This sand lenses out to the east and fingers into shale, decreasing from 100 feet in thickness to nothing, as shown by Figs. 61 and 62. Along the west margin of the field the oil rests on salt water in the Bartlesville sand about 950 feet below sea level. A cross-section after Smith is shown by Fig. 190.

In the Wilcox sand oil is accumulated on small domes with barren areas between. Wells to this sand averaged 100 barrels a day initial production, but the oil is of low gravity and the development disappointing. Wilson believes that the lighter oil from the Wilcox escaped during the period of erosion represented at the top of the sand. Oil has been developed also in the Hominy sand and Turkey Mountain limestone, the latter lying 2,250 feet deep.

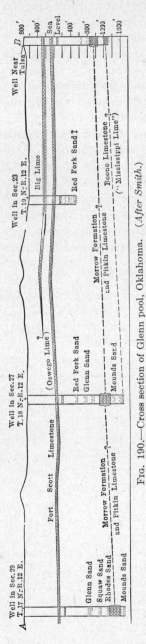

FIG. 190.—Cross section of Glenn pool, Oklahoma. (After Smith.)

[1] MARTIN, H. M., Depew Area, Creek County, Oklahoma, "Structure of Typical American Oil Fields, vol. 2, pp. 365–377, 1929.

[2] SMITH, C. D., The Glenn Oil and Gas Pool and Vicinity, Oklahoma, U. S. Geol. Survey Bull. 541, pp. 34–48, 1914.

WILSON, W. B., Geology of the Glenn Pool of Oklahoma, Am. Assoc. Pet. Geol. Bull., vol. 11, pp. 1055–1065, 1927.

The Sapulpa-Pumpkin Center field is located northwest of the Glenn pool. Oil is found in the Pennsylvanian sands including the Perryman, Red Fork, Glenn (Bartlesville 1,365 feet deep), Taneha, and Dutcher. Gas is found in several other Pennsylvanian sands and in the Mississippian limestone, which lies 2,060 feet deep. The Wilcox sand, which lies 2,290 feet deep, produces gas and some oil. The Kiefer pool is part of the Sapulpa district. The Mounds district is about 9 miles south of Sapulpa. The chief production is from the Glenn, Dutcher, and Wilcox sands.

Kelleyville, 8 miles west of Sapulpa, produces oil from the Oswego, Red Fork, Glenn, Dutcher, and Mississippi formations. Scott, south of Kelleyville, produces oil from the Taneha and Dutcher sands. The Prairie district, southeast of Scott, produces oil from the Glenn, Dutcher, and Wilcox sands. The Slick field, southeast of Bristow, produces oil from the same formations and also from the Misener sand. The Donnelly district, south of Slick, produces from the same formations.

The Continental field, 5 miles north of Bristow, produces from the Glenn and Dutcher sands, the latter lying 2,900 feet deep. The Bristow[1] field produces from these sands and from the Mississippian limestone and the Wilcox sand. Structurally, this field is a westward-dipping monocline cut by many small faults that strike northwest. Depew is 6 miles southwest of Bristow. The Layton, Cleveland, Prue, Dutcher, and Wilcox sands produce oil. At the Poor Farm field between Bristow and Depew, and Prue, Bartlesville, and Dutcher sands produce oil. The Pure district, 4 miles southeast of Depew, produces oil from the same sands and also from the Wilcox. At Billingslea, 10 miles southeast of Depew, the chief production is from the Prue, Bartlesville, and Wilcox sands.

Mannford in north Creek County produces oil chiefly from the Wilcox sand which lies 2,980 feet deep. Jennings, 10 miles west of Mannford, produces oil chiefly from the Skinner, Bartlesville, and Wilcox sands. The Olive district, 10 miles southwest of Mannford, produces from the Bartlesville sand 2,560 feet deep and also from the Tucker, Dutcher, and Burgess sands. Dropright, Drumright, and Shamrock are all sub-districts of the Cushing field and are shown on Fig. 192.

The Cushing field was opened in 1912 and soon became the foremost oil field in Oklahoma. The peak of production was reached in May, 1915, when the field yielded 305,000 barrels a day. It had produced to January 1, 1928, 283,894,274 barrels of oil. The producing area of the field is 21,850 acres, and the average yield per acre is 12,993 barrels.

[1] FATH, A. E., Geology of the Bristow Quadrangle, Creek County, Oklahoma, U. S. Geol. Survey *Bull.* 759, pp. 1–63, 1925.

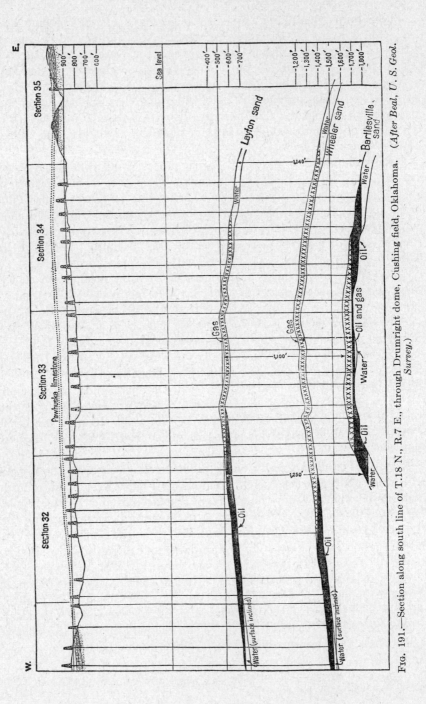

Fig. 191.—Section along south line of T.18 N., R.7 E., through Drumright dome, Cushing field, Oklahoma. (*After Beal, U. S. Geol. Survey.*)

The Cushing[1] field is on a long anticline or dome that strikes north and is one of the longest anticlines in northern Oklahoma. On it are developed four smaller domes from north to south: Dropright, Drumright, Mount Pleasant, and Shamrock.

The following table gives the geologic formations of the Pennsylvanian series as reported by Buttram in the vicinity of the Cushing field—the youngest at the top:

Neva limestone.
Sandstones and shales and thin limestones (556.5 feet).
Pawhuska limestone is 2,340 feet above Fort Scott limestone and 1,243 to 1,262 feet above Lost City limestone.
Shales and sandstones (134 feet).
Elgin sandstone.
Interval.
Lost City limestone.
Interval. Includes Layton sand at 700 to 810 feet above Wheeler sand.
Fort Scott or Oswego limestones (75 feet) (= Wheeler sand).
Interval.
Bartlesville sand (in Cherokee shale).

The most prominent outcropping stratum is a limestone that is equivalent to the Pawhuska limestone of northern Oklahoma.

Oil and gas are found on the crest of the anticline. The productive strata, in order of age, are Layton sand, Jones sand, Oswego limestone, Prue, Skinner, Redfork, and Bartlesville sands, Tucker ("Wilcox") sand and Arbuckle limestone. The Layton sand produces throughout an area of 14 square miles, the Wheeler in an area of 11 square miles, and the Bartlesville in an area of 28 square miles. The Wilcox sand and Arbuckle limestone produce only in small areas on crests of the domes. More than half of the production has come from the Bartlesville sand (Fig. 191). The Tucker sand at places lies directly below the Bartlesville sand and at other places is separated from the latter by 200 feet of strata. It is characterized by rounded and "frosted" grains intermingled with green shale. It is now correlated with the "Wilcox" sand in the main, although some of the so-called Tucker sand is probably older than the Wilcox.

The distribution of the pre-Pennsylvanian rocks is shown by Fig. 192*A*. This figure illustrates, approximately, conditions at the beginning of Cherokee time and shows how the rocks would appear if the Cherokee and later formations were removed. The oldest rocks exposed would be the Arbuckle limestone and the youngest the Mississippian limestone.

[1] BUTTRAM, FRANK, The Cushing Oil and Gas Field, Oklahoma, Okla. Geol. Survey *Bull.* 18, pp. 1–60, 1914.

BEAL, C. H., Geologic Structure in the Cushing Oil and Gas Field, Oklahoma, and Its Relation to the Oil, Gas, and Water, U. S. Geol. Survey *Bull.* 658, pp.1–64, 1917.

WEIRICH, T. E., Cushing Oil and Gas Field, *Nat. Petroleum News*, pp. 90–94, May 9, 1928; "Structure of Typical American Oil Fields," vol. 2, pp. 396–406, 1929.

The structure is shown by contours on top of "Wilcox" sand (Fig. 192*B*). A section through the Shamrock dome is shown as Fig. 193. The dip to the west is about 2 degrees; the dip to the east is 12 degrees. Some have interpreted the steep drop of beds to the east as due to pre-Pennsylvanian faulting, but Weirich interprets the drop as due to folding.

The section shows granite overlain by the Arbuckle limestone. This limestone is 1,405 feet thick at Dropright dome but only 630 feet thick

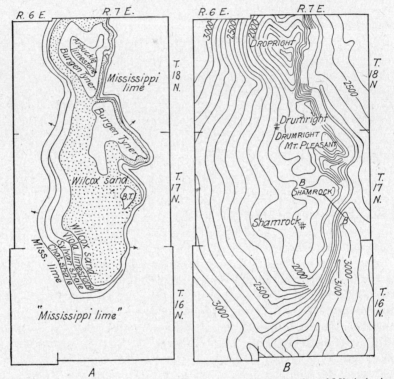

FIG. 192.—*A*. Geologic map of Cushing oil field; shows distribution of Mississippian and older rocks below the Pennsylvanian or Cherokee shale. (*After Weirich.*)

B. Structure map of pre-Pennsylvanian rocks in Cushing oil field. Contours based on upper surface of Wilcox sand and inferred at crests of domes where Wilcox sand has been removed. Numbers show elevations of Wilcox sand below sea level. (*After Weirich.*)

at Shamrock dome, indicating upwarping and erosion before the later Ordovician strata were deposited above it. There were erosion intervals also at the ends of the Silurian or Devonian and at the end of Mississippian time and gentle arching of the Cushing anticline continued after the Pennsylvanian time. Later, the region was tilted to the west, which decreased the east dip of the anticline. This interpretation of the structure implies gentle folding in the region of the Cushing anticline at several different times.

Payne County.—In Payne County,[1] west of Creek County, the Carboniferous beds at the surface are chiefly the transitional beds between the Pennsylvanian and Permian. The rocks dip west 40 to 50 feet per mile. The chief producing strata are the Bartlesville, Misener, and Wilcox sands, although other formations are productive in certain fields. Lenses of the Misener sand produce oil in Olean, Ingalls, and elsewhere. The "Wilcox," which is probably the most important oil sand in the county, is found at 3,800 feet below the surface in the eastern part of the county and 4,300 to 5,000 feet deep in the western part.

The Yale-Quay field is in the northern part of Payne County and extends northward into Pawnee County. The field is on a faulted

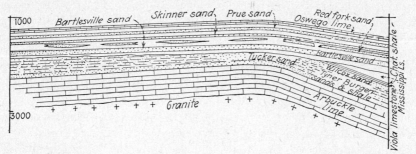

Fig. 193.—Cross section on line BB, Fig. 192*B*. (*After Weirich., Nat. Petroleum News,* May 9, 1928.)

anticline and derives oil from the Oswego, Prue, Skinner, Bartlesville, and Burgess sands, and from the Wilcox(?) sand. The Bartlesville sand lies 3,150 feet deep and the Wilcox(?) 3,580 feet deep. The March field, west of the town of Cushing, produces oil from six formations of the Pennsylvanian series and also from the Wilcox sand. It is situated on an anticline that is shown at the surface. Ingalls, 10 miles northwest of Cushing, is located on the Ingalls dome. Oil is found in the Oswego, Skinner, and Bartlesville formations, the latter lying about 3,400 feet deep. Recently, oil was developed in the Misener sand at about 3,750 feet deep. The Wilcox sand is dry.

The Ripley field is about 6 miles west of Cushing on the Ripley dome. Gas is found in the Bartlesville sand at 3,400 feet, in the Viola lime at 4,030 feet, and in larger amounts in the Wilcox sand at 4,128 feet. The Deep Rock or Mehan field, west of Ripley, is also located on a dome. The oil is found chiefly in the Bartlesville and Wilcox sands. The Bartlesville sand lies 3,100 feet deep and the Wilcox 4,300 feet deep.

West of Payne County, in Kingfisher and Canadian[2] counties, the Pennsylvanian and older strata probably lie deep, although it is possi-

[1] KOSCHMANN, A. H., Geology of Payne County, Okla. Geol. Survey *Bull.* 40X, pp. 1–13, 1928.

[2] KITE, W. C., Geology of Kingfisher and Canadian Counties, Okla. Geol. Survey *Bull.* 40O, pp. 1–13, 1927.

ble that these are raised up by folding in line with folds of Kay County. In Cleveland and McLain counties[1] to the southeast of Canadian County deep wells are being drilled to test the deep formations. The discoveries of a great oil field near Oklahoma City have stimulated exploration in western Oklahoma.

Pawnee County.—The strata that are developed in Payne County extend northward into Pawnee County. The productive fields derive oil chiefly from Pennsylvanian beds, although the Wilcox sand yields oil in the western part of the county. The Keystone field in the east end of Pawnee County produces oil from the Cleveland, Oswego, Skinner, and Hominy formations. The field also produces gas, the initial pressure ranging from 125 to 750 pounds per square inch. Lauderdale, west of Keystone, produces oil from the Layton, Cleveland, Skinner, and Bartlesville sands, the latter lying at a depth of 2,350 feet. The Wilcox sand also produces oil. The Terlton field west of Lauderdale produces oil from the same sands and from the Wheeler and Tucker sands. The Bartlesville sand is 2,680 feet deep. Hallet, west of Terlton, produces oil from the Skinner sand which lies 2,565 feet deep.

The Maramec field, west of Hallet, produces oil from seven sands of the Pennsylvanian system, including the Bartlesville sand which lies 3,080 feet deep. One well produces from the Wilcox sand. The Duquesne field near Casey, north of Maramec, contains small wells which find oil in the Prue sand of the Pennsylvanian. The Cleveland field north of Terlton produces oil chiefly from the Cleveland sand. Ralston (Fig. 180), which is located on the Ralston anticline 20 miles northwest of the Cleveland district, produces oil from the Skinner, Bartlesville, and Burgess sands, the Bartlesville lying about 3,200 feet deep. Donahue or Masham (Fig. 180), 10 miles southwest of Ralston, is located on an anticlinal structure and produces oil from the Wilcox sand and gas from the Cleveland and Oswego formations. The Morrison or Watchorn field southwest of Donahue has been mentioned in connection with the oil fields to the northwest; it is located on an anticline and produces oil from the Peoples sand, the Mississippi lime and from the Wilcox sand.

Lincoln, and Logan Counties.—In Lincoln County (Fig. 175), south of Payne County, oil and gas are developed at Agra near the north border of the county. Several Pennsylvanian formations are productive and the Wilcox, which lies about 4,100 feet deep, yields both oil and gas. The Kendrick field (Skelly-Ford), which is 10 miles southeast of Agra, produces oil from Pennsylvanian sands and also from Hunton limestone.

[1] ANDERSON, G. E., Geology of Cleveland and McLain Counties, Okla. Geol. Survey *Bull.* 40N, pp. 1–18, 1927.

Davenport, 6 miles south of Kendrick, produces oil from the Layton and chiefly from the Prue sand, the latter lying about 3,400 feet deep. Stroud is located about 10 miles east of Davenport. Oil is found in several Pennsylvanian sands which lie below the Layton sand and chiefly in the Wilcox formation. Near Chanler, west of the Davenport field, oil is found in several Pennsylvanian sands and in the Viola limestone.

In northwest Logan County[1] near Lovell, about 20 miles northwest of Guthrie, some oil is found in the Tonkawa sand which is 4,000 feet deep. In the Roxana field near by (Fig. 155), the Wilcox sand produces oil at a depth of 5,984 feet. In 1929 Roxana field yielded 5,646,800 barrels of oil.

Western Oklahoma.—In western Oklahoma the surface rocks are mainly of Permian age but Cretaceous and Tertiary rocks at places lie above the Permian beds.[2] Near Zea, in Cimarron County (Fig. 207), gas is discovered at a depth of 2,610 feet, probably in the Cottonwood formation. In Texas County a well with a large flow of gas was drilled in 1922 near Texhoma (Fig. 155). In 1925 a well near Redpoint (Fig. 155), passed through about 200 feet of Tertiary beds and 2,075 feet of Permian beds. It encountered a flow of 15,000,000 cubic feet of gas per day. In 1927 oil was found near Ramsay 10 miles northeast of Redpoint at a depth of 4,100 feet. Gas wells are found northeast of Redpoint and also farther north near Liberal in Kansas (Fig. 155). This region is regarded as prospective oil territory, although the Pennsylvanian beds over most of it lie deep.

The Sayre field,[3] 3 miles south of Sayre, is 20 miles east of the Texas line and nearly in line with the axis of Wichita range (Fig. 207). In 1922 a well with an initial flow of gas estimated to be 50,000,000 cubic feet and 20 barrels of oil was brought in at a depth of 2,755 to 2,806 feet. Another well producing 200 barrels of oil a day was drilled soon afterward. The structure of the district is an elongated dome with 100 feet of closure with an axis trending N. 30° E., and most of the oil and gas is found in a dolomitic horizon at the top of the Cisco of Pennsylvanian age. The

[1] BALE, H. E., Logan County, Okla. Geol. Survey *Bull.* 40, Part 2, pp. 225–238, 1930.

[2] GREEN, G. C., Subsurface Stratigraphy of Western Oklahoma, Okla. Geol. Survey *Bull.* 40D, pp. 1–12, 1926.

CLIFTON, R. L., Woods, Harper, Major, Woodward, and Ellis Counties, Okla. Geol. Survey *Bull.* 40A, pp. 1–24, 1926.

GOULD, C. N., and J. T. LONSDALE, Geology of Texas County, Oklahoma, Okla. Geol. Survey *Bull.* 37, pp. 1–62, 1926.

[3] BIRK, R. A., The Sayre Field, Beckham County, Oklahoma, Am. Assoc. Pet. Geol. *Bull.*, vol. 8, pp. 347–349, 1926.

GOUIN, F., Geology of Beckham County, Oklahoma, Okla. Geol. Survey *Bull.* 40M, pp. 1–17, 1927.

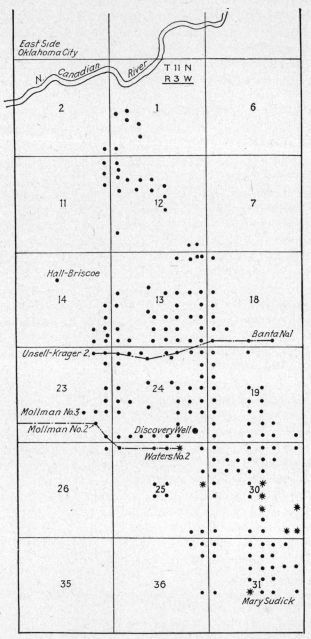

FIG. 194a.—Sketch map of Oklahoma City oil field showing oil wells (dots) May, 1930. Wells in Oklahoma city and certain other wells not shown. (*Data mainly from map by W. H. Atkinson.*)

wells drilled thus far have declined rapidly and some have had trouble with water.

South of the Sayre field in Beckham County (Fig. 207), Permian rocks crop out along the axis joining the Wichita Mountains and the buried range of the Texas Panhandle ("Amarillo Mountains"). This county and adjoining counties are regarded as in part possible oil-bearing territory. A little oil and gas have been found in the Granite field, Greer County, about 20 miles southeast of Sayre. In the Gotebo[1] field, 30 miles east of Granite, oil and gas in small amounts are found in several wells.

Oklahoma City.—The Oklahoma City oil field is at Oklahoma City (Fig. 196) south of the Garber field, nearly in line with the Blackwell-Garber anticline. It is frequently stated that the field is on the south extension of the Nemaha Ridge-Blackwell anticline and that may be true, but the subsurface structure between Oklahoma City and Garber is not yet disclosed by drilling. It may be a buried extension of the Arbuckle Mountains and intersect the Nemaha trend at a high angle.

The Oklahoma City pool[2] (Fig. 194a and b) was discovered December, 1928, when a 5,000 barrel well was brought in at a depth of 6,420 feet. Subsequent drilling has outlined an area 6 miles long and 2½ miles wide; which is said to have a potential production of 1,000,000 barrels of oil per day. It is one of

[1] CLIFTON, R. L., Geology of Herman, Greer, Jackson, and Tillman Counties, Okla. Geol. Survey *Bull.* 40Y, pp. 1–24, 1928.

[2] TRAVIS, A., Oklahoma County, Okla. Geol. Survey *Bull.* 40SS, pp. 1–31, 1930.

ZAVOICO, B. B., Oklahoma City Pool, Oklahoma, Am. Assoc. Pet. Geol. *Bull.*, vol. 13, pp. 1387–1394, 1929.

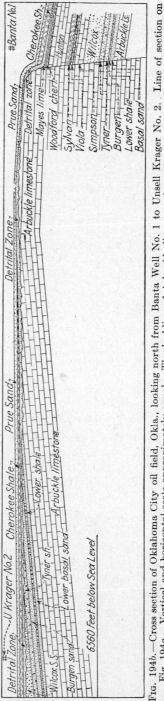

FIG. 194b.—Cross section of Oklahoma City oil field, Okla., looking north from Banta Well No. 1 to Unsell Krager No. 2. Line of section on Fig. 194a. Vertical and horizontal scale approximately equal. The bedding of Arbuckle limestone is assumed. (*After Hubert E. Bale.*)

the greatest oil fields in the United States. The surface of the Oklahoma City field is about 1,300 feet above sea. The rocks cropping out are of Permian age and a structural dome is mapped at the surface on the contact between the Garber and Hennessey formations of the Enid group of Permian age. This dome has 120 feet of closure at the surface. Drilling has shown that the oil field lies on a buried domatic hill several hundred feet high.

The base of the Permian series lies about 1,650 feet deep in the productive area. The Pawhuska limestone series is encountered at 3,100 to 3,300 feet. The upper Tonkawa limestone and sand series is at

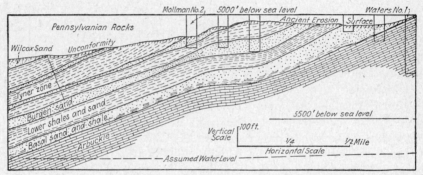

Fig. 195.—Section looking north from Waters No. 1 well to Mollman No. 2 and westward, Oklahoma City oil field. See line of section Fig. 194a. (*Data from J. B. Umpleby.*)

4,000 to 4,570 feet. The Layton series lies about 4,700 feet deep and the Checkerboard limestone at 5,100 to 5,300 feet. The detrital zone is at 6,000 to 6,220 feet and the unconformity at about 6,220 feet. Below this unconformity are found the Arbuckle limestone and other Ordovician strata.

The general relations of the rocks are shown by the cross-section (Fig. 194b), which is a generalized section[1] looking north and approximately between the Banta No. 1 and Unsell Krager No. 2 wells. The Mississippian and older rocks are faulted down on the east side of the field by a great fault, probably with about 1,800 feet of displacement. After the area was folded to form a great dome and after the faulting on its east side, erosion reduced the area almost to base level. Since the Mayes sand and older formations are faulted, the age of the faulting is probably post-Mississippian; and since the Prue sand is not faulted, the faulting is older than the Prue sand. Thus it appears probable that the major deformation of the area took place between Mississippian and Middle Pennsylvanian time, which is one of the periods of great deformation in the region of the Arbuckle Mountains. On the west side of the

[1] The data for this section were kindly supplied by Hubert E. Bale of Oklahoma City. (W.H.E.)

dome the formations from the Arbuckle limestone to the "Wilcox" sand (Ordovician) are shown dipping west and the Ordovician rocks are covered over with "Detrital" material of Lower Pennsylvanian age. The detrital material consists of sandstone and shale and is the waste of pre-Pennsylvanian rocks that accumulated above the ancient dome during the period of erosion that succeeded the early folding and faulting of the area and before the Prue sand was deposited. The Prue sand is nearly parallel with the unconformity, which shows that the buried hill was practically worn down to a plane surface before the Middle Pennsylvanian beds were deposited. On the cross-section (Fig. 194*b*) the crest of the anticline in the Arbuckle limestone is assumed to be where the largest wells are found. The attitude of the limestone in this part of the field is not accurately determined. According to Travis there was some deformation also between the deposition of the Oswego and Checkerboard limestones.

The oil is found in the Arbuckle limestone which is highly porous and is oil bearing to depths of at least 500 feet below the eroded surface of the limestone. The wells in the Arbuckle limestone have initial productions of 5,000 to 20,000 barrels of oil or more per day. This oil has a gravity of 38 to 41° Bé., and a temperature of about 72° F., although with the appearance of salt water the temperature rises to 110° F. in certain wells. The salt-water level in the producing field is estimated by some to lie at a depth of about 5,700 feet below sea, or 7,000 feet deep. Oil is found also in the Simpson, Burgen, "Wilcox," and other sands of the Simpson series, and also in the detrital sandy beds above the unconformity. Several sands above the unconformity yield gas in large amounts. The oil is highly charged with gas, and many of the wells get out of control when brought in. In the spring of 1930 the Mary Sudick and several other wells came in flowing large amounts of oil and gas, which were discharged with violence, spraying the countryside with oil 10 miles or more away from the wells. The gas pressure of the well was estimated to be 2,300 pounds per square inch.

The great fault seems to limit production on the east side of the field. During the summer of 1930 very large wells were brought in yielding large amounts of oil from the Wilcox sand. These wells are found on the west side of the dome and the productive belt extends into the southeast part of Oklahoma City.

Cleveland County lies south of Oklahoma County and McClain County joins Cleveland County on the west. These counties are not far west of the Seminole group of oil fields and are being actively explored. A cross section by Anderson[1] shows the relations of the rocks in this

[1] ANDERSON, G. E., Cleveland and McClain counties, Okla. Geol. Survey *Bull.* 40N, pp. 1–18, 1927.

region which dip west away from the Hunton arch in west Seminole County.

GENERALIZED GEOLOGIC SECTION, GREATER SEMINOLE DISTRICT

(*After Levorsen*)

System	Formation	Thickness, feet	Character of sediments
Quaternary	Recent	0–40	Alluvium, sand, clay, and conglomerate
			————————Unconformity————————
	Pleistocene		Guertie sand and gravel
			————————Unconformity————————
Pennsylvanian	Vanoss	250–500	Shale, sand, conglomerate and limestone
	Ada	0–50	Sand and shale. Thins northward
	Vamoosa	270–525	Conglomerates, sands, shale. Thins southward
	Belle City limestone	0–30	Gray, fossiliferous limestone. Thins northward
	Francis	370–500	Shale with interbedded sandstone
	Seminole Holdenville shale Wewoka	800–1,000	Shale with interbedded sandstone
	Wetumka shale Calvin sandstone	250–300	"Calvin sand series" extending from base of Calvin to top of basal sand of Wewoka
	Boggy McAlester shale	600–1,400	Shale with several variable sandstones including Earlsboro sand
			————Unconformity——
	Pottsville — Wapanucka	Wapanucka limestone	0–40	structural and erosional Present only in
		Cromwell sand	0–100	Little River area
			————Unconformity——
Mississippian	Caney	Caney shale member	0–600	structural and erosional Bluish gray, fine-grained shale overlain unconformably by formations up to Boggy shale
		"Mayes" limestone member	90–110	Argillaceous, dark limestone. Sycamore limestone at base
			————Unconformity(?)——
	Chattanooga shale Misener sand at base	20–250	Uniform, black shale, thickens southward. Woodford chert of Arbuckle Mountain section
			————Unconformity——
Devonian	Bois d'Arc limestone Haragan shale		structural and erosional Hunton limestone of oil fields. Produces oil from weathered zone near top or from porous horizons. Faunal hiatus separates each member below Haragan shale
Silurian	Henryhouse shale Chimneyhill limestone Pink crinoidal member Glauconitic member Oolitic member	0–415	
Ordovician	Sylvan shale	35–100	Gray-green shale
	Viola limestone (Fernvale)	20–40	White to gray limestone
			————————Unconformity————————
	Simpson	Dense lime member	5–50	
		First dolomite member	30–125	
		"Seminole" sand	0–80	Main producing horizon. "First Wilcox"
		Second dolomite	15–100	
		"Wilcox" sand	500+	Locally productive "Second Wilcox"

Seminole County.—Seminole[1] County (Fig. 175) joins Okfuskee County on the west and lies north of the Arbuckle Mountains. Petro-

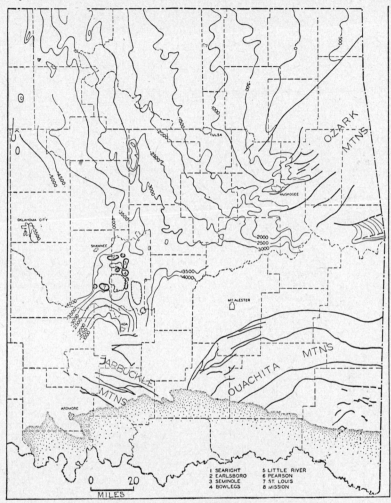

Fig. 196.—Map showing structure of part of Oklahoma by contours on top of Ordovician beds. (*After Levorsen, Thom and others.*)

[1] LEVORSEN, A. I., Geology of Seminole County, Okla. Geol. Survey *Bull.* 40BB, pp. 1–70, 1928.

———, Greater Seminole District, Seminole and Pottawatomie Counties, Oklahoma, "Structure of Typical American Oil Fields," vol. 2, pp. 315–351, 1929.

CRAM, I. H., "Structure of Typical American Oil Fields," vol. 2, pp. 351–361, 1929.

POWERS, S., The Seminole Uplift in Oklahoma, Am. Assoc. Pet. Geol. *Bull.*, vol. 11, pp. 1097–1108, 1927.

MORGAN, G. D., Geology of the Stonewall Quadrangle, Okla. Bur. Geol., vol. 2, 1924.

DOTT, R. H., Pennsylvanian Paleogeography, Okla. Geol. Survey *Bull.* 40J, 1927.

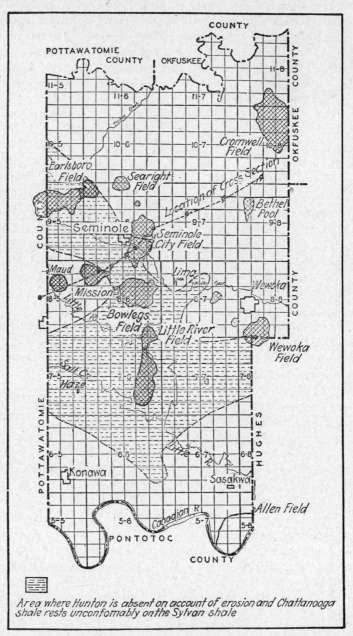

Fɪɢ. 197.—Map of Seminole County, showing positions of main oil fields, the location of the cross section (Fig. 198*a*) and the area where the Hunton limestone has been removed and the Chattanooga shale rests unconformably on the Sylvan shale. (*After Levorsen.*)

leum was discovered in the Wewoka field in 1923, and in 1925, in this field, a deep well was drilled to the Seminole sand of the Simpson formation. This well had an initial daily production of 4,000 barrels. This discovery was followed by the discovery of oil in the Seminole City field and later in other fields of the Greater Seminole region, and by August, 1927, the production of this region reached a daily output of 527,400 barrels of oil and exceeded that of light oil of any other field in the United States. The oil is high in gasoline and has a gravity of about 38 to 42° Bé.

Seminole County is 800 to 1,050 feet above sea. The rocks exposed are the upper beds of the Pennsylvanian system. The regional structure is shown by Fig. 196, and a map of the oil fields by Fig. 197. A section of the rocks on the broken line is shown as Figs. 198*A*, *B*. The field lies in a structural saddle between the Ozark Mountains and the Arbuckle Mountains. The Pennsylvanian rocks dip gently westward, the average dip being 70 feet per mile. At places, however, the rocks are nearly flat lying or show low arches plunging northwest, and locally the beds are faulted by normal faults that strike northwest. At such places, marked by flat dips, by open folds, or by faults, most of the oil fields are found.

The Pennsylvanian strata increase in thickness to the southeast and at places this increase is greater than the dip of the beds at the surface. The small folds pitching northwest, which are open at the surface, are closed with depth in the lower beds of the Pennsylvanian rocks. Thus in the Garrison field, as shown by Levorsen, a low open anticline in the surface rocks lies directly over a dome in the Cromwell sand (Fig. 25). The Pennsylvanian rocks lie unconformably on the Mississippian rocks. The Mississippian and lower strata at the close of Mississippian time dipped eastward at higher angles than they do today. They were tilted to the northwest at the time the Pennsylvanian rocks were tilted. If it is assumed that the Calvin beds were laid down essentially flat, the attitude of the lower rocks at the time of the deposition of the Calvin formation is illustrated by Fig. 198*b*. This figure shows also faulting which probably dropped the depressed blocks of the Mississippian and older strata, but which did not depress the Pennsylvanian rocks to the same extent. The faulting is largely pre-Pennsylvanian. Over a considerable part of Seminole County the Hunton limestone is lacking and the Chattanooga shale rests directly on the Sylvan shale. This area is believed to represent an area of uplift of pre-Mississippian age.

Briefly, a gentle doming of Hunton formation and older rocks took place before the Chattanooga shale was deposited and erosion removed the Hunton from the area indicated on Fig. 197. Later the Mississippian rocks were laid down over this area, tilted to the east, and probably faulted and eroded. The Pennsylvanian rocks were laid down on the tilted peneplained surface in a sea that expanded gradually to the north-west, so that the thickness of Pennsylvanian strata decreases greatly to the northwest. At this stage in the history of the region, the structure

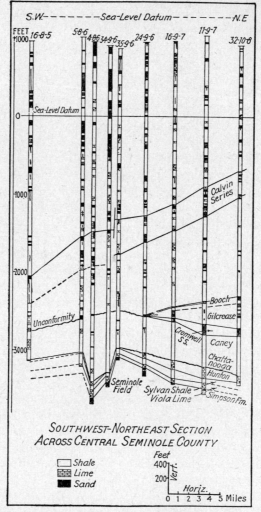

Fig. 198a.—Cross section of Seminole County, Oklahoma, on line shown on Fig. 197. Logs are referred to sea-level datum and show present structure. (*After Levorsen.*)

was like that shown on Fig. 198b. Later, the region was tilted to the northwest and the east dip of the beds below the Mississippian as a result of this tilting was greatly diminished. The structure after this period of tilting is shown on Fig. 198a.

The Cromwell field[1] is in the northeast part of Seminole County and in the southwest part of Okfuskee County. A well drilled in 1923 encountered oil in the Cromwell sand at a depth of about 3,467 feet, near the bottom of the Pennsylvanian series. The initial production

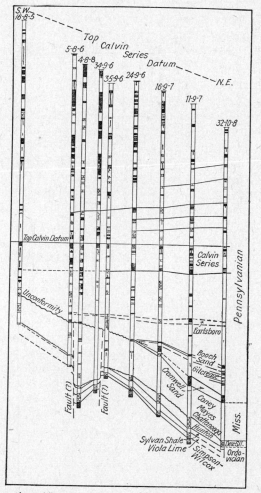

Fig. 198*b*.—Cross section of Seminole County, Oklahoma, on line shown on Fig. 197; same logs as 198*a* referred to the Calvin series datum. (*After Levorsen.*)

was 312 barrels per day. The peak production was reached in 1924, when 75 wells had a combined daily output of 63,391 barrels. The rocks exposed at the surface are shales, sandstone, and a conglomerate of the Vamoosa and Francis formations of the Pennsylvanian. These

[1] LANGWORTHY, A. A., Cromwell Field, Seminole and Okfuskee Counties, Oklahoma, "Structure of Typical American Oil Fields," vol. 2, pp. 300–314, 1929.

rocks lie on a northwest pitching terrace, which shows several folds plunging northwest and are cut by faults that strike northwest. Oil is found in small amounts in the Calvin, Booch, Gilcrease, and Wilcox sands, but nearly all of the oil produced has come from the Cromwell sand, which lies at the base of the Pennsylvanian series and is about 3,500 feet deep. The oil has a gravity of 38 to 40° Bé. and is associated with gas rich in gasoline vapor. The Cromwell sand is locally calcareous and of relatively low porosity. In the main the most productive portions of the field are in the structurally high areas. In the south part of the field the oil-bearing rocks dip west away from a fault that has a throw of 200 feet, and this fault has aided in sealing the reservoir on the east side. In the north part of the area the oil has accumulated on a dome which has a closure of 70 feet or more. The Wilcox sand, about 700 feet below the Cromwell sand, yields oil in a few wells.

In the Bethel field, five miles southwest of Cromwell, oil was found in the Booch sand (Hartshorne) in 1924 at a depth of 3,275 to 3,300 feet. The Cromwell and the Ordovician beds have not proved productive. The structure shows a low fold in the Booch sand. The wells are small but have a slow decline. The oil has a gravity of 38 to 40° Bé.

The Wewoka[1] field is in Seminole County, 2 miles southeast of the town of Wewoka. The rocks exposed at the surface are the Francis and Seminole formations of the Pennsylvanian which dip westward and are faulted. The structure of the Smith sand is an irregular dome faulted on the west side which roughly outlines the limits of production. Oil is found at a depth of 3,150 feet in the Smith sand of the upper part of the Cromwell horizon, which is at the base of the Pennsylvanian, and in the Sykes sand, also in the Cromwell horizon, and 50 feet below the Smith sand. Oil is found also in the Hunton limestone about 3,880 feet deep and in the Seminole sand ("First Wilcox") about 4,080 feet deep. At its peak of production in the week of August 20, 1926, the Seminole sand yielded 29,023 barrels per day. The Hunton limestone is thin or missing over the highest part of the Ordovician structure, indicating an uplift of pre-Mississippian age. The Ordovician rocks show a dome with 200 feet of closure.

The Seminole City field is in western Seminole County, adjoining Seminole City on the east. Oil was discovered March, 1926, in the Hunton limestone at a depth of 3,975 feet, the well (Jones No. 1) yielding 1,100 barrels a day. In July of the same year the Amerada Company drilled a well to the Seminole sand which was encountered at a depth of 4,258 feet. This well yielded 60 barrels of oil per day. Active drilling

[1] LEVORSEN, A. I., Geology of Seminole County, Okla. Geol. Survey *Bull.* 40BB, pp. 40–43, 1929.

SHEA, E. F., and L. G. MOSSBERG, The Wewoka Oil Field, Oklahoma, Am. Assoc. Pet. Geol., paper read at Tulsa meeting, March, 1927.

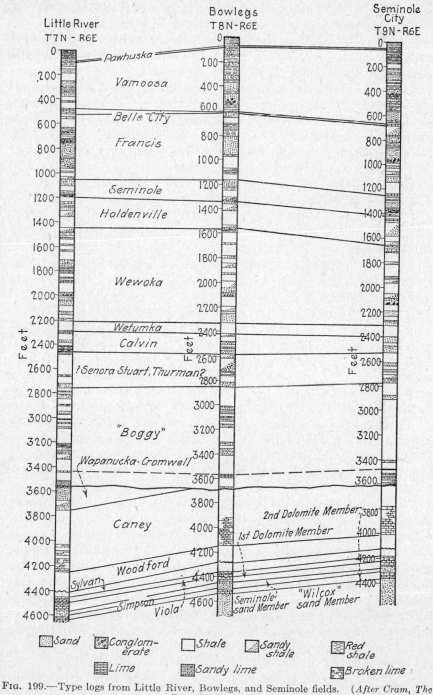

Little River
T7N – R6E

Bowlegs
T8N–R6E

Seminole
City
T9N–R6E

Pawhuska

Vamoosa

Belle City

Francis

Seminole

Holdenville

Wewoka

Wetumka

Calvin

?Senora Stuart, Thurman?

"Boggy"

Wapanucka-Cromwell

Caney

Woodford

Sylvan

Simpson

Viola

2nd Dolomite Member

1st Dolomite Member

Seminole
sand Member

"Wilcox"
sand Member

Feet

Feet

Feet

Sand   Conglom-   Shale   Sandy   Red
        erate   shale   shale

Lime   Sandy lime   Broken lime

FIG. 199.—Type logs from Little River, Bowlegs, and Seminole fields. (*After Cram, The Pure Oil Company.*)

followed, and in the week ended February 28, 1927, the field produced 253,192 barrels of oil per day from 211 wells. The high initial production was obtained by shooting the wells or by using air and gas lifts. The gravity of the oil is between 40 and 42° Bé. The field as outlined covers 3,600 acres.

The rocks cropping out are the Vanoss and Vamoosa formations, and the chief datum plane is the Pawhuska limestone at the base of the Vanoss formation (Fig. 199). The surface shows small anticlines plunging northwest cut by several faults that strike northwest (Fig. 200). The oil is found in the Hunton limestone, the Seminole ("Wilcox") sand,

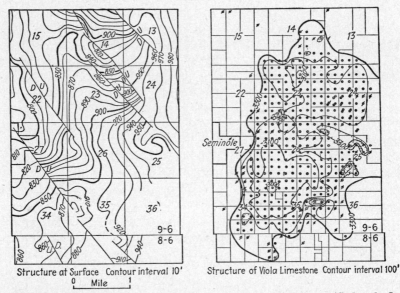

Structure at Surface Contour interval 10'

0   Mile   1

Structure of Viola Limestone Contour interval 100'

FIG. 200.—Map showing structure Seminole City oil field, Oklahoma. (*Geology by Indian Territory Illuminating Oil Co. and by A. I. Levorsen.*)

and in smaller amounts in the second "Wilcox" sand. The structure of the Ordovician rocks shows 3 domes, each of which underlies small surface folds (Fig. 200). The structural relief of the field as a whole is 250 feet, but at places within the field the oil sand is found 600 feet or more below its highest elevation, and in some of the low areas within the field the oil sand is productive. These low places in the structure are believed, by certain investigators, to be due to sharp folding after the oil had accumulated in the dome, but, according to Levorsen, some are probably downthrown fault blocks. Other blocks, apparently raised, are probably due to crooked holes. Since the Pennsylvanian rocks do not show faulting of the same magnitude, it follows that the faulting took place in pre-Pennsylvanian time (Fig. 198B). If the low places within the dome were due to folding the beds would lie at high angles and wells would pass through them at places where they would show dips of about 45 degrees. Increases in thickness of beds as shown in drill holes should be noted in logs of wells that passed through the tilted beds, but, according to Levorsen, the beds penetrated do not show corresponding increases in thickness.

The Bowlegs[1] field is a mile or two south of the Seminole City field. In January, 1927, oil was discovered in the Seminole sand at a depth of 4,194 feet and a well completed with an initial daily production of 5,500 barrels of oil. In August, 1927, 173 wells reached a combined daily production of 190,408 barrels of oil. The field covers an area of 2,800 acres. The oil has a gravity between 40 and 42° Bé.

The formations exposed at the surface are the same as those exposed in the Seminole City field and are similarly faulted and thrown into gentle open folds. The oil is derived from the Hunton limestone and from the Seminole and Wilcox sands of the Simpson formation. The subsurface structure is that of a broad dome, which outlines the limits of production and has a closure of 300 feet. At places within the dome the oil-bearing sands are found 600 or more feet below the top of the dome. Two such areas show definite evidence of faulting. Other apparently high areas are probably due to crooked holes.

The Little River field is 3 miles south of the Bowlegs field. In February, 1927, oil was found in the Seminole sand at a depth of 4,017 feet and on November 1, 1927, the daily production was 45,361 barrels of oil, this being derived from 59 wells. The surface conditions are similar to those found at Seminole City and Bowlegs fields, and the conditions underground are probably similar also, although the subsurface structure is not well defined.

The Earlsboro[2] field is 6 miles northwest of Seminole City. Oil was discovered March, 1926, and the maximum daily production was reached during the week of August 9, 1927, when 135 wells produced 205,286 barrels of oil. On November 1, 1927, the production had fallen to 148,361 barrels per day from 248 wells and to this date the total production was 28,230,350 barrels. About one-fifth of the wells are showing water. The gravity of the oil is between 40 and 42° Bé. The field has an area of 2,830 acres. The rocks cropping out are the shales and sands of the Vanoss formation. The surface shows several terraces and minor flattenings of dip, and there is a low broad arch in the western part of the field. The Pennsylvanian rocks extend to a depth of 3,900 feet and the Earlsboro sand, which is a lens-shaped body and produces oil in several wells, is found 250 feet above the base of the Pennsylvanian. The Earlsboro sand is at about the same stratigraphic horizon as the Salt or Glenn sand. The Ordovician rocks show a dome with a closure

[1] LEVORSEN, A. I., Okla. Geol. Survey *Bull.* 40BB, pp. 58–64, 1929.
[2] LEVORSEN, A. I., *idem*, p. 54.

of 150 feet, but locally the oil sands seem to lie below the main structure, and the total structural relief is 360 feet. There are probably blocks depressed by faulting, but some of the apparently high areas are probably due to crooked holes. The chief oil production is from the Seminole sand member and the Wilcox sand, both in the Simpson formation. The Seminole sand member is 50 to 100 feet thick, and its average depth is from 4,200 to 4,300 feet.

The Searight field is 5 miles north of Seminole City. Oil was discovered in this field on April 21, 1926, and during the week of June 21, 1927, 42 wells produced 39,857 barrels of oil per day. On November 1, 1927, the field had produced a total of 11,282,174 barrels of oil. At that

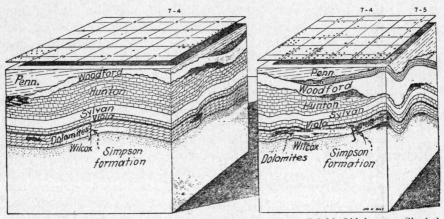

Fig. 201.—Diagram showing structural relations in St. Louis oil field, Oklahoma. Shaded portions of Hunton and Simpson formations indicate oil. (*After Levorsen.*)

date production was 25,663 barrels of oil per day and about one-fourth of the wells showed water. The gravity of the oil is between 39 and 42° Bé. Shales and sands of the Vanoss formation crop out at the surface and show a low anticline pitching west with faults on the east side of the field. The Ordovician rocks show a low dome with 100 feet of closure which is broken probably by faults. The oil is in the Hunton limestone and in the Seminole sand member, the latter lying at depths between 4,300 and 4,400 feet.

Pottawatomie County.—In Pottawatomie County, west of Seminole County, the St. Louis district (Fig. 201), which is about 8 miles west of the Little River field, produces oil from the Hunton and Simpson formations. Most of the St. Louis pool is underlain by the Hunton limestone, which has a thickness of over 400 feet. This limestone is an important producing horizon over most of the field. Locally, however, the Hunton limestone is absent, due to pre-Chattanooga erosion, and the Wilcox sand is found productive in small areas. Wells up to 20,000 barrels per day initial production have been drilled. The structure of the Simpson in these producing areas is that of small sharp dome folds, probably formed before the Chattanooga shale was deposited. The Maud pool, 3 miles northwest of Maud, produces oil from the Misener sand at depths around 4,150 feet. Some wells have initial daily production of 4,500 barrels, but the average is 1,500 barrels initial production. The Hunton also yields oil. In the Pearson Switch field, 5 miles west of St. Louis, oil is found in the Hunton limestone.[1] At Asher, 6 miles south of the St. Louis field, the Viola limestone 3650 feet deep yields oil on a small steeply dipping dome.

Southern Oklahoma.—The Arbuckle, Wichita, and Amarillo Mountains form a great anticlinorium that strikes northwest (Fig. 117). This great uplifted area has been folded many times, but the major deformation took place in middle and late Pennsylvanian time, and, subsequently, after erosion, the larger part of it was buried by Permo-Pennsylvanian rocks and the latter at places by Comanchean beds. Only the tops of the mountains are exposed, but drilling has shown numerous buried hills on the flanks of the mountains and between the Arbuckle and Wichita groups. The Amarillo Mountains are completely buried. The middle Pennsylvanian and older rocks are highly folded. The Permo-Pennsylvanian beds are only gently folded and the Comanchean rocks are folded still less. The oil fields in the main are in areas of Permian beds that are only gently folded, but the axes of the folds are traced great distances through them, and many oil fields lie on their axes (Figs. 202, 203). Drilling has revealed the buried hills and the complicated underlying structures with which the oil deposits are associated.

The Cement[2] field (Fig. 202) is in eastern Caddo County, 50 miles southwest of Oklahoma City, was drilled in 1916 and in 1927 there were 125 wells in the area. The oil is black and has a gravity of 34.7 to 37° Bé. The oil wells in general are small but decline slowly. The strata of Caddo County vary laterally and vertically. Reeves regards the Permian and Upper Pennsylvanian of central and western Oklahoma as a delta deposit formed by rivers rising in the area of what is now the Rocky Mountains. The rocks cropping out above the center of the Cement

[1] WEIRICK, T. E., Pottawotomie County; Okla. Geol. Survey *Bull.* 40TT, pp. 1–15, 1930.

[2] BECKER, C. M., Geology of Caddo and Grady Counties, Oklahoma, Okla. Geol. Survey *Bull.* 40I, pp. 1–18, 1927.

REEVES, F., Geology of the Cement Oil Field, Caddo County, Oklahoma, U. S. Geol. Survey *Bull.* 726B, pp. 41–85, 1921.

GOULD, C. N., Geology and Water Resources of Oklahoma, U. S. Geol. Survey *Water Supply Paper* 148, p. 40, 1905.

DECKER, LAV., Structural Trends in Southern Oklahoma, Okla. Geol. Survey *Bull.* 40P, pp. 1–13, 1927.

HONESS, C. W., Okla. Geol. Survey *Bull.* 40R, pp. 1–32, 1927.

dome belong to the Whitehorse formation, a cross-bedded sandstone 250 feet thick, which is generally brownish red but which changes to pink,

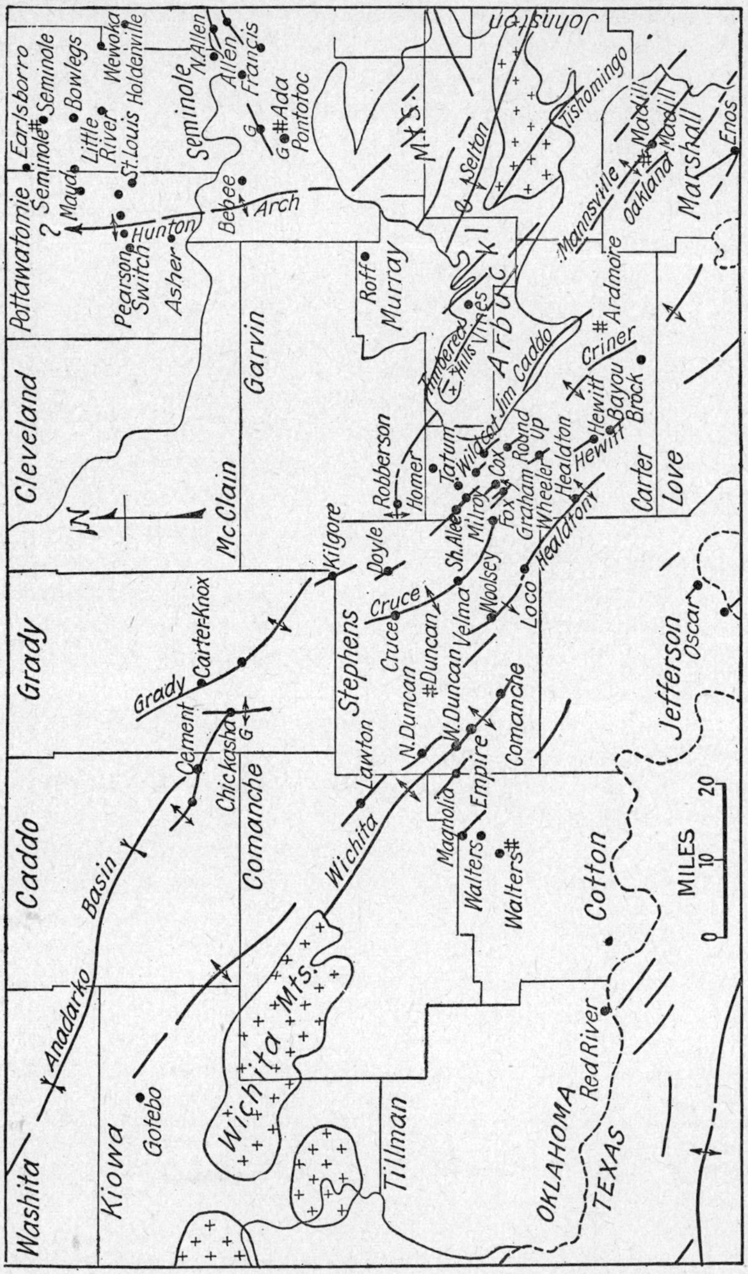

FIG. 202.—Map showing anticlines and oil and gas fields (dots) in Southern Oklahoma.   (Data from La Verne Decker and others.)

white, and yellow near the crest of the dome. According to Reeves, this change is due to alteration produced by carbonate waters rising in the region of the dome, and the changes were localized by reason of fracturing near the crest of the fold. The base of the Permian is placed tentatively at a depth of 1,500 feet. The oils are produced mainly from

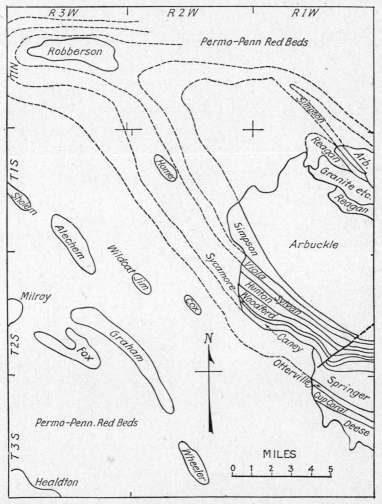

Fig. 203.—Sketch showing the present Arbuckle Mountains and their former westward extension toward Robberson oil field where the mountains were buried in late Carboniferous time. Figure shows also oil fields on southwest flank of mountains. Most of these fields are located where hills and folds were buried by Permo-Pennsylvanian Red beds. (*After Roth, with additions.*)

sands a depths from 1,500 to 3,180 feet. In October, 1929, a well 3,280 feet deep was brought in with an initial daily yield estimated to be 1,000 barrels.

The Chickasha gas field in Grady County, 5 miles southeast of Cement, is located on the same anticline. Gas is found at depths from 1,350 to 2,500 feet, probably at the base of the Permian and lower. The Carter-Knox field on the Grady anticline, east of Chickasha, produces oil at depths between 1,600 and 2,100 feet.

GENERALIZED SECTION OF CRETACEOUS AND PERMIAN ROCKS OF SOUTHERN OKLAHOMA
(*After Gould and others*)

Formation	Thickness, feet	Description
Upper Cretaceous:		
Eagle Ford................	300–400	Clay and shale, dark blue, black; thin sandstone
Woodbine.................	0–200	Sand, brown, friable; ferruginous shale, shaly sandstone
Comanche (Lower Cretaceous):		
Washita Group:		
Bennington................	0–150	Limestone, massive, blue
Bokchito..................	0–150	Shale, red and blue; ferruginous limestone, lenses of sandstone
Caddo....................	0–150	Limestone, yellow and white with marly beds
Kiamichi..................	30–150	Shale, blue, friable; thin limestone in upper part
Permian:		
Quartermaster.............	300	Sandstone, soft red, sandy clay, shale
Cloud Chief...............	0–115	Red clay shales, gypsum
Day Creek................	1–5	Dolomite
Whitehorse................	200–275	Sandstone, red, poorly cemented, cross-bedded; becomes shaly to north
Dog Creek................	30–400	Red clay shales, dolomite
Blaine....................	75–125	Red gypsiferous shale and gypsum, red clay shale, dolomite
Enid:		
Chickasha.................	75–175	Sandstone, red, green, and purple, with clay partings; gypsum-bearing shales
Duncan...................	30–200	Loose uncemented sand, sandstone, shales
Clear Fork-Wichita.........	400–1,000	Red and gray-banded shales not differentiated, red and gray sandstone, calcareous sandstone
Pennsylvanian:[1]		
Pontotoc group............	1,000–1,500	Sandstone, conglomerate, shales, thin limestone

[1] The beds including and below the Vanoss formation which is a member of the Pontotoc group, are described by Levorsen (p. 318) for Seminole County where they are best known. The Glenn formation referred to on following pages includes the Seminole and lower Pennsylvanian beds.

The Robberson[1] field is in southwest Garvin County on the westward extension of the Timbered Hills anticline which is the main anticline of the southern Arbuckle Mountains. Pre-Cambrian gabbro crops out on its axis, above which are Cambrian and Ordovician rocks. The axis is in line with a group of buried hills, above which is developed the Robberson dome in southwest Garvin County (Fig. 203). Gas was discovered in the field in 1920 and oil soon afterward. In June, 1923, the field produced 6,482 barrels of oil daily from 148 wells. An anticline shows indistinctly at the surface. The surface rocks are Permian shales and sandstones. Permian red beds and limestones called the Garvin beds extend to depths of 1,200 feet or more. Below these beds are 200 to 400 feet of sands and shales, with lenticular gas sands called the Mauldin horizon of the Permian. Below these sands are beds of Pennsylvanian (Pontotoc) (Fig. 82) which lie on buried hills. The Pennsylvanian strata below the base of the Permian lie on a well-defined anticline that forms the surface of the ancient hills. At the top of the anticline are four or more domes. The maximum production is on the north side of the anticline and is derived from the Newberry sands of the Pennsylvanian and from the Simpson sands of the Ordovician. The oil ranges in gravity from 25 to 33° Bé. The lightest oil is in the Simpson sand; heavier oil is found in the higher sands in the Permian.

Homer field is in northwestern Carter County about 8 miles southeast of the Robberson field. It is located on a plunging anticline and derives its oil from the Pontotoc series. The wells are small and produce an oil high in lubricants. Tatum is southwest of Homer. Both fields are believed to lie on buried structures. Sholem Alechem field, 8 miles south of the Robberson field, is located on an anticline which strikes southeast.[2] The rocks cropping out are of Permian age and the anticline is an upfold of at least 1,200 feet. The numerous oil sands range from 1,800 to about 4,000 feet deep. Wildcat Jim field east of Sholem Alechem is probably on a buried anticline covered with Permian rocks. In the Cox field, southeast of Wildcat Jim, the Permian beds crop out. The oil is derived from the Pennsylvanian formations.

In the Doyle[3] district, about 7 miles west of Robberson, the Duncan sandstone crops out on top of a small flat dome. The oil is found at

[1] DENISON, A. R., The Robberson Field, Garvin County, Oklahoma, Am. Assoc. Pet. Geol. *Bull.*, vol. 7, pp. 625–644, 1923.

ROTH, R., The Robberson Field, Okla. Geol. Survey *Bull.* 40K, pp. 32–52, 1927.

[2] MEYER, A. M., Sholem Alechem, Oil and Gas geology of Carter County, Okla. Geol. Survey *Bull.* 40Z, pp. 48–58, 1928.

TOMLINSON, C. W., Okla. Geol. Survey *Bull.* 40Z, pp. 1–77, 1928.

[3] GOUIN, F., The Geology of the Oil and Gas Fields of Stephens County, Oklahoma, Okla. Geol. Survey *Bull.* 40E, pp. 1–44, 1926.

WEGEMANN, C. H., The Duncan Gas Field, Stephens County, Oklahoma, U. S. Geol. Survey *Bull.* 621D, pp. 43–50, 1915.

depths of 1,200 to 1,500 feet in sands associated with red and gray shales. Below the producing sands are post–Glenn formations of the Pennsylvanian.

On the Cruse anticline southwest of Doyle are located the Cruse, Velma, and Milroy fields. In the Cruse district the surface rocks are Wichita and Duncan formations, which, probably, according to Gouin, overlie a buried hill. Gas is found at a depth of 850 feet and oil at 1,700 feet. The oil has a gravity of 28° Bé.

At Velma[1] the rocks dip gently southwest and more steeply to the northeast. The surface rocks are sandstones and shales belonging to the Wichita-Clear Fork series, and oil is found in the Permian at depths of from 350 to 900 feet and in the Pennsylvanian at about 2,400 feet down the west side of the fold. The oil is about 28° A.P.I. and the wells yield initially about 5 to 25 barrels. The core of the anticline, found at a depth of 1,745 feet, is limestone, probably Ordovician. The Milroy field, 10 miles southeast of Velma is on the same anticline which is clearly shown on the surface. Oil is found in the lower part of the Permian.

The Fox[2] field, north of Healdton, was opened as a gas field in 1916, when a well with an initial production of 25,000,000 cubic feet was drilled. Subsequently, oil wells were drilled, and in May, 1922, the average daily production was 3,230 barrels from 58 wells. The gravity of most of the oil is about 35° Bé. The Permian rocks crop out and show an anticline striking northwest with about 60 feet of closure. Oil or gas is found in 15 horizons at depths between 150 and 2,450 feet. The beds below 1,200 feet are Pennsylvanian and probably belong to the Glenn formation. The best producing sand is between 2,225 and 2,380 feet deep.

The Graham[3] field is 10 miles northeast of Healdton. The first oil well was drilled in April, 1921, and in 1924 the field was producing about 14,000 barrels of oil daily and also large amounts of gas. The area is covered with a thick series of Permian strata that dip about 1 degree northeast. These beds are 800 to 1,200 feet thick near Graham. A short distance northeast of the field they dip into a syncline and rise again near the Arbuckle Mountains. The Pennsylvanian rocks lie unconformably below the Permian and are thrown into a steep anticline that strikes northwest. On it an oil field is developed about 6 miles on strike and

[1] STORM, W., The "2–4" Shallow Field and the Velma Oil and Gas Field, Oklahoma, Am. Assoc. Pet. Geol. *Bull.* vol. 5, pp. 626–629, 1924.

[2] STORM, W., Fox Oil and Gas Field, Carter County, Oklahoma, Am. Assoc. Pet. Geol. *Bull.*, vol. 6, pp. 367–369, 1922.

TOMLINSON, C. W., Buried Hills near Mannville, Oklahoma, Am. Assoc. Pet. Geol. *Bull.*, vol. 10, pp. 138–143, 1926.

BUNN, J. R., Okla. Geol. Survey *Bull.* 40Z, pp. 21–28, 1928.

[3] TOMLINSON, C. W., and W. STORM, The Graham Field, Oklahoma, Am. Assoc. Pet. Geol. *Bull.*, vol. 8, pp. 593–620, 1924.

WOODS, S. H., and J. P. McKEE, Okla. Geol. Survey *Bull.* 40Z, pp. 29–37, 1928.

nearly a mile wide. On the northeast flank of the fold dips average 28 degrees and on the southwest side 22 degrees. The Pennsylvanian rocks belong to the Glenn formation and consist of shales, limestones, sandy limestones, and sandstones. A little oil was found in the Permian strata but not in commercial quantity. In the Glenn formation the oil or gas is found in 8 zones within a vertical distance of 2,100 feet within a depth of 3,300 feet below the surface. The oil ranges in gravity from 27 to 43° Bé. (page 35). The oils of the deeper sands are lighter than the oils in the beds nearer the surface. In a single sand, however, the lighter oils are found near the crest of the dome, and the oil is heavier near edge water. The wells having largest production are near the top of the dome in the area adjoining the gas deposits. To July, 1928, the Graham field produced nearly 16,000,000 barrels of oil. The Wheeler[1] field is located southeast of Graham on a dome that is shown at the surface. Oil is found at the base of the "Red Beds" about 1,000 feet deep.

The Crinerville[2] oil field near Brock is 15 miles southeast of Healdton field and 7 miles southwest of Ardmore. Oil was discovered in this field in 1922. By June 30, 1927, the field had produced about 2,300,000 barrels. The oil is 27 to 39° Bé. and is high in gasoline. The field lies along a surface anticline in the Pennsylvanian strata on the west side of and faulted against the Criner Hills (Fig. 204). The production comes from sands in the Pennsylvanian which overlap the Ordovician limestones of the Criner Hills. The oil, which, according to Powers, originated in Pennsylvanian shales, migrated into the Pennsylvanian sandstones and small amounts migrated into the Ordovician beds. Although the oil wells are located upon a buried ridge of the Ordovician rocks, the production is not confined to the anticline but the accumulation is up the dip near the edge of the sands, where the latter either thin out or become impervious or lap against the Ordovician rocks. Down dip, below the oil blanket, salt water is found in the beds. The chief production is from the Pennsylvanian beds below the Hoxbar in sands below the heavy oil series, as shown in Fig. 204.

The Healdton[3] district (Fig. 205) is located on the Healdton anticline in the western part of Carter County. Oil was discovered in 1913 and

[1] TOMLINSON, C. W., Okla. Geol. Survey *Bull.* 40Z, pp. 62–63, 1928.

[2] TAFF, J. A., Preliminary Report on the Geology of the Arbuckle and Wichita Mountains, U. S. Geol. Survey *Prof. Paper* 31, pp. 1–97, 1904.

POWERS, S., Crinerville Oil Field, Carter County, Oklahoma, Am. Assoc. Pet. Geol. *Bull.*, vol. 11, pp. 1067–1086, 1927.

[3] WEGEMANN, C. H., and K. C. HEALD, The Healdton Oil Field, Carter County, Oklahoma, U. S. Geol. Survey *Bull.* 621, pp. 13–30, 1915.

POWERS, S., The Healdton Oil and Gas Field, Oklahoma, *Econ. Geol.*, vol. 12, p. 604, 1917.

MERRITT, J. W., Am. Assoc. Pet. Geol. *Bull.*, vol. 4, pp. 47–52, 1920.

TOMLINSON, C. W., Okla. Geol. Survey *Bull.* 40Z, pp. 37–42, 1928.

within 3 years the field was one of the most productive in Oklahoma, yielding about 60,000 barrels of oil per day. The total production to December 31, 1927, was 148,211,277 barrels of oil. The surface rocks are the Permian red beds and consist of red and gray shales alternating with brown, white, and red sandstone and thin conglomerate beds. Several domes are developed on the Healdton anticline (Figs. 34, 35), and the oil is concentrated in the domes. Oil or gas is produced from 10 or more horizons. All of these are of Pennsylvanian, and Ordovician age. There is an unconformity between the Pennsylvanian and the red beds, and there is an angular unconformity between the Ordovician and Pennsylvanian strata, the Ordovician constituting a buried hill of pre-Pennsylvanian age. According to Tomlinson, at places this ancient hill projects several hundred feet into the basal Pennsylvanian strata, and some of the latter are cut out. The bulk of the oil of the Healdton field has come from Pennsylvanian sands, although some is derived from Ordovician sandy limestone, the latter at depths from 2,100 feet to 4,200 feet.

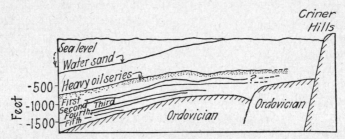

Fig. 204.—Cross section of Crinerville oil field, Oklahoma. The oil is accumulated in Pennsylvanian sands which overlap the Ordovician strata and are sealed up dip where they thin out or become impervious against the Ordovician beds. (*After S. Powers.*)

The Hewett field is about 3 miles east of Healdton. The rocks cropping out are the Clear Fork-Wichita formation of Permian age. The field is located on two domes, connected by a saddle, which lie above a buried hill of limestone. Oil and gas are found in six sands in the Pennsylvanian, which lies unconformably below the Permian, and also in the porous limestone below the Pennsylvanian near the plane of the unconformity between Pennsylvanian and Ordovician beds. The main production, which to the end of 1929 was 60,349,876 barrels, has come from the Pennsylvanian sands. One well completed in 1923 at a depth of 2,940 feet in pre-Pennsylvanian strata gaged 12,800 barrels of oil per day. The oil of the Hewett field[1] is lighter than that of Healdton and

[1] Swigart, T. E., and F. X. Schwarzenbek, Petroleum Engineering in the Hewett Field, Oklahoma, Chamber of Commerce, Ardmore, Oklahoma, and U. S. Bureau of Mines, pp. 1–132, 1921.

Burton, G. E., Hewett Oil Field, Carter County, Oklahoma, "Structure of Typical American Oil Fields," vol. 2, pp. 290–299, 1929.

has a gravity between 32 and 34° Bé. A cross-section of the field is shown by Fig. 205.

The Lawton-Hanbury field[1] is east of Lawton and near the east end of Comanche County. The producing part of the field is on a flat dome 10 miles east of Lawton. The surface rocks are Wichita-Clear Fork formation which extend to depths of about 1,400 feet. Below this depth are shales, sands, and gravels probably of the Pontotoc group. A well in August, 1925, at 2,010 feet, found high-gravity oil in a Pontotoc sand and produced 400 barrels a day. Other wells found oil in sands at higher horizons. Below the sands are beds of dry gravels which, when penetrated, appear to drain the oil from the sands so that production rapidly declines.

The Woolsey field 8 miles southwest of Velma is on an anticline that strikes southeast extending through the Loco and Healdton fields. At Woolsey the base of the red beds lies at a depth of 1,300 feet, and oil

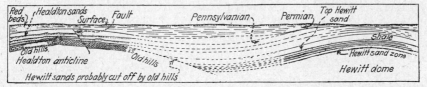

Fig. 205.—Cross section of Healdton and Hewett oil fields, Oklahoma. (*After Hubbard.*)

is found at a depth of 1,750 feet in the Glenn formation. The Loco[2] field is 7 miles southeast of Woolsey on the same anticlinal axis. The surface rocks are part of the Wichita-Clear Fork formation of the Permian which consists of red shale and sandstone. The base of the Permian lies at a depth of 600 feet below which are Pennsylvanian blue shales, sandstones and thin limestone. The thickness of the Pennsylvanian rocks increases down the flanks of the fold, the field being located on a buried pre-Pennsylvanian ridge. Gas is found in the 700- and 850-foot sand of the Glenn formation of the Pennsylvanian and deeper sands. The wells yield initially from 10 to 25 barrels of oil having a gravity of 24° A.P.I. A well drilled near the axis of the fold found a thick pre-Pennsylvanian limestone.

The North Duncan[3] field southeast of the Lawton-Hanbury field is on a low flat dome elongated in the northwest direction in line with

[1] WEGEMANN, C. H., and R. W. HOWELL, The Lawton Oil and Gas Field, Oklahoma, U. S. Geol. Survey *Bull.* 621, pp. 71–85, 1916.

[2] WEGEMANN, C. H., The Loco Gas Field, Stephens and Jefferson Counties, Oklahoma, U. S. Geol. Survey *Bull.* 621C, pp. 31–42, 1916.

GOUIN, F., The Geology of the Oil and Gas Fields of Stephens County Oklahoma, Okla. Geol. Survey *Bull.* 40E, pp. 41–43, 1926.

[3] GOUIN, F., *op. cit.*, pp. 35–48.

the dome on part of the Lawton-Hanbury area.   The rocks at the surface
are the red sandstones and shales of the Wichita (Permian), which have
a general northeast dip.   A well drilled near the top of the dome in 1921
had an initial production of 1,600 barrels from the Thomas sand at 2,000
feet.   Later, oil was found in sand at a depth of 2,300 feet in the southwest side of the dome.   The producing sands are probably of Pennsylvanian age.   A deep well encountered limestone probably the Arbuckle
formation.   The total production of the field to 1926 was 4,867,017
barrels.   The gravity of the oil is about 39° A.P.I.

The Wichita anticline, which is in line with the main trend of the
Wichita Mountains, passes through the south part of the Lawton area and
is followed southeast through the West Duncan, Empire, and Comanche
fields in Stephens County.   In all of these fields the beds cropping out
are the red sandstones and shales of the Wichita formation (Permian).
The regional dip is north, and, in the Comanche field, south dips are
prominent, and an elongated dome on the Wichita anticline can be
outlined at the surface.   The structure of the domes at Empire and West
Duncan is obscure at the surface and the discovery well of the Empire
was located where it was believed to be in line with the axis of the Wichita
uplift.   In the Empire field oil was discovered in 1920 and by January
1, 1926, the field had produced 10,604,728 barrels.   The oil has a gravity
between 38 and 42° A.P.I.   Drilling developed a well-defined dome with
small folds on its crest.   From the surface to about 1,200 feet the wells are
in the Permian; from that depth to 1,700 feet is post-Glenn Pennsylvanian; between that depth and 3,400 feet are dark shales, sandstone,
and some thin limestone; below 3,400 feet are the Arbuckle limestones.
There are 10 producing sands between the depths of 1,000 and 2,600 feet.
Of these the Surber at 1,700 feet and the Blaydes at 2,200 feet have yielded
most of the oil.

The West Duncan field 2 miles northwest of Empire field is on a flat
dome separated from the Empire dome by a shallow saddle.   This dome
is not clearly defined at the surface but is mapped from drill holes.   The
producing sands are the same as those developed in the Empire field, the
chief production coming from the Surber sand at 1,700 feet and the Brown
sand at 2,100 feet, both probably of Pennsylvanian age.   The district
produced 3,327,926 barrels to January 1, 1926.   On the summit of the
dome there were large accumulations of gas.

In the Comanche pool, 7 miles southeast of Empire, gas is found in a
sand at a depth of 800 feet, the initial pressure being 300 pounds per square
inch.   Oil is found at a depth of 1,400 feet approximately at the base of
the Permian and at a depth of 1,800 feet in the Pennsylvanian strata.
The field to January 1, 1926, produced 1,297,188 barrels of oil.   The
Magnolia pool is 3 miles west of West Duncan on an axis that lies southwest of the Wichita axis and is nearly parallel to it.

The Walters field is about 8 miles southwest of the Magnolia field. Oil and gas are found in several sands but the yield of the wells decreases rapidly. In the Red River field on Red River, 25 miles southwest of Walters, the rocks cropping out are of Permian age. Oil is found at three horizons probably belonging to the Cisco formation. In the Oscar field located on an anticline 20 miles southwest of Healdton, oil is found at a number of horizons included in the Glenn formation. The oil has a gravity of about 35° Bé.

The Madill field near Madill,[1] about 25 miles east of Ardmore, is located on a gentle anticline, which is shown in the Trinity formation of the Lower Cretaceous system, and which is probably a more acute anticline in older underlying rocks.[2] The oil is of light gravity and of high gasoline content. It is found in sandstone and conglomerate at the base of the Trinity formation. It is believed to have migrated from underlying rocks. The wells exploited are shallow and of small yield.

The Enos[3] gas field is about 12 miles south of Madill. The rocks exposed at the surface are Trinity sands which are folded into a gentle anticline. A little oil is found in the Trinity at a depth of about 450 feet, and gas is found at 600 feet. The anticline is the north extension of the Preston anticline of Texas.

The Vines (Scott) field is in Murray County about 20 miles north of Ardmore. A little heavy oil is found in the Simpson formation. In the Roff field, northern Murray County, a little oil is found, probably in the Simpson formation, which produces asphalt in the field.

Near Ada, Pontotoc County, gas is encountered in several sands of the Pennsylvanian series, and some oil has been found in the Hunton limestone at a depth of 2,300 feet. In the Allen field,[4] northeast of Ada, there is a dome with 80 feet of closure. The long axis of the dome strikes northeast, and small oil and gas wells are developed in sand lenses at shallow depth near the center of the dome. In 1929 large production of oil was obtained from the Wilcox sand. Some of the oil is derived from the Allen sand of the Pennsylvanian series at a depth of about 750 to 800 feet. The North Allen field is on a structural dome. The Allen sand is about 900 feet deep. An oil sand lies at a depth of about 2,300 to 2,400 feet and is correlated with the Wapanucka, or upper part of the Caney, by Conklin, and by others with the Savanna. Oil has recently

[1] Taff, J. A., U. S. Geol. Survey, Tishomingo *Folio* 98, 1903.

Taff, J. A , and W. J. Reed, The Madill Oil Pool, Oklahoma, U. S. Geol. Survey *Bull.* 381, pp. 504–513, 1910.

[2] Tomlinson, C. W., Buried Hills near Mannsville, Oklahoma, Am. Assoc. Pet. Geol. *Bull.*, vol. 10, pp. 138–143, 1926.

[3] Hopkins, O. B., S. Powers, and H. M. Robinson, The Structure of the Madill-Denison Area, Oklahoma and Texas, with Notes on Oil and Gas Developments, U. S. Geol. Survey *Bull.* 736, pp. 1–34, 1922.

[4] Conklin, R. A., Okla. Geol. Survey *Bull.* 40S, p. 23, 1927.

been found in the Wilcox sand about two miles north of Ada. In the
Beebe field northwest of Ada, oil is produced from the Boggy formation
and from the Viola limestone, which lies 2,300 feet deep. The wells are
on the flanks of the Beebe anticline.

Additional References for Oklahoma

ADAMS, G. I., The Carboniferous and Permian Age of the Red Beds of Eastern
Oklahoma from Stratigraphic Evidence, *Am. Jour. Sci.*, ser. 4, vol. 12, pp. 383–
386, 1901.
———, Lithologic Phases of the Pennsylvanian and Permian of Kansas, Indian
Territory, and Oklahoma, *Science*, new ser., vol. 15, No. 379, pp. 545–546, 1902.
AURIN, FRITZ, Correlation of the Oil Sands of Oklahoma, Okla. Geol. Survey *Circ.* 7,
pp. 1–16, chart, 1917.
———, Geology of the Red Beds of Oklahoma, Okla. Geol. Survey *Bull.* 30, pp. 1–66,
1917.
BEEDE, J. W., The Bearing of the Stratigraphic History and Invertebrate Fossils on
the Age of the Anthracolithic Rocks of Kansas and Oklahoma, *Jour. Geol.*, vol.
17, pp. 710–729, 1909.
———, Origin of the Sediments and Coloring Matter of the Red Beds of Oklahoma,
Science, new ser., vol. 35, No. 896, pp. 348–350, 1912.
BIRK, R. A., The Extension of a Portion of the Pontotoc Series around the Western
End of the Arbuckle Mountains, Am. Assoc. Pet. Geol., *Bull.*, vol. 9, pp. 983–989,
1925.
BLOESCH, E., Fort Scott-Wetumka Correlation, Am. Assoc. Pet. Geol. *Bull.*, vol. 10,
pp. 810–812, 1926.
BUCHANAN, G. S., The Distribution and Correlation of the Mississippian in Oklahoma,
Am. Assoc. Pet. Geol. *Bull.*, vol. 11, pp. 1307–1320, 1927.
BULLARD, F. M., Geology of Love County, Oklahoma, Okla. Geol. Survey *Bull.* 33,
pp. 1–77, 1925.
———, Geology of Marshall County, Oklahoma, Okla. Geol. Survey *Bull.* 39, pp.
1–101, 1926.
BUNN, J. R., Petroleum Engineering in the Papoose Oil Field, Okfuskee and Hughes
Counties Oklahoma, Okla. Geol. Survey *Bull.* 36, pp. 1–61, 1926.
EDSON, FANNY CARTER, Notes on the Simpson Formation, Oklahoma, Am. Assoc.
Pet. Geol. *Bull.*, vol. 7, pp. 558–564, 1923.
FOLEY, L. L., Origin of Folding in Oklahoma, Am. Assoc. Pet. Geol. *Bull.*, vol. 11, pp.
639–640, 1927.
GOLDSTON, W. L., JR., Differentiation and Structure of the Glenn Formation, Am.
Assoc. Pet. Geol. *Bull.*, vol. 6, pp. 5–23, 1922.
GARDNER, J. H., Oil Pools of Southern Oklahoma and Northern Texas, *Econ. Geol.*,
vol. 10, pp. 422–434, 1915.
———, Rock Distortion on Local Structures in the Oil Fields of Oklahoma, Am.
Assoc. Pet. Geol. *Bull.*, vol. 6, pp. 228–243, 1922.
———, The Mid-Continent Oil Fields, Geol. Soc. Am. *Bull.*, vol. 28, pp. 685–720, 1917.
GOULD, C. N., Correlation of the Permian of Kansas, Oklahoma, and Northern Texas,
Am. Assoc. Pet. Geol. *Bull.*, vol. 10, pp. 144–153, 1926.
———, Geology and Water Resources of Oklahoma, U. S. Geol. Survey *Water Supply
Paper* 148, pp. 1–178, 1905.
———, Index to the Stratigraphy of Oklahoma, Okla. Geol. Survey *Bull.* 35, pp.
1–116, 1925.

GOULD, C, N., On the Southern Extension of the Marion and Wellington Formations Kan. Acad. Sci. *Trans.*, vol. 17, pp. 179–181, 1901.

———, Stratigraphy of the McCann Sandstone, Kan. Univ. *Quart.*, pp. 175–177, 1905.

———, and J. T. LONSDALE, Geology of Beaver County, Oklahoma, Okla. Geol. Survey *Bull.* 38, pp. 1–71, 1926.

——— and ———, Geology of Texas County, Oklahoma, Okla. Geol. Survey *Bull.* 37, pp. 1–62, 1926.

HAGER, DORSEY, Gas Pressures and Water Pressures in Oklahoma, *Fuel Oil Jour.*, vol. 6, p. 64, April, 1915.

HONESS, C. W., Geology of the Southern Ouachita Mountains of Oklahoma, Okla. Geol. Survey *Bull.* 32, pt. 1, pp.1–278, 1923; pt. 2, *Econ. Geol.*, pp. 1–76, 1923.

HUTCHINSON, L. L., Rock Asphalt, Asphaltite, Petroleum, and Natural Gas in Oklahoma, Okla. Geol. Survey *Bull.* 2, pp. 1–256, 1911.

KIRK, C. T., A Preliminary Report on the Contact of the Permian with the Pennsylvanian in Oklahoma, Okla. Geol. Survey *Third Bienn. Rept.* 1903, pp. 5–14, 1904.

MISER, R. D., Geological Map of Oklahoma, Okla. Geol. Survey and U. S. Geol. Survey, 1926. (Scale 1 to 500,000.)

MONNETT, V. E., Topographic Criteria of Oil-field Structure, Am. Assoc. Pet. Geol. *Bull.* Vol. 6, pp. 37–41, 1922.

MUNN, M. J., Reconnaissance of the Grandfield District, Oklahoma, U. S. Geol. Survey *Bull.*, 547, pp. 1–85, 1914.

OHERN, D. W., Stratigraphy of the Older Pennsylvanian Rocks of Northeastern Oklahoma, Okla. Univ. Research *Bull.* 4.

———, and GARRETT, R. E., The Ponca City Oil and Gas Field, Okla. Geol. Survey *Bull.* 16, 1915.

POWER, S., The Healdton Oil Field, Oklahoma, *Econ. Geol.*, vol. 12, pp. 594–606, 1917.

PURDUE, A. H., Winslow Arkansas-Oklahoma *Folio* 154, 1907.

REED, R. D., Some Suggestions in Regard to Pennsylvanian Paleogeography in the Henryetta District, Oklahoma, Am. Assoc. Pet. Geol. *Bull.*, vol. 7, pp. 50–57, 1923.

ROSS, G. S., Evidence of Slumping Previous to Consolidation in the Pennsylvanian of Oklahoma, Am. Assoc. Pet. Geol. *Bull.*, vol. 8, pp. 505–510, 1924.

ROTHROCK, E. P., Geology of Cimarron County, Oklahoma, Okla. Geol. Survey *Bull.* 34, pp. 1–110, 1925.

RUEDEMANN, P., and H. E. REDMON, The Turkey Mountain Lime Pools, Oklahoma, Am. Assoc. Pet. Geol. *Bull.*, vol. 11, pp. 933–944, 1927.

SAWYER, R. W., Areal Geology of Part of Southwestern Oklahoma, Am. Assoc. Pet. Geol. *Bull.*, vol. 8, pp. 312–321, 1924.

SHANNON, C. W., and others, Petroleum and Natural Gas, Okla. Geol. Survey *Bull.* 10, pt. 2, pp. 1–536, 1917.

———, and L. E. TROUT, Petroleum and Natural Gas in Oklahoma, Okla. Geol. Survey *Bull.* 19, pt. 1, pp. 1–133, 1915.

SNIDER, L. C., Geology of a Portion of Northeastern Oklahoma, Okla. Geol. Survey *Bull.* 24, pt. 1, pp. 1–122, 1915.

TAFF, J. A., Atoka Quadrangle, U. S. Geol. Survey *Folio* 79, 1902.

———, Coalgate Quadrangle, U. S. Geol. Survey *Folio* 74, 1901.

———, Muskogee Quadrangle, U. S. Geol. Survey *Folio* 132, 1906.

———, U. S. Geol. Survey, Tallequah *Folio* 122, 1905.

———, U. S. Geol. Survey, Tishomingo *Folio* 98, 1903.

———, Preliminary Report on the Geology of the Arbuckle and Wichita Mountains, Indian Territory and Oklahoma, U. S. Geol. Survey *Prof. Paper* 31, pp. 1–75, 1904; reprinted as Okla. Geol. Survey *Bull.* 12.

————, and M. K. Shaler, Notes on the Geology of the Muskogee Oil Field, U. S. Geol. Survey *Bull.* 260, pp. 441–445, 1905.

Trout, L. E., and G. H. Myers, Bibliography of Oklahoma Geology, Okla. Geol. Survey *Bull.* 25, pp 1–105, 1915.

Wallis, B. F., The Geology and Economic Value of the Wapanucka Limestone of Oklahoma, with Notes on the Economic Value of Adjacent Formations, Okla. Geol. Survey *Bull.* 23, pp. 1–102, 1915.

White, L. H., and F. C. Green, Correlation of the Wilcox Sand in the Okmulgee District with the Osage, Oklahoma, Am. Assoc. Pet. Geol. *Bull.*, vol. 5, pp. 399–408, 1921.

Wood, R. H., Oil and Gas Development in Northeastern Oklahoma, U. S. Geol. Survey *Bull.*, 531, pp. 27–53, 1913.

CHAPTER XIII

MID-CONTINENT REGION (*Continued*)

TEXAS AND SOUTH NEW MEXICO

General Features.—Nearly all of Texas lies south of the Ouachita-Arbuckle-Wichita Mountains system and east of the Rocky Mountains. The buried Amarillo Mountains in the northern Panhandle, however,

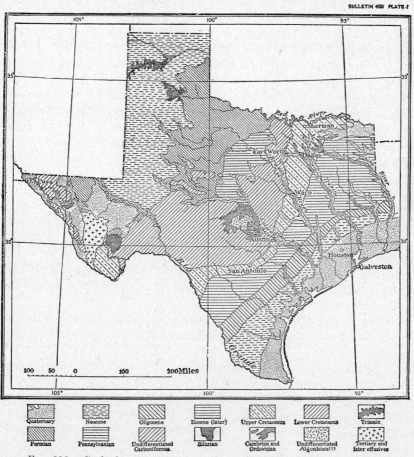

FIG. 206.—Geologic map of Texas. (*After Hill, Willis, Paige and others.*)

are the northwest extension of the Wichita range, and the region along the Rio Grande southeast of El Paso includes foothill ranges of the Rocky

Mountains.　An area of pre-Cambrian rocks is found near the center of the state (Fig. 206).　Between the Amarillo Mountains and the Rocky Mountains ranges, along the Rio Grande and the central pre-Cambrian area, there is a great structural basin containing Permian rocks, which extends northward into New Mexico and is called the Permian basin of West Texas and New Mexico.

North of the central pre-Cambrian area there is a great buried anticline extending northward toward Oklahoma which is known as the Bend arch.　On this arch Mississippian, Pennsylvanian, and Permian rocks are found.　The arch plunges gently to the north, and younger formations crop out successively toward the north.　East of this arch and east of the central pre-Cambrian area Cretaceous and younger rocks dip gently southeast to the coast, the successively younger belts of strata lying southeast of the older ones.

The Balcones fault zone is a great belt of deformation which extends from northeast Texas southwestward almost to the Rio Grande.　It bends near San Antonio.　On the Balcones fault zone upper Cretaceous rocks are highly deformed.　East of the Balcones fault zone is found the Palestine zone along which are situated ten or more salt domes.　In these domes rocks of Tertiary age are greatly deformed by movements attending the rise of the great bodies of salt that form the cores of the salt domes. Southeast of the Palestine zone, in an area extending for several hundred miles along the Gulf Coast of Texas and Louisiana, salt domes surrounded by highly deformed Tertiary rocks are found at many places.

The chief oil and gas regions of Texas include:

1.　The north Panhandle in which oil and gas fields are found in Permian rocks above and on the flanks of the buried Amarillo Mountains.

2.　The West Texas-New Mexico Permian basin (in part) in which oil and gas fields are found in Permian rocks.

3.　The north-central Texas region in which oil and gas fields are found in Mississippian, Pennsylvanian, and Permian rocks mainly along and on the flanks of the Bend arch.

4.　The Balcones fault region, including the Mexia fault zone in which the oil and gas fields are found chiefly in Upper Cretaceous but also in Comanchean strata.

5.　The Palestine zone of deformation and west edge of the Sabine uplift.

6.　The Reynosa (Bordas) escarpment region of south Texas, in which oil and gas are found in Tertiary rocks.

7.　The salt dome region of the Gulf Coast in which oil is found in Tertiary rocks.

Practically all of these regions are known to contain large amounts of oil or gas or both.　In 1927 Texas produced 213,768,000 barrels of oil valued at $249,600,000.　In 1926 the state produced 175,392,000 thousand cubic feet of gas valued at $28,165,000. In 1927 Texas produced 316,600,000 gallons of natural gas gasoline valued at $18,110,000.

Panhandle Region.—In the Panhandle[1] district of north Texas (Figs. 207, 208) gas was discovered in Potter County in 1918, and oil was

FIG. 207.—Map of Panhandle oil field, Texas. The main prospective gas bearing area is stippled; oil fields black. (*Data from Bauer and others.*)

[1] BAUER, C. M., Oil and Gas Fields of the Texas Panhandle, Am. Assoc. Pet. Geol. *Bull.*, vol. 10, pp. 733–746, 1926.

———, Gas a Big Factor in the Texas Panhandle, Am. Assoc. Pet. Geol. *Bull.*, vol. 12, pp. 165–176, 1928.

GOULD, C. N., The Geology and Water Resources of the Eastern Portion of the Texas Panhandle, U. S. Geol. Survey, *Water Supply Paper* 154, pp. 1–64, 1906.

———, The Geology and Water Resources of the Western Portion of the Texas Panhandle, U. S. Geol. Survey *Water Supply Paper* 191, pp. 1–70, 1907.

———, Geology and Structure of the Amarillo Region, Am. Assoc. Pet. Geol. *Bull.*, vol. 4, No. 3, pp. 269–275, 1920.

PATTON, L. T., The Geology of Potter County, Univ. Texas *Bull.* 2330, pp. 1–180, 1923.

PRATT, W. E., Oil and Gas in the Texas Panhandle, Am. Assoc. Pet. Geol. *Bull.*, vol. 7, pp. 237–246, 1923.

HARRISON, T. S., Porphyry at Amarillo, Am. Assoc. Pet. Geol. *Bull.*, vol. 7, pp. 434–439, 1923.

POWERS, S., Reflected Buried Hills and Their Importance in Petroleum Geology, *Econ. Geol.*, vol. 17, pp. 233–259, 1922.

RUEDEMANN P., and L. M. OLES, Am. Assoc. Pet. Geol. *Bull.*, vol. 13, pp. 799–810, 1929.

discovered in Carson County in 1921. A 600-barrel well was brought in in Carson County in 1925, and since then the field has been developed rapidly. In 1927 the oil production reached about 131,500 barrels a day and the field has proved to be one of the greatest gas fields in North America (Fig. 209a). The oil is high grade, about 34 to 37° Bé. and is rich in gasoline and paraffin. It congeals at 50° F. and causes trouble in pipe lines and in the waxing of the oil sands.

TENTATIVE CORRELATION OF THE PERMIAN RED BEDS OF KANSAS, OKLAHOMA, AND NORTHERN TAXAS

(*After Gould*)

Kansas	Oklahoma	Texas
Big Basin[1]	Quartermaster	Red sandy shales
Hackberry	Cloud Chief ("Greer")	Gypsiferous red shales
Day Creek	Day Creek	
Whitehorse ("Red Bluff")	Whitehorse	Whitehorse ("Lake Trammel")
Dog Creek	Dog Creek	Gypsiferous red shales
Blaine ("Cave Creek")	Blaine	Blaine ("Eskota," "Greer")
Flowerpot Cedar Hills Salt Plain	Chickasha	Gypsiferous red shales
Harper	Duncan	San Angelo
Wellington Marion		Choza Vale

(left bracket labels: Cimarron; "Woodward"; Enid. right bracket labels: Double Mountain; Clear Fork)

[1] The relations of the Big Basin and Hackberry of Kansas to the Quartermaster and Cloud Chief of Oklahoma are not clearly understood at present.

The rocks exposed are chiefly of Recent, Tertiary, and Triassic age. Below the Triassic is a great series of Permian beds, the top of which is exposed on several anticlines, some of which are outlined at the surface by the Alibates dolomite bed. The upper division of the Permian includes (Fig. 209b) red beds, sandstone, and clay, in all 700 feet or more. Below this group is the second group of strata 500 feet thick, which includes a similar red group with much gypsum. In a third group of red rocks, salt is abundant. This series is bottomed at depths of 1,500 to 2,200 feet, and below it is a limestone series which is about 800 feet thick. The rocks[1] of the limestone series include limestone, dolomite, shale,

[1] GOULD, C. N., The Correlation of the Permian of Kansas, Oklahoma, and Northern Texas, Am. Assoc. Pet. Geol. *Bull.*, vol. 10, pp. 144–153, 1926.

PATTON, L. T., The Geology of Potter County, Univ. Texas *Bull.* 2330, pp. 1–180, 1923.

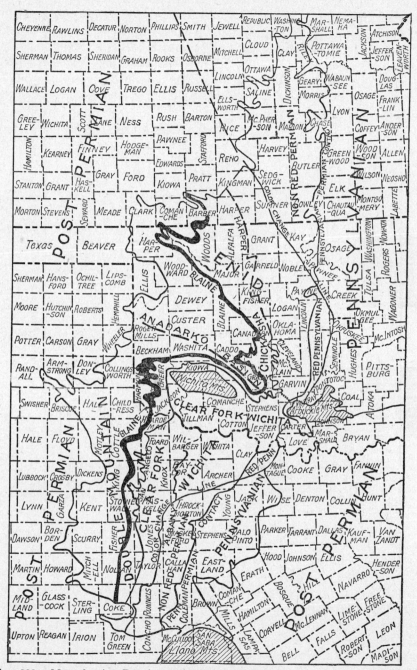

Fig. 208.—Map showing Permian rocks of parts of Kansas, Oklahoma and Northern Texas. (*After C. N. Gould.*)

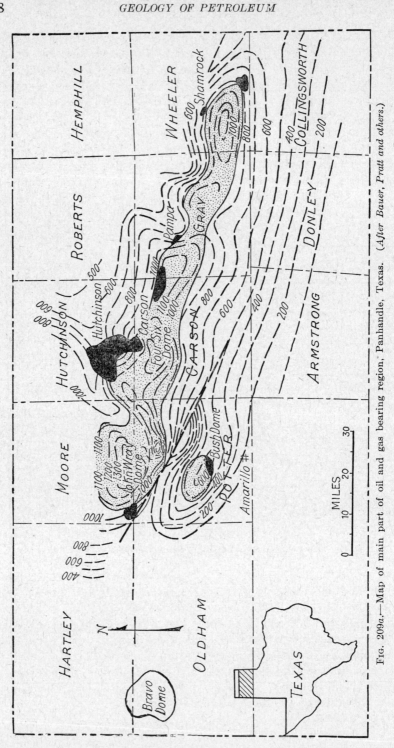

Fig. 209a.—Map of main part of oil and gas bearing region, Panhandle, Texas.   (After Bauer, Pratt and others.)

anhydrite, etc., and they are not red. This series is the main zone producing oil and gas, which are found in pores and fractures of oolitic dolomites and in limestone. Oil and gas are found also in ancient granite wash or arkose near a ridge of buried hills. Below the Lime series is one of shales and below that are probably Pennsylvanian shales.

A great buried ridge consisting of granite, schists, gneisses, etc., extends westward from the Wichita Mountains of Oklahoma almost across the Panhandle. The Permian and later beds were laid down on this ridge, and on its flanks the Permian beds are more than 900 feet thicker than on the top of the ridge. After the beds were arched above the ridge, they formed the anticline, 100 miles long, which is shown in Fig. 207. Faults striking parallel to the ridge displace the strata.[1]

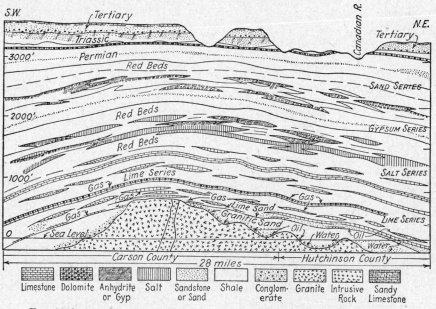

Fig. 209b.—Section of Panhandle oil and gas region, Texas. (After Bauer.)

As stated, gas is abundant above the crest of the buried ridge in crevices and pores of a thick limestone bed. The gas occurs at depths of 1,600 to 2,400 feet along the crest of the anticline and at 2,900 feet down the flanks. It has a pressure of about 430 pounds per square inch, and the pressure is fairly uniform, which suggests interconnection. The gas usually appears 320 feet below the top of the Lime series and below that point, in a section of 500 feet, from three to seven porous beds are reached. The thickness of the gas pay sands varies but, according to Bauer, will average together 36.2 feet for each well.

[1] FATH, A. E., U. S. Geol. Survey *Prof. Paper* 128, pp. 75–84, 1920.

Oil is found in several areas on the north side of the gas area and at a few places on the south side. It lies in a horizontal zone on a water body which, according to Bauer, is at sea level or within about 20 feet of sea level throughout the field. The upper limit of the oil zone is 200 feet above sea level, where the oil is in the arkose sand or dolomitic limestone or dolomite. The arkose sand which rests on the ancient ridge is from a few feet to 80 feet thick. The "lime sand" reservoir is generally

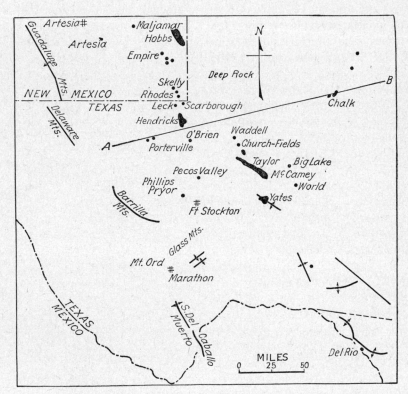

Fig. 210.—Map of part of Permian basin of West Texas; for Section on the line *AB* see Fig. 211.

150 feet above the granite sand and is about 200 feet thick. At places it contains 50 per cent anhydrite, and in it are several porous layers from 15 to 30 feet thick.

The gas pressure of about 430 pounds per square inch is nearly uniform and suggests interconnection of reservoir rocks which lie along the pre-Cambrian-Permian unconformity. This pressure is less than half of what would be expected if the gas were in balance with water in saturated beds extending up to the surface.

According to Bauer, the oil-bearing beds are not known to crop out at any place that is higher than the elevation of the district. Ruedemann and Oles suggest a connection with beds that crop out near the Wichita Mountains to the east.

The amount of gas present in the field is enormous. Bauer estimates that the gas field covers 949,120 acres, and uses an estimate of Roth that the oil reservoir rock averages 36.2 feet of pay. He assumes a porosity of 20 per cent and estimates that the amount of recoverable gas present when the field was opened to be equivalent to 4,436,000,000,000 cubic feet of gas at one atmosphere of pressure (p. 149). The gas contains about 68.7 per cent methane and 17.4 per cent ethane, and in parts of the field it is high in hydrogen sulphide. The first gas encountered was dry or free from gasoline vapor, but subsequent drilling revealed large quantities of gas high in vapor of gasoline, which is now recovered. Notwithstanding the low closed pressure of the wells, the initial daily discharge is high, in some wells 100,000,000 cubic feet per day. This, Pratt[1] attributes to the very open character of the reservoir rocks. The gas of parts of the field contains considerable helium, that of central Potter County and eastern Hartley County being especially high in helium.[2]

West Texas-New Mexico Permian Basin.—The Permian basin of

[1] PRATT, W. E., *op. cit.*, discussion, p. 247.

[2] RUEDEMANN, P., and L. M. OLES, Helium, Its Probable Origin and Concentration in the Amarillo Fold, Texas, Am. Assoc. Pet. Geol. *Bull.*, vol. 13, pp. 799–810, 1929.

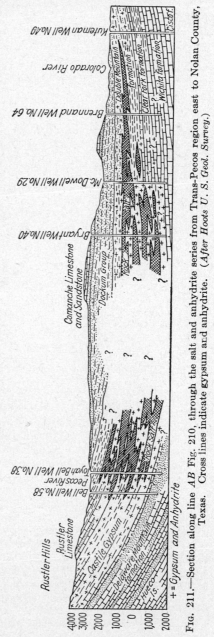

FIG. 211.—Section along line *AB* Fig. 210, through the salt and anhydrite series from Trans-Pecos region east to Nolan County, Texas. Cross lines indicate gypsum and anhydrite. (*After Hoots U. S. Geol. Survey.*)

western Texas[1] and southeastern New Mexico (Figs. 210, 211) is a great
structural trough that lies west of the Bend arch and Llano Mountains

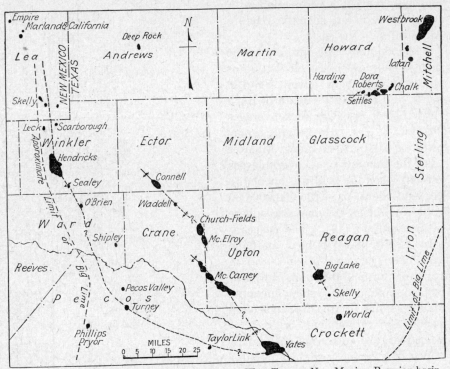

Fig. 212.—Sketch showing main producing area West Texas—New Mexico, Permian basin.

of central Texas and east of the southern extension of the Rocky Mountains, which includes the somewhat isolated chains and foreland ranges

[1] Cummins, W. F., Tex. Geol. Survey *First Ann. Rept.*, pp. 185–197, 1890; *Second Ann. Rept.*, pp. 394–435, 1891; *Third Ann. Rept.*, pp. 129–223, 1892.

Osann, C. A., Tex. Geol. Survey *Fourth Ann. Rept.*, pp. 177–238, 1893.

Hoots, H. W., Geology of a Part of Western Texas and Southeastern New Mexico, U. S. Geol. Survey *Bull.* 780, pp. 33–126, 1925.

Darton, N. H., Permian Salt Deposits of South-central United States, U. S. Geol. Survey *Bull.* 715, pp. 205–230, 1921.

————, "Red Beds" and Associated Formations in New Mexico, U. S. Geol. Survey *Bull.* 794, pp. 1–356, 1928.

————, A Comparison of Paleozoic Sections of Southern New Mexico, U. S. Geol. Survey *Prof. Paper* 108, pp. 31–55, 1917.

Beede, J. W., Notes on Geology and Oil Possibilities of Northern Diablo Plateau in Texas, Univ. Texas Geol. Survey *Bull.* 1852, 1920.

Baker, C. L., Geology and Underground Water of the Northern Llano Estacado, Univ. Texas *Bull.* 57, pp. 1–225, 1915.

————, Exploratory Geology of Part of Southwestern Trans-Pecos, Texas, Univ. Texas. *Bull.* 2745, 1927.

————, and W. F. Bowman, Geology of the Southeastern Front Range of Trans-Pecos, Texas, Univ. Texas *Bull.* 1753, pp. 63–177, 1917.

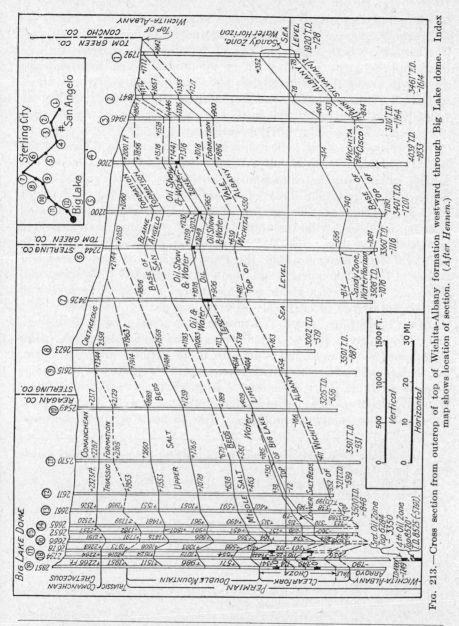

Fig. 213.—Cross section from outcrop of top of Wichita-Albany formation westward through Big Lake dome. Index map shows location of section. (*After Hennen.*)

Udden, J. A., Notes on the Geology of Glass Mountains, Univ. Texas. *Bull.* 1753, pp. 3–59, 1917.

———, C. L. Baker, and E. Böse, Review of the Geology of Texas, Univ. Texas Geol. Survey *Bull.* 44, 1916; 3rd ed. rev., 1919.

Liddle, R. A., The Marathon Fold and Its Influence on Petroleum Accumulation, Univ. Texas Geol. Survey *Bull.* 1847, 1920.

of the group, namely, the Guadalupe Mountains in New Mexico, the Delaware Mountains, Glass Mountains, and Marathon uplift of Texas. The basin is separated from the area of Permian rocks of western Oklahoma by the great buried chain of mountains near Amarillo. The country is a high nearly featureless plain that slopes gently south and southeast. It is arid and given over mainly to stock raising. Numerous water wells of the basin found small amounts of oil, and attempts were made to develop the oil at several localities.

The discovery of oil in Permian rocks near Amarillo, Texas, in the Big Lake field, Reagan County, Texas, and in the Artesia field, New Mexico, greatly stimulated exploration of the west Texas Permian basin. Between 1924 and 1928 discoveries were made which showed that this basin is one of the world's greatest oil-bearing regions. It is estimated that the oil fields of the basin are capable of producing several million barrels of oil per day. The oil is mainly of medium gravity and is high in sulphur. To January 1, 1928, the Permian basin of west Texas had produced 76,753,000 barrels of oil from proved areas of 45,764 acres, and, according to Watson,[1] there was an indicated ultimate recovery of 715,000,000 barrels of oil. This estimate is probably conservative.

West Texas (Figs. 212, 213) is now in the process of being developed, and there is a great variety of opinions as to the geologic structure. The mountains to the west and south are being studied with great care, but the geologic section is difficult to interpret. Well records show great differences within short distances. Variations from 5,000 feet of limestone to 5,000 feet of anhydrite and salt are found in wells 20 miles apart. There are many unsolved problems. The oil fields occupy domes and

RICHARDSON, G. B., Reconnaissance in Trans-Pecos, Univ. Texas Min. Survey *Bull.* 9, pp. 1–119, 1904.

EDWARDS, E. C., Stratigraphic Position of the Big Lime of West Texas, Am. Assoc. Pet. Geol. *Bull.*, vol. 11, pp. 721–728, 1927.

KING, P. H., and R. E. KING, The Pennsylvanian and Permian Stratigraphy of the Glass Mountains, Contributions to Geology 1928, Univ. Texas *Bull.* 2801, pp. 109–145, 1928.

———, and ———, Stratigraphy of Outcropping Carboniferous and Permian Rocks at Trans-Pecos, Texas, Advance Sheets, Am. Assoc. Pet. Geol. *Bull.*, pp. 1–4, Forth Worth meeting, 1929.

ADAMS, J. E., Triassic of West Texas, Advance Sheets, Am. Assoc. Pet. Geol. *Bull.*, pp. 1–10, Forth Worth meeting, 1929.

CRANDALL, K. H., Permian Stratigraphy of Southeastern New Mexico and Adjacent Portions of Western Texas, Advance Sheets, Am. Assoc. Pet. Geol. *Bull.*, pp. 1–23, Fort Worth meeting, 1929.

LLOYD, R. E., Capitan Limestone and Associated Formations of Texas and New Mexico, Advance Sheets, Am. Assoc. Pet. Geol. *Bull.*, pp. 1–12, Fort Worth meeting, 1929.

[1] WATSON, C. P., Economic Significance of West Texas Development, *Oil Weekly*, vol. 48, No. 11, pp. 31 32, Mar. 2, 1928.

anticlines. Some of the fields are located on refolded buried anticlinal hills. Low folds are found in Cretaceous rocks but these are generally obscured by a mantle of wind-blown sand. The low folds, when drilled, are found commonly to reflect stronger folds with depth, in rocks that lie unconformably below the Cretaceous beds.[1] Certain thick limestones are probably ancient coral reefs.

Unconformities are found within the Permian strata, between the Permian and the Triassic and between the Triassic and Comanchean rocks. The earth movements that marked the close of the Paleozoic era and raised the Appalachian and Ouachita Mountains affected also parts of the Rocks Mountains area. The earth movements shown in the Rocky Mountains, which involved rocks of Mesozoic and Tertiary age, probably are to be correlated with those that caused the minor folding that is shown in the Comanchean rocks of eastern New Mexico and west Texas.

On the east side of the basin the oil is found in the Big Lake limestone. The Permian formations, which near the margins of the basin consist chiefly of limestone, shales, and some gypsum and anhydrite, change character near the center of the basin, where they contain 3,000 feet or more of salt, anhydrite, gypsum, and potash salts. Owing to the burial of the Permian below later rocks and unconformities between those rocks, correlations of the Permian beds on the east and west sides of the basin are difficult. The oil, as stated, is found in limestones, which nearly everywhere are overlain by great beds of salt, gypsum, and anhydrite. It is not certain whether the oil-bearing limestone in the east part of the basin is the same as that in the southwest and at Artesia, New Mexico, although that is considered probable. The general relations are shown by Fig. 211 after Hoots, and generalized sections are given on pages that follow. According to Hennen, the Big Lake limestone in the Big Lake field is in the Choza member of the Clear Fork formation (Permian). It is believed that many of the oil-bearing structures are buried hills in which the limestone was eroded, leached, and made porous by ground water before burial. This theory is supported by the fact that the limestone in the structural basins between the oil fields often has very low porosity, wells drilled into it several hundred feet finding very little water, whereas the limestone on and near the tops of the domes is very porous. Some believe the "Big Lime" was originally in part coral reefs.

Surface and shallow indications of oil, as already stated, are numerous on the borders of the basin. At many places in wells sunk for water small amounts of oil are found. On the east side of the basin shallow

---

[1] POWERS, S., Buried Ridges in West Texas, Am. Assoc. Pet. Geol. *Bull.*, vol. 11, pp. 1109–1115, 1927.

wells found oil in Tom Green, Howard, Coleman, and McCulloch counties. In Coke County, 3 miles southwest of Edith postoffice, an outcrop of sandstone 2 feet thick, of the Greer stage of the Double Mountain formation heavily stained with oil[1] and similar occurrences are found near Robert E. Lee. In the Turney district, a few miles northeast of Fort Stockton, the basal sands of the Comanchean crop out. Oil seeps are found and several wells encountered oil or gas at depths between 50 and 1,058 feet.[2] One well obtained an estimated production of 1,000 barrels of oil a day at a depth of 96 feet. The oil, according to Adkins, has probably risen through fractures or cavernous rock from the Permian

FORMATIONS ON EAST SIDE WEST TEXAS BASIN

Formation	Thickness, feet	Description
Pleistocene and Tertiary(?):............	0–800	Unconsolidated sands, gravels, clays, etc.
Comanchean:		
Edwards............	0–158	Limestone, argillaceous limestone
Walnut..............	0–10	Yellowish brown clayey limestone, locally sandy and clay
Trinity..............	0–150	Soft friable sandstone, cross-bedded variegated
Unconformity Triassic:		
Dockum Group......	150–1,200	Red clay, micaceous sandstone, cross-bedded sandstone
Unconformity Permian:		
Double Mountain....	2,000–4,000	Red and blue sandstone, shale, clay, dolomitic limestone, dolomite, gypsum, salt, oil in dolomite
Clear Fork..........	750–1,000	Red sandstone, red shale, blue shale, dolomite
Wichita-Albany......	1,000–1,500	Dolomite and blue shale, sand near base Oil in porous dolomite, marine
Pennsylvanian:		
Cisco..............	750–1,000	Blue and red clay and shale, sandstone, conglomerate, some limestone
Canyon............	800–1,000	Limestone, clay, shale, red sandstone, conglomerate, coal
Strawn.............	950–4,700	Sandstone, conglomerate, shale, limestone, coal
Smithwick..........	225–600	Carbonaceous shale, some sandstone
Marble Falls........	450–650	Dark limestone, limestone conglomerate at base

[1] BEEDE, J. A., Geology of Coke County, Univ. Texas *Bull.* 1850, p. 1, 1918.
   JONES, R. A., Am. Assoc. Pet. Geol. *Bull.*, vol. 9, p. 1215, 1925.
[2] ADKINS, W. S., The Geology and Mineral Resources of the Fort Stockton Quadrangle, Univ. Texas. Bur. Econ. Geol. *Bull.* 2738, pp. 1–166, 1927.

TRIASSIC-PERMIAN-PENNSYLVANIAN SECTION, EAST-CENTRAL NEW MEXICO
(After E. R. Lloyd)

System	Formation	Character	Thickness, feet
Triassic	Dockum beds	Santa Rosa sandstone at base	1,700 ±
	Unconformity		
Permian	Upper red beds	Red shale and sandstone	
	Salt anhydrite group	Thick salt beds interbedded with anhydrite and gypsum	
	"Red sand" group	Red and white sandstones interbedded with anhydrite and gypsum	1,500 ±
	"Red sand" group	Red and white sandstones interbedded with anhydrite and gypsum	600–800
	San Andres	Limestone, grading northward into salt, anhydrite and gypsum	1,100 ±
	Glorieta sandstone	Medium-grained, buff sandstone, locally interbedded with limestone	10–400
	Yeso	Interbedded gypsum (anhydrite) salt, shale, limestone, and sandstone; predominantly light-red colors	1,000 ±
	Abo	Brick red sandstone, arkose, red sandy shale and beds of limestone	800 ±
	Unconformity		
Pennsylvanian	Magdalena	Predominantly limestone with interbedded shale and sandstone	1,500–2,000

GEOLOGIC SECTION OF GLASS MOUNTAINS
(After Baker, King, and others)

Cretaceous:
Unconformity.
Permian:
  Bissett. Conglomerate, shale, thin dolomite

Thickness, Feet

Unconformity.
  Tessey. Massive dolomite, a little gypsum...................... 1,000
  Gilliam. Thin bedded dolomite, a little gypsum.................. 900
  Vidrio. Thick bedded gray dolomite, some sandstone and red shale.. 500–900
  Ward. Limestone, shale, sandstone............................. 700–1,500
  Leonard. Shale, limestone, quartzite, conglomerate............... 300–1,800
  Hess. Limestone, dolomite, shale, conglomerate at base............ 700–2,100
Unconformity.
  Wolfcamp. Shale and limestone................................. 700
Unconformity. Strong folding
Pennsylvanian:
  Gaptank. Limestone, sandstone, shale, conglomerate............... 1,800
  Haymond. Sandstone, shale, conglomerate...................... 1,800
  Dimple. Massive limestone, some sandstone at base and shales at top 1,100
  Tesnus. Sandstone, shale....................................... 3,370
Unconformity.
Devonian(?):
  Caballos. Novaculite

rocks.   The wells near Fort Stockton were short lived, and the oil was soon followed by sulphur water.   The oil was opaque, dark; specific gravity 22° Bé.   One well drilled in 1915 produced a heavy black oil from which ichthyol, a medicinal preparation, was distilled.   This oil is said to have sold for $7.50 a barrel.

Near the southwest border of the basin in the Pecos and Porterville fields, 15 miles northeast of Toyah, a small group of wells once produced 1 or 2 barrels each per day.   This oil probably originated from the Delaware Mountains limestone which is exposed in the mountains southwest

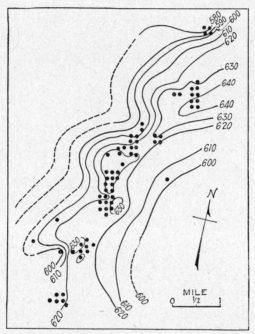

Fig. 214.—Map of Westbrook oil field, Mitchell County, Texas, contoured on a key horizon in the Permian system.   (*After Edwards and Orynski.*)

of the field, where the limestone contains asphalt.   Near Artesia in southeast New Mexico, oil was found in many wells drilled for water.

The Westbrook[1] field (Fig. 212) is in Mitchell County, Texas, 2 miles northwest of the town of Westbrook.   The field began production in 1920 and in 1926 there was a production of 3,400 barrels a day from 77 wells.   The rocks dip northwest at low angles.   The outcropping rocks are of Triassic age, below which, at depths between 500 and 1,500 feet, are Permian red sands and shales with salt, gypsum, and anhydrite. Below 1,500 feet the Permian consists chiefly of dolomitic limestone. The regional dip is northwest.   An anticline with an axis striking north-

[1] EDWARDS, E. C., and L. W. ORYNSKI, Westbrook Field, Mitchell County, Texas, Am. Assoc. Pet. Geol. *Bull.*, vol. 11, pp. 467–476, 1927.

east shows 30 feet of reversal on the southeast side (Fig. 214).   The field is 6 miles long and 1½ miles wide.   Oil is encountered in the Permian limestone at depths of 2,400 and at 3,000 feet, the latter, according to Edwards and Orynski, being near the base of Clear Fork and top of Wichita.   There are two zones of porous limestone from 10 to 40 feet thick.   Nearly all the wells are on the northwest side of the fold in the direction of the regional dip.   This, however, is attributed by Edwards and Orynski to differences in porosity.   The oil is probably derived from marine Permian limestone and shale.   It is about 25.8° Bé. and is high in sulphur.   The oil is accompanied by wet gas yielding over 4 gallons of gasoline per 1,000 cubic feet.

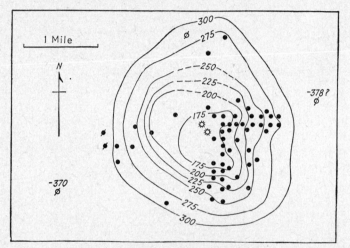

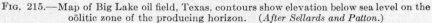

Fig. 215.—Map of Big Lake oil field, Texas, contours show elevation below sea level on the oölitic zone of the producing horizon.   (*After Sellards and Patton.*)

The Big Lake[1] oil field (Fig. 215) is in southwest Reagan County about 75 miles southwest of San Angelo.   The field, which is the property of the University of Texas, was drilled in 1923, when an 80-barrel well was brought in.   The total production of the field to October, 1928, was 36,238,451 barrels.   The rocks of the district are shown in Fig. 216.   The regional dip is westward as shown by Fig. 213.   The oil is found at two horizons in the Permian, one in the Pennsylvanian, and one in the Ordovician.   The Permian consists of red shales, sandstones, gypsum, anhydrite, limestone, and dolomite.   Below the dolomite there is a great thickness of black shale.   The Permian rocks include three salt beds with a total thickness of 500 feet.   The upper salt carries much anhydrite and also the potash minerals polyhalite and sylvite.

[1] SELLARDS, E. H., and L. T. PATTON, The Subsurface Geology of the Big Lake Oil Field, Am. Assoc. Pet. Geol. *Bull.*, vol. 10, pp. 365–381, 1926.

HENNEN, R. V., Big Lake Oil Pool, Reagan County, Texas, "Structure of Typical American Oil Fields," vol. 2, pp. 500–541, 1929.

The highest oil zone is in the Choza member of the Clear Fork formation about 2,500 feet deep. This is called the "Shallow" oil sand. The second zone, which is the chief oil-producing horizon, is 50 to 100

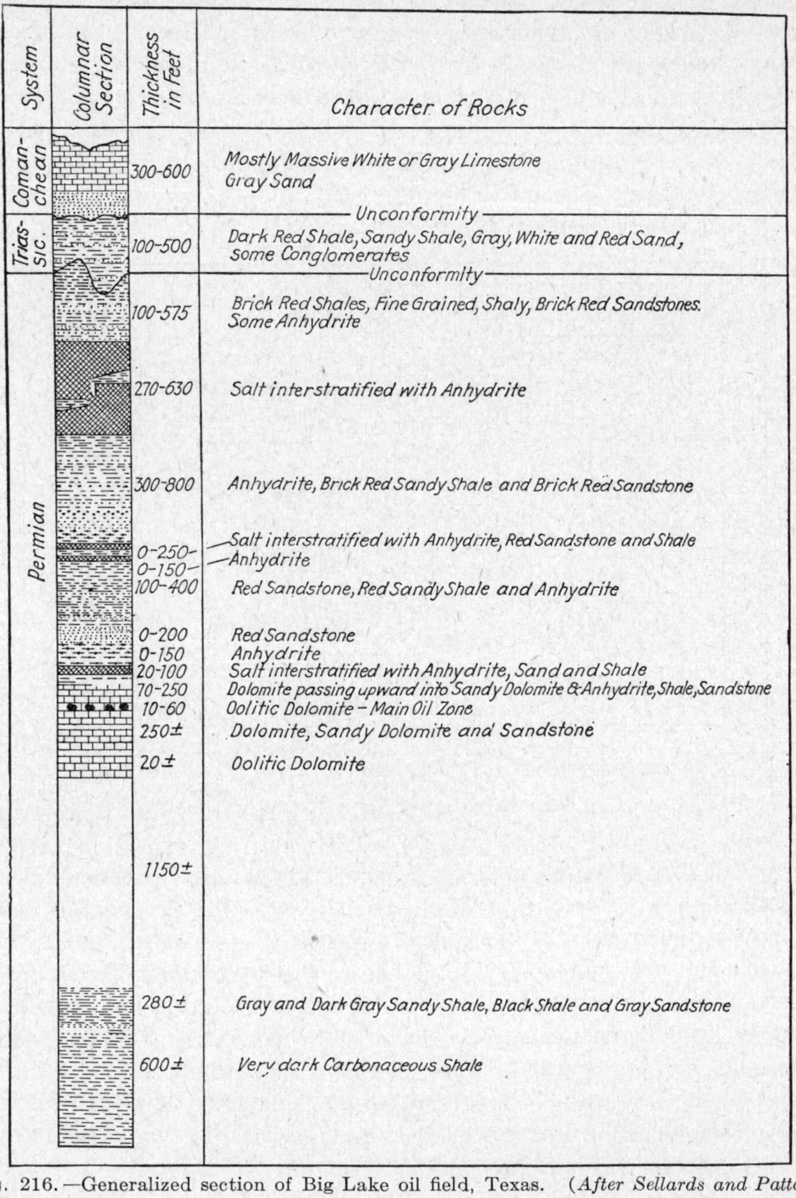

System	Columnar Section	Thickness in Feet	Character of Rocks
Coman-chean		300-600	Mostly Massive White or Gray Limestone Gray Sand
			──────── Unconformity ────────
Trias-sic.		100-500	Dark Red Shale, Sandy Shale, Gray, White and Red Sand, Some Conglomerates
			──────── Unconformity ────────
Permian		100-575	Brick Red Shales, Fine Grained, Shaly, Brick Red Sandstones. Some Anhydrite
		270-630	Salt interstratified with Anhydrite
		300-800	Anhydrite, Brick Red Sandy Shale and Brick Red Sandstone
		0-250-	Salt interstratified with Anhydrite, Red Sandstone and Shale
		0-150-	Anhydrite
		100-400	Red Sandstone, Red Sandy Shale and Anhydrite
		0-200	Red Sandstone
		0-150	Anhydrite
		20-100	Salt interstratified with Anhydrite, Sand and Shale
		70-250	Dolomite passing upward into Sandy Dolomite & Anhydrite, Shale, Sandstone
		10-60	Oolitic Dolomite – Main Oil Zone
		250±	Dolomite, Sandy Dolomite and Sandstone
		20±	Oolitic Dolomite
		1150±	
		280±	Gray and Dark Gray Sandy Shale, Black Shale and Gray Sandstone
		600±	Very dark Carbonaceous Shale

FIG. 216.—Generalized section of Big Lake oil field, Texas. (*After Sellards and Patton.*)

feet below the top of the Big Lime and is called the "Texon" zone. It is an oolitic dolomite, very porous, and has an average thickness of 22 feet. A third zone is found at 6,284 feet and is probably in the Strawn formation. As shown by Harlton, Bush, Lowman and others, the Big Lake deep well passes through Pennsylvanian and Silurian beds into the Ordovician limestone[1] from which oil is obtained at 8,514 feet.

The oil is found in a dome about 3 miles in diameter, which has a slight closure in Comanchean rocks at the surface. This closure is greater in the Shallow oil zone and greater still where contoured on the Texon zone. The oil of both of these zones is associated with gas, and that of

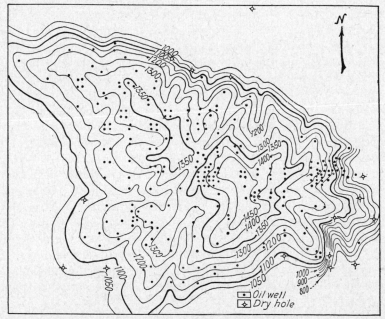

FIG. 217.—Structural map of Yates field, West Texas, contours on top of "Big Lime." Width of figure about 8 miles. (*After F. R. Clark.*)

the Texon zone contains much hydrogen sulphide and is poison. The oil in both of these zones is circled by edge water on the flanks of the dome. In 1929 a well sunk 8,525 feet encountered oil in the fourth zone. This was then the world's deepest well. The oil was associated with much gas; a short time after it was brought in, the well increased its flow so that it soon was producing about 1,900 barrels of oil per day. This oil has a gravity of 58° Bé. and is a sweet oil of excellent grade. As stated it is from Ordovician strata. That is noteworthy, for nearly all of the oils of the west Texas Permian basin are high in sulphur. The oil of the Texon zone, which has yielded the bulk of the production of the Big Lake field, has a gravity of 38° A.P.I. and carries about 0.36 per cent sulphur. In the World district, a few miles south of Big Lake and probably on the

[1] LOWMAN. S. W., Amer. Assoc. Pet. Geol. *Bull.*, vol. 14, pp. 798–806, 1930.

same structural axis, oil is found in the Big Lime series at depths between 2,500 and 2,700 feet.   The oil is heavier than that of Big Lake.   Production is small.

The Yates[1] oil field (Fig. 217) is located in northeast Pecos County, with a few edge wells in Crockett County along the Pecos River.   The pool ranks as one of the greatest oil fields in the world.   Many wells produce initially at the rate of 75,000 barrels per day and a few exceed 100,000 barrels per day.   The field has a shut-in production rated at several million barrels per day.   The discovery well was drilled in November, 1926, and was rated at 75 barrels per day, flowing by heads.   Later, it was drilled deeper and produced at the rate of 70,000 barrels per day. The field was developed rapidly, with 282 oil-well completions to the end of 1928, which is about 18 per cent of the proved 10-acre locations.   The oil is about 30° Bé. gravity and is high in sulphur.   The original oil-gas bottom hole pressure was about 705 pounds per square inch.   The oil reservoir is a highly porous dolomitic limestone, belonging to the Big Lime formation of the Big Lake field, presumably Permian in age.   It is found at depths ranging from 1,000 to 1,650 feet, depending on the topography and the folding.   The structure of the Yates field is that of an elongated dome with the major axis trending northwest.   It has about 500 feet of closure and contains about 16,000 acres of oil-producing territory.   The dome is relatively flat on top with steeply dipping flanks and is on one of the major lines of folding of the west Texas Permian basin.   Possibly it is on the intersection of two lines of folding.[2]   The structure map representing the attitude of the top of Big Lime strongly suggests an erosional surface with ridges and valleys radiating from the axis of the fold.

The surface rocks include Edwards and Georgetown limestones, Walnut clay and the Basement sands, all of Comanchean age.   The Basement sands rest unconformably on a series of blue and gray shale interbedded with sandstone and limestone, aggregating 100 to 200 feet in thickness.   Below this, on the top of the fold, is about 600 to 700 feet of anhydrite and some dolomite with stringers of interbedded shale and sand.   This member increases greatly in thickness on the flanks of the dome toward the basins.   Several hundred feet of salt and red beds, which are absent on the top of the fold, are present above the anhydrite member in the basins and on the flanks of the fold.   The Big Lime is found below the anhydrite member.   The evidence appears to indicate a major unconformity between the anhydrite member and the Big Lime. Fragments blown from the wells appear to be water worn and suggest

[1] This description of the Yates oil field was kindly supplied by Frank R. Clark of Tulsa.

[2] GESTER, G. C., and H. J. HAWLEY, Yates Field, Pecos County, Texas, "Structure of Typical American Oil Fields," vol. 2, pp. 480–499, 1929.

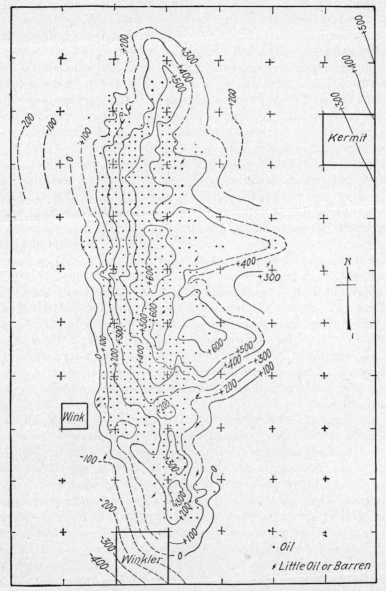

Fig. 218.—Structure map of Hendricks oil field, Winkler County, Texas. Contours on top of Permian limestone. It is uncertain whether contours show top of burned reef, an unconformity or a structural dome. Crosses show section corners. (*By J. M. Brown, Independent Oil and Gas Co.*)

ground-water leaching.   The leached zone extends at least 200 feet below the present top of the Big Lime.   The probable unconformity may be confined to the top and near-by flanks of the fold, with the basins sinking or the fold rising during the deposition of the anhydrite and the salt and red bed members.   Although nearly all of the oil has come from the "Big Lime," the sands above the latter have produced small amounts.

In the McCamey field, 25 miles northwest of Yates, a narrow anticline strikes northwest.   Oil is found along the strike for about 12 miles in the upper part of the Permian (Big Lake) limestone at a depth of about 1,800 to 2,300 feet.   The field is about 1 mile wide and sulphurous water appears in most of the wells.

The McElroy field is about 10 miles north of the McCamey field. An anticline strikes northwest and the northwest continuation of the field is known as the Church and Fields district.   The oil is developed in the upper part of the "Big Lime" and is found at depths of between 2,800 and 3,200 feet.   The oil contains considerable gasoline but is high in sulphur, many samples containing about 2.5 per cent.   Vertrees[1] states that some of the fragments blown from the wells seem to be weather worn, suggesting a buried erosion surface.

Hendricks field is in Winkler County about 50 miles northwest of McElroy (Fig. 218).   The field was brought in in 1926 and by 1928 had developed many large wells.   It ranks with Yates among the greatest oil fields of the world.   The field is on the west side of the basin where the regional dip is east.   It is located on a dome with a long axis that strikes north and is probably 8 miles long or more.   The rocks cropping out are of Triassic age.   The wells are drilled through red beds, anhydrite, gypsum and salt, with thin limestone and dolomite, and encounter the Permian Big Lime about 2,400 feet deep.   The top member of the Big Lime is the "Brown lime" about 300 feet thick, including the basal sandy beds.   The Brown lime carries oil.   Below the Brown lime is the "White lime" which is the main oil bearing member.   The chief production is found about 200 feet below the top of the "White" lime.[2]

Lea and Eddy counties, New Mexico, lie to the northwest of and on the general strike of the Hendricks oil field in Winkler County, and, owing to the great amount of oil developed in the Hendricks pool, these counties are under active exploration (Fig. 210).   The country is relatively level and drained by the Pecos River.   The land along the river is irrigated by artesian water, good flows of which are found at Artesia, Dayton, and Lakewood.   In this region hundreds of water wells have been drilled, ranging in depths from 300 to 1,000 feet.   In most of them water rises to points near the surface or flows out under pressure.   In 1910 gas under

[1] VERTREES, C. D., Am. Assoc. Pet. Geol. *Bull.*, vol. 12, p. 1158, 1928.

[2] ACKERS, A. L., DeChicchis, R., and SMITH, R. H., The Hendricks field, Winkler County, Texas, Am. Assoc. Pet. Geol. *Bull.*, vol. 14, pp. 923–944, 1930.

strong pressure was encountered in a water well 2 miles southeast of Dayton, and later a heavy black oil was found in the Williams well 2½ miles east of Dayton.[1] In 1924 oil was found in the Artesia oil field, 15 miles southeast of the town of Artesia and about 12 miles east of Dayton, by Flynn, Welch, and Yates. To March, 1927, the field produced 1,896,965 barrels of oil. The oil has a paraffin base and a gravity of 35° Bé.

The Artesia field is located on the west side of the west Texas-New Mexico Permian basin on a dome that lies on an anticline that strikes

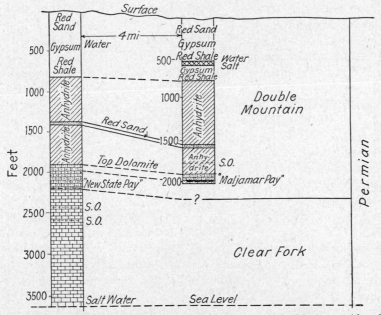

Fig. 219.—Geologic sections of Permian strata southeast New Mexico. (*After M. J. Davis.*)

northeast. Permian rocks crop out and wells pass through red beds, gypsum, and thick beds of anhydrite into a thick series of dolomites, all of Permian age. A section of the area, after Davis,[2] is shown as Fig. 219. The oil is found on top and on the southeast flank of the dome in a somewhat porous dolomite about 300 feet below the top of the dolomite, where the rock is somewhat sandy. Most of the wells are about 2,000 to 3,000 feet deep. They are shot with heavy charges and make up to

[1] Fisher, C. A., Preliminary Report on the Geology and Underground Waters of the Roswell Artesian Area, New Mexico, U. S. Geol. Survey *Water Supply Paper* 158, pp. 1–29, 1908.

Richardson, G. B., Petroleum near Dayton, New Mexico, U. S. Geol. Survey *Bull.* 541, pp. 135–140, 1914.

Yates, Martin, written communication.

[2] Davis, M. J., Artesian Field, Eddy County, New Mexico, "Structure of Typical American Oil Fields," vol. 1, pp. 112–123, 1929.

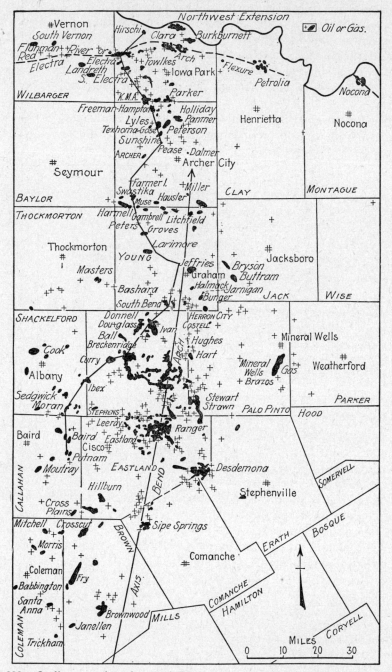

Fig. 220.—Outline map of north central Texas showing position of main oil and gas fields.

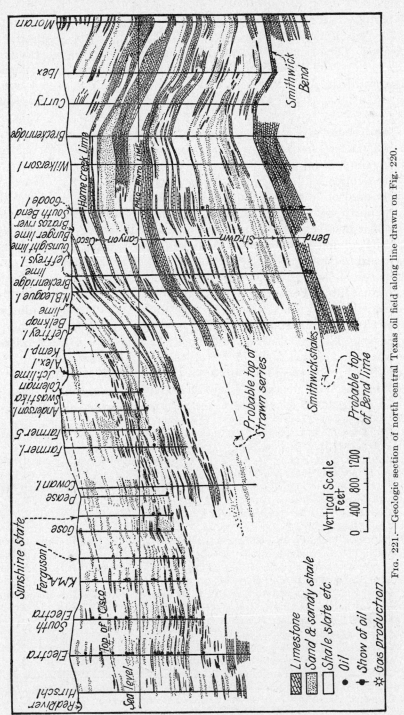

FIG. 221.—Geologic section of north central Texas oil field along line drawn on Fig. 220.

250 barrels of oil a day or more, initial production. The oil is accompanied by gas under heavy pressure from which casing-head gasoline is recovered. The Empire well (Fig. 210) obtained oil on a small structural dome. In a well recently drilled, about 12 miles northeast of Artesia field toward the Maljamar field, a thick salt bed is found. This well is more than 3,300 feet deep and has encountered gas and some oil at several horizons.

The Rhodes well in the southeast corner of Lea County, at a depth of about 3,216 feet, found a flow of gas estimated to be 23,000,000 cubic feet per day, and oil estimated to be about 120 barrels a day.

The Hobbs field is in Lea County about 70 miles east of Artesia. It is located on a structural dome which lies on an anticlinal axis that strikes northwest (Fig. 210). The Big Lime is encountered at a depth of about 4,000 feet. The limestone is altered and porous. It carries oil generally at depths about 50 feet in the formation and the oil extends downward to depths about 150 feet below the top of the formation. The field is one of the greatest in the Permian basin.

North-central Texas.—The north-central Texas[1] oil producing area is included within a belt about 180 miles long and 100 miles wide that extends from the Llano uplift to Red River (Figs. 220, 221). The country is relatively flat, semiarid, and in the main is given over to stock raising. Superficial indications of oil are rare, although in the Llano region to the south of the belt, according to Paige, the Carboniferous strata have a petroliferous odor and asphalt is found in fractures in limestone.[2] North-

[1] GIRTY, G. H., The Bend Formation and Its Correlations, Am. Assoc. Pet. Geol. *Bull.*, vol. 3, pp. 71–81, 1919.

GOLDMAN, M. I., Lithologic Subsurface Correlation of the Bend Series of North-central Texas, U. S. Geol. Survey *Prof. Paper* 129, pp. 1–22, 1921.

HAGER, D., Geology of the Oil Fields of North-central Texas, Am. Inst. Min. Eng. *Bull.* 118, pp. 1115–1116, 1918.

MATTESEN, W. G., A Review of the Development of the North-central Texas Oil Fields during 1918, *Econ. Geol.*, vol. 14, pp. 95–146, 1919.

MOORE, R. G., The Bend Series of Central Texas, Am. Assoc. Pet. Geol. *Bull.*, vol. 3, pp. 216–241, 1919.

PLUMMER, F. B., Preliminary Paper on the Stratigraphy of North-central Texas, Am. Assoc. Pet. Geol. *Bull.*, vol. 3, pp. 132–150, 1919.

PRATT, W. E., Geologic Structure and Producing Areas of North Texas Petroleum Fields, Am. Assoc. Pet. Geol. *Bull.*, vol. 3, pp. 44–70, 1919.

SHAW, E. W., G. C. MATSON, and C. H. WEGEMANN, Natural Gas Resources of Parts of Northern Texas, U. S. Geol. Survey *Bull.* 629, pp. 1–126, 1916.

ADAMS, H. H., Geologic Structure of Eastland and Stephens Counties Texas, Am. Assoc. Pet. Geol. *Bull.*, vol. 4, pp. 159–167, 1920.

GORDON, C. H., Geology and Underground Waters of the Wichita Region, North-central Texas, U. S. Geol. Survey *Water Supply Paper* 317, pp. 1–88, 1913.

GLENN, L. C., Some Paleontologic Evidence on the Age of the Oil-bearing Horizon at Burkburnett, Texas, Am. Assoc. Pet. Geol. *Bull.*, vol. 5, pp. 154–158, 1921.

[2] PAIGE, S., Mineral Resources of the Llano Burnet Region, Texas, U. S. Geol. Survey *Bull.* 450, p. 93, 1916.

central Texas has produced relatively small quantities of oil from shallow wells for many years. In 1916, however, important discoveries were made in the Breckenridge field in Stephens County and the following year near Ranger, Eastland County, a well was drilled which produced 1,200 barrels a day. This discovery led to rapid drilling of the Ranger field, and its production reached 80,000 barrels a day in 1919. Since then the north Texas region has been steadily productive, the daily average yield being over 100,000 barrels for many years. The oil is light and high in gasoline. It has a gravity in general between 39 and 42° Bé. and it is nearly uniform in composition, although it comes from many different sands.

The rocks cropping out in north-central Texas are of Pennsylvanian and Permian age. They strike northeast, dip northwest, and overlap the older rocks of the Llano uplift. They include the Strawn, Canyon, and Cisco formations which are overlain with no great discordance by the Permian beds. The Llano Mountains are older than the Strawn beds; the Strawn overlaps the mountains without change of strike. These formations do not form circles about the mountains. The Bend arch is not a northward extension of the Llano Mountains. It is a buried arch that is due to two periods of folding. There is no indication of its presence at the surface.

ROCK SYSTEMS OF NORTH-CENTRAL TEXAS
(*After Cheney*)

Permian:

Double Mountain. Shale, sand, thin dolomite, anhydrite, gypsum, salt. Oil in west Texas.

Clear Fork. Sandy shales, sands, some dolomite; oil in "Morrison," pay at 3,000 feet in Westbrook field, Mitchell County.

Wichita-Albany. Thick limestone and shale, a little sandstone; some shallow oil in Wichita County.

Pennsylvanian:

Cisco. Shale, sandstone, and limestone; oil in sandstone and limestone; has produced more oil than any other group of beds in north-central Texas.

Canyon. Thick limestone with interbedded shale, some sandstone; produces oil at four limestone horizons, the highest being the Ranger limestone.

Strawn. Sands, shales, coals, etc.; oil at eight or more horizons.

Bend Group:

Smithwick. Shale, limestone and some sandstone; oil at four or more horizons.

Marble Falls. Limestone and shale, some sandstone; oil at many horizons.

Mississippian:

Barnett group. Limestone, shales.

Pre-Mississippian:

A limestone, producing oil in South Bend pool, is of Lower Silurian age (Viola).

Another limestone, probably Ordovician, is correlated with the Ellenburger of Llano Burnet area. The Simpson formation is probably represented in part of the area.

EASTERN OKLAHOMA
INTERVAL BETWEEN TOP OF
CALVIN SERIES-OSWEGO LIME
AND TOP OF MORROW-PITKIN
AND WAPANUCKA LIME

Contour Interval=1000 Feet
Scale 0 6 12 18 24 30 Miles

NORTH CENTRAL TEXAS
INTERVAL BETWEEN TOP OF
PALO PINTO LIME AND TOP
OF BEND FORMATION

Contour Interval=500 Feet
Scale 0 6 12 18 24 30 Miles

FIG. 222.—Map showing convergence of beds to northwest in North Texas and East Oklahoma. Contour interval 500 feet. The beds between the Palo Pinto limestone and Bend formation converge to northwest. (*After Levorsen.*)

As shown by Levorsen (Figs. 222, 223), there is a noteworthy similarity of conditions between the Bend[1] arch and the southwest end of the Ozark uplift.   In early Paleozoic time after the Bend was deposited, there was sinking to the southeast, and, later, the Strawn formation was deposited in a sinking sea which continued to expand to the northwest, so that the Strawn formation converges and overlaps earlier beds to the northwest.

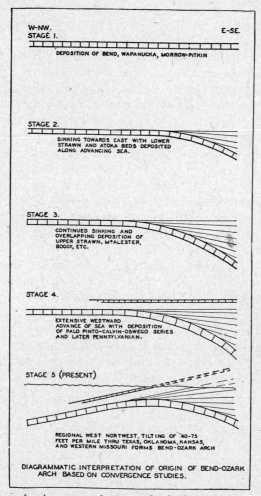

FIG. 223.—Diagram showing progressive stages in the formation of the Bend-Ozark arch based on convergence relations.   (*After Levorsen.*)

The Palo Pinto limestone was deposited in the expanded sea almost horizontally.   After the Palo Pinto limestone was deposited and subsequently, after Permian time, the entire system was tilted 40 to 75 feet

[1] LEVORSEN, A. I., Convergence Studies in the Mid-Continent Region, Am. Assoc. Pet. Geol. *Bull.* 11, pp. 657–682, 1927.

per mile to the northwest. This tilting decreased the east dips, increased the northwest dips, and formed the Bend-Ozark arch. Thus the Bend-Ozark arch is the result of two regional tiltings which were in opposite directions.

According to Cheney,[1] the Bend flexure is really two flexures, which he calls the San Saba-Callahan and the Comanche-Young flexures. Cheney's map of the pre-Mississippian surface shows a broad elevated area called the Electra arch, which lies just south of Red River and which has been termed also the Red River uplift (Fig. 220).

The Red River uplift[2] is traced with difficulty. According to Hager, it probably extends east as far as Cooke County. To the west in Foard County, according to Liddle, the Carboniferous strata are at least 500 feet above their normal undisturbed position. Still further west in Cotton, Motley, Floyd, and Hale counties there is probably an uplift that is either an extension of the Red River uplift[3] or a parallel anticline that lies between the latter and the Wichita arch. The Red River uplift, according to Kendrick and McLaughlin, is probably a buried ridge comparable to the Nemaha Ridge of Kansas and Oklahoma.

Figure 221 is a cross-section drawn along the line indicated on Fig. 220. It shows the flattening of the strata and a small arching of some of the beds near Electra.[4] Cheney's map shows much more arching at Electra on pre-Mississippian beds.

According to Hubbard and Thompson,[5] the Bend series has produced 43 per cent of the oil of north Texas, the Strawn 4 per cent, the Cisco 53 per cent. The Canyon formation consists chiefly of limestone sand shales and has produced little oil.

In the southern part of the region the oil is from the Bend series which lies within 1,400 to 3,400 feet of the surface and subordinately from the Strawn and Cisco. At Putnam oil is found in the Cisco formation 450 feet below the surface and at Moran within 600 feet of the sur-

[1] CHENEY, M. G., Stratigraphic and Structural Studies in North-central Texas, Univ. Texas, Bur. Econ. Geol. *Bull.* 2913, pp. 1-27, 1929. This bulletin includes convergence sheets showing the thickness of the Strawn, a contour map of the pre-Mississippian surface, and cross-sections of north-central Texas.

[2] UDDEN, J. A., and D. McN. PHILLIPS, Geology of the Oil and Gas Fields of Wichita and Clay Counties, Texas, Univ. Texas *Bull.* 246, pp. 1-308, 1912.

HAGER, L., *Oil Gas Jour.*, vol. 18, p. 64, Oct. 17, 1919.

LIDDLE, R. A., The Marathon Fold and Its Influence on Petroleum Accumulation, Univ. Texas *Bull.* 1847, p. 15, 1918.

[3] HOOTS, H. W., Geology of Part of Western Texas and Southeastern New Mexico, U. S. Geol. Survey *Bull.* 780B, pp. 33-120, 1926.

[4] This section is the north half of a section, from W. C. Thompson and W. E. Hubbard, appearing in *Oil Gas Jour.*, vol. 24, Aug. 20, 1925.

[5] HUBBARD, W. E., and W. C. THOMPSON, The Geology and Oil Fields of Archer County, Texas, Am. Assoc. Pet. Geol. *Bull.*, vol. 10, pp. 457-481, 1926; also "Structure of Typical American Oil Fields." vol. 1, pp. 421-439, 1929.

face. In Palo Pinto County near Strawn, shallow oil is found in the Strawn formation. In Eastland and Stephens counties the bulk of the oil is from the Bend series, which lies about 3,000 feet deep or more, although considerable oil is found also in the Strawn formation. In Young County oil is found in the Strawn, Cisco, and the Bend series. In the South Bend field in the southern part of the county, a well drilled in July, 1927, encountered oil in the Marble Falls at a depth of 4,219 feet. This well,[1] December 1 of that year, had yielded 600,000 barrels of 42° Bé.

In Archer and Wichita counties nearly all of the oil is derived from the Cisco formation. Both of these counties have large production and are characterized by fields with many producing sands. In Archer County there are 6 or more producing sands, and in Wichita County in the Electra Pool production has been obtained from 14 sands, all above the base of the Cisco. The Cisco formation in this part of north Texas, as stated by Thompson and Hubbard, is characterized by near-shore deposition. The formations consist chiefly of shales and sands with a little limestone, and they are correlated with difficulty. Probably the most nearly continuous sand is the Gose (Texhoma-Gose) sand which is productive in 29 of 33 pools in Archer County. This sand, which is about 1,350 feet below the Coleman Junction limestone, lies within a 50-foot zone, the top of which is 1 to 20 feet below the Gunsight limestone. At places it is a mere streak and at other places it is 30 feet thick, the average thickness being 6 or 7 feet. At some places there are two distinct pay streaks 40 feet apart. The abrupt changes in thickness and intervals cause producing wells to alternate with dry holes. Near Graham a shale rich in carbonaceous material is seen to underlie the sand, which carries marine fossils. This suggests that the shale formed on a tidal flat or in a lagoon, and that the sand was formed as a bar or barrier beach above a coastal marsh. In a sea advancing on a land area a succession of bars and beaches would form one after the other. Such a sand would be spread out over a large area but would consist of many thick lenses between which sands would be thin or absent.

The main productive areas of north Texas are localized near the axis of the Bend arch and near the axis of the Electra arch. In limestone, production is found where porosity is high. In sands production is concentrated where the sands are thickest. There are also small plunging anticlines and, due to convergence, these in depth form domes which are favorable for accumulation. These small flutings or folds in the Ranger district are reflected at the surface, but in Archer County, according to Hubbard and Thompson, they have little relation to surface folds. In the Ranger district the thickness of the McClesky oil sand on tops of

---

[1] BOWEN, J. P., Marble Falls Production in South Bend, Texas, Am. Assoc. Pet. Geol. *Bull.*, vol. 12, p. 97, 1928.

small anticlines is noteworthy. Since faulting is pronounced in some parts of the north-central Texas region, it appears probable that some of the minor structures are due to earth deformation by tangential stresses. Faults are found in the Ranger district and in a zone of deformation that extends westward from Jack County into Throckmorton and Haskell counties.[1]

In the Breckenridge field[2] Stephens County, near the crest of the Bend arch, oil is found in the Bend series of lower Pennsylvanian age. The surface rocks dip west and are marked by small plunging anticlines and terraces only, but the Bend series, which is about 3,000 feet deep, forms a dome with about 200 feet of closure. The oil is found in limestone and sandy limestone, and gas is found above and salt water below the oil. Subordinately, however, the accumulation is influenced by porosity and crevices in the limestone. Stephens County has produced 113,777,926 barrels of oil, half of it coming from the Breckenridge field.

The Ranger[3] field is in Eastland County about 25 miles southeast of Breckenridge. Oil was discovered in this district in 1917 when a well on the McClesky farm was drilled to a sand 200 feet below the top of the Black Lime at a depth of 3,431 feet. From this well oil flowed at the rate of 1,200 barrels a day. The oil is of high grade with a gravity of 35 to 40° Bé. The field was rapidly developed and by July 1, 1920, had produced 20,000,000 barrels of oil. The production declined rapidly, because the gas which issued from some of the wells under high pressure was allowed to flow freely into the air, and, according to Reeves, the ultimate recovery of the field will probably be less than one-fourth of the oil in the sands.

The rock formations are shown in the table on page 376. The rocks cropping out in the district are shown in Fig. 224. The rocks of the region at the surface dip northwest at angles of 50 feet or more to the mile. Superimposed on this monocline are low folds that commonly plunge northwest. The subsurface structure corresponds in a certain measure with the surface structure, but the folds are much steeper, the dips being locally 250 feet to the mile. The closures of structures in the Bend

[1] A map of this zone in Throckmorton County, by R. A. Reynolds, appeared in the *Oil Gas Jour.*, vol. 24, p. 80, Aug. 20, 1925; and one of its southwestern extensions in Haskell and Shackleford counties appeared in the same issue, p. 94. The faults of this region have small throws but are traced on strike for many miles.

[2] Esgen, W. K., Relation of Accumulation of Petroleum to Structure in Stephens County, Texas, "Structure of Typical American Oil Fields," vol. 2, pp. 470–479, 1929.

[3] Reeves, F., Geology of the Ranger Oil Field, Texas, U. S. Geol. Survey *Bull.* 736, pp. 111–170, 1923.

Ross, C. S., The Lacasa Area, Ranger District, North-central Texas, U. S. Geol., Survey *Bull.*, 726, pp. 303–314, 1921.

Dobbin, C. E., Geology of the Wiles Area, Ranger District, Texas, U. S. Geol. Survey *Bull.* 736, pp. 55–69, 1923.

formation are due mainly to westward convergence or thinning of the Strawn formation.

The oil is found in the Ray, Scott, and Harris sands of the Strawn formation, in the Smithwick "lime" and shale, in the base of the Black Lime of the Marble Falls formation, in the McClesky sand 200 feet below the top of the Black Lime and in the lower part of the Marble Falls limestone. About 90 per cent of the oil produced to 1921 came from the Marble Falls limestone and from the McClesky sand in that formation. The McClesky sand is from medium to coarse grained and is 140 feet thick on anticlines and thins to almost nothing on synclines. This relationship is accounted for, according to Reeves, by uplift of the sea bottom during deposition of the sand which was brought within reach of the action of waves that washed out the clay and mud from the sand.

In Young County in the Larimore (Riggs) field northwest of Graham and 4 miles north of Newcastle, large deposits of oil are found at shallow depths in sands sealed up dip.

In Wilbarger[1] County, near Red River, the Red River uplift strikes east approximately at right angles to the Bend arch. On this uplift are several domes, including South Vernon, Castleberry, Gulf-Waggoner, Landreth, Murchison, and Petrolia. At South Vernon, Permian beds crop out and extend to depths of 1,100 feet, below which are 1,400 feet of Pennsylvanian strata, and below the latter 400 feet of Cambro-Silurian beds that rest on igneous rocks. The oil is found on domes which, owing to convergence of beds above the productive sands, are much less regular and less accentuated at the surface than at depths of the producing horizons. In the South Vernon field seven horizons are

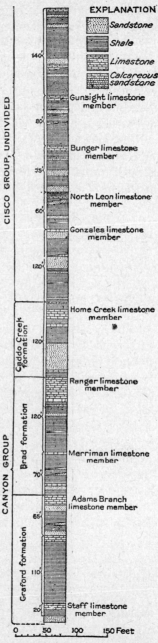

Fig. 224.—Section of rocks cropping out in Ranger oil field, Texas. (*After Reeves.*)

[1] Fuqua, H. B., and B. E. Thompson, Relation of Production to Structure in Central Wilbarger County, Texas, "Structure of Typical American Oil Fields," vol. 1, pp. 293–303, 1929.

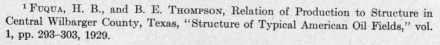
State Teachers College Library
Willimantic, Conn.

producing; of these the two most important are the 1,300-foot sand and the limestone "pay" encountered 2,300 feet deep, both of Pennsylvanian age. In the Petrolia[1] field, Clay County (Fig. 225) drilling has revealed an ancient buried hill of Ordovician(?) limestone which lies above granite. Gas and oil are found mainly in sands of the Cisco formation, which extends over the top of the buried hill. The surface closure is about 50 feet, but in depth on the "Big gas" zone the closure is 150 feet. The gas of Petrolia is high in helium.

In Shackleford, Callahan, Coleman, and Brown counties there are numerous shallow oil fields. Many of them yield oil from the Cisco and Strawn formations. Some of them are on low domes that are marked at the surface by terraces or noses.

ROCK FORMATIONS IN THE SOUTH PART OF NORTH TEXAS FIELD
(*After Reeves*, with additions)

System or series	Group or formation		Thickness, feet	Character
Lower Cretaceous, 0–50 feet	Trinity sand		0–50	Coarse conglomerate, sandstone, and sand
	—Unconformity—			
Pennsylvanian, 4,200+ feet	Cisco group		800	Gray and blue clay and shale, brown and gray cross-bedded sandstone and blue to gray thin-bedded fossiliferous limestone. Oil bearing
	Canyon groun		800–1,000	Gray multiple-bedded and yellow thin-bedded fossiliferous limestone, brown cross-bedded ferruginous and gray even-bedded calcareous sandstone, and gray and blue shale and clay
	Strawn formation		1,750–2,000	Fine-grained thin-bedded and coarse-grained, heavy-bedded gray sandstone, blue and black shale, and siliceous thin-bedded limestone. Oil bearing
	—Unconformity—			
	"Bend series," 1,000–1,280 feet	Smithwick shale	230–330	Black shale and black thick-bedded limestone. Oil bearing
		Marble Falls limestone	600–650	Black shale, black and gray limestone, and gray lenticular sandstone. Oil bearing.
		"Lower Bend" limestone	150 ±	Black limestone
Mississippian		"Lower Bend" shale		Black shale
		—Unconformity—		
Ordovician and Cambrian, 545+ feet	Ellenburger limestone		545+	White dolomite, crystalline limestone, and sandstone

[1] KENDRICK, F. E., and H. C. MCLAUGHLIN, Relation of Petroleum Accumulation to Structure, Petrolia Field, Clay County, Texas, "Structure of Typical American Oil Fields," vol. 2, pp. 542–555, 1929.

GEOLOGICAL SECTION IN REGION OF ARCHER COUNTY

Permian:

Wichita, 500 feet light to red sandstone and red shale. Sandstones make escarpments. Beaverburk limestone at top.

Pennsylvanian:

Cisco, 900 to 1,800 feet sandstone, shale and thin limestone with some coal; thickens northward. Chief oil series of Pennsylvanian in north-central Texas. Outcrops in southeast Archer County.

    a. Coleman Junction limestone (top of Cisco) outcrops at Harmell-Swastika.

    b. Dalmar sand about 1,050 feet below Coleman Junction; some oil in sand.

    c. Upper Wilmot sandstone 1,150 feet below Coleman Junction. Production in Wilmot, Peterson, Sunshine State, Oil Investment, Freeman, Hampton.

    d. Texhoma-Gose sand (Archer, Miller, Swastika) about 1,350 feet below Coleman Junction limestone and just below Gunsight limestone. It is the main oil-producing sand in Archer County. Texhoma-Gose is not continuous, varies from 0 to 30 feet, average thickness 6 to 7 feet.

    e. Lower Freeman-Hampton sand, about 160 feet below Texhoma-Gose sand. Average thickness 7 feet. Oil in Freeman-Hampton, Orton, Tad Wilson, and Shappell pools.

    Canon, 900 to 1,000 feet limestone and snale. Four massive limestone members from top down: Home Creek, Ranger, Adams Branch, Palo Pinto. Becomes sandy to north and northeast. Oil in Brown County, gas in Archer County.

    Strawn, 3,800 to 5,000 feet sandstone, shale, a little limestone, and coal. Thins to east. Oil and gas in Eastland, Stephens, Young, and Shackelford.

Pennsylvanian:

Smithwick, 200 to 400 feet, black fissile shale, sandy near top. Thickens northward and contains thin limestone members. Contains "gray-lime" which produces oil in Stephens County.

Marble Falls, 200 to 600 feet, gray and black limestone with black and green shale. Oil in black lime fields of Eastland and Stephens Counties.

Mississippian:

Barnett shale (lower Bend) 50 to 150 feet dark gray and black shale.

Ordovician:

Ellenburger, limestone (Arbuckle limestone). Several hundred to several thousand feet of massive and siliceous limestone.

In Brown County the shallow sand fields that are found in the northwest part of the county include Crosscut, Smith-Ellis, Fry, and Byler. The sand in the Smith-Ellis field in the Strawn formation according to Storm,[1] is probably an ancient buried sand spit that was formed in a coastal marsh. This field produces light oil at a depth of 1,350 feet and to January 1, 1928, had yielded 846,660 barrels. The field at the surface shows a very low dome which, according to Storm, is probably due to differential settling above the sand lens.

[1] STORM, W., Smith-Ellis Field, Brown County, Texas, "Structure of Typical American Oil Fields," vol. 2, pp. 556–570, 1929.

Balcones Fault Region.—In east Texas the rocks dip southeast away from the Llano uplift of central Texas, the Arbuckle Mountains of Oklahoma, and the Ouachita Mountains of eastern Oklahoma and western Arkansas. They form part of a great structural basin which lies south of the Ouachita Mountains element and east of the Llano uplift and the Bend arch. In this great synclinal area, between the Llano uplift and the

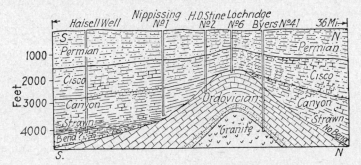

Fig. 225.—Cross section through Petrolia oil and gas field South to Halsell Well, Clay County, Texas. The exact character of contact of Ordovician and granite is unknown. (*After Kendrick and McLaughlin.*)

Mississippi River there are many subordinate zones of uplift and deformation. These are the Preston anticline, Balcones fault zone, Mexia fault zone, Palestine zone of salt dome upthrust, Sabine uplift, Monroe uplift, and other uplifts. The Angelina-Caldwell flexure, which strikes northeast, is a region in which the rocks dip steeply to the south, and, although it lies within the basin described above, it separates the east Texas border region and the province of northern Louisiana from the salt dome region of the southern Texas and Louisiana Coast.

The Balcones[1] fault zone (Fig. 226) is a great zone of faulting and folding that lies east of the Llano uplift and is traced from Rockwell

[1] HILL, R. T., Geography and Geology of the Black and Grand Prairies, Texas, U. S. Geol. Survey *Twenty-first Ann. Rept.*, pt. 7, pp. 1–666, 1900; also Geol. Soc. Am. *Bull.*, vol. 5, pp. 297–338, 1893; *Am. Jour. Sci.*, p. 292, October, 1887.

DUMBLE, E. T., Tex. Geol. Survey *Second Ann. Rept.*, pp. 5–88, 1890.

KENNEDY, A. A., Section from Terrill, Kaufman County, to Sabine Pass, Tex. Geol. Survey, *Third Ann. Rept.*, 1891.

ADAMS, G. I., Oil and Gas Fields of the Upper Cretaceous and Tertiary Formations of the Western Gulf Coast, U. S. Geol. Survey *Bull.* 184, pp. 37–64, 1901.

STEPHENSON, L. W., Notes on the Stratigraphy of the Upper Cretaceous Formations of Texas and Arkansas, Am. Assoc. Pet. Geol., *Bull.*, vol. 11, pp. 1–18, 1927.

FOHS, F. J., Structural and Stratigraphic Data of Northeast Texas Petroleum Area; *Econ. Geol.*, vol. 18, pp. 709–721, 1923.

ROBINSON, H. M., Origin of Structure of the Northeast Texas Petroleum Area, *Econ. Geol.* vol. 18, pp. 722–731, 1923.

HULL, J. P. D., Guide Notes on the Midway of Southwest Arkansas, Am. Assoc. Pet. Geol. *Bull.*, vol. 9, pp. 167–170, 1925.

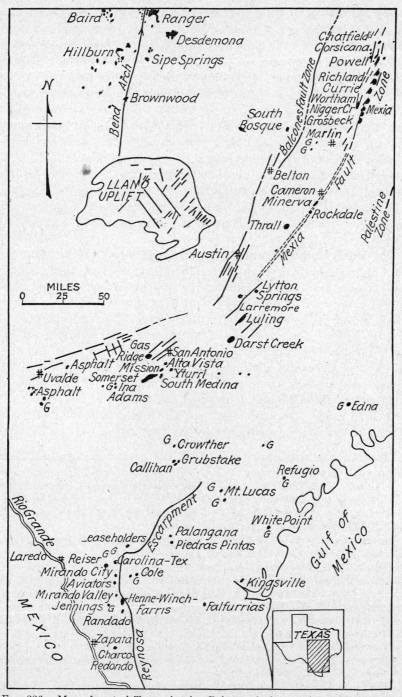

Fig. 226.—Map of central Texas showing Balcones fault zone, its westward extension and the relation to the Reynosa escarpment. Many oil fields omitted are shown on other maps.

County southwest to Uvalde County, a distance of about 360 miles. The zone of faulting is 5 to 15 miles wide. From Austin, Travis County, to the Rio Grande on the northwest side of the fault zone, an escarpment of hills and low mountains rises 200 to 1,000 feet above the valley that lies on the southeast side of the fault. Nearly everywhere on the west side of the main fault, as stated by Fohs, there is a group of overlapping small faults with total displacement of 100 to 800 feet. Near Austin[1] there are 13 faults within 6 miles. To the west, in Uvalde County,[2] the fault zone is represented by a monoclinal flexure, and farther west in Val Verde County it is represented by small subordinate folds.[3] The west end of the Balcones fault is almost in line with the Angelina-Caldwell flexure and has the same general strike. At places along the fault zone, in Travis,[4] Uvalde, and other counties, small intrusions of igneous rocks appear and serpentine and tuffs are found farther north in drill holes and oil wells.

The Mexia fault zone is about 30 miles east of the Balcones fault zone and is approximately parallel to it. The Mexia zone is traced about 100 miles, is 5 or 6 miles wide, and marked by displacements from 100 to 700 feet along overlapping parallel faults that are traced 3 to 8 miles on strike. These faults strike about N. 10° E. to N. 30° E. and slice the country into blocks. The strike of the fault zone is more nearly north than that of the individual faults. They are in part ruptured folds, and on the east sides of the faults along the east side of the fault zone, eastward dipping beds are bent over to the west, dipping to the fault plane and forming small anticlines and domes that constitute the chief oil reservoirs of the fault zone. Thus the reservoirs which lie east of the faults in the footwall blocks are closed in part by faulting and in part by folding.

HAMMILL, C. A., The Cretaceous of Northwestern Louisiana, Am. Assoc. Pet. Geol. *Bull.*, vol. 5, pp. 298–310, 1921.

UDDEN, J. A., Observations of Two Deep Borings Near Balcones Fault, Am. Assoc. Pet. Geol. *Bull.*, vol. 3, pp. 124–131, 1910.

SCOTT, G., The Woodbine Sand of Texas Interpreted as a Regressive Phenomenon, Am. Assoc. Pet. Geo. *Bull.*, vol. 10, pp. 613–624, 1926.

STEPHENSON, L. W., and C. H. DANE, Notes on the Taylor and Navarro Formations of East-central Texas, Am. Assoc. Pet. Geol. *Bull.*, vol. 12, pp. 41–58, 1928.

FOLEY, L. L., Mechanics of the Balcones and Mexia Faulting, Am. Assoc. Pet. Geol. *Bull.*, vol. 10, pp. 1261–1269, 1926.

[1] HILL, R. T., and T. W. VAUGHAN, U. S. Geol. Survey, Atlas of the United States, *Folio* 76, Austin, Texas, 1902.

[2] VAUGHAN, T. W., U. S. Geol. Survey, Atlas of the United States, *Folio* 64, 1900.

[3] ROBERTS, J. R., and J. P. NASH, The Geology of Val Verde County, Univ. Texas, Bur. Econ. Geol. *Bull.* 1803, p. 22, 1918.

[4] BYBEE, H. P., and R. T. SHORT, The Lytton Springs Oil Field, Univ. Texas, Bur. Econ. Geol. *Bull.* 2539, pp. 5–69, 1925.

The Palestine zone of deformation is east of the Mexia fault zone and approximately parallel to it, and lies near the bottom of and nearly parallel to the axis of the east Texas syncline. Along the zone are found

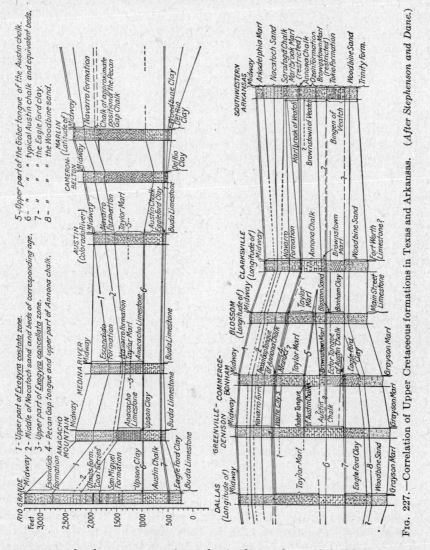

FIG. 227.—Correlation of Upper Cretaceous formations in Texas and Arkansas. (*After Stephenson and Dane.*)

numerous salt domes approximately in line where the older rocks are thrust up thousands of feet (p. 397).

The Preston[1] anticline, which is a great upfold plunging to the south at the Red River, strikes southeast across Red River and, if con-

[1] HOPKINS, O. B., S. POWERS, and H. M. ROBINSON, The Structure of the Madill-Denison Area, Oklahoma and Texas, with Notes on Oil and Gas Developments, U. S. Geol. Survey *Bull.* 736, pp. 1–34, 1923.

tinued, would cross the continuation of the strike lines of the Balcones, Mexia, and Palestine zones of deformation. In the area where this extension would cross, however, no pronounced uplifts are discovered. Certain investigators believe that the Choctaw fault extended would join the Balcones zone. The long axis of the Sabine uplift in northwest Louisiana is rudely parallel to and in line with the Preston anticline, but the two are not joined by any pronounced structural feature. A belt of salt domes lies along the east side of the Sabine uplift. About 100 miles east of the axis of the Sabine uplift there is a group of oil fields that strikes northwest and includes Smackover, Arkansas, Monroe, and Richland, Louisiana.

In east Texas, as stated, the rocks strike northeast nearly parallel to the Balcones fault zone and dip southeast to the Gulf. The Upper Cretaceous rocks crop out in a belt about 50 miles wide, which includes part of the Mexia zone of deformation and the northern part of the Balcones zone. This belt of rocks has been studied by Stephenson[1] from the Rio Grande to Arkansas, and sections are compared in Fig. 227. The Woodbine sand, which is the chief oil-bearing stratum on the Mexia fault zone, extends to the northeast into Arkansas and Louisiana where it is a reservoir rock.

The Woodbine lies unconformably on various formations of the Lower Cretaceous or Comanchean. Deep wells have discovered oil in the Edwards limestone in the Luling, Texas, field, and oil and much gas in the Glen Rose formation in the Pine Island field on the east border of the Caddo field, Louisiana. This formation produces gas at Cotton Valley, Louisiana, and it is probably a gas sand in the Richland field south of Monroe, Louisiana. At Thrall oil is found in a tuffaceous igneous rock and at Lytton Springs in serpentine.

The chief production of oil of east Texas comes from the Mexia fault zone pools (Figs. 66, 67, 68) and from the fields at Thrall, Lytton Springs, and Luling. The area between this great group of oil fields and the Sabine uplift fields of Louisiana has naturally been regarded as promising and has been drilled at many places. Deep holes have been sunk around several of the salt domes of the Palestine zone and some oil was found, but the explorations in general are disappointing. Recently large deposits of oil have been discovered at Van, east of the Mexia fault zone.

Before the fields along the Mexia fault were drilled to the Woodbine sand, oil and gas had been produced at shallow depths from a number of pools in the faulted region, and gas, oil, or asphalt had been discovered at places over an area extending from Cash on the north to Uvalde near the southwest end of the zone. Of these fields the Corsicana[2] group was

[1] STEPHENSON, L. W., Am. Assoc. Pet. Geol. *Bull.*, vol. 11, pp. 1–18, 1927.

[2] MATSON, G. C., and O. B. HOPKINS, The Corsicana Oil and Gas Field, U. S. Geol. Survey *Bull.* 661, pp. 211–252, 1918.

Generalized Section of Formations in the Mexia Oil and Gas Region, Texas

Series	Group	Formation	Thickness, feet	Character
Recent				Alluvial deposits along streams
Pleistocene				Terrace deposits
Eocene		Wilcox	Thin basal	Sandstones, gray shales, lignite. Fresh water
		Midway	350–675	Micaceous sandy clays, fine argillaceous sands, and limestone concretions; limestone
Gulf (Upper Cretaceous)		Navarro	800–1,000	Gray calcareous clay, sandy clay, and lenticular beds of sand; includes Nacatoch sand
		Taylor marl	800–1,200	Massive calcareous clay marl, little sand, limestone and glauconite; includes Corsicana sand
		Austin chalk	350–480	Gray to white chalky limestone containing some hard beds
		Eagle Ford shale	300–400	Light to dark colored shale or clay and thinly laminated impure limestone; high in organic remains
		Woodbine sand	200–450	Sand, sandy lignitic clay, sandstone, ferruginous sand, and clay. Main oil sand
Comanche (Lower Cretaceous)	Washita	Buda	40±	Limestone
		Del Rio	80±	Clays and shales
		Georgetown	50±	Impure limestone
	Fredericksburg	Edwards limestone	300–730	White chalky limestones, and in places fine arenaceous beds
		Comanche Peak	?	Limestone
		Walnut clay	100–200	Calcareous clays and impure marly and chalky limestones
	Trinity	Paluxy sand	125–200	Fine-grained sand and lenticular beds of clay
		Glen Rose limestone	300–1,450	Impure limestone, marl, and calcareous shales
		Travis Peak sand	250±	Conglomerate, sand, sandstone, shales, and impure limestones

most productive.   This group extends northward to Chatfield and eastward to the Mexia fault.   Light oil and gas are derived from the Taylor
and heavy oil and gas from the Navarro formation.   The oil and gas are
found mainly on domes.   The rocks generally dip at low angles, although
in the Burke Pool, 1 mile south of Powell, the dip is about 185 feet to
the mile to the northwest and southeast.   In the Mexia-Groesbeck
gas field, southeast of Corsicana, gas is found in the Nacatoch sand of
the Navarro formation along the Mexia fault zone in an area over 12
miles long and 1 mile or more wide.   The wells passed through the Midway formation into the Navarro[1] and encountered porous sandstone with
gas at a pressure of 276 pounds to the square inch.   At Cash, 50 miles
northeast of Dallas and 10 miles south of Greenville, gas and salt water
under pressure are found in shallow Cretaceous sands and deeper wells to
the Woodbine sand encountered a little oil and gas.   At Mabank, south
of Cash, and in the Conner well, south of Mabank, gas is found in the
Upper Cretaceous sands.

Mexia-Powell.—The Mexia[2] fault zone, which lies 30 or 40 miles east
of the Balcones fault, is traced from Kosse, 15 miles south of Groesbeck,
to Trinity River, about 65 miles.   It strikes about N. 25° E., and in
general the faults dip west about 45 degrees, although locally the faults
dip east.   At places two or more faults are present and locally brecciation
is pronounced.   In general the Midway formation crops out and the
wells are sunk to the Woodbine sand.   The regional dip of the beds is
east, and, on the east side of the fault, the oil is trapped against the fault,
forming areas about $\frac{1}{2}$ to $1\frac{1}{2}$ miles wide, which in several fields are
highly productive.   The chief fields of the fault zone are South Groesbeck,
North Groesbeck, Mexia, Wortham, Currie, North Currie, Richland,
and Powell.   In some of the fields, due to the drag, the beds are slightly
arched east of the fault and the oil is accumulated below the arches;
elsewhere the oil lies against the fault where no arching appears to be
present.   The source of the oil of the Woodbine is uncertain, but the
overlying Eagle Ford shale is petroliferous and is regarded by Pratt and
Lahee as a probable source.   These fields to December 31, 1927, produced
212,544,366 barrels of oil.

Gas production of the Nacatoch sand in the Mexia-Groesbeck[3]
district began in 1912.   In 1920 the Humphreys Oil Company discovered

[1] MATSON, G. C., Gas Prospects South and Southeast of Dallas, U. S. Geol. Survey Bull. 629, pp. 77–119, 1916.

[2] LAHEE, F. H., Comparative Study of Well Logs on the Mexia Type of Structure,
Am. Inst. Min. Eng. Trans., vol. 71, pp. 1329–1350, 1925.

———, Oil and Gas Field of the Mexia and Tehuanaca Fault Zones, "Structure
of Typical American Oil Fields," vol. 1, pp. 304–388, 1929.

[3] MATSON, G. C., Gas Prospects South and Southeast of Dallas, U. S. Geol. Survey
Bull. 629, p. 87, 1916.

PRATT, W. E., and F. H. LAHEE, Faulting and Petroleum Accumulation at Mexia,
Texas, Am. Assoc. Pet. Geol. Bull., vol. 7, pp. 226–236, 1923.

large deposits of oil at a depth of about 3,000 feet in the Woodbine sand. The Mexia field is 7 miles long and 7,000 feet wide and lies east of the Mexia fault. The fault in general dips 35 degrees west, but at the north end of the field the fault steepens. Production extended down dip 150 feet and edge water appeared at 2,530 feet below sea level. The oil sand west of the fault is barren. Along the fault the beds are dragged down, forming an anticline the axis of which moves westward with depth. The sand east of the fault is highest near the center of the field and descends at either end. The greatest accumulation of oil is in the highest parts of the arch near the axis of the fold. The gravity of the oil is 35 to 37° Bé. and the lightest oil is highest on the dome.

At Wortham, 7 miles north of Mexia, a large deposit of oil was discovered November, 1924, along the Wortham fault of the Mexia zone. This fault lies about 1 mile west of the north end of the Mexia fault and is essentially parallel to it. The Wortham field, like the Mexia field, developed a large production from the Woodbine sand. The field is 4 miles long and about 2,000 feet wide. The oil-water contact is 2,560 feet below sea level.

In the Currie[1] field, 12 miles north of Mexia, a few shallow gas wells suggested deep drilling along the Mexia fault and in 1921 a well found oil in the Woodbine sand. The field is 11,000 feet long and 3,000 feet wide, and the strata form a half dome against the westward-dipping fault. The rocks dip east away from the Mexia fault about 100 feet per mile. There is a slight arching locally on the east side of the fault but accumulation is not confined to the area where arching is noted. The fault at Currie is a fault zone with two or more faults having a total displacement of 250 to 400 feet. Edge water appears at a depth of 2,540 feet below sea level. The gravity of the oil ranges from 40 to 45° Bé.

The North Currie field (Fig. 66) was drilled on a small arch, and the discovery well had a flush gas production estimated to be 50,000,000 cubic feet per day. Subsequent drilling showed a fault with a throw of 400 feet, along the east side of which gas and oil have accumulated. The field yielded chiefly gas, with oil at the north and south ends of the field in the Woodbine "pay" and oil in the "Swink pay" below the main pay of the Woodbine. The Richland field, discovered in 1923, is east of a fault that dips 55 degrees west and has a downthrow of 500 feet. The structural relief is between 30 and 50 feet and edge water lies about 2,610 feet below sea level.

[1] LAHEE, F. H., The Currie Field, Navarro County, Texas, Am. Assoc. Pet. Geol. *Bull.*, vol. 7, pp. 25–36, 1923.

———, Further Notes on the Currie Structure. Am. Assoc. Geol. *Bull.*, vol. 10, pp. 61–71, 1926

The Powell field (Fig. 228) was worked first for oil and gas in the Nacatoch and Corsicana sands.[1] The field shows a pronounced dome, and deep drilling in 1923 brought in large wells deriving their oil from the Woodbine sand. The daily production reached a maximum of 350,000 barrels. The field is 40,000 feet long and 4,000 feet wide and lies east of a fault of the Mexia zone which dips west and shows a displacement of 400 feet or more. The oil blanket banks against the fault and extends down the dip of the beds about 150 feet and reaches edge water about 2,590 feet below sea level.

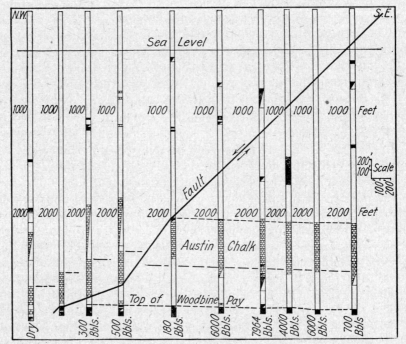

Fig. 228.—Section of Powell field Texas. Black, sand; brick pattern, limestone or chalk; blank, shale. Scale in feet. (*After Lahee.*)

Nigger Creek[2] field, 3 miles west of Mexia field, is located in the graben between the Balcones and Mexia fault zones. The field lies on the side of a fault that is parallel to the Mexia fault and dips 43 degrees west. Oil was discovered in the Woodbine sand in 1926 at a depth of 2,846 feet. The oil deposit lies east of the fault in a low dome that has a structural relief of 35 feet and is arched along an axis parallel to the

[1] Matson, G. C., and O. B. Hopkins, The Corsicana Oil and Gas Field, Texas, U. S. Geol. Survey *Bull.* 661, pp. 211–252, 1918.

[2] Pepperburg, L. J., Nigger Creek Field Limestone County, Texas, "Structure of Typical American Oil Fields," vol. 1, pp. 409–420, 1929.

Hull, J. P. D., Am. Assoc. Pet. Geol. *Bull.*, vol. 10, pp. 997–998, 1926.

fault. In two years the field yielded 2,690,000 barrels of oil, the gravity being about 40° A.P.I. The Cedar Creek field south of Nigger Creek lies east of a fault and produces oil from the Woodbine sand at a depth of about 2,886 feet.

As a result of discoveries along the Mexia fault zone, many deep wells have been drilled at each end of the zone. In the speckled shale at the base of the Eagle Ford formation just above the Woodbine sand there are abundant organic remains, and it is believed that the oil of the Woodbine formation may have originated in that shale. The speckled shale plays out north of Kaufman County, according to Lahee. In the region south of Groesbeck the Woodbine sand becomes shaly. At Kosse, 15 miles south of Groesbeck, the Woodbine sand is said to be absent. A deep well which was stopped in the Georgetown limestone yielded oil and salt water and fragments of limestone from the Glen Rose formation (Comanchean) which lies some hundreds of feet below the Georgetown, suggesting that the oil came up through a fault from a deep source. The Glen Rose formation carries oil also in a small field near Waco. In the Van district, Van Zandt County, 55 miles northeast of Powell, an anticline discovered by geophysical methods was drilled, and a large amount of oil was found in the Woodbine sand at a depth of 2,710 feet. The oil is light, 35.4° A.P.I., similar to that of Powell.[1]

Minerva.—The Minerva[2] field in Milam County is 1 mile west of the town of Minerva and 10 miles south of Cameron. It lies just east of the probable continuation of the Mexia fault and about 60 miles southwest of Groesbeck. The rocks at the surface are sands and shales of the Wilcox formation, and oil is found in a sand of the Navarro at depths between 650 and 1,200 feet, about 130 feet below the top of the Navarro formation. The rocks dip southeast and the oil is accumulated on a structural terrace marked by small anticlines. These small folds are shown in both the Midway (Eocene) and in the Navarro (Upper Cretaceous). The wells generally have initial flows of about 11 barrels a day. The oil has a gravity of 37° Bé.

Thrall.—At Thrall field, 1 mile southeast of Thrall and 20 miles southwest of the Minerva field, oil was discovered in the Taylor marl at a depth of 850 feet. It is brecciated and altered and is probably a fine-grained tuff. The top of the tuff is arched to form a low dome, and the oil accumulation is above the dome (Fig. 229). The oil is of low gravity, has a paraffin base, and is heavier than the oil of Corsicana that comes from the Taylor marl. It deposits paraffin rapidly in pipes and casing, so that the wells readily become clogged.

[1] LIDDLE, R. A., Am. Assoc. Pet. Geol. *Bull.*, vol. 13, pp. 1557–1558, 1929.
[2] HAGER, D. S., and I. O. BROWN, The Minerva Oil Field, Milan County, Texas, Am. Assoc. Pet. Geol. *Bull.*, vol. 8, pp. 632–640, 1924.

Lytton Springs.—The Lytton Springs[1] oil field is about 40 miles southwest of Thrall. Near San Marcos, in Hays County southwest of Thrall, the Balcones fault changes strike and trends more nearly west. A system of faults 30 miles wide or more extends southeast. These faults are nearly parallel, strike northeast, dip northwest, and drop the beds

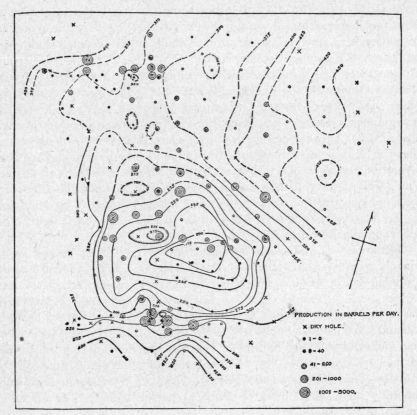

Fig. 229.—Sketch showing distribution and production of wells in Thrall oil field, Texas. Contour lines show position of upper surface of oil bearing rock in feet below sea level. (*After Udden and Bybee.*)

of the hanging walls on their northwest sides. The Lytton Springs oil field is in the block on the upraised southeast side of one of these faults. The Lytton Springs field was discovered March, 1925, and reached a

[1] Bybee, H. P., and R. F. Short, The Lytton Springs Oil Field, Univ. Texas, Bur. Econ. Geol. *Bull.* 2539, pp. 1–67, 1925.

Brucks, E. W., Geology of the San Marcos Quadrangle, Am. Assoc. Pet. Geol. *Bull.*, vol. 11, pp. 825–851, 1927.

Collingwood, D. M., and R. E. Rettger, Lytton Springs Oil Field, Texas, Am Assoc. Pet. Geol. *Bull.*, vol. 10, pp. 953–975, 1926.

production of 15,000 barrels of oil per day in July of that year. Soon afterward it settled to a production of 8,000 barrels per day. The oil is high grade with paraffin base and is light oil (gravity about 38° Bé.).

The formations present in this region are shown below:

Formation	Thickness, feet	Description
Eocene:		
Wilcox.....................	300–400	Dark micaceous shale
Midway....................	350–450	Clays with concretions
Upper Cretaceous:		
Navarro....................	650 ±	Clay, sands
Taylor.....................	650 ±	Clays, calcareous clays
Serpentine.................		Oil in upper part
Austin.....................	180–350	Chalk
Eagle Ford.................	10–60	Shale and limestone
Comanchean (Lower Cretaceous):		
Buda......................	40–60	Glauconitic limestone
Del Rio....................	45–80	Blue clay, shale, marl
Georgetown................	50–80	Limestone, shale, and marl
Edwards and Comanche Peak	700 ±	Oil in porous dolomitic limestone near top of Edwards at Luling field, 20 miles south of Lytton Springs
Glen Rose..................	......	Yields oil near Waco

The rocks cropping out are the Wilcox and Midway formations which strike parallel to the Balcones escarpment and dip 1 to 2 degrees southeast. These rocks are faulted and lie in the Luling-Mexia fault zone. In the producing area they are either domed or faulted up (Fig. 89). A well-defined dome is shown by contours at the top of the Austin chalk. A mass of serpentine more than a mile in diameter appears near the top of the Austin and the bottom of the Taylor formation at depths of 1,200 to 1,500 feet. The top of the mass is a dome, and from its highest point it slopes on all sides about 500 feet. The serpentine mass is an altered intrusive and in part an extrusive basalt with lava and ash phases. This volcanic activity probably continued to late Austin time, and the eruption is said to have been submarine. The serpentine is fractured and brecciated and in part vesicular. It is at places highly porous. Most of the wells are in the upper 200 feet of the serpentine.

Some gas and a little salt water are associated with the oil but no well-defined edge water area is developed around the oil field. The oil carries paraffin which tends to choke the wells near the surface, where deposition of paraffin takes place on lowering the temperature of the oil. This is relieved by warming the oil in the upper parts of the tubing.

In the Dale field, 4 miles southeast of Lytton Springs, and at Yost 6 miles north of Lytton Springs, oil is found in serpentine.

Luling.—The Luling[1] oil field is 40 miles southeast of Austin, 50 miles northeast of San Antonio, and about 6 miles west of Luling. The field is located on the southeast side of a fault that strikes N. 35° E. and is parallel to the faults of the Mexia system. In 1922 a well sunk 2,155 feet deep brought in oil flowing by heads 100 barrels a day. Closely spaced wells sunk along the southeast side of the fault outlined a field 7 miles long and about ½ mile wide, extending south from Caldwell into Gaudalupe County. The total production December 31, 1926, was 31,672,000 barrels, the oil having a gravity of about 27° Bé.

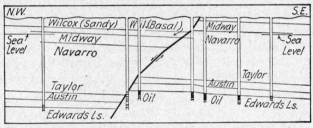

Fig. 230.—Section of Luling oil field, Texas. (*After Bruchs.*)

The structural relations (Fig. 230) are nearly similar to those that exist in the Mexia group of oil fields. The sequence of strata is nearly the same as at Lytton Springs. The fault dips northwest about 55 degrees and drops the hanging wall about 500 feet. In the footwall the beds dip east away from the fault about 200 feet per mile. Locally, low domes are developed by drag to the east of the fault, and cross-faults are found at both the north and south ends of the field, thus apparently sealing the reservoir up dip and on the sides. The oil is found in the dolomitic Edwards limestone of Lower Cretaceous age, particularly at the top and in the porous upper part of the limestone in a zone between 15 and 150 feet below the top of the limestone. The Edwards formation consists of alternating beds of limestone, dolomitic limestone, marl, and thin shales. The dolomite layers are crystallized, highly porous, and cavernous, and, according to Sellards, the porous zone lies just below a buried

[1] PRATT, W. E., Oil at Luling, Caldwell County, Texas, Am. Assoc. Pet. Geol. *Bull.*, vol. 7, pp. 182–183, 1923.

SELLARDS, E. H., The Luling Oil Field, Caldwell County, Texas, Am. Assoc. Pet. Geol. *Bull.*, vol. 8, pp. 775–788, 1924; also Univ. Texas *Bull.* 2239, November, 1922.

BRUCHS, E. W., Luling Oil Field, Caldwell and Guadalupe Counties, Texas, "Structure of Typical American Oil Fields," vol. 1, pp. 256–281, 1929.

———, The Geology of the San Marcos Quadrangle, Am. Assoc. Pet. Geol. *Bull.*, vol. 11, pp. 825–851, 1927.

erosion surface.[1] The Salt Flats field 2 miles north of Luling is developed along a parallel fault and produced much oil from the Edwards limestone.

The Darst Creek oil field is 10 miles southeast of Seguin, Guadalupe County, Texas. A structural dome is found at the surface along a fault that crosses the Guadalupe River. A well drilled in 1929, found oil producing 1,200 barrels a day from the Edwards limestone and large deposits of oil were developed.

San Antonio.—Near San Antonio[2] in Bexar County the Cretaceous rocks in a belt 25 miles wide are sliced by closely spaced normal faults that in the main strike a little north of east. The regional dip is southeast, although there are local reversals of dip. The faulting and folding are such that blocks elongated northeast are raised. Oil and gas fields are developed on these blocks or upfolds in the main on the south sides of the upraised structures. The fields include Gas Ridge, Alta Vista, Mission, Somerset, South Medina. Production of oil or gas or oil showings have been obtained from several of the Upper Cretaceous formations. At Somerset the production is 500 feet above the Austin at the horizon of the Taylor and Navarro formations. Oil is found in the Ina field near Somerset. The pay sand lies at a depth of about 925 feet.

Uvalde is west of San Antonio in Uvalde County. In Uvalde quadrangle, 17 miles northeast of Uvalde on the east side of Blanco River ½ mile south of the Southern Pacific Railway bridge, asphalt is found impregnating the Anacacho limestone of the Cretaceous which rests on Austin chalk. About 10 miles southwest of Uvalde asphalt is found impregnating sandstone. Outcrops are found here and there down stream for 5 miles to Asphalt Falls, the belt extending across the county line into Zavalla County at Nueces River.[3]

The Balcones fault, as stated, is not traced into Val Verde[4] County. There is, however, a wide zone of deformation in this region which involves rocks of Cretaceous age and was probably formed at the time of the Balcones faulting (Fig. 210). The prevailing structural trend is northwest, parallel to the Rocky Mountains folds. Over most of the county the regional dip is southwest, but this regional dip is interrupted by northwest striking anticlines. In this region the Rio Grande flows in a

[1] DUESSEN, A., U. S. Geol. Survey *Prof. Paper* 126, 1–139, 1924.

Row, C. H., Darst Creek Fault, Guadalupe County, Texas, Am. Assoc. Pet. Geol. *Bull.*, vol. 13, p. 1387, 1929.

[2] SELLARDS, E. H., The Geology and Mineral Resources of Bexar County, Univ. Texas, Bur. Econ. Geol. *Bull.* 1922, 1920; also Univ. Texas, Bur. Econ. Geol. *Bull.* 2230, (with map) pp. 30–40, 1926.

[3] VAUGHAN, T. W., U. S., Geol. Survey *Folio* 64, p. 7, 1900.

[4] CALVERT, W. R., Geologic Features of Val Verde County, Texas, and Adjacent Area, *Oil Gas Jour.*, vol. 26, p. 81, Jan. 26, 1928.

ROBERTS, J. R., and J. P. NASH, The Geology of Val Verde County, Univ. Texas *Bull.* 1803. 1918.

ROCK SECTION VAL VERDE COUNTY

Formation	Thick- ness, feet	Description
Upper Cretaceous: Eagle Ford.......	450	Thin flaggy sandstone merging upward into thin-bedded limestone and shales locally bituminous
Comanchean: Buda............	45–80	White chalky limestone, thins to north and northwest
Del Rio..........	200	Dark shale and clay, weathers yellow
Devil's River.....	1,000	Limestone, thins to north and northwest; marly bed weathering yellow about 90 feet below top
Glen Rose		

major syncline, the rocks dipping toward the river from two anticlinal areas. Oil seepages are found just east of the city limits of Del Rio, and this oil was once collected and distilled. The oil seeps out of the Devil's River limestone. A well drilled in this vicinity found a little light oil in Pennsylvanian rocks at a depth of 2,800 feet. The Owens well in the northwest part of the county found a small flow of wet gas in Pennsylvanian rocks at a depth of 2,500 feet.

Laredo District.—The rocks of the oil region of the south point of Texas,[1] east of Laredo (Fig. 231), are Tertiary and Quaternary beds that strike north and dip east. The Reynosa or Bordas escarpment, about 40 miles east of Laredo, marks a zone which is due in part to faulting and is traced 150 miles through the area. Chalcedony veins are numerous near the escarpment. Drilling has discovered large amounts of gas in Eocene rocks. The gas is piped to San Antonio, Houston, and smaller cities. The field had produced, also, altogether about 13,375,371 barrels of oil to June 30, 1927. The rocks of the area are shown in the table that follows. The Reynosa unconsolidated rocks cover most of the area and exposures are poor. In general a group of faults strike about N. 25° E. and the oil fields are related to these faults. At places the faults seal the reservoirs up dip, and at other places the sands play out near faults, due

[1] McFarland, P. W., Laredo District, Texas, "Structure of Typical American Oil Fields," vol. 1, pp. 389–408, 1929.

Jones, R. A., The Relation of the Reynosa Escarpment to Oil and Gas Fields of Webb and Zapata Counties, Texas, Am. Assoc. Pet. Geol. *Bull.*, vol. 7, pp. 532–545, 1923.

Deussen, A., and R. B. Dole, Ground Water in LaSalle and McMullen Counties, Texas, U. S. Geol. Survey *Water Supply Paper* 375, pp. 140–177, 1916.

Dumble, E. T., Geology of Southwestern Texas, Am. Inst. Min. Eng. *Trans.*, vol. 33, pp. 913–987, 1903.

Sardeson, F. W., Oil from Cone Domes in Texas, *Pan-American Geologist*, Vol. 52, pp. 118–124, 1929.

to conditions of erosion and deposition that prevailed during the times the sands were deposited.

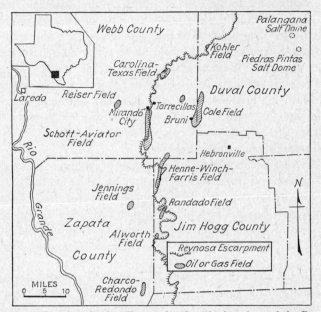

Fig. 231.—Map of Laredo District, Texas, showing the locations of the Reynosa escarp-ment and of oil and gas fields. (*After McFarland.*)

FORMATIONS, LAREDO DISTRICT

(*After Dumble, Duessen, McFarland, and others*)

Formation	Thick-ness, feet	Description
Pleistocene:		
Reynosa...........	175	Sands, gravels, etc.
Miocene:		
Oakville...........	200	Sandstone, conglomeratic sands
Miocene or Oligocene:		
Gueydan...........	850	Volcanic conglomerate, sandstone, tuffs.
Eocene:		
Frio..............	200	Clays and shales, some sand, volcanic material
Fayette...........	700–1,000	Sand, sandy shale, volcanic material, Cole and Mirando oil and gas sands
Yegua.............	700	Shale, gumbo, sands, Schott oil sand
Cook Mountain.....	1,000	Micaceous sands, sandy shale, shale. Webster and Carolina-Texas oil and gas sands
Mount Selman......	700	Brown and blue sands and shales, iron ore, lignitic material
Carrizo...........	80	Brown sandstone, carries artesian water (Wilcox)

The Cole gas field at the town of Bruni is 8 miles long and 1 to 3 miles wide. Gas is found in the Cole sand of the Fayette formation about 1,700 feet deep, and in smaller amounts in the Mirando sand about 2,300 feet deep. The field was opened in 1924 when large gas wells were brought in. The accumulation is due to sand lensing and folding. The sand plays out to the west of the field along a line that strikes N. 20° E., which is about parallel to many of the faults in this region. This, according to McFarland, is due probably to an old shore line that was dependent on a line of faulting farther west. The field has produced large amounts of gas from the Cole sand in which the pressure is 500 pounds, and small amounts from the Mirando sand about 700 feet deeper in which the pressure is 700 pounds per square inch.

The Carolina-Texas field, 8 miles north of Mirando City, is located on an anticline cut off to the west of its axis by a normal fault that strikes northeast and dips southeast, displacing the beds 200 feet. In a dome on the anticline that is sealed, probably in part by the fault, gas is accumulated in the Mirando, Webster, and Carolina-Texas sands, the latter being about 3,050 feet deep (Figs. 232, 233). The field has produced a little light oil.

The Schott-Aviator field south of Mirando City is located in an area of faults which have influenced accumulation. The district has produced 8,000,000 barrels of oil. That in the Mirando sand, 1,700 feet deep, has a gravity of 21° Bé. and that of the Schott sand, 300 feet deeper, and in the Yegua formation has a gravity of 42° Bé.

The Henne-Winch-Farris field, northwest Jim Hogg County, is 8 miles long, ½ mile wide, and located along the east side of a normal fault that strikes east of north and dips west. The rocks dip east from the fault about 150 feet per mile and oil and gas are found in the Mirando sand at depths of about 2,100 feet. The oil-bearing area parallels the fault and lies a short distance east of it. The field produced 2,666,110 barrels of oil to June 30, 1927.

In the Randado field oil and gas are found in the Cole sand 1,300 feet deep. The gravity of the oil is 21° Bé. In this field the rocks dip southeast at low angles. The accumulation is due to the lensing of the sand. In the Charco-Redondo field, 20 miles southwest of Randado, small oil wells are sunk 160 feet deep.

In the Jennings field west of the Randado field gas is obtained from the lower part of the Fayette formation at depths of about 1,300 feet and also from a deeper sand. The Reiser field near the north end of the district produced gas from the Fayette formation.

Palangana[1] salt dome is 70 miles east of Laredo and 60 miles west of Corpus Christi. A ring of low hills surrounds a basin below which, at a

[1] BARTON, D. C., The Salt Domes of South Texas, Am. Assoc. Pet. Geol. *Bull.*, vol. 9, pp. 536–589, 1925.

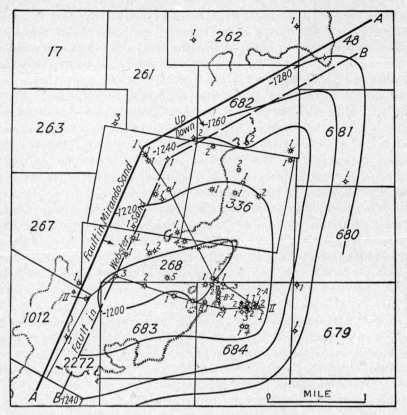

Fig. 232.—Map of Carolina-Texas oil field, Webb County, Texas, showing fault in the Mirando sand and in the Webster sand. Datum, Mirando sand. (*After McFarland.*)

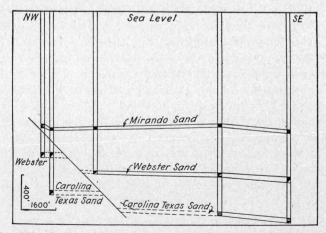

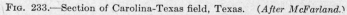

Fig. 233.—Section of Carolina-Texas field, Texas. (*After McFarland.*)

depth of 100 feet, is disclosed the top of a circular salt core about 2 miles in diameter. A cap rock 300 feet thick composed of anhydrite, gypsum, and calcite overlies the salt. Anhydrite from this dome, described by Goldman,[1] is schistose. The anhydrite is capped by the Reynosa formation. Some wells show oil; considerable sulphur is developed. The Piedras Pintas salt dome, 4 miles south-southeast of Palangana, is probably a circular dome of approximately the same size as the Palangana dome. Above the Piedras Pintas dome a black oil was found in water wells. Later, commercial wells yielding an oil rich in lubricants were drilled to oil sands, one 170 feet below the surface. Falfurrias dome, 40 miles southeast of Piedras Pintas, is a mound of gypsum 50 feet high, which is believed to be the cap rock of a salt dome. It is an ellipse about a mile in diameter with the long axis striking northwest toward Piedras Pintas. A well 1,000 feet deep is said to be bottomed in gypsum.

Near Kingsville, 30 miles southwest of Corpus Christi, oil and gas are found and a gas field is developed at Aqua Dulce, 20 miles north of Kingsville. At the White Point field 7 miles northwest of Corpus Christi, and at Saxet a few miles southwest of White Point, gas fields are developed. In the Refugio field, 35 miles north of Corpus Christi, oil and gas are produced from sands 3,700 feet and 5,200 feet deep and gas is produced from several shallower sands. The oil is derived from Lower Tertiary beds which lie on an uplift but probably not on a salt dome.

East Texas.—Oil and gas are found on the east side of the synclinal basin of east Texas at several places near the east border of Texas.[2] Bethany, Fig. 234 which is situated on a dome in northeast Panola County, extending into Louisiana, has produced gas from four horizons: Nacatoch at 1,050 feet, Blossom sand at 1,725 feet, Woodbine at 2,650 and at a depth of 3,000 feet from the Lower Cretaceous. The Waskom field north of Bethany is of similar character. The rocks dip southwest from Bethany and at Carthage, 22 miles southwest of Bethany, are 200 or 300 feet lower. Several wells are drilled at Carthage, and some of them found a little high-grade oil, probably in the Blossom sand. The Van field (Fig. 234) is on a great faulted structural dome. The oil is in the Woodbine sand which has a thickness of 320 feet or more, and much of the sand is saturated. Large deposits are developed. The gravity of the oil is 35° Bé. Large deposits are developed also in Rusk County.

At Nacogdoches[3] in the southeastern part of the syncline the marine formation (Claiborne group) crops out. Wells found small amounts of oil

[1] GOLDMAN, M. I., Am. Assoc. Pet. Geol. *Bull.*, vol. 9, p. 56, 1925.

[2] SELLARDS, E. H., Well Records in Panola County, with Structural Contour Map, Univ. Texas, Bur. Econ. Geol. *Bull.* 2232, pp. 1–33, 1922.

HULL, J. P. D., and W. C. SPOONER, Am. Assoc. Pet. Geol. *Bull.*, vol. 6, No. 2, pp. 179–192, 1922.

[3] DUMBLE, E. T., Geology of East Texas, Univ. Texas, Bur. Econ. Geol. *Bull.* 1869, pp. 1–388, 1918.

and gas at depths of 400 feet or less near the middle of the Cook Mountain beds. At Palestine asphaltic sands of the Lower Claiborne series were used for street paving.

Palestine Group of Salt Domes.—About 40 miles east of the Mexia fault there is a group of salt domes which constitute the interior group of salt domes of Texas. Most of these domes lie in a zone that strikes northeast nearly parallel to the Mexia fault. This zone of deformation is

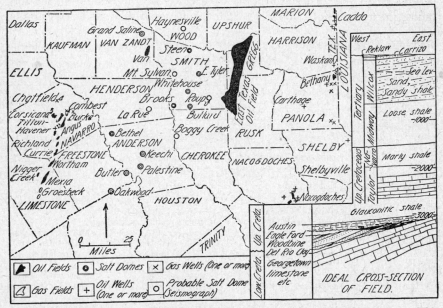

Fig. 234.—Map and section of East Texas oil field (data chiefly from Levorsen). This field, discovered in 1930, is 40 miles long, covers 110,000 acres and has over 10,000 producing wells which reach depths of about 3700 feet. Produces oil from Woodbine (Upper Cretaceous) sand where overlain unconformably by Austin chalk and shale. Production to January 1, 1933, about 234,000,000 barrels. Reserves estimated to be 2,000,000,000 barrels. Average thickness of sand 20 feet, porosity 20 %. High permeability. Initial pressure 900 to 1600 pounds per square inch. Oil high grade, light gravity.

called the Palestine zone (Fig. 234) and it lies near the bottom of a syncline between the Llano and the Sabine uplifts.[1]

[1] Powers, S., Interior Salt Domes of Texas, Am. Assoc. Pet. Geol. *Bull.*, vol. 10, pp. 1–60, 1926.

———, and O. B. Hopkins, The Brooks, Steen, and Grand Saline Domes, U. S. Geol. Survey *Bull.* 736 G, pp. 179–239, 1923.

Levorsen, A. I., Int. Petrol. Tech., vol. 8, pp. 261–268, 1931.

Minor, H. E., and Hanna, M. A., *Bull.* Amer. Assoc. Pet. Geol., vol. 17, pp. 757–791, 1933.

Lahee, F. H., *Trans* A.I.M.E., Petrol. Div., pp. 279–294, 1932.

Steen dome is 24 miles southeast of Grand Saline dome.   It is marked by a salt marsh surrounded by low hills.   The upthrust salt plug is capped by Wilcox formation and lies in an area of Mount Selman formation.   The upthrust of the rocks around the core is estimated to be 500 feet.

Brooks dome is 27 miles south of Steen dome.   The surrounding beds are steeply tilted, at places about on edge, and the Austin formation is brought up into an area normally covered by Mount Selman formation, indicating an uplift of 4,300 feet.   The formations are identified by fossils.

GEOLOGIC FORMATIONS FOUND IN THE REGION OF THE INTERIOR SALT DOMES IN TEXAS AND LOUISIANA

(After Powers)

System	Central Texas	Eastern Texas	Northern Louisiana

Eocene..........	Claiborne group
	  Yegua formation
	  Cook Mountain formation
	  Mount Selman formation
	
	Wilcox group
	  Carrizo sandstone
	  Indio formation
	  Midway formation
		Claiborne group
		  Yegua formation
		  Cook Mountain form
		  Mount Selman form
		
		Wilcox group
		  Carrizo sandstone
		  Indio formation
		Midway formation
			Claiborne group
			  Yegua (Cockfield)
			  form
			  St. Maurice form
			  Sparta sand
			  Cane River
			Wilcox formation
			
			Midway formation

Upper Cretaceous..	Navarro formation Taylor marl Austin chalk Eagle Ford clay Woodbine sand	Arkadelphia clay Nacatoch sand Unnamed shale Pecan Gap chalk Wolfe City sand Annona tongue Blossom sand Unnamed clay and sand (including Ector chalk) Eagle Ford formation Woodbine sand	Arkadelphia clay Nacatoch sand Marlbrook marl (including Saratoga chalk) Annona chalk Brownstown marl Bingen group Unconformity Washita group
Lower Cretaceous..	....	Washita group Fredericksburg group Trinity group	Fredericksburg (locally absent) Trinity group
Pennsylvanian (?). Permian (??)...... Pre-Cambrian.....			

At the Bullard dome, 10 miles east of Brooks, rock salt is encountered at a depth of 527 feet.   The Boggy Creek dome, about 20 miles south of Brooks dome, was discovered in 1927.   A salt core lies 2,142 feet deep. Oil was encountered probably in the Bingen formation.   To 1930 Boggy Creek produced 1,500,000 barrels of oil.[1]

[1] LIDDLE, R. A. "Petroleum Development and Technology in 1927," Am. Inst. Min. Eng., p. 632, 1928.

Keechi[1] dome (Fig. 235) is 30 miles southwest of Brooks dome. The country near by is covered by Mount Selman formation which dips southeast away from the dome. Near the core dips of 45 degrees are noted and a mile away the dips are 2 degrees. A good showing of heavy oil (8° Bé.) was found in a marginal drill hole.

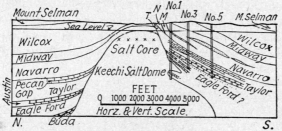

Fig. 235.—Cross-section of Keechi salt dome. (*After Powers.*)

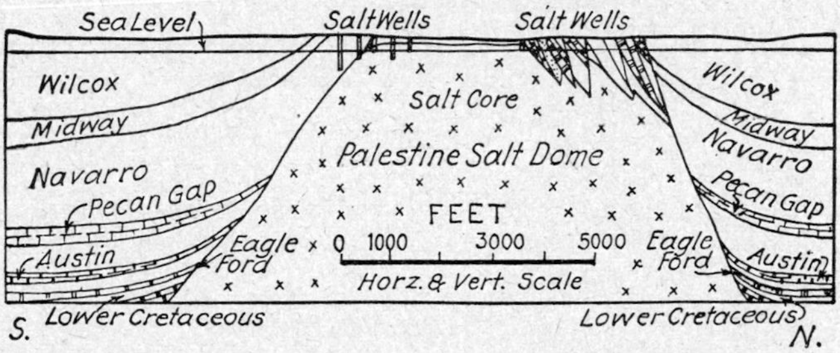

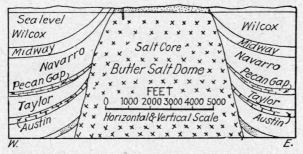

Fig. 236.—Cross-section of Palestine salt dome, Texas. (*After Powers and Hopkins.*)

Fig. 237.—Cross-section of Butler salt dome, Texas. (*After Powers.*)

The Bethel dome northwest of Keechi, located in 1927 by the seismograph, showed salt at a depth of 1,600 feet. A little heavy oil was found.

Palestine dome (Fig. 236) is 6 miles south of Keechi dome. It is a low area surrounded by hills and marked by salt springs, gas seeps, and small mud volcanoes. The beds dip away from the salt core at high angles and the Buda limestone is brought up into a region where the

[1] Hopkins, O. B., The Palestine Salt Dome, Anderson County, Texas, U. S. Geol. Survey *Bull.* 661, pp. 253–270, 1918.

Mount Selman is the normal surface formation, indicating an upthrust of 5,500 feet near the top of the dome. The salt core has been extensively eroded.

The Butler dome is 6 miles southwest of Palestine dome. It is marked by a saline surrounded by hills and by small mounds that are formed by the creep of wet clay below springs on the edge of the saline and by water springs that carry gas. The top of the salt core has been eroded and has probably suffered solution. The wells of the core, as shown by wells drilled around it, are very steep. A section of the dome is shown by Fig. 237.

Fig. 238.—Map showing oil and gas fields of southern Arkansas and northern Louisiana.

SOUTHERN ARKANSAS AND NORTHERN LOUISIANA

The oil-bearing area of southern Arkansas and northern Louisiana (Fig. 238) lies south of the Ouachita Mountains of Arkansas from which the rocks dip southeast, and it is bounded on the south by the Angelina-Caldwell flexure. The rocks of the region are raised along three belts which strike northwest. These are the Sabine uplift,[1] of north-west

[1] Harris, G. D., Oil and Gas in Louisiana, U. S. Geol. Survey *Bull.* 429, pp. 1–192, 1910.

Powers, S., The Sabine Uplift, Am. Assoc. Pet. Geol. *Bull.*, vol. 4, pp. 117–136, 1920.

Huntley, L. G., The Sabine Uplift, Am. Assoc. Pet. Geol. *Bull.*, vol. 7, pp. 179–181, 1923.

Louisiana the Haynesville-Homer uplift east of the Sabine uplift and the Smackover-Monroe-Richland uplift. On these broad zones of gentle warping there are many smaller anticlines and domes. The axes of some of these smaller folds are aligned with the long axes of the great zones of warping, but a large number of them strike northeast rudely parallel with the strike of the Angelina-Caldwell flexure (Figs. 239, 240).

GENERALIZED SECTION SHOWING STRATA IN SOUTHERN ARKANSAS AND NORTHERN LOUISIANA

Formation	Thickness, feet	Description
Tertiary		
Eocene:		
St. Maurice	100–400	Clay, shale, sand, green sand, calcareous shale, marine
Sparta.........	400–500	Sand, shale, lignite, brown clay shale at base
Cane River.....	200–400	Fossiliferous shale, green clay, green sand at top, locally calcareous in lower part
Wilcox.........	200–2,000	Sand, clay, shale, lignite, glauconite; becomes thicker to south. Oil at Urania, oil shows at Zwolle, Louisiana, and Nacogdoches, Texas
Midway........	250–500	Clay, marine limestone, chalk, lignite, gypsum
Cretaceous:		
Arkadelphia....	100–500	Clay, shale, chalk near base, marine, fossiliferous, at places has a layer of green waxy bentonite clay (volcanic ash?) about 40 feet above Nacatoch
Nacatoch	100–350	Sand, shale, chalk, limestone, glauconite. Oil at Smackover, El Dorado, Homer, Bellevue, Caddo. Gas at Waskom, Bethany, Elm Grove, Bull Bayou, Monroe, etc.
Saratoga.......	100	Chalk
Marlbrook	125–350	Marl, chalk, shaly sand, Meakin sand at Smackover
Annona........	100–250	Chalk, shale, sand; oil at Caddo, Pine Island, etc.
Ozan..........	0–250	Shale, chalk, and sand. Oil at Homer, Caddo, Cotton Valley, Smackover etc. Probably same as Buckrange and Blossom sands.
Brownstown....	100–300	Marl, clay, shale
Tokio..........	0–330	Shale and sandstone. Oil at Caddo, etc.
Eagleford......	0–100	Shale, calcareous shale, red shale, sandy at base
Woodbine......	0–150	Sand, shales, lignite, clays; oil at Caddo, Bull Bayou, etc., Sligo; gas at Elm Grove, Shreveport, etc.
Comanchean:		
Washita and		Shale, red shale, sandstone limestone
Fredericksburg .	1,000+	Gas at Waskom; oil near Pleasant Hill, etc.
Glen Rose......	3,200+	Limestone shale, sandstone, red beds anhydrite; oil and gas at Pine Island; gas at Cotton Valley, probably at Richland

The oil and gas are found in the smaller upfolds, mainly in the Cretaceous strata.   Many of the formations are approximately the same as

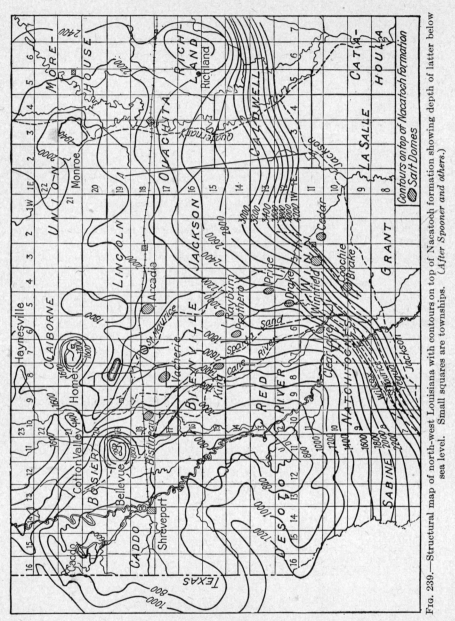

Fig. 239.—Structural map of north-west Louisiana with contours on top of Nacatoch formation showing depth of latter below sea level. Small squares are townships. (*After Spooner and others.*)

those described in east Texas but differ in thickness and character. Oil has been found also in the Wilcox sand of the Tertiary in the Urania field, and, 40 miles to the northeast of it on the west side of the Richland

TERTIARY SECTION ON ANGELINA-CALDWELL FLEXURE, BETWEEN PACKTON AND GEORGETOWN

(After Teas)

Formation	Thickness, feet	Description
Oligocene:		
Fleming.........	1,150	Clays, gray, calcareous sandy; sandstone, some volcanic ash
Catahoula.......	1,500	Sands, yellow, gray, massive volcanic ash and green-gray clay
Eocene:		
Jackson..........	550	Green and yellow calcareous clay, glauconitic sandy clays and sands, basal fossiliferous limestone ledges
Cockfield........	470	Gray sandy and chocolate-colored clays and sands, lignite, limonite concretions, silicified wood, cone-in-cone fragments
St. Maurice......	100	Brown to green glauconite, clays and sands, fossiliferous
Jonesboro.......	130	Light-green calcareous and brownish fossiliferous clays
Sparta..........	470	Chocolate-colored clays and gray sandy clays and sands
Cane River......	278	Upper brown clays, lower green glauconitic clays with pyritic and glauconitic sands at base 5 to 8 feet thick
Wilcox..........		Lignite or brown clay at top, 1 to 4 feet thick, directly above the oil sand at Urania; below the lignite is 125 feet of white sand with beds of clay and some thin glauconitic fossil zones

gas field, a gas well has been brought in, probably deriving its flow from the Wilcox formation.

The rocks of the region are shown in the following generalized geologic section. Not all of the beds are found in the positions indicated, for

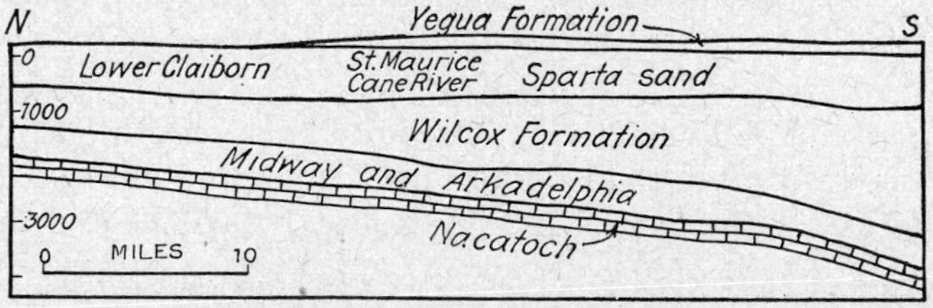

FIG. 240.—Diagram showing southward thickening of Wilcox formation in Louisiana. Location of section, *AA*, Fig. 239. (*After Spooner.*)

there are unconformities in the section. The area was above sea during certain periods of Cretaceous and Tertiary times. At still other periods parts of the area were covered by extensive bodies of fresh water. There is an unconformity at the base of the Upper Cretaceous, another at the base of the Nacatoch, still another at the top of the Upper Cretaceous, and another still at the top of the Oligocene. Extensive deformation occurred near the close of Comanchean time (Fig. 241). In the Bellevue oil field faults with vertical displacements of 800 feet involved Comanchean beds. The country was peneplained by erosion and the Upper Cretaceous was laid down on a nearly level surface. In the Pine Island field Comanchean rocks were folded, and on an eroded anticline Upper Cretaceous beds were deposited and, later, folded on earlier lines of

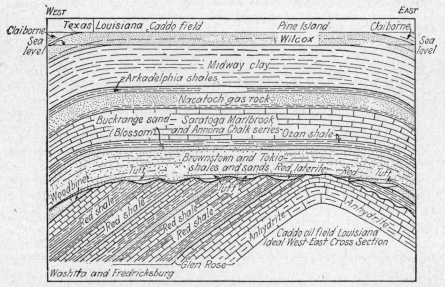

Fig. 241.—Ideal cross-section through Pine Island, Caddo oil field, Louisiana. Upper Cretaceous to scale. Lower Cretaceous to exaggerated scale. (*After Fletcher.*)

weakness. In this district the structure recalls the refolded buried anticlinal hills, which are developed in many fields of Oklahoma. The second period of folding probably followed Oligocene time, for the early Tertiary beds are folded in many districts.

Caddo and Pine Island.—In Caddo[1] Parish, northwest Louisiana (Fig. 239), are located the Caddo, Pine Island, and Hosston oil fields, which together to the end of 1928 produced 114,548,365 barrels of oil.

[1] Fletcher, C. D., Structure of Caddo Field, Caddo Parish, Louisiana, "Structure of Typical American Oil Fields," vol. 2, pp. 183–195, 1929.

Crider, A. F., Pine Island Deep Sands, Caddo Parish, Louisiana, "Structure of Typical American Oil Fields," vol. 2, pp. 168–182, 1929.

Matson, G. C., The Caddo Oil and Gas Field, Louisiana and Texas, U. S. Geol. Survey *Bull.* 619, pp. 1–62, 1912.

Hammill, C. A., The Cretaceous of Northwestern Louisiana, Am. Assoc. Pet. Geol. *Bull.*, vol. 5, pp. 298–310, 1921.

These fields are on the northwest side of the Sabine uplift which strikes northwest. Smaller folds strike northeast across the axis of the main uplift. These include the Hosston and Pine Island anticlines on which are located important oil fields. The reservoir rocks of Caddo Parish are the Nacatoch "gas rock," the "chalk rock" in the Saratoga, Marlbrook, and Annona formations, the Buckrange sand (Blossom) of the Ozan formation, the "Woodbine" sands and four horizons in the Comanchean. The so-called "Woodbine," which is the main source of oil, according to Fletcher, probably includes three or more horizons: a sand in the Tokio formation, a laterite at the unconformity between the Upper and Lower Cretaceous series, and one or more sands of the Comanchean series.

The Nacatoch sand has produced much gas in the Caddo field and oil and gas in the Hosston field. At some places it is a sand, at other places a sandy limestone. In general the oil and gas are in the anticlines. The chalk rock produces a rather light oil (31 to 36° Bé.), from a fractured zone along a fault and has been a prolific source of oil in the Pine Island field. The Buckrange sand has produced a little oil (24° Bé.). The "Woodbine sand," as stated, probably includes three or more sands, which together have supplied the bulk of the oil of Caddo Parish. The concentration of oil in the "Woodbine" pools, according to Fletcher, depends chiefly upon the amount of sand present. The production appears to be largely from sand lenses near the unconformity between the Upper and Lower Cretaceous beds (Fig. 241).

In the Pine Island field, 20 miles north of Shreveport, oil was produced from the Cretaceous sands for many years. The Upper Cretaceous rocks are gently arched. Deep drilling has shown that the Lower Cretaceous rocks are more highly arched, and in a circular area at the center of the uplift the Washita red shales are wanting. These appear at the sides of the uplift, indicating that the Lower Cretaceous was arched and eroded before the Upper Cretaceous was laid down. In the Lower Cretaceous rocks oil is found in the lateritic beds of the formation at the top of the series, in the anhydrite bed near the top of the series and about 2,700 feet deep at Pine Island, in a fractured limestone at 2,900 feet, in the "Dillon" gas horizon at 3,623 feet, in the "Dixie" oil horizon 90 feet deeper, where oil is found in fractured limestone, and in the Herndon sand 193 feet below the Dixie horizon.

[1] In the Dixie Pool, 10 miles north of Shreveport, oil is found in basal sands of the Tokio formation that rest unconformably upon the Trinity shales.

In the Carterville district, north Bossier Parish, oil, gas, and salt water are found in the Blossom sand. A sand was encountered in

[1] SHEARER, H. K., and HUTSON, E. B., Dixie oil pool, Caddo Parish, Louisiana, *Am. Assoc. Pet. Geol. Bull.*, vol. 14, pp. 743–764, 1930.

Woodley and Collins No. 1 well, at a depth of 3,086, and found gas with an estimated daily flow of 35,000,000 cubic feet.

Shreveport, Elmgrove, and Sligo.—A small field adjoining Shreveport on the west produced gas from the Nacatoch and Woodbine sands. The gas field is now exhausted and no oil was found. Elmgrove field, about 18 miles southeast of Shreveport, is located on a broad dome. Gas is

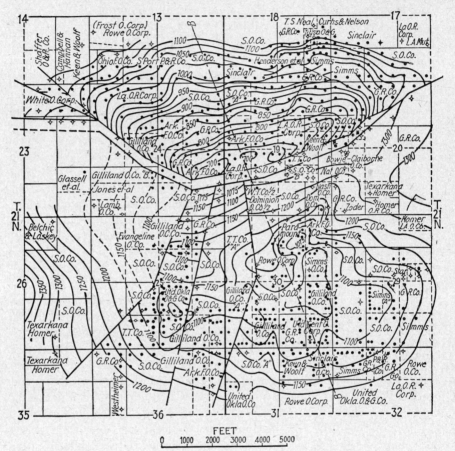

FEET

0 1000 2000 3000 4000 5000

FIG. 242.—Structure map of Homer oil field, Louisiana. Contours drawn on top of Nacatoch sand. (*After Spooner.*)

derived from the Nacatoch and Woodbine formations. The Blossom sand also carries some gas and from the very top of the structure it has yielded a small amount of oil. The gas pressure of the field is low, owing to large withdrawals and to wild wells that were allowed to blow themselves out. Compressor stations are installed for recovering the small amount of gas remaining in the sands. A deep test drilled in 1923 found in the Glen Rose formation a light gravity oil at 4,412 feet, which on exposure congealed to a vaseline-like mass. The Sligo gas field is about

7 miles north of Elmgrove field and is located on a similar structure separated from Elmgrove by a low structural saddle. It was discovered in 1922 and produces gas and some oil from the Woodbine sand.

Bellevue.—The Bellevue[1] field, 20 miles northeast of Shreveport, is located in a flat area on a pronounced structural dome which shows, above the dome, the Wilcox formation surrounded by younger rocks. The dome has a closure of about 800 feet and the oil-bearing rocks are higher than elsewhere in northern Louisiana. The Nacatoch, which is the main oil-bearing horizon, is a medium-grained sand with glauconite, locally, with calcareous and gumbo layers. Wells only 300 feet deep were brought in with an initial production of 400 barrels per day. The oil has a gravity of 19.3° Bé. and is low in gasoline. The two oil pools of the field are about a mile apart and these have produced 8,500,000

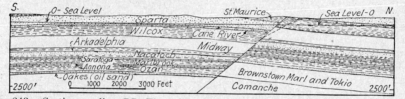

Fig. 243.—Section on line *BB*, Fig. 242, Homer oil field, Louisiana. (*After Spooner.*)

barrels of oil from the Nacatoch sand. The Nacatoch formation is crossed by several faults[2] with throws of between 20 and 250 feet, and in general the oil-bearing areas are limited by these faults, the oil occupying the higher parts of the dome. There is a great unconformity between the Eagle Ford clay at the base of the Upper Cretaceous and the Glen Rose formation at the top of the Lower Cretaceous. The beds of the Lower Cretaceous were faulted up 800 feet and eroded before the Upper Cretaceous was deposited.

Homer.—In the Homer field,[3] 40 miles northeast of Shreveport, oil was discovered in 1919. Some of the earlier wells drilled came in with initial productions as high as 10,000 barrels a day. To January 1, 1928, the production was 56,053,456 barrels of oil. The field (Figs. 242, 243) is a high area topographically, 225 to 335 feet above sea level, in which

[1] VEATCH, A. C., U. S. Geol. Survey *Prof. Paper* 46, pl. 3, 1905.

HULL, J. P. D., and W. C. SPOONER, A Review of Oil and Gas Pools in North Louisiana, Amer. Assoc. Pet. Geol. *Bull.*, vol. 6, pp. 179–192, 1922.

HOLMAN, E., and R. B. CAMPBELL, The Bellevue Oil Field, Louisiana, Am. Assoc. Pet. Geol. *Bull.*, vol. 7, pp. 645–652, 1923.

[2] TEAS, L. P., Bellevue Oil Field, Bossier Parish, Louisiana, "Structure of Typical American Oil Fields," vol. 2, pp. 229–253, 1929.

[3] HULL, J. P. D., and W. C. SPOONER, A Review of Oil and Gas Pools in Northern Louisiana Territory, Am. Assoc. Pet. Geol. *Bull.*, vol. 6, pp. 186–187, 1922.

SPOONER, W. C., Homer Oil Field, Claiborne Parish, Louisiana, "Structure of Typical American Oil Fields," vol. 2, pp. 196–228, 1929.

GENERALIZED SECTION OF FORMATIONS IN THE HOMER FIELD
(After W. C. Spooner)

System	Series	Group	Formation	Thickness, feet	Character
Tertiary	Plio-cene(?)		Superficial gravels	0–2	
	Eocene	Claiborne	St. Maurice	0–300	Mainly sands with ferruginous clay and sandstone. Glauconite
			Sparta sand	400–450	Massive reddish and light-colored sands with thin beds, and nodules of white clay and ferruginous sandstone
			Cane River	75	Glauconitic sands and chocolate-colored clays. Siderite concretions
			Wilcox	400–600	Lignitic sands and clays
			Midway	450 ±	Non-calcareous clays in upper part. Dark clay in basal part. Siderite concretions
Cretaceous	Gulf	Navarro	——Unconformity—— Arkadelphia clays	90–125	Dark-colored clays with some chalk in the lower half. Fossiliferous
			Nacatoch sand	250	Sand, sandy limestone with shale at the base. Fossiliferous. Oil producing
			Saratoga chalk	80–100	Hard white and gray chalk
		Taylor	Marlbrook marl	125	Light-colored chalky shale and marl
			Annona chalk	100	Hard white chalk. Fossiliferous
			Ozan (Oakes sand at the base 50–60 feet)	275	Gray calcareous shale with 50–60 feet of sand at the base. Oil producing
		Austin	Brownstown marl (200 feet)	650	Mainly gray and bluish-green sands, sandy shales and gray clays; in part lignite. Volcanic ash
			Tokio (450 feet)		
			Woodbine sand		Doubtfully present in the lower 30 feet
	Comanche	Trinity	——Unconformity—— Upper Glen Rose	850	Red and brown clay and shale. Argillaceous limestone, gray and black shale. Thin beds of sand and sandstone
			Anhydrite zone	500	Anhydrite interbedded with limestone
			Lower Glen Rose		Chiefly gray to black shale and argillaceous limestone. Some red and brown shale and lenses of fine sand
			Red sand and shale zone	1,800 ±	Red and brown shale and clay. White, gray, and red sand and sandstone

the Eocene rocks crop out, the domatic structure being shown at the surface. The structural relief is about 1,000 feet, and the dome is cut by numerous faults, one striking east having a downthrow of 500 feet on the south side. This fault dips about 45 degrees south. Oil is found in the Nacatoch and Oakes (Blossom) sands which are 700 feet apart. The oil of these sands is similar in character and, according to Spooner, has migrated upward from the lower sand along fault planes. The Nacatoch sand produces oil on both sides of the fault (Fig. 243) and the Oakes sand produces oil on the south or downthrown side of the fault but contains water only on the north side. The oil occurs on the high parts of the dome on both sides of the fault, and salt water is encountered below the oil.

Spring Hill and Haynesville.—The Spring Hill-Sarepta[1] gas field is located 30 miles northeast of Shreveport. The rocks are thrown into very gentle folds and are faulted. The Sarepta fold, on which gas is located, is believed to be a dome. The Spring Hill fold is probably a structural nose. A sand tentatively correlated with the Blossom sand is encountered at a depth of about 2,650 feet. Several wells to this sand have initial flows of between 25,000,000 and 60,000,000 cubic feet of gas per day. The productive area is estimated to be about 50 square miles and the porosity of the sand is estimated at 20 per cent. The initial pressure is about 1,200 pounds per square inch. The gas carries 45 gallons of gasoline per 1,000,000 cubic feet. In the Haynesville oil field, east of the Sarepta field, the same sand produces oil. This field is located probably on a dome. The pay sand is only 8 to 16 feet thick. Wells with initial production of several thousands of barrels daily were brought in, but some of the larger wells soon yielded oil, salt water, and basic sediment.[2] The salt-water line to which the sand slopes is in general 2,500 feet below sea level.

Cotton Valley.—In the Cotton Valley[3] oil field, 10 miles west of Homer, a large gas well in the Blossom sand was brought in in August, 1922. The following year a well was drilled which had an initial daily production of 25,000,000 feet of gas and a slight spray of oil. This spray increased until the well yielded commercial supplies of oil. Later, wells making 1,000 to 10,000 barrels a day were drilled. The field is on a well-defined dome

---

[1] Ponton, G. M., and J. W. Whitehurst, The Spring Hill-Sarepta Gas Field, Louisiana, Am. Assoc. Pet. Geol. *Bull.*, vol. 7, pp. 546–554, 1923.

Belchic, G., and C. A. Breitung, Gas Production of the Spring Hill-Sarepta Gas Field, Am. Assoc. Pet. Geol. *Bull.*, vol. 7, pp. 555–557, 1923.

[2] Teas, L. P., Am. Assoc. Pet. Geol. *Bull.*, vol. 6, pp. 371–372, 1922.

———, "Petroleum Development and Technology in 1927," p. 668, 1928.

[3] McDonald, M. W., The Cotton Valley, Louisiana, Oil Field, Am. Assoc. Pet. Geol. *Bull.*, vol. 9, pp. 875–885, 1925.

Powers, S., Am. Assoc. Pet. Geol. *Bull.*, vol. 8, pp. 245–247, 1924.

Crider, A. F., *Oil Gas Jour.*, vol. 26, p. 122, Feb. 17, 1927.

that shows the Blossom sand 2,280 feet below sea level at the top of the dome and the closure is 140 feet or more. Edge water lies about 2,350 feet below sea level and the oil occupies a narrow circle around the disc of gas near the top of the dome. The oil is 30° Bé. and low in gasoline. Initial gas pressure was about 900 pounds per square inch. A well was recently drilled producing gas high in gasoline vapor from the upper part of the Glen Rose formation at a depth of 4,198 feet.

Waskom and Bethany.—Waskom and Bethany[1] are on the Texas border line, the chief parts of the fields lying in Texas. These fields lie on the west border of the Sabine uplift. They are on the same high structure but are separated by a saddle that does not yield oil or gas. The Waskom field yields gas from the Nacatoch Blossom, and from the Washita formations. The rock pressure in the Nacatoch was originally 410 pounds per square inch and in 1927 was 215 pounds. The pressure in the Blossom sand at Waskom was 800 pounds per square inch and has decreased one half. The Bethany field, 6 miles south of Waskom, originally produced gas from the Nacatoch and from the Adams sand of the Washita. The gas of this field is piped to Shreveport and to coast cities.

Bull Bayou.—The Bull Bayou[2] (DeSoto-Red River) field is 35 miles southeast of Shreveport and near the south edge of the Sabine uplift. Between 1914 and 1921 the field produced 37,837,360 barrels of oil. The field is on a dome which is crossed by the Gusher Bend fault which has a downthrow of 200 feet to the south. Gas is found in the Nacatoch sand but most of the oil is produced from the Woodbine sand which lies at a depth of 2,450 to 2,700 feet. Small low anticlines are developed on the dome. The dome where crossed by the fault was particularly productive from wells of large flow.

The Pleasant Hill[3] or Pelican field is 12 miles southwest of the Bull Bayou field. The field occupies a dome and the geologic section is similar to that of Bull Bayou field. The Nacatoch sand is reached at a depth of 900 feet in the northern part of the field and 1,350 feet in the southern part. A sand in the northern part of the field 3,200 feet deep yields light oil, probably from the Fredericksburg formation.

Monroe.—The Monroe[4] gas field is 100 miles east of Shreveport, Louisiana, and 60 miles southeast of Smackover, Arkansas. The surface

---

[1] *Op. cit.*, p. 333.

[2] MATSON, G. C., and O. B. HOPKINS, The DeSoto-Red River Oil and Gas Field, Louisiana, U. S. Geol. Survey *Bull.* 661, pp. 101–140, 1918.

[3] TEAS, L. P., "Petroleum Development and Technology in 1927," p. 669, 1928.

[4] BELL, H. W., and R. A. COTTRELL, The Monroe Gas Field, Louisiana, Dept. Conservation *Bull.* 9, 1921.

STROUD, B. K., and F. P. SHAYES, The Monroe Gas Field, Am. Assoc. Pet. Geol. *Bull.*, vol. 7, pp. 565–574, 1923.

BELL, H. W., The Monroe Gas Field, Louisiana, Dept. Conservation *Bull.* 12, pp. 1–8, 1926; also SPOONER, W. C., "Geology."

is about 100 feet above sea level. It is on the south end of the Ouachita uplift of Arkansas and Louisiana, which is similar to and roughly parallel to the Sabine uplift. Drilling was suggested by a gas spring. The field occupies about 300 square miles and is one of the world's greatest gas fields. The rocks above the Nacatoch are somewhat similar to those of the Smackover district (p. 415), but below the Nacatoch correlation is uncertain. The gas is found in the Nacatoch formation below the chalky shales and chalk of the Arkadelphia.[1] The Nacatoch is from 100 to 250 feet thick and is made up of limestone, chalk, and tuffs with shale and sand in the lower half of the formation. The porosity of the rock is generally high but is lowest in the northwest part of the field.

As shown by Figs. 244 and 245, the field is on a great structural dome. There is 300 feet of closure as measured on the red beds below the Nacatoch with less than that on the top of the Nacatoch, because the Nacatoch thickens greatly to the north and west. On this part of the dome, however, the Nacatoch is relatively impervious and that has the effect of increasing the closure of the reservoir. The reservoir thus appears to be due in part to the domatic structure and in part to the low permeability of the gas rock up dip near the crest of the dome. The top of the Nacatoch formation on top of the dome is 1,940 feet below sea level and 2,050 feet deep. The southeast part of the field shows a wide terrace. Stroud and Shayes estimate that the gas rock has a porosity of 23 per cent, the average pressure of the field is estimated to be 1,050 pounds per square inch, and the average thickness of the producing bed is about 25 feet.[2] The reservoir is estimated to have contained 3,420,000,000,000 cubic feet of gas at 8 ounces above atmospheric pressure. In 1925 when 628,000,000,000 cubic feet of gas had left the rock, the pressure was reduced one-sixth. Bell, using this figure, estimated that the field originally contained six times that amount, or 3,768,000,000,000 cubic feet. Salt water around the edge of the field has an elevation of 2,200 feet below sea level. It does not rise and restore pressure appreciably as gas is removed. There is little or no trouble with bottom water. Since the gas is rather high in gasoline, the flanks of the field are drilled for oil, but so far the exploration has been disappointing. A second sand from 147 to 432 feet below the Nacatoch also contains gas, three wells having a combined initial daily flow of 53,000,000 cubic feet. The gas of the field is used for making carbon black and for gasoline recovery, but a large generating plant has been built for supplying power for long-distance transmission, and gas lines have been installed to supply gas to distant cities.

[1] Some consider the "Monroe gas rock" to be the Annona Chalk.
[2] They estimate 25 feet for 254 square miles and 20 feet for 44 square miles of gas rock.

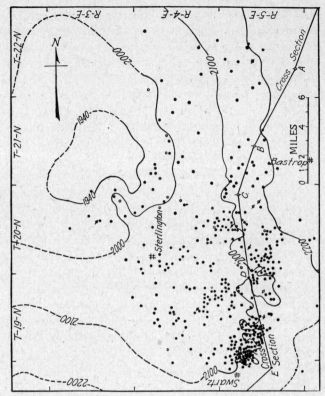

FIG. 244.—Map of Monroe gas field, Louisiana, with contours on top of the Nacatoch formation or "Monroe gas rock." Cross-section *ABCDE* is Fig. 245. Elevations on contours are below sea. (*After Wilson.*)

GENERALIZED SECTION OF FORMATION IN THE MONROE GAS FIELD
(*After Spooner*)

	Feet
Recent:	
River terraces and alluvium	0–100
Tertiary:	
Eocene:	
St. Maurice beds ⎫	
Sparta sand ⎬ Lower Claiborne	700–850
Cane River beds ⎭	
Wilcox formation, sand clay lignite	700–900
Midway formation, dark shales	400–500
Unconformity.	
Cretaceous:	
Gulf Series:	
Arkadelphia formation, chalky shale, chalk	150–200
Nacatoch formation (includes Monroe gas rock)	100–250
Unnamed sand and red clay, red clay shales. Include rocks	
of volcanic origin	300–1,000+
Unconformity.	
Comanche Series:	
Washita group ⎫	
Fredericksburg group ⎬ Undifferentiated	1,000+
Trinity group ⎭	

Richland.—The Richland[1] gas field, about 10 miles southeast of the Monroe field, was opened in 1926. It is 11 miles long or more and of

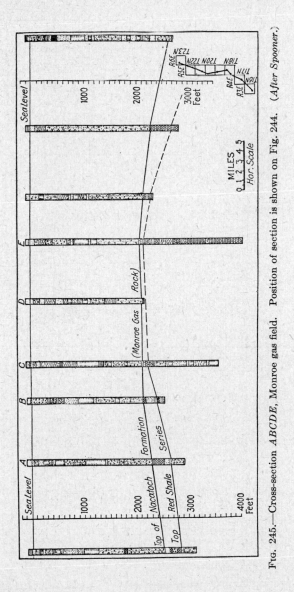

Fig. 245.—Cross-section *ABCDE*, Monroe gas field. Position of section is shown on Fig. 244. (*After Spooner.*)

unknown width. The chief gas is found at a depth of about 2,430 feet or more and comes from the base of the upper Cretaceous and at a domed unconformity between the Upper and Lower Cretaceous where the Lower

[1] Teas, L. P., "Petroleum Development and Technology in 1927," p. 671, 1928.

Cretaceous forms a buried hill. The gas carries about 125 gallons of
gasoline per 1,000,000 cubic feet.

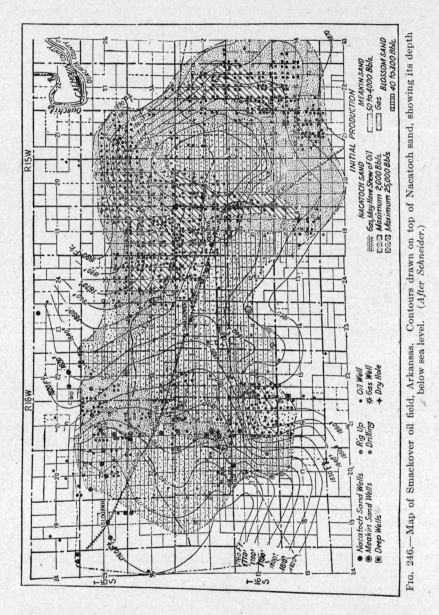

Fig. 246.—Map of Smackover oil field, Arkansas. Contours drawn on top of Nacatoch sand, showing its depth below sea level. (*After Schneider.*)

In western Richland Parish,[1] about 40 miles northeast of Urania,
a well in 1926 found gas in the Tertiary, probably Midway formation.

[1] Teas, L. P., *Oil Gas Jour.*, vol. 25, p. 125, Feb. 17, 1927.

Urania.—Urania[1] field is located 50 miles south of Monroe (Fig. 238) on the Angelina-Caldwell flexure, from 60 feet to 130 feet above sea. The field is 10 miles long and 3 miles wide and is near the towns of Urania and Tullos. A flowing well was brought in March 25, 1925, and to September, 1927, the field had produced 6,588,819 barrels of oil. Rocks of Eocene age crop out, and the top of the Wilcox sand, which produces the oil, is found about 1,500 feet deep. The field is located on a flat terrace 8 miles wide on the Angelina-Caldwell flexure. On this terrace there is a low anticline with a closure of 50 feet, and the oil is found in this fold, particularly in low domes superimposed upon it. The oil-producing horizon is an ancient erosion surface, as is shown by the irregularity of the producing sand. The oil has a gravity of 21.5° Bé. and is associated with a little gas and with salt water. The 1,450 contour marks the salt water level. Some of the oil is emulsified with water and is dehydrated before sale.

Smackover.—The Smackover field (Figs. 246, 247) is in south-central Arkansas about 10 miles north of El Dorado. The field is 12 miles long and 6 miles wide, and the productive area is about 55 square miles. It is divided into two areas, one east, the other west of the town of Smackover. Oil was discovered in May, 1922, when a gas well with an initial open flow of 30,000,000 cubic feet per day was drilled to the Nacatoch sand. In July of that year an oil well was brought in. The field rapidly developed into one

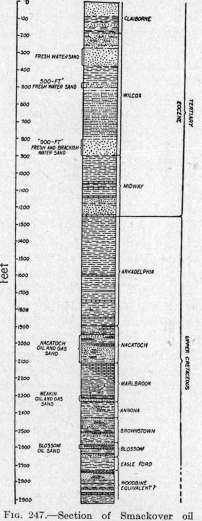

FIG. 247.—Section of Smackover oil field, Arkansas. (*After Schneider.*)

of the most productive oil and gas fields of North America.

The country is in the Coastal Plain and is underlain by Tertiary and Cretaceous rocks that dip about 20 feet per mile eastward. The oil and gas are produced from three sands: Nacatoch, Meakin, and Blossom.

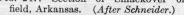

[1] SCHNEIDER, G. W., Urania Oil Field, LaSalle, Winn, and Grant Parishes, Louisiana, "Structure of Typical American Oil Fields," vol. 1, pp. 91–104, 1929.

The Nacatoch is 200 feet thick and consists of sand, shale, and gumbo with argillaceous limestone at the top of the formation. The sand is cleaner in the east part of the field than in the west part, where it consists chiefly of shale and gumbo with lenses of sand. About 95 per cent of the sands are quartz and about 5 per cent glauconite grains. The Meakin sand is 360 feet below the Nacatoch. It produces gas near Kenova and oil and gas in the west part of the Smackover field. It is 18 feet thick. The Blossom sand, 600 feet below the Nacatoch, is 10 feet thick or more and is overlain and underlain by shale. The oil in the Nacatoch is from 19 to 26° Bé., that in the Meakin is about 26° Bé., and in the Blossom is 17 to 20° Bé.

The structure of the Smackover field is shown by Fig. 246, in which the contours show the elevation of the top of the Nacatoch sand below sea level. The field occupies a structural nose on the east-dipping monocline. This nose is 13 miles long and 6 miles wide. At the east end of the nose, occupying nearly half the field, is a dome which Schneider[1] designates the Norphlet dome. West of that is the Kenova saddle and farther west the Louann structural terrace. The oil and gas cover essentially these three structures. The Nacatoch sand on the dome at the east end of the field is clean. At the top of the dome are gas wells with initial daily flows of 45,000,000 cubic feet and a pressure of 850 pounds per square inch. On the sides of the dome below the gas the sand carries oil, and some of the wells had initial production of about 25,000 barrels per day. The oil blanket met salt water on the north and east sides of the dome at a depth of 1910 feet below sea level and on the south side about 30 feet higher. West of the dome the Nacatoch sand is impure. It carries beds of gumbo, shale, and indurated sandstone in large amounts. The porous sands occur in lenses and pockets and the recovery of oil and gas is controlled by porosity of localized areas.

The Meakin sand is productive in the western part of the area. It is cleaner than the overlying Nacatoch. The oil and gas have accumulated in the higher part of the monocline and salt water underlies the oil blanket at a depth of about 2,150 feet below sea level.

The Blossom sand has been highly productive in the Smackover fields. The areas of production are indicated only in a general way on Fig. 246. Mt. Holly 5 miles west of Smackover field produces oil probably from the Tokio sand.

El Dorado.—The El Dorado[2] field is about 10 miles south of Smackover. A gas well with a flow of 40,000,000 cubic feet a day was brought

[1] SCHNEIDER, H. G., Smackover Oil Field, Ouachita and Union Counties, Arkansas, Am. Inst. Min. Eng. *Trans.*, vol. 70, pp. 1076–1099, 1924.

[2] HEALD, K. C., and W. W. RUBEY, El Dorado Field in Arkansas, Am. Assoc. Pet. Geol. *Bull.*, vol. 6, pp. 358–367, 1922.

CRIDER, A. F., The El Dorado Arkansas Oil Field and Its Relation to North Louisiana Structures, Am. Assoc. Pet. Geol. *Bull.*, vol. 6, pp. 193–198, 1922.

in in 1920, and the following year wells flowing 10,000 barrels of oil daily were drilled into the Nacatoch sand, which lies at a depth of 2,150 feet below surface. In August, 1921, the daily production reached 82,000 barrels. The oil has a gravity of 34.2° Bé. and contains 30 per cent gasoline. The rocks are nearly flat lying and are cut by northeast faults. The Nacatoch probably lies on a very flat dome, where the first gas well was brought in. The oil probably originated in the Marlbrook marl and moved from it into the Nacatoch sand above. The Nacatoch is 180 to 190 feet thick and consists of sandstone, gumbo, and shale. There are three pay streaks in the upper part of the sand and one 40 feet below the top of the sand yields most of the oil, although other lenses above and below are productive. In these pay streaks the oil is underlain by salt water over almost the entire field, and the water and sediment in the oil have caused many difficulties in operating wells.

Champagnolle is 12 miles northeast of El Dorado. In 1928 wells flowing about 300 barrels per day were drilled. The oil is found in lenses in the red bed or red shale formation at depths of about 3,153 feet.

In the Stephens[1] field, 15 miles west of the Smackover district, oil is found on a low structural nose that plunges southeast and is limited on the north by a fault. Oil and gas are found in the Buckrange (Blossom) sand, and gas is found in small amounts in the Nacatoch sand. The Buckrange sand lies about 2,100 feet deep, and the distribution of the oil in it depends mainly on the lenticular character of the sand rather than its structure.

The Irma[2] field is about 35 miles northwest of Smackover. The field was opened in 1921 when wells sunk about 1,200 feet encountered heavy black oil (14.4° A.P.I.). To September 1, 1927, the field had produced 1,878,478 barrels of oil. The country is an area of Tertiary strata that dip southeast at low angles. A normal fault exposed at the surface strikes N.60° E., dips northwest, and drops the northwest side about 400 feet. The beds are slightly arched along a low fold, and the axis of the fold is cut by the fault so that there is a closure of 50 feet at the fault plane, where the highest part of the reservoir is found. The oil occurs in the Nacatoch sand of Upper Cretaceous age and is developed in a belt parallel to and on the southeast side of the fault. Gas with an original pressure of 750 pounds per square inch is associated with the oil, and the oil rests on brackish water. Some 25 miles up dip the Nacatoch sand crops out, and, according to Teas, the salt water in the sand has been diluted by influx of ground water. The Midway black shale is a possible source of the oil. A parallel fault dipping southeast is found 2

[1] SPOONER, W. C., Stephens Oil Field, Columbus and Ouachita Counties, Arkansas, "Structure of Typical American Oil Fields," vol. 2, pp. 1–17, 1929.

[2] TEAS, L. P., Irma Oil Field, Nevada County, Arkansas, "Structure of Typical American Oil Fields," vol. 1, pp. 1–17, 1929.

GENERALIZED SECTION OF FORMATIONS IN THE STEPHENS FIELD ARKANSAS
(*After Spooner*)

System	Series	Group	Formation	Thickness, feet	Character
Tertiary	Eocene	Claiborne	Undifferentiated	300–400	Sand, sandy clay, and ferruginous sand and clay. Glauconitic sand at base
		Wilcox	Wilcox	550	Sand, sandy clay, and clay, lignitic. Non-marine
		Midway	Midway clay	500	Gray clay and shale. Lower 50 feet gray and dark blue shale
			Unconformity		
Cretaceous	Gulf series	Navarro	Arkadelphia	90–100	Dark shale, in part chalky
			Nacatoch sand	315	Sand, sandy shale, calcareous sandstone, sandy limestone, lower 100 feet gray shale
			Saratoga chalk	15–30	Gray and white chalk
		Taylor	Marlbrook marl	225	Gray marl and shale, in part chalky
			Annona chalk	30–50	White and bluish-gray chalk
			Ozan (Buckrange sand at base)	110	Gray shale and fine sandy shale. Buckrange sand 30 to 50 feet at the base
			Brownstown marl		Medium to dark gray shale and fine-textured sandy shale and sand
		Austin	Tokio	450	Gray shale, sandy shale, sand, glauconite, volcanic ash
			Woodbine sand		Arkosic sand with matrix of volcanic ash
			Unconformity Absent		
	Comanche series	Washita			
		Fredericksburg	Absent		
		Trinity	Glen Rose limestone	1,000–1,100	Gray shale, red and brown shale. Clayey limestone and sand
			Red sand and shale		Red shale and sand, light-colored fine sand

miles northwest of one which outlines the northwest side of the oil fields. In the Urbana field east of El Dorado wells sunk to the Nacatoch sand are reported to have initial flows as high as 35,000,000 cubic feet of gas.

Interior Salt Domes.—A group of salt domes is found on the east side of the Sabine uplift (Fig. 239). The Arcadia[1] dome, 50 miles east of

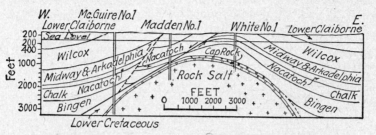

FIG. 248.—Cross-section of Arcadia salt dome. (*After Spooner.*)

Shreveport, is in an area of St. Maurice formation but the Arkadelphia outcrops above the dome. The cap rock and top of the salt plug have not been eroded. The dome (Fig. 248) is elongated and strikes northwest.

The Bistineau dome is 25 miles east of Shreveport and 12 miles southeast of Bellevue oil field. A saline[2] area with the salt incrusting the soil marks the surface. The surrounding area is covered by the Cane River or a younger formation and on the dome the Marlbrook crops out. The

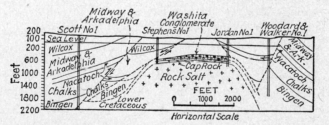

FIG. 249.—Cross-section of Vacherie salt dome showing faulting of sedimentary rocks around the salt core; the cap rock is anhydrite. (*After Spooner.*)

area of uplift is 3 miles in diameter and the amount of uplift 2,000 feet or more.

The Vacherie dome is 10 miles southeast of Bistineau dome. The long axis strikes northwest. The top is not removed by erosion and the cap rock consists of anhydrite 90 to 120 feet thick. The rocks above and around the dome are faulted (Fig. 249).

[1] SPOONER, W. C., Interior Salt Domes of Louisiana, Am. Assoc. Pet. Geol. *Bull.*, vol. 10, pp. 217–292, 1926.

[2] VEATCH, A. C., The Salines of Northern Louisiana, La. Geol. Survey Rept. 1902, *Special Paper* 2, pp. 81–89, 1902.

Prothro[1] dome is 25 miles southeast of Vacherie dome.   Cretaceous
rocks steeply dipping rise through the surrounding Eocene (St. Maurice),
which dips away from the Cretaceous.

Kings dome is 8 miles northwest of Prothro dome.   The Marlbrook is
brought up into a region of Cane River formation.   The area of uplift is 3
miles in diameter and the salt core is 172 feet deep.   The cap rock is about
50 feet thick and consists of gypsum and anhydrite.   Formations above
the cap rock are eroded.

Rayburn salt dome (Fig. 250) is 7 miles northeast of Prothro dome.
A central salt marsh is surrounded by low hills.   The steep core is overlain by cap rock 30 feet thick, consisting of calcite, gypsum, and anhydrite, and the latter by alluvium.   The top of the salt plug is eroded.

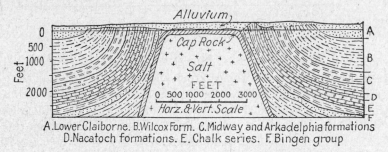

A.Lower Claiborne. B.Wilcox Form. C.Midway and Arkadelphia formations
D.Nacatoch formations. E. Chalk series. F. Bingen group

Fig. 250.—Cross-section Rayburn salt dome, Louisiana.   (*After Spooner.*)

Price dome is 12 miles south of Rayburn.   The uplift is about 2,000
feet and is marked by a salt lick.   No salt core is discovered.

At Drake dome, 6 miles southwest of Price dome, a central mound
a mile in diameter contains a marsh bordered by salt barrens.   The
top of the salt core lies 900 feet deep and is covered by a cap rock 600 feet
thick consisting of very porous limestone.   The cap rock becomes very
thin on the flanks of the dome.

Winnfield dome is 10 miles southeast of Drake.   A well on top of the
dome penetrated 990 feet of outcropping limestone cap rock and below
this drilled into the salt core.   The cap rock, according to Goldman, is
white limestone full of cavities, at places twisted, shattered, and faulted.

Cedar Creek dome is 6 miles east of Winnfield.   The cap rock lies
about 700 feet below the surface and consists of gray banded limestone,
like that at Winnfield.   The vertical uplift is probably 2,700 feet or
more.

Coochie Brake, 12 miles southwest of Winnfield, probably covers a
salt dome not yet proved.

[1] Hull, J. P. D., Prothro Salt Dome, Bienville Parish, Louisiana, Am. Assoc.
Pet. Geol. *Bull.*, vol. 9, pp. 904–906, 1925.

CHAPTER XIV

GULF COAST REGION

Eastern Texas and Louisiana are underlain by Mesozoic and Cenozoic rocks, which crop out as broad belts in which the younger rocks lie successively nearer the sea. The younger beds extend farther north in the region of the Mississippi River than east or west of it. Structurally the region has been characterized as a gently pitching trough with its axis lying along the river. The beds in general dip at very low angles, though locally they are sharply flexed.[1]

The country is approximately flat, and details of structure are derived principally from drilling. At many places low mounds or hills rise above the generally level plain. On some of these there are small lakes from which gas bubbles escape. Sulphur, sulphur dioxide, sulphuric acid, saline water, gas, oil, asphalt, or "paraffin dirt" are sought for as evidences of oil-bearing areas. These indications are found also at some places where there is no mound or rise of the land. Drilling has shown that cores of salt with petroliferous beds underlie many of the mounds or the other places where one or more of the indications noted above are present. The distribution of the salt domes is shown by Fig. 251. Many

---

[1] HARRIS, G. D., Oil and Gas in Louisiana, with a Brief Summary of Their Occurrence in Adjacent States, U. S. Geol. Survey *Bull.* 429, 1910.

FENNEMAN, N. M., Oil Fields of Texas and Louisiana Gulf Coastal Plain, U. S. Geol. Survey *Bull.* 282, 1906.

DEUSSEN, ALEXANDER, Geology and Underground Waters of the Southeastern Part of the Texas Coastal Plain, U. S. Geol. Survey *Water Supply Paper* 335, 1914.

VEATCH, A. C., Geology and Underground Water Resources of Northern Louisiana and Southern Arkansas, U. S. Geol. Survey *Prof. Paper* 46, 1906.

HAYES, C. W., and WILLIAM KENNEDY, Oil Fields of the Texas-Louisiana Gulf Coastal Plain, U. S. Geol. Survey *Bull.* 212, 1903.

KENNEDY, WILLIAM, Coastal Salt Domes, Southwestern Assoc. Pet. Geol. *Bull.*, vol. 1, pp. 34-59, 1917.

ELLISOR, A. E., and H. T. KNICKER, Subsurface Stratigraphy of the Coastal Plain of Texas and Louisiana, Am. Assoc. Pet. Geol. *Bull.*, vol. 9, pp. 79-122, 1925.

DEGOLYER, E., Origin of North American Salt Domes, Am. Assoc. Pet. Geol. *Bull.*, vol. 9, pp. 831-874, 1925.

———— and others, Geology of Salt Dome Oil Fields, Am. Assoc. Pet. Geol. pp. 1-797, 1926.

POWERS, S., Interior Salt Domes of Texas, Am. Assoc. Pet. Geol. *Bull.*, vol. 10, pp. 1-60, 1926.

SPOONER, W. C., Interior Salt Domes of Louisiana, Am. Assoc. Pet. Geol. *Bull.*, vol. 10, pp. 217-292 1926.

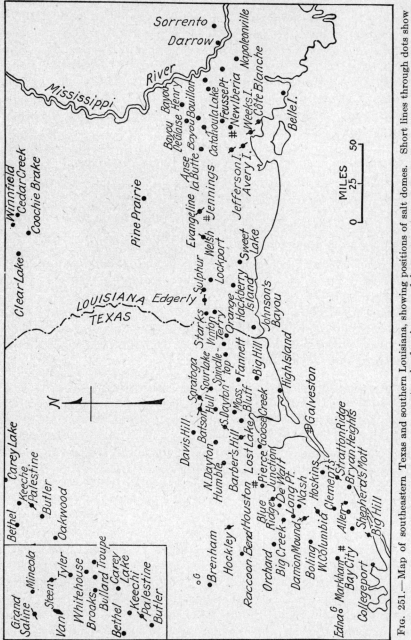

Fig. 251.—Map of southeastern Texas and southern Louisiana, showing positions of salt domes. Short lines through dots show trends of major axes of domes.

of the salt domes have been mined for salt. The rocks above some of them contain large deposits of sulphur, and the overlying beds and the beds near the domes have produced large amounts of oil and gas.

General Features of Salt Domes.—The salt masses rise at places within about 50 feet of the surface. At other places they are found 3,000 feet or more below the surface. In general the part of a dome developed has approximately the shape of the frustum of a steep cone. The domes extend downward to unknown depths, for, although some have been drilled for thousands of feet, the bases of the salt masses are not discovered. The tops of the salt masses are commonly one or two miles in diameter. Many of them are not truly conical, but their horizontal cross-sections are rudely elliptical, one axis being a little longer than the other.

The salt found in the domes is crystalline and some of it is nearly pure. At places, however, it contains considerable anhydrite and gypsum and in the salt of the dome of Avery Island a bed of quartzite with grains of quartz sand cemented by silica has been found. The salt of Avery Island consists of interbedded

FIG. 252.—Cross-section of core of sulphur, Big Hill, Matagorda County, Texas. (*After Wolf.*)

layers of dark- and light-colored salt, and these are folded by strong pressure so that the salt has taken on a schistose structure. The salt is in part at least of sedimentary origin, since in that of the Markham dome the remains of algae are found.

Above the salt in many of the domes are beds called the "cap rocks." They are from a few feet to several hundred feet thick. At some places they do not completely cover the salt masses but thin out near the edges. At other places they not only cover tops of the salt masses but extend down on the domes as a thimble covers the finger. The cap rock is composed of anhydrite, gypsum, limestone, and dolomite, and in six or more of the domes there are large deposits of sulphur associated with the limestone (Fig. 252). The cap-rock materials are generally crystalline. The anhydrite alters to form gypsum, and it is believed that the sulphur is derived from the sulphates. The limestone is very cavernous and consists in the main of crystalline calcite or dolomite. Oil and gas have accumulated at places in the porous limestone.

At Bryan Heights near Freeport, Texas, the sulphur-bearing beds are chiefly gypsum veined with sulphur. At Big Hill (Gulf), Texas, the top of the cap rock is a thin zone of porous limestone barren of sulphur, below which is a porous limestone high in sulphur, and below that is anhydrite. Residuary anhydrite is found in the sulphur-bearing zone. At Damon Mound the sulphur is below the limestone cap rock

Cenozoic Deposits of the Texas Coastal Plain
(*After Deussen*)

System	Series	Formation	Thickness, feet	Lithology and characteristic fossils	
Quaternary	Recent		0–50	Fluviatile deposits, consisting of brown, red, or black sandy clay or silt of the low, overflow terraces of the streams; flood-plain materials, including sand and gravel bars. Recent buffalo bones, etc. Seaward, these fluviatile deposits grade into interstream deposits consisting of yellow and blue clays and yellow wave-formed sand, sand and shell beaches, bars, and barriers, carrying *Rangia cuneata* and other fossils	
	Pleistocene	Beaumont clay	800 max.	Blue, calcareous clay, with numerous lime concretions about 1 inch through. Lenses of sand and sandy clay. The clays carry *Rangia cuneata*, etc.; embedded logs are common	Farther inland the Lissie gravel and Beaumont clay are represented along the stream valleys by the lowest and the middle of the three Pleistocene terraces
		Lissie gravel	Thin to 900	Gravels and coarse sands, with some small lenses and pockets of red clay in places; limy clays, gravels, and limy conglomerates or "adobe" in others. The fossils include *Equus semiplicatus*, Megalonyx, etc.	
		–Unconformity–			
		Highest Pleistocene terrace (farther inland)	0–50	Fluviatile deposits consisting of granitic gravels in and adjacent to certain drainage areas; flints, limestone débris, and limy conglomerates in others; ferruginous sands and silts, with fragments of iron ore, in still others. In the stream valleys these materials appear as terraces lying 200 to 225 feet above the level of the present stream channels, and grading laterally into an interstream or upland phase veneering the uplands with a sheet of gravel where the Yegua and Jackson formations constitute the country rock, but thinning and disappearing south of the Yegua-Catahoula or the Jackson-Catahoula boundary. No fossils	
Tertiary		–Unconformity–			
	Pliocene	Uvalde (late Pliocene)	0–100	Fluviatile deposits, consisting of flint gravel and limestone débris embedded in a clay matrix. In the plateau region west of the Coastal Plain the formation appears as the uppermost terrace of the major streams, lying about 350 feet above the levels of the present stream channels. Along the Cretaceous-Tertiary boundary, the terraces grade laterally into an upland gravel deposit, which caps the interstream areas, but thins and disappears a distance to east and south	

CENOZOIC DEPOSITS OF THE TEXAS COASTAL PLAIN.—(*Continued*)

System	Series	Formation	Thickness, feet	Lithology and characteristic fossils
Tertiary	Miocene	–Unconformity– Dewitt[1]	1,250–1,500	Lacustrine and littoral deposits, consisting of cross-bedded, coarse, gray, semi-indurated, highly calcareous sandstones. Lenses of clay in places. *Aceratherium* and other fossils. East of the Brazos these beds are almost completely overlapped by the Lissie gravel. Seaward, the time equivalent of the Dewitt formation is represented by about 800 feet of marine sands and clays, carrying *Arca carolinensis* and other upper Miocene marine fossils and believed to involve some of the lower Pliocene. These marine deposits do not outcrop and are not a part of the lacustrine Dewitt formation, which also includes some deposits of early Pliocene age
		Fleming clay	200–500	Palustrine deposits, consisting of gray, white, and bluish-white, bedded, calcareous clays, with numerous small concretions of lime and some lenses of sand
	Oligocene	–Unconformity– Catahoula sandstone	500–800	Littoral deposits, consisting of hard, blue, semi-quartzitic, noncalcareous sandstones, with interbedded lenticular masses of green clays
	Eocene	Jackson	0–250	Marine deposits, consisting of calcareous blue clays, with large limestone concretions. Carry *Levifusus branneri* and other Eocene forms
		Claiborne group — Yegua	375–750	Palustrine deposits, consisting of green clays with concretions of selenite; in places, lenses of sand and lignite
		Claiborne group — Cook Mountain	400	Palustrine and marine deposits, consisting of lenticular masses of yellow sand and clay; in places, lenses of green calcareous, glauconitic, fossiliferous marl. Beds of limonite and lignite. Some of the clays carry fossiliferous calcareous concretions. Formation as a whole is decidedly ferruginous. Fossils: *Ostrea sellaeformis*, *Ostrea divaricata*, *Anomia ephippioides*, and others
		Claiborne group — Mount Selman	350	Palustrine and marine deposits, consisting of red, ferruginous, indurated, and probably altered green sand, with casts of shells, lenses of lignite and clay, beds and concretions of limonite. The formation as a whole is conspicuously ferruginous. Carries casts of *Venericardia planicosta*
	Eocene	Wilcox	800–1,100	Palustrine, marine, and littoral deposits. The littoral deposits comprise the Queen City sand member, at the top of the formation, consisting of 50 to 200 feet of white, porous, loose, water-bearing sands, with some interstratified clays. The palustrine deposits consist of lenticular masses of sand, clay, and lignite, carrying large, especially characteristic concretions (20 to 30 feet in diameter) of hard flintlike sandstone; the palustrine clays are leaf bearing, and in places carry teeth of *Crocodylus grypus*. The marine deposits consist of calcareous, glauconitic, fossiliferous marls, alternating with beds of sand, clay, and lignite; they are exposed only on Sabine River. Characteristic fossils of the marine phase are *Kellia prima*, *Natica aperta*, and *Pleurotoma silicata*
		Midway	250–500	Marine deposits, consisting of black and blue clays with interbedded strata of limestone and some lenses of sand, which are somewhat rare north of the Brazos. *Plejona limopsis*, *Enclimatoceras ulrichi*, and other fossils

[1] What is here called the Dewitt formation is probably represented along the Sabine by the beds described as the Fleming clay.

and extends downward to near the top of the salt core.   It is disseminated in pores of gypsum and anhydrite which the sulphur replaces in part.

In the Sulphur dome, Louisiana (Fig. 253) the sulphur is in porous cavernous limestone of the cap.   In this dome, according to Kelley, sulphur is present only where calcium sulphates contain considerable lime carbonate, or where the lime rock passes downward into anhydrite. A series of sections from the core of a hole drilled to salt on Sulphur dome, Louisiana, was studied by Goldman.[1]   The anhydrite bed is believed to be of sedimentary origin.   Part of the anhydrite bed contains breccia fragments of a banded finer grained anhydrite.   The upper part of the anhydrite bed is altered to gypsum, veined, and almost completely

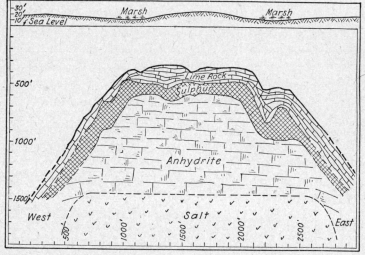

Fig. 253.—Cross-section Sulphur salt dome, Sulphur, Louisiana. (*After Kelley.*)

replaced by calcite, the intensity of replacement increasing upward.   The calcite cap, which rests on the anhydrite-gypsum bed, is believed to be an alteration or replacement of the upper part of the anhydrite and gypsum cap, as is also the sulphur which is characteristically associated with the calcite.   The alteration of calcium sulphate rock to calcite and sulphur is believed to have resulted through the agency of hydrocarbons, which are present in adjacent beds.   Although the field relations strongly indicate that the gypsum through the agency of hydrocarbons has altered to sulphur or to sulphur and calcite, this alteration has not been accomplished in the laboratory at any temperature which has probably prevailed in the alteration of the salt dome cap rocks.   The work of Bastin[2] suggests that bacteria may play a part in the alteration.

[1] GOLDMAN, M. I., Petrography of Salt Dome Cap Rock, Am. Assoc. Pet. Geol. *Bull.*, vol. 9, pp. 42–78, 1925.

[2] BASTIN, E. S., and others, The Problem of the Natural Reduction of Sulphates, Am. Assoc. Pet. Geol. *Bull.*, vol. 10, pp. 1270–1299, 1926.

———, and F. E. GREER, Am. Assoc. Pet. Geol. *Bull.*, vol. 14, pp. 153–159, 1930.

DeGolyer and certain other students of the salt domes believe that the cap rock materials represent residuary matter that has accumulated through dissolution of the salt. This theory is supported by certain gypsum caps above the salt domes of Germany. Salt is more soluble than anhydrite, gypsum, and calcite. This solution would go on through the agency of ground water which would attack the tops and also the edges of the salt masses. Moreover, certain of the domes seem to have been thrust above the surface of the ground in former geologic times and to have been partly dissolved and eroded. They were subsequently buried under later sediments. This would give further opportunity for the accumulation of the less soluble materials above the salt.

The cap rock at Damon Mound,[1] which is a plug that has been eroded, is covered with unconsolidated beds 68 feet deep or more. The cap is 375 to 575 feet thick above the center of the salt plug. It thins to nothing on the sides. It is composed of an upper layer of limestone 10 to 150 feet thick, and below that a layer, chiefly anhydrite, below which is one mainly of gypsum. The three materials, however, are very irregular in occurrence and poorly sorted. Crystals of sulphur, pyrite, calcite, and barite are common in the cavernous cap material, and a valuable deposit of sulphur is developed midway between limestone and salt. The arrangement of the materials, calcite, anhydrite, gypsum, and salt, is in the order of their solubilities, the least soluble being near the surface. If the calcite remained at the top because the more soluble sulphates and chlorides were removed, this supports the theory that the cap is a residuary deposit. In certain other domes, however, the order is calcite, gypsum, anhydrite, and salt. In these anhydrite is probably altering to gypsum.

In a few of the domes the limestone cap is several hundred feet thick, and there is little else above the salt. It is not unlikely that some of the limestones of the caps are true beds and that in the upthrust of certain of the salt masses, associated shales, muds, and sands were squeezed out, leaving the more consolidated limestone intact. The belief that the limestones of some of the cap rocks are true sedimentary beds is supported also by the occurrence of unconsolidated limestone or marl, and of dense limestone which at places, according to Deussen,[2] grades into the secondary limestone or calcite.

Drilling for oil has shown that the rocks dip away from the salt plugs at all angles. In general the beds are poorly consolidated except the older beds and sands and limestones. At places they are faulted. As a salt plug rose it forced itself through the overlying beds. Some of these

[1] BEVIER, G. M., Am. Assoc. Pet. Geol. *Bull.*, vol. 9, pp. 505–535, 1925.

[2] DEUSSEN, A., Geology of the Coastal Plain of Texas West of Brazos River, U. S. Geol. Survey *Prof. Paper* 126, p. 129, 1924.

beds rose from great depths along with the salt, particularly the more competent layers.   These were squeezed past the softer more yielding beds above them.   This process of by-pass and of thinning of incompetent beds (diapirism) is a common feature of domes of central Europe and is shown in many of the oil fields that are located on salt domes.

In many of the areas of the salt domes oil is discovered.   The oil is accumulated in the porous cap rock, in sands above the cap rock, and in sands around the domes in reservoirs where the tops of the beds are sealed.   These beds may be sealed against salt or where they rest against beds that were thrust up with the salt and passed by the reservoir rocks. The oil-bearing rocks are of Tertiary age.

As a rule the beds around a salt core are little affected at the surface 2 or 3 miles or less away from the center of the domed area.   It is not known whether the areas affected in depth are larger, but that seems probable.   The wells drilled around the domes are generally too close to the cores to show whether that is true or not, but if the folding involved only a small area in depth, it would appear improbable that beds sealed up dip by the salt plug and associated material would be highly productive on all sides of the salt plug.   Where the beds dip away from the salt domes, the gathering grounds supplying oil are generally greater than on sides where the regional dip is toward the domes.   At such places movement of oil would be up dip away from the dome.   The regional dip is south and in general the south sides of the domes are more productive than the north sides.   At Spindletop and Markham the greater part of the production is on the southwest sides of the domes.   At Boling the chief production is on the west side, but recently wells have been brought in on the east side of the dome.   At Humble there is large production on the east, south, and north sides of the dome, and at West Columbia oil is found on the northwest as well as on the southeast sides of the dome. At Damon Mound oil is found on the north and southwest sides of the dome.   Altogether there is larger production on the south, west, and east sides of the domes than on the north sides, yet at places there is no very striking predominance of oil on the southeast sides in the direction of the regional dip.   If, as seems probable, there is a direct relation between the gathering areas and amounts of accumulations, the areas of quaquaversal folding probably increase appreciably with depth.

Harris[1] as early as 1910 noted that certain of the salt domes were arranged in belts that are parallel to the Balcones fault.   Since his paper appeared other domes have been found, and some of the domes have been developed so that the positions of their longer axes are known. This work supports Harris' view that there are lines of domes parallel

[1] HARRIS, G. D., Oil and Gas in Louisiana, U. S. Geol. Survey *Bull*. 429, pp. 1–192, 1910.

to the Balcones fault. They are not straight lines, but they are probably narrow zones of deformation. Some of the domes in these narrow zones lie with their longer axes in the direction of the trend, but others seem to cross the trend nearly at right angles. There are clearly structural lines striking northeast parallel to the Balcones fault and other lines striking northwest.

A line drawn from Brenham dome to Butler will pass near Palestine, Keechi, and Brooks domes. The long axis of Palestine dome strikes northeast nearly parallel to the line, but the axis of Steen dome is across the line. This line of domes is nearly parallel to the Balcones fault, as is pointed out by Deussen, Pratt, Powers, and others.

The best defined line of domes in the Texas Gulf group is one which extends 85 miles north-northeast from the Gulf and includes from southwest to northeast Bryan Heights, Stratton Ridge, Hoskins, Goose Creek, Barbers Hill, South Dayton, and Batson. These domes are not only approximately in line but, some of them are long ellipses with their longer axes striking nearly in line with the line of domes. This suggests that the domes are on a general northeast fold. The Bryan Heights dome is circular; Stratton Ridge strikes N. 55° E; the axis of Goose Creek fold is not determined; Barbers Hill strikes northwest; South Dayton strikes N. 30° E. Thus it appears that some of the salt domes lie on tectonic lines parallel to the Balcones fault.

The Five Islands, near the Gulf Coast in Louisiana, are essentially in line and have long been regarded as controlled by a fissure or a fold. Vaughn contoured the tops of the salt masses in most of these islands. While in general the tops of the salt cores strike northwest, the agreement with the tectonic line is not exact. The tops of the salt plugs have probably been modified by solution since the plugs were raised, and in some cases this may have materially changed the contours of the upper surfaces of the domes. There is, however, a fairly close agreement with the elongation of the salt plugs that are known to be elliptical in horizontal cross-sections, and the tectonic lines that have been assumed to control the distribution of the domes.

Origin of the Salt Domes.—When the salt domes were first discovered, their peculiar shapes, resembling certain igneous stocks and plugs, led certain investigators to the belief that the salt plugs also were of igneous origin. Later Harris proposed the theory that they had formed by precipitation of salt in fissures and that the force of crystallization had thrust up the overlying beds. As the domes were developed these hypotheses were generally discarded, and it is now believed that the salt plugs are parts of salt beds thrust up from an underlying stratum of salt, probably of Lower Cretaceous or Permian age. In the process of folding the salt bed was probably thickened at the crests of anticlines.

Balcones   Mexia Zone   Salt   Tertiary and Upper Cretaceous   Lower Cretaceous   Salt

MILES
0 5 10 15 20 25 30 35 40 45 50

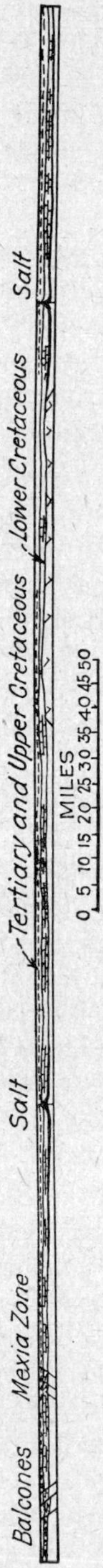

FIG. 254.—Ideal geologic section across region of interior salt domes of Texas and of Louisiana, showing formation of salt cores by upfolds of thick salt beds. Vertical and horizontal scale are same. (*Based on a section by Powers*).

In Germany and in Roumania[1] thick anticlines of salt are developed, and some of them have been explored below the salt.

The Gulf Coast domes are not elongated anticlines like certain of the salt anticlines of Europe, but are approximately conical in shape, probably because the bed was folded as a result of stresses that were relieved in two directions, and in some of them it is probable that the axes of deformation crossed. Salt flows readily under pressure.[2] The domes were deformed throughout a long period. The salt plugs were lifted and some were eroded more than once, as is shown by unconformities in beds surrounding them and by fossils of earlier beds worked over and deposited in later beds. It is believed by some that certain plugs have continued to rise almost to the present day, for tilted beds of Recent rocks are found above them, and some of the mounds of unconsolidated easily eroded rocks above the domes reflect the shapes of the tops of the underlying salt cores.

The salt domes of the United States include those of the Interior group of Louisiana and Texas, the Gulf Coast domes of Louisiana and Texas, and the domes of eastern Utah and western Colorado. The Interior group of Texas and Louisiana includes about 30 domes. Most of these domes have been drilled for oil, but, with a few exceptions, thus far they appear to be essentially barren. Several of the domes have been exploited for salt. None of the group has been worked for sulphur. The Interior domes in Louisiana are located in a belt that strikes northwest and on the west side of a syncline between the Sabine and the Monroe uplifts. The domes of Texas are in a belt that strikes northeast between the Balcones fault and Sabine uplift. The beds thicken in the synclines, and the domes rise through the beds, probably along faults. These relations are indicated by Fig. 254. The maximum upthrust is about a mile, as indicated by the positions of beds that have

[1] STILLE, H., The Upthrust of Salt Masses of Germany, Am. Assoc. Pet. Geol. *Bull.*, vol. 9, pp. 417–441, 1925.

VAN DE GRACHT, W. A. I. M. van W. The Saline Domes of Northwestern Europe, Am. Assoc. Pet. Geol. *Bull.*, vol. 1, pp. 85–92, 1917.

ROGERS, G. S., Intrusive Origin of Gulf Coast Salt Domes, *Econ. Geol.*, vol. 13, pp. 447–485, 1918.

[2] ADAMS, F. D., An Experimental Investigation into the Action of Differential Pressure on Certain Minerals and Rocks, *Jour. Geol.*, vol. 18, p. 489, 1910.

been raised to the surface on the sides of the domes. The actual upthrust is probably greater, for the central salt core appears to have moved up more than the adjoining sedimentary rocks, and the older rocks near the core have been squeezed upward by the force of the rising salt mass, so that they have passed by younger rocks that lie on the side farther away from the salt. The process of by-pass and squeezing gives the kind of arm-in-sleeve structure already noted.

The beds dip away from the salt cores at angles that decrease gradually from the cores outward. The normal core is about 1 to 1½ miles in diameter, and the area of quaquaversal dips around the core is about 4 miles in diameter. With a few exceptions the salt plugs of the Coast group have been thrust above the surface of the earth and peneplanation has removed the tops of the cores along with the upturned sedimentary rocks surrounding it. Where the cores did not reach the present surface, the beds above the cores are probably thinned out by pressure. Complicated faulting is generally shown in the rocks above the domes and on their sides. The age of the salt bodies of the Gulf area is not known. At South Liberty (South Dayton) Texas, Upper Cretaceous rocks are found above the salt and below the limestone cap rock.[1] The production of the Gulf Coast area in 1928 amounted to 47,070,650 barrels of oil.[2]

LOUISIANA COAST

The Five Islands include Jefferson Island, Avery Island, Weeks Island, Côte Blanche, and Belle Isle. They constitute a group of mounds in southwestern Louisiana that form a chain that extends from Jefferson Island, 10 miles west of New Iberia, southeast to the Gulf. These islands rise 100 feet or more above a marshy flat, and each marks the surface above a great salt dome which has thrust up the mound. A little oil has been found at Belle Isle, but no production is developed in any of the islands. They afford, however, the best opportunity for investigation of the salt cores, since salt mines are opened in them, and they supply convincing data on the origin of the salt domes. The salt of Avery Island shows bands highly contorted by flowage, and the salt includes a red sandstone shattered during the process of flowage. The domes are believed to have been thrust up thousands of feet, and the period of upthrust did not end until Recent time, since, at Belle Isle, Recent fossils are found above the salt in beds dipping 25 degrees. The high dips, however, may be due in part to slumping of beds over places where salt was dissolved. None of the islands shows elevated beaches. In the salt plugs of this group only one is known to have a considerable cap rock. At Belle Isle the salt is impure and carries con-

[1] MORRISON, T. E., Am. Assoc. Pet. Geol. *Bull.*, vol. 13, p. 1065, 1929.
[2] BOWMAN, W. F., and J. M. VETTER, Texas-Louisiana Gulf Coast operations in 1928, "Petroleum Development and Technology, 1928–1929," New York, 1930.

siderable anhydrite, gypsum, and beds of limestone. These materials have accumulated at the top of the dome by the solution of salt, and thus the cap rock was formed as a residuary deposit. Jefferson, Avery, and Weeks islands have pure salt, and, according to Vaughn,[1] the caps are wanting or very thin.

Some of the salt plugs have probably been exposed to surface erosion, and the overlying anhydrite accumulated as a relatively insoluble residuary blanket, which was subsequently submerged and buried under sands and gravels, but the general absence or scarcity of rounded bodies of limestone, anhydrite, or gypsum in the material above the domes suggests that in many instances, at least, the solution of salt took place through the agency of ground water when the cap rock and salt were below the surface of the earth.

The New Iberia[2] salt dome lies east of the axis of the Five Islands and 5 miles east of the town of New Iberia. Escaping gas and "paraffin" beds led to drilling the field. Salt was found at 800 feet and a little oil was developed. The salt mass has no typical cap rock.

The Evangeline[3] or Jennings oil field, 7 miles northeast of Jennings, is marked by a depression 10 feet above sea level which adjoins a low mound 32 feet above sea. Gas escaped from the mound. The rocks at the surface are Pleistocene sands and clays; in depth Tertiary rocks are found. The doming of the area is between 300 and 500 feet. The dome is a very short ellipse and the long axis of the main productive area strikes west of north nearly in line with the axis of the Five Islands. The wells pass through clays containing beds of sand and some of them end in a porous limestone at about 2,100 feet which may be the cap rock of a salt plug, although no salt is discovered. The main productive zone is a series of fine sands at depths between 1,700 and 1,900 feet. The Evangeline field is one of the largest fields of the Gulf Coast group in Louisiana. To 1923 the total production was 46,000,000 barrels of oil.

At Anse Le Butte, about 40 miles east of Evangeline dome, a salt dome lies 260 feet below the surface. Some oil was found and a salt mine was opened on the dome.

Catahoula, or Section 28 salt dome,[4] 8 miles northeast of St. Martinville, is marked by gas seeps and "paraffin dirt." A well drilled in 1918

[1] VAUGHN, F. E., The Five Islands, Louisiana, Am. Assoc. Pet. Geol. *Bull.*, vol. 9, pp. 756–797, 1925.

[2] DEUSSEN, A., Review of the Developments in the Gulf Coast Country, Am. Assoc. Pet. Geol. *Bull.*, vol. 2, pp. 16–37, 1918.

[3] BARTON, D. C., and R. H. GOODRICH, The Jennings Oil Field, Acadia, Louisiana, Am. Assoc. Pet. Geol. *Bull.*, vol. 10, pp. 72–92, 1926.

   HARRIS, G. D., Oil and Gas in Louisiana, U. S. Geol. Survey *Bull.* 429, pp. 50–97, 1910.

[4] DONOGHUE, D., Section 28 Salt Dome, St. Martin Parish, Louisiana, Am. Assoc. Pet. Geol. *Bull.*, vol. 9, pp. 1290–1293, 1925.

found a showing of oil at 900 feet and salt at 1,250 feet, which continued to the bottom of the hole at 2,500 feet.   No cap rock was found.

Bayou Bouillon, northeast of Catahoula and 15 miles northeast of St. Martinville, is marked by inflammable gas boiling from the bayou, and by "paraffin dirt" on its banks.   The gas led to drilling, which outlined a conical salt dome.[1]   The dome in 1928 produced about 217,600 barrels of oil.

Pine Prairie[2] salt dome, north of Evangeline, is marked by an outcrop of limestone which is the cap rock of the dome.   A well drilled on the west flank of the dome in 1912 yielded oil having an initial flow estimated to be 1,000 barrels a day, but later wells were small.   The limestone cap rock is 520 feet thick and about a mile in diameter.   The beds involved are Oligocene to Pliocene in age.

Welch[3] field, 20 miles west of Evangeline, occupies a low structural dome, the longer axis striking east of north.   The surface rocks are Beaumont clays below which are Lafayette gravels, and below the Lafayette are Pliocene sands and clays.   The oil is heavy 11 to 19° Bé., and occurs at depths of about 1,000 feet near the top of the dome in the Pliocene sands.   No salt core has been discovered.

The Sulphur[4] salt dome, 13 miles west of Lake Charles, is marked by a low ridge, below which is the circular top of a salt core.   The top (Fig. 253) has an area of little more than 75 acres and is almost circular in plan.   The cap is about 1,000 feet thick and consists of an anhydrite mass with a thin lime carbonate covering, and between the two is a transition zone rich in sulphur.   The deposit is worked by the Union Sulphur Company, using the Frasch process, and has yielded 9,000,000 tons of sulphur having a value of $150,000,000.   A heavy oil and also gas were found in some of the sulphur wells and oil is developed on the sides of the salt core.

The wells sunk to the cap pass through 250 feet of Beaumont clays and, below these, Lafayette gravels.   These gravels are upthrust very little, if any, and are thicker around the dome than above it, suggesting that the cap of the dome was exposed to erosion before Lafayette time. Kelley states that sulphur is present only where the calcium sulphates are high in calcium carbonate, or where the lime rock passes downward into anhydrite.

[1] DONOGHUE, D., The Bayou Bouillon Salt Dome, St. Martin Parish, Louisiana, Am. Assoc. Pet. Geol. *Bull.*, vol. 9, pp. 1283–1289, 1925.

[2] BARTON, D. C., Pine Prairie Salt Dome, Am. Assoc. Pet. Geol. *Bull.*, vol. 9, pp. 738–755, 1925.

[3] REED, L. C., The Welch, Louisiana, Oil Field, Am. Assoc. Pet. Geol. *Bull.*, vol. 9, pp. 464–477, 1925.

[4] KELLEY, P. K., Sulphur Salt Dome, Louisiana, Am. Assoc. Pet. Geol. *Bull.*, vol. 9, pp. 479–496, 1925.

The Edgerly oil field, Louisiana, is ½ mile north of Edgerly. It is in a featureless plain and is marked by "paraffin dirt" and seeps of hydrogen sulphide gas. The oil field is an oval 5,000 feet long and 1,400 feet wide, with the long axis striking east almost in line with Starks, Sulphur, and Welch. The field is broken by many small faults.[1] The oil lies in several Pliocene sands at depths between 2,700 and 3,100 feet and some parts of the field have yielded 55,000 barrels of oil per acre. No salt core is discovered. The average daily yield for the week ended May 26, 1928, was 1,198 barrels.

The Lockport dome, southeast of Sulphur, is one of the most productive salt domes in Louisiana, having a daily yield in May, 1928, of about 3,900 barrels of oil. The Starks salt dome,[2] was discovered in 1925 by seismograph methods. Wells about 4,300 feet deep on the north side of the structure are productive. These are flowing wells averaging about 900 barrels of relatively high-gravity oil. A 33-foot bed, with sulphur, was met at a depth of 1,639 feet. At Vinton, 15 miles southwest of Edgerly, cap rock is met at 500 feet in depth and salt at 1,000 feet. Oil and gas in large amounts are found in several sands at depths between 2,100 and 3,000 feet. In 1928 the field had a daily production of over 4,500 barrels of oil. At Johnson Bayou seeps of sulphur gas led to the discovery of a little oil. In east Louisiana, Sorrento yields oil.

At Hackberry,[3] southeast of Vinton, the cap rock is 1,580 feet deep. This field in May, 1928, was producing about 2,700 barrels daily. A small production of oil is developed at Sweet Lake, east of Hackberry. At Kelso Bayou dome, east of Hackberry, a well yielding 500 barrels of oil a day was brought in at a depth of 3,925 feet in 1928. Five successful completions had been made in this field May 11, 1928. The oil is heavy with a gravity of 22° Bé.

TEXAS COAST

At Bryan Heights,[4] Freeport, south of Houston near the Gulf Coast, a mound rises 25 feet above sea level and 23 feet above the surrounding area of Quaternary rocks. A well sunk 900 feet brought in an initial flow of 6,000,000 cubic feet of gas, mainly hydrogen sulphide. Subsequent drilling revealed the circular top of a salt core with an area of 300 acres and surrounding Tertiary beds dipping away from the core. The cap rock contains large deposits of sulphur worked by the Freeport Sulphur Company. Wells above the cap pass through 300 feet of

[1] MINOR, H. E., The Edgerly Oil Field, Louisiana, Am. Assoc. Pet. Geol. *Bull.*, vol. 9, pp. 497–505, 1925.

[2] WILLIAMS, H., *Oil Gas Jour.*, pp. 184–185 (map), Sept. 29, 1927.

[3] LOGAN, J., *Oil Weekly*, vol. 49, p. 45, May 11, 1928.

[4] KENNEDY, W., The Bryan Heights Salt Dome, Brazoria County, Texas, Am. Assoc. Pet. Geol. *Bull.*, vol. 9, pp. 613–625, 1925.

Quaternary clays, 400 to 500 feet of Miocene sands and clays to the cap, which is about 250 feet thick. The cap includes 175 feet or more of porous limestone, gypsum, anhydrite, and sulphur, carrying hot sulphur water and hydrogen sulphide. Below the sulphur-bearing zone is one 75 feet thick of limestone with pyrite, gypsum, and sandstone but without

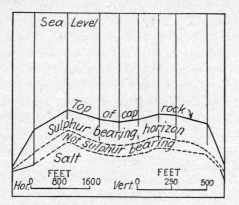

FIG. 255.—Geologic cross-section of Bryan Heights sulphur field, Texas. Bryan Heights salt dome. (*After Kennedy.*)

deposits of sulphur. The sulphur-bearing beds are mainly gypsum veined with sulphur, and at places water worn pebbles of barite are present. In the richer parts of the deposits sulphur constitutes 10 to 50 per cent of the mass (Fig. 255).

Stratton Ridge[1] salt dome (Fig. 256) is 7 miles north of Freeport, Texas, and midway between Hoskins Mound and Bryan Heights. It is marked by a low dome and gas seeps. Drilling has discovered a salt

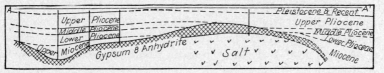

FIG. 256.—Section through Stratton Ridge salt dome, Texas. Cross-lined beds are gypsum and anhydrite. (*After Applin.*)

core with an elliptical top, 2 miles long, striking N. 25° E., which has a gypsum and anhydrite cap. Tertiary beds including the Miocene dip away from the core, and their truncated edges are overlain by Pliocene beds. Most of the deformation took place between the Oligocene and upper Pliocene time. Some oil has been found.

At Hoskins Mound, northeast of Stratton Ridge, salt lies at 1,250 to 1,750 feet below the surface. Shallow wells found oil and gas. The cap rock contains sulphur.

[1] APPLIN, P. L., The Stratton Ridge Salt Dome, Brazoria County, Texas, Am. Assoc. Pet. Geol. *Bull.*, vol. 9, pp. 1–34, 1925.

Goose Creek[1] oil field is 25 miles east of Houston.   The country is flat and is marked by gas seeps and paraffin beds. In 1908 a well was completed at 1,600 feet yielding 800 barrels of oil a day.   Development was slow until 1916, when a well at 2,030 feet brought in oil flowing at a rate of 10,000 barrels a day.   In 1925 the field had produced 50,000,000 barrels, and in May, 1928, the field had a daily production of 7,106 barrels.   The rocks encountered in Goose Creek (Fig. 257) wells are Recent, Pliocene, Miocene, and Oligocene.   These include surface sands; blue, red, and brown clays with interbedded water sands; red and pink shale and clays with brackish water sands, in which the salt water content increases with depth; dark shales and gumbo with closely spaced sand lenses.   The beds, including the Pliocene, are gently arched, and the productive area is near the top of the fold.   Oil was encountered at a

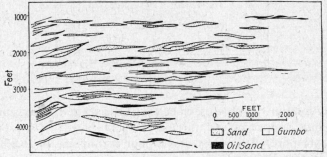

FIG. 257.—Geologic cross-section of Goose Creek oil field, Harris County, Texas.   (*After Minor.*)

depth of 1,000 feet, but the main production is found at depths between 2,200 and 4,500 feet.   It is a heavy green oil 22 to 27° Bé. and has the odor of cedar.   No cap rock or salt plug is discovered.   Since the field was developed the surface has subsided 2.7 feet above the area where the oil was removed.   This is probably due to slumping above sands that are readjusted into a closer system of packing, due to removal of oil, gas, and water.

Barbers Hill,[2] 11 miles northeast of Goose Creek, rises 45 feet above the surrounding country.   Gas seeps, sulphur water, and paraffin dirt are found near the hill.   The cap rock is found at a depth of 350 feet and is 850 feet thick near the center of the dome.   It is made up of anhydrite, gypsum, and limestone, which occur in confused relations, although, in general, the limestone is near the top, gypsum below limestone, and anhydrite below gypsum.   Some sulphur is present.   The long axis of the dome strikes northwest.   The surrounding sediments

[1] MINOR, H. E., Goose Creek Oil Field, Harris County, Texas, Am. Assoc. Pet. Geol. *Bull.*, vol. 9, pp. 286–297, 1925.
[2] BEVIER, G. M., The Barbers Hill Oil Field, Chambers County, Texas, Am. Assoc. Pet. Geol. *Bull.*, vol. 9, pp. 958–973, 1925.

dip about 45 degrees away from the dome and are displaced by circum-
ferential step faults with downthrow on the sides of faults away from the
dome.   Wells are sunk to the Oligocene on the south side of the dome.
The oil is found in the cap rock and in overlying sand lenses.   The
productive area is small and lies on the southwest side of the dome.

The South Dayton[1] salt dome (Fig. 258) is on Trinity River, 38
miles northeast of Houston.   A salt core comes within 500 feet of the

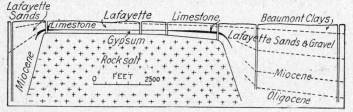

FIG. 258.—Geologic cross-section of South Dayton salt dome, Texas.   (*After Bowman.*)

surface.   The long axis strikes N. 30° E.   The Lafayette is raised 500
feet and older formations more than that.   The cap rock is 150 to 260
feet thick and consists of gypsum and anhydrite with a thin capping of
limestone, at places 40 feet thick, at the top of the cap.   A well on the
northeast flank of the dome, drilled in 1924, brought in an initial daily
flow of 500 barrels of oil, 22° Bé.

Batson[2] oil field, 1 mile north of Batson and 6 miles west of Saratoga,
is marked by a slight rise of the surface and by paraffin dirt.   Samples

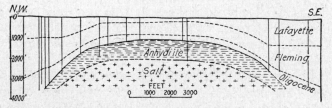

FIG. 259.—Geologic cross-section of Batson oil field, Texas.   (*After Sawtelle.*)

of the latter submitted to a chemist in Beaumont and reported to carry
paraffin led to the drilling of the field which, to 1925, had produced
32,000,000 barrels of oil.   An elliptical salt plug, with its longer axis
striking west-northwest, is capped by anhydrite above which are found
Oligocene, Fleming, and Lafayette formations (Fig. 259).   The anhydrite
rises to within 1,081 feet of the surface.   The oil comes from the cap
rock and from sands drilled on the southwest side of the dome.   Some

[1] BOWMAN, W. F., The South Dayton Salt Dome, Liberty County, Texas, Am.
Assoc. Pet. Geol. *Bull.*, vol. 9, pp. 655–666, 1925.

[2] SAWTELLE, G., The Batson Oil Field, Hardin County, Texas, Am. Assoc. Pet.
Geol. *Bull.*, vol. 9, pp. 1277–1282, 1925.

of the wells had initial flows of 10,000 barrels daily. The oil in the main is heavy, although it ranges from 14.6 to 40° Bé.

At Saratoga[1] oil field the surface is nearly flat and marked by sour water, sulphur water, gas seeps, and asphaltic material. The field has been known as a health resort since an early date, and shallow wells sunk in 1895 produced a little oil. After Spindletop was developed (1901), Saratoga was actively drilled, and in 1905 the annual production had reached nearly 3,000,000 barrels. The rocks of the district are as follows:

	Feet
Pleistocene:	
Columbia sands. Gray sands, gray and brown mottled clays........	100–150
Pliocene:	
Lafayette sands and gravels locally, sandstones, fresh water.........	400–1,300
Miocene:	
Fleming equivalent, blue gumbo, shales and sands..................	700–1,200
Oligocene:	
Green, gray, lavender, and black shales and gumbo, sandy shales.....	200–700
Eocene:	
Jackson sandstone	

The cap rock of the Saratoga dome rises to within 1,500 feet of the surface and consists of limestone anhydrite and gypsum. The dome is broad and flat (Figs. 260, 261). It is elliptical with its long axis striking northeast. The is oil heavy (18° Bé.) and high in sulphur. It is found in sand lenses, probably connected, in Oligocene and younger beds lying above the cap rock. Where the cap was penetrated, it carried hot black sulphur water. A considerable quantity of barite[2] is bailed out from certain wells.

Sour Lake is 20 miles northwest of Spindletop and 10 miles southeast of Saratoga. The surface is marked by sour water, gas, oil seeps, and asphalt. The salt is encountered at a depth of 880 feet. The cap rock is cavernous limestone and yielded large amounts of oil. Production was obtained also at depth on the flanks of the dome.

At Hull, west of Sour Lake, salt is found at relatively shallow depths. Drilling deep wells on the flanks of the dome discovered large amounts of heavy oil (21 to 27° Bé.) and some oil of lighter grade. In 1923 the field was one of the most productive of the salt-dome group. In May, 1928, the daily production was about 13,000 barrels.

[1] SUMAN, J. R., The Saratoga Oil Field, Hardin County, Texas, Am. Assoc. Pet. Geol. *Bull.*, vol. 9, pp. 263–285, 1925.

[2] MOORE, E. S., Oolitic and Pisolitic Barite from Saratoga Oil Field, Texas, Geol. Soc. Am. *Bull.*, vol. 25, pp. 77–79, 1914.

At Spindletop,[1] 3 miles south of Beaumont, a mound rising 10 to 15 feet above the coastal plain, gas seeps, sulphur, and sour water marks the position of a salt dome. The top of the dome is a mile in diameter, circular in outline, and lies about 1,600 feet deep. Wells pass through

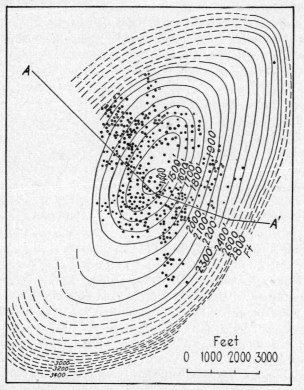

Fig. 260.—Structural map of Saratoga oil field, Texas. (*After Suman.*) Contours show elevation of cap rock below sea level.

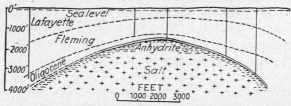

Fig. 261.—Cross-section of Saratoga oil field, Texas, on line *AA'*, Fig. 260. "Lafayette" includes Columbia. (*After Suman.*)

clay, sand, and gravel of the Lissie formation, and clay, sand, and limestone below which is the limestone cap which overlies a thick disc of gypsum and anhydrite that nearly covers the salt (p. 95). The limestone is a very porous dolomite estimated to contain 33 per cent pore

---

[1] BARTON, D. C., and R. B. PAXSON, The Spindletop Salt Dome and Oil Field, Jefferson County, Texas, Am. Assoc. Pet. Geol. *Bull.*, vol. 9, pp. 594–612, 1925.

space, and, until recently, it was the chief producing reservoir of the field, although the sandy layers above the limestone also were productive, particularly one about 120 feet above the cap. The oil is dark and heavy (22° Bé.) and is low in gasoline. The reservoir originally contained gas, with high pressure and the first wells had large initial flows. The gas is wet and high in hydrogen sulphide. The field probably produced over 50,000,000 barrels of oil to 1924. Since that date large wells have been brought in by drilling the beds on the southwest sides of the dome which dip away from the salt core. Certain wells show considerable deposits of sulphur above the oil rock and also associated with gypsum below the oil rock. The average daily production for the week ended May 28, 1928, was 40,425 barrels of oil, the field having the highest production of the salt-dome fields of the Gulf region.

At Orange (Cow Bayou), 8 miles northeast of Spindletop, the surface of the ground rises slightly. Drilling at depths between 1,701 and 5,490 feet has discovered considerable oil. Pliocene fossils are found at depths between 3,000 and 3,400 feet. No salt dome has been encountered.[1]

The Big Hill[2] district, 25 miles southwest of Beaumont and 10 miles from the Gulf of Mexico, is marked by a low mound, below which a steep dome is outlined by wells drilled to a cap rock composed of limestone, anhydrite, and gypsum. The wells have not encountered the salt dome that is assumed to lie below the gypsum. At High Island, 20 miles southwest of Big Hill, the cap rock is found at depths between 300 and 1,500 feet, below which salt, oil and gas occur in the cap rock. The Moss Bluff[3] dome, in southern Liberty County near Chambers County line, is marked by a slight elevation. It was discovered by the seismograph.

Lost Lake[4] dome, 2 miles northwest of Wallisville, Chambers County, is marked by a low marshy area and gas seepage. The dome was discovered by seismographic methods.

The Big Hill[5] ("Gulf") salt dome is in Matagorda County, 20 miles south-southeast of Bay City and about 1 mile from Matagorda Bay. An elliptical mound with its long axis trending north rises 37 feet above sea. Below the mound is discovered a salt dome about a mile in diameter,

[1] POWERS, S., and O. B. HOPKINS, U. S. Geol. Survey Bull. 736, p. 185, 1923.

[2] HENLEY, A. S., The Big Hill Salt Dome, Jefferson County, Texas, Am. Assoc. Pet. Geol. Bull., vol. 9, pp. 590–593, 1925.

[3] PRATT, W. E., Two New Salt Domes in Texas, Am. Assoc. Pet. Geol. Bull., vol. 10, p. 1171, 1926.

[4] WASSON, T., Lost Lake Salt Dome, Texas, Am. Assoc. Pet. Geol. Bull., vol. 11, p. 633, 1927.

[5] WOLF, A. G., The Big Hill Salt Dome, Matagorda County, Texas, Am. Assoc. Pet. Geol. Bull., vol. 9, pp. 711–737, 1925.

WOLF, A. G., The Origin of Salt Domes, Eng. Mining Jour., vol. 115, pp. 412–414, 1923.

its long axis striking north. The surface formation is Beaumont clay. The unconsolidated sedimentary rocks extend to a depth of 800 feet, below which is the cap rock of the salt dome (Fig. 262). At the top of the cap rock is a thin zone of porous limestone barren of sulphur, below which is a zone of similar rock high in sulphur, and below that a thick layer of anhydrite. Residuary anhydrite is found in the sulphur and limestone zones. Small amounts of pyrite, galena, and sphalerite are present in the cap rock, and pyrite is noted in the anhydrite as deep as it has been sampled. The sulphur and calcite are believed to be alteration products of the anhydrite. Little gypsum is present. The Big Hill dome was first worked for oil and a considerable amount, probably not over 500,000 barrels, was recovered from cavities in the limestone cap

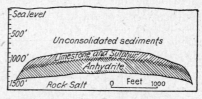

FIG. 262.—Geologic cross-section of Big Hill salt dome of Texas Gulf Sulphur Company, Matagorda County, Texas. (*After Wolf.*)

rock. It was a greenish oil with a gravity of 20° Bé. Early wells yielded gas and the discovery well had a high initial flow, the gas being chiefly hydrogen sulphide. In 1919 exploitation of the sulphur was begun on a large scale.

Markham[1] salt dome, 8 miles west of Bay City and 6 miles northwest of Markham station, is marked by a low rounded hill which trends northeast. Oil was discovered in wells drilled in 1908 at depths between 1,301 and 1,371 feet. The oil occurs in limestone cap rock and on the southwest side of the dome in sandy beds dipping away from the dome. According to DeGolyer, the salt of this dome contains the remains of algae showing the sedimentary character of the salt.

At Collegeport, west of Big Hill (Gulf), the surface of the ground rises somewhat, but the district is not known to be a salt dome. At Shepperd's Mott, 10 miles north of Big Hill, there is a rise of ground 40 feet high, and shows of oil are reported to have been found. Near Edna, west of Bay City, gas wells with considerable flow are drilled. This gas is piped to Houston. The gas and oil associated with the gas have a turpentine-like odor.

The West Columbia[2] salt dome (Kaiser's mound), 30 miles northwest of Bryan Heights, is one of the most productive domes in the Gulf Coast

[1] DeGolyer, E., Origin of North America Salt Domes, Am. Assoc. Pet. Geol. *Bull.*, vol. 9, p. 870, 1925.

Powers, S., Am. Assoc. Pet. Geol. *Bull.*, vol. 10, p. 10, 1926.

[2] Ellisor, A. C., Coral Reefs in the Oligocene of Texas, Am. Assoc. Pet. Geol. *Bull.*, vol. 10, pp. 976–985, 1926.

Barton, D. C., The West Columbia Oil Field, Brazoria County, Texas, Am. Assoc. Pet. Geol. *Bull.*, vol. 5, pp. 212–251, 1921.

Carlton, D. P., West Columbia Salt Dome and Oil Field, "Structure of Typical American Oil Fields," vol. 2, pp. 451–469, 1929.

region, having yielded 68,637,000 barrels of oil to 1929. The top of the salt core is flat and is found 800 feet deep and is about 3,000 feet in diameter. The field is slightly elongated on a line that strikes about N.55° E. The cap rock consists of anhydrite and gypsum 100 to 150 feet thick. This does not cover the entire salt mass, but pinches out to the south. No oil is found in the cap or supercap rocks. The oil occurs on the sides of the salt mass at depths about 3,000 to 4,000 feet in sands of Miocene age (Fig. 263). The bulk of production has come from the southeast side of the salt plug.

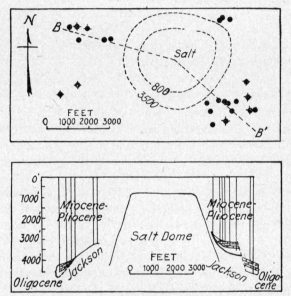

Fig. 263.—Map and geologic cross-section of West Columbia oil field, Texas. (*After A. C. Ellisor.*)

Damon Mound,[1] 40 miles southwest of Houston and 15 miles northwest of West Columbia, is marked by a mound 83 feet above the surrounding prairie and by gas seeps, sour dirt, sulphur, etc. This mound has been raised by a salt plug, the top of which is oval in plan with a long axis that strikes N.32° W. The salt plug is capped by gypsum, anhydrite, sulphur, and limestone. Oil has accumulated on the flank of the dome. To 1924 the field produced 5,008,870 barrels of oil (22° Bé.) from two areas with a total of 280 acres. One area is on the north, the other on the southwest side of the field. The oil is believed to have originated in Jackson (Eocene), Oligocene, and Miocene beds. It accumulated chiefly in the limestone sands of the Oligocene, which abut against and dip 40 degrees away from the salt core. Certain Oligocene beds around the

[1] BEVIER, G. M., The Damon Mound Oil Field, Texas, Am. Assoc. Pet. Geol. Bull., vol. 9, pp. 505–535, 1925.

dome are ancient coral reefs.[1] At Nash, 6 miles east of Damon Mound, oil is developed on the south side of a dome. The field had an average daily yield of 1,732 barrels for the week ended May 26, 1928. At Orchard, 20 miles northwest of Big Creek, oil is developed on top of a dome.

At Boling dome oil is found in the cap rock and on the southwest and east sides of a salt dome. The first large well was drilled southwest of the dome and had an initial production of 10,000 barrels per day. East of Boling dome a well with 200 barrels initial daily capacity was drilled in 1928. The oil has a gravity of 26° Bé. and is found at a depth of about 3,781 feet. Large deposits of sulphur are worked in the cap rock of the dome.

Big Creek[2] is 15 miles north of Damon Mound. Oil is found in a cap rock at a depth of 650 feet and salt is found at 750 feet. The average daily production for a week ended May 26, 1928, was 1,495 barrels.

The Blue Ridge[3] salt dome is 15 miles southwest of Houston. The top of the salt dome is marked by a low ridge that rises 20 feet above the surrounding country. The top of the salt dome rises to within 143 feet of the surface, is elongated and is developed about 1½ miles on the long axis which strikes southeast. The top of the dome is relatively narrow and uneven. A cap rock of lime and gypsum is locally developed. The rocks above and around the dome are Beaumont clays, Lafayette gravels, Fleming (Pliocene-Miocene), and Oligocene. The oil ranges from 22 to 46° Bé. and lies in sands and sandstone lenses. It is accumulated in three pools, one on the northeast flank, another on the west flank, and another field to the southeast of the dome.

At Pierce Junction, 8 miles southwest of Houston, salt is met at a depth of 950 feet, and above it is cap rock 100 to 200 feet thick. Oil wells with large yield are drilled on the west side of the dome.

Humble field is 25 miles northeast of Houston. It is one of the most productive fields in the Gulf Coast region, the productive area covering about 4 square miles. A salt plug is met at a depth of 1,400 feet and above it is a cap rock 50 to 250 feet thick, containing oil of about 22° Bé. gravity. On the east, north, and south flanks of the dome, in beds dipping away from the core, lateral sands yielding oil are found at depths between 1,000 and 4,200 feet. This oil is somewhat higher in gravity than the oil of the cap rock. At North Dayton, Myrtle Ridge, 15 miles northeast of Humble, salt is met at a depth of 674 feet and above it is a cap rock of anhydrite. Some oil is found above the dome. At Davis Hill,

[1] ELLISOR, A. C., Coral Reefs in the Oligocene of Texas, Am. Assoc. Pet. Geol. *Bull.*, vol. 10, pp. 976–985, 1926.

[2] WILLIAMS, N., *Oil Gas Jour.*, p. 51, May 31, 1928.

[3] HAGER, D. S., and E. STILES, The Blue Ridge Salt Dome, Fort Bend County, Texas, Am. Assoc. Pet. Geol. *Bull.*, vol. 9, pp. 304–316, 1925.

north of North Dayton below a hill 140 feet high, at a depth of 1,395 feet, salt rock with anhydrite cap is discovered. Some oil is encountered at depths of 500 to 3,700 feet.

Hockley[1] dome, 30 miles northwest of Houston, is marked by gas seeps and sulphur water. The top of the core is 3 miles long and 2 miles wide, and the long axis strikes N.22° W. Wells pass through 130 feet of the Fleming (Late Tertiary), 450 feet of porous limestone locally saturated with sulphur, 700 feet or more of anhydrite, and into salt. Sulphur,[2] possibly in amounts of economic value, occurs in the cavernous limestone of the cap rock. The anhydrite contains sandstone fragments. Oil is not encountered in quantity in the cap rock. Wells on the northeast side of the dome found oil in small amounts. According to Duessen and Lane, the upthrust of salt did not end until late Pleistocene time.

Brenham[3] dome is about 70 miles northwest of Houston and 35 miles west of Hockley dome. A well encountered cap rock of anhydrite at 1,124 feet, and salt was found at 1,383 feet. Oil is found in Cook Mountain formation at 1,360 feet. The oil lies in sandstone that probably abuts against the core and was tilted up by the rising salt plug. The strike of the axis of the Brenham dome is not known, but the dome is in line with the zone of Butler, Palestine, Keechi, and Brooks domes and this line is nearly parallel to the Balcones fault.

Large deposits of oil and gas have lately been developed at Raccoon Bend, 30 miles southeast of Brenham. The oil is found chiefly in the Jackson formation, and no salt dome is discovered.

PROSPECTS IN MISSISSIPPI, ALABAMA, AND GEORGIA

Mississippi.—The Vicksburg-Jackson area of[4] Mississippi lies east of the Louisiana fields. The main features are the broad, flat valleys that cross the region in general from north to south and the interstream tracts, which in the western part of the area are much dissected and have angular topographic features, and in the eastern part are flat or rolling plains.

[1] DUESSEN, A., and L. L. LANE, Hockley Salt Dome, Harris County, Texas, Am. Assoc. Pet. Geol. *Bull.*, vol. 9, pp. 1031–1060, 1925.

CHAPMAN, L. C., The Hockley Salt Dome, Am. Assoc. Pet. Geol. *Bull.*, vol. 7, pp. 297–299, 1923.

[2] GOLDMAN, M. I., Am. Assoc. Pet. Geol. *Bull.*, vol. 9, p. 56, 1925.

[3] DEUSSEN, A., Geology of the Coastal Plain of Texas, West of Brazos River, U. S. Geol. Survey *Prof. Paper* 126, pp. 134–135, 1924.

HOPKINS, O. B., The Brenham Salt Dome, Washington and Austin Counties, Texas, U. S. Geol. Survey *Bull.* 661, pp. 271–280, 1918.

[4] HOPKINS, O. B., Structure of the Vicksburg-Jackson Area, Mississippi, U. S. Geol. Survey *Bull.* 641, pp. 93–120, 1917.

CRIDER, A. F., Geology and Mineral Resources of Mississppppi, U. S. Geol. Survey *Bull.* 283, 1906.

————, Oil and Gas Possibilities in Mississippi, Southwestern Assoc. Pet. Geol. *Bull.* 1, pp. 152–155, 1917.

The city of Jackson is near the center of a broad gentle fold, which shows a domelike arch in cross-section from northwest to southeast and a terrace-like form from northeast to southwest. Near the southwestern and southern parts of the anticline the dips are as much as 60 to 70 feet to the mile; in the northwestern and southwestern parts they are 30 feet or less to the mile. The northern extent of this fold has not been determined. This fold is said to lie above a buried igneous mass.

SECTION OF FORMATIONS IN VICKSBURG-JACKSON AREA
(After Hopkins)

System	Series	Group or formation	Thickness, feet	Character
Quaternary	Recent	Alluvium	. . . .	Sand, clay, and silt along present streams
	Pleistocene	Loess and yellow loam	0–100	Clay, fine gray to buff, calcareous, and yellow to brown loam
		Alluvial terrace deposits	0–50	Sand, gravel, and clay
Tertiary	Pliocene	Sand and gravel	0–50	Terrace sand and gravel
	Oligocene	Catahoula sandstone	0–75	Unconsolidated sands, sandstones, gray siliceous clay, and some lignitic material
		Vicksburg limestone	80–130	Marl and clay above, containing marine shells; limestone and impure limestone and marl below
	Eocene	Jackson formation	250–500 (?)	Sand above, cross-bedded, green to yellow nonfossiliferous; gray clay weathering black below and sand beds at base. Both clay and sand beds contain marine shells
		Claiborne group	500–1,000	Marls, sands, lignitic clays, and lignite above; quartzite, clay stone, and marl below
		Wicox group	850–1,500 (?)	Lignitic clays and sands, with sand predominating in middle part
Cretaceous	Upper	Midway group[1]	100–300	Clay, dark gray to black, and micaceous sandstone, with hard limestone and sandy marl below
		Ripley formation	50–300	Sands, clays, marls, and impure limestones of marine origin
		Selma chalk	600–1,000	Chalky limestone with argillaceous and sandy beds
		Eutaw formation	300–400	Sands, massive and cross-bedded
		Tuscaloosa formation	100–300	Irregularly bedded sands, clays, and gravels, containing clay and lignitic layers at top

[1] The Midway group is generally placed at base of Eocene.

In 1930 a well near Jackson encountered gas at a depth of 2,520 feet. The well was reported to have a flow of 10,000,000 cubic feet per day.

The rocks of the Vicksburg-Jackson region are sedimentary in origin and relatively young, the exposed rocks ranging in age from Claiborne (Eocene) to Recent, as shown in the upper part of the following table. The formations below the Claiborne are below drainage level. The gas is probably in the Selma chalk. Northeast Mississippi is treated on page 201.

Alabama.—Gas and some oil have been discovered in the Pennsylvanian series in northwestern Alabama, but the production has not been

GENERALIZED GEOLOGIC SECTION OF WESTERN ALABAMA

Geologic age	Group	Formation	Thickness, feet	Character
Pliocene-Pleistocene		Lafayette	25	Gravel, sands, clays
Lower Miocene		Grand Gulf	50	Soft sandstones and clays
Lower Oligocene		St. Stephens limestone	300	Unusually soft limestone, easily cut with saw
Eocene	Claiborne	Gosport green sand	30	Glauconitic sands
		Lisbon	115	Calcareous clays and sandy clay
		Tallahatta buhrstone	400	Aluminous sandstones and siliceous clays
	Chickasaw (Wilcox)	Hatchetigbee	175	Sandy clays and cross-bedded sands
		Bashi	80	Sands and clays. Fossiliferous greensand
		Tuscahoma	140	Gray and yellow cross-bedded sands
		Nanafalia	200	Siliceous clays
	Midway	Naheola	150	Gray sandy clays Glauconitic clays
		Sucarnochee clay	100	Dark-brown clay
		Clayton	50	Impure limestone
Upper Cretaceous		Ripley	300	Calcareous and siliceous sands
		Selma chalk	950	Argillaceous limestones
		Eutaw sands	500	Glauconitic sands, cross-bedded
		Tuscaloosa	1,000	Irregular bedded sands, clays, and gravels

large. In southern Alabama, according to Hager,[1] there are several localities where oil possibly may be found in the Cretaceous beds.

The Hatchetigbee fold (Fig. 264), described by Hopkins,[2] runs in a general southeasterly direction through portions of Choctaw, Clarke, and Washington counties and is about 20 miles long and 4 to 5 miles

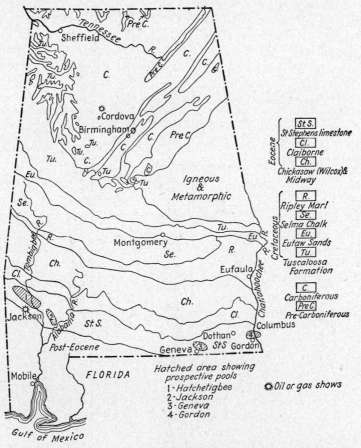

Fig. 264.—Index map of Alabama, showing anticlines in southern part of state. (*After Hager.*)

wide. Along the axis the Hatchetigbee formation crops out. This formation is about 550 feet lower stratigraphically than the St. Stephens limestone, which crops out on all sides of the fold. The reversal is not much less than 500 feet. The pitch of the strata away from the axis of the anticline ranges from 1 to nearly 2 degrees.

[1] HAGER, DORSEY, Possible Oil and Gas Fields in the Cretaceous Beds of Alabama, Am. Inst. Min. Eng. *Bull.* 134, pp. 469–476, 1918.

[2] HOPKINS, O. B., Oil and Gas Possibilities of the Hatchetigbee Anticline, Alabama, U. S. Geol. Survey *Bull.* 661, pp. 281–313, 1918.

The Jackson anticline is in all probability a part of the same fold as the Hatchetigbee anticline. Along the axis of the Jackson anticline, rocks of the Claiborne group are exposed, and the reversal is not much less than that of the Hatchetigbee anticline, from which this fold is separated by a saddle.

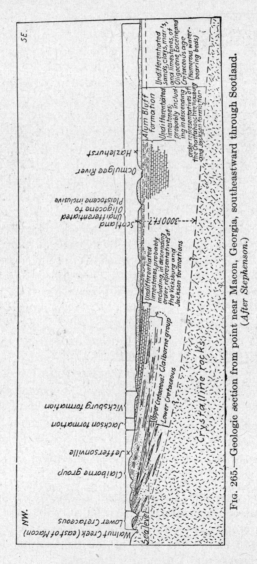

Fig. 265.—Geologic section from point near Macon, Georgia, southeastward through Scotland. (After Stephenson.)

Toward the east, according to Hager, no strong folding is noted until Geneva County is reached. In an area near Geneva, covering possibly 20 square miles, the Claiborne rocks are exposed at the surface, with the St. Stephens limestone surrounding them. The reversal on this fold is probably more than 100 feet. In this area exposures are meager, owing to the covering of the Grand Gulf and Lafayette formations.

East of Geneva, near Gordon, there is another anticlinal fold, on the Georgia state line. It has a reversal of 40 feet and covers 10 square miles.

A well on the Hatchetigbee anticline is reported to have had showings of gas at 750 and 1,500 feet and of oil at 2,250 feet. The 750-foot gas horizon is probably in the Ripley formation, and the 1,500-foot horizon is in the Selma chalk. The oil at 2,250 feet is below the Selma chalk and probably in the Eutaw sands.[1]

Georgia.—A seep of petroleum was reported to be found in 1919 about 1 mile south of Scotland, Telfair County, Georgia.[2] The surface deposits throughout the interstream areas in this region consist of 100 feet or less of irregularly bedded sandy clays and sands with subordinate interbedded layers of argillaceous sandstone. They are underlain by 100 feet or more of soft sandy clays and sands, in part water bearing, with interbedded thin layers of sandstone and quartzite that belong to the Alum Bluff formation. The Alum Bluff formation is underlain by 500 feet or more of limestone with interbedded layers of calcareous sandstone and marl, which probably represent, in descending order, the Chattahoochee and Vicksburg formations of the Oligocene and perhaps the Jackson formation of the Eocene. These formations contain water-bearing beds. Beneath the limestones are sediments of Eocene and Cretaceous age, which probably have an aggregate thickness of 1,500 feet or more, and which rest upon a basement of ancient crystalline rocks. These also contain important water-bearing beds.

The dip of the beds is southeastward and increases with the age of the beds from 4 to 5 feet to about 30 feet to the mile. The general stratigraphic relations of the formations are shown in Fig. 265.

Examination of the underlying rocks where they come to the surface about 75 miles north of Scotland shows them to be largely of marine origin, with remnants of plant and animal life. These rocks belong to the Cretaceous system, which is oil bearing in Louisiana and Texas.

[1] HAGER, DORSEY, *op. cit.*, p. 475.

[2] VEATCH, OTTO, and L. W. STEPHENSON, Preliminary Report on the Geology of the Coastal Plain of Georgia, Ga. Geol. Survey *Bull.* 26, pp. 60–61, 1911.

HULL, J. P. D., and L. P. TEAS, Oil Prospect Near Scotland, Telfair County, Georgia, Ga. Geol. Survey, pp. 3–5, 1919.

CHAPTER XV

ROCKY MOUNTAIN REGION

MONTANA

The western part of Montana is made up chiefly of igneous and pre-Cambrian sedimentary rocks with relatively small intermontane basins of later rocks (Fig. 266). The sedimentary rocks in general dip away from the Rocky Mountain Front. East of the Rocky Mountain Front, Paleozoic and Mesozoic rocks are present in force, and these cover most of the central part of the state. In the eastern one-third of the state they are covered with Tertiary rocks. East of the Rocky Mountain Front

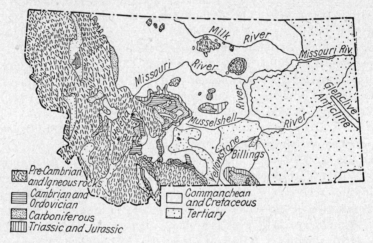

Fig. 266.—Geologic sketch map of Montana. Silurian, Devonian, and undifferentiated Paleozoic rocks are included in other systems.

(Figs. 267, 268), there are foreland ranges or mountain groups which are isolated and in general the rocks dip away from these in all directions. Such groups include the Bearpaw, Little Rockies, Judith, Big Snowy, Black Hills, and others. Many of the oil structures are developed on the flanks of these foreland ranges or on extensions of them. The rocks that are productive in Wyoming are present also in Montana, and they are thrown into anticlines and domes that form the prospective oil structures; thus far, however, oil has been found at relatively few places in Montana, although a large number of structures have been drilled.

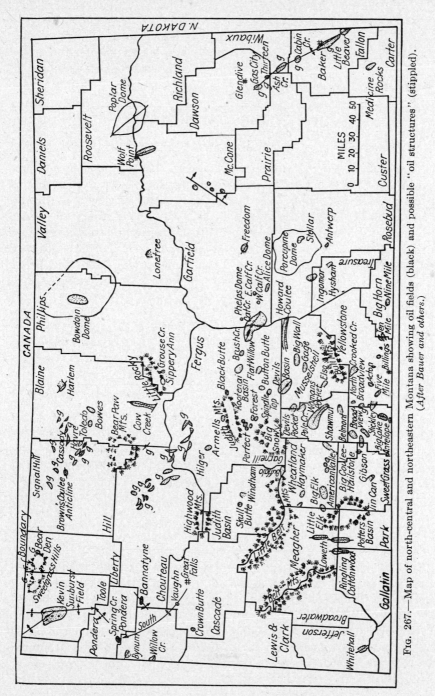

FIG. 267.—Map of north-central and northeastern Montana showing oil fields (black) and possible "oil structures" (stippled). (After Bauer and others.)

Oil occurs in Montana through a considerable geologic range. In Kevin-Sunburst and Soap Creek fields it is found in the Madison (Mississippian) limestone, in Soap Creek in the Amsden formation, and in the Tensleep (Pennsylvanian) sandstone. In Devil's basin oil is found in the Quadrant formation of the Carboniferous. In Kevin-Sunburst

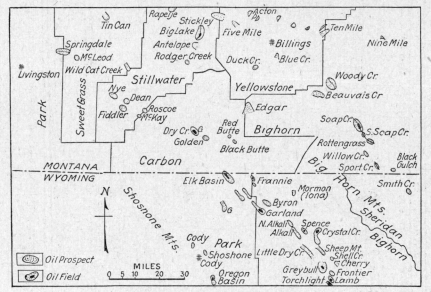

Fig. 268.—Map showing oil and gas fields and prospects in south-central Montana and part of Wyoming.

district gas is found in the Sunburst sand (Kootenai). In the Cat Creek field oil is found in the Kootenai and probably in the Dakota formation. In Big Lake area the oil is found in the Dakota. In Elk basin the oil and gas are in the Frontier sands of the Colorado. The Eagle sandstone of the Montana group carries gas at Havre, Bowes, and in many other fields,

MONTANA OIL PRODUCTION
(Barrels)

Field	1928	Total to Dec. 31, 1928
Cat creek..................	601,655	11,486,661
Devil's Basin..............	1,853	21,500
Elk Basin.................	16,240	867,991
Kevin-Sunburst............	3,174,027	18,704,360
Lake Basin................	47,149	195,227
Pondera...................	146,575	146,575
Soap Creek................	Shut in	25,000
Total.................	3,987,499	31,447,314

and the sandstone of the Judith River formation, also of the Montana group, is the chief gas horizon in the domes on the Glendive-Baker anticline.

Owing to the proximity of high mountains, the sands generally carry water under high pressure. It is believed that from many structures the oil has been carried out by movement of the water. Faulting interferes with the water circulation and tends to preserve the oil. It is noteworthy that some of the most productive domes, Kevin-Sunburst, Cat Creek, and Elk Basin are cut by closely spaced faults.

FORMATIONS EXPOSED IN THE BIRCH CREEK-SUN RIVER AREA, MONTANA
(*After Stebinger*)

System	Series	Group or formation		Thickness, feet	Character
Quaternary	Recent	Alluvium			Silt, sand, and gravel, chiefly along stream bottoms
	Pleistocene	Glacial drift		0–150	Boulder clay, gravel, and sand. Contains boulders of various rocks derived from the mountains
Tertiary	Pleistocene and late Tertiary	Terrace gravels		5–50	Limestone gravels on terraces and plains
Tertiary (?)	Eocene (?)	St. Mary River formation		650+	Clay, clay shale, and soft sandstone, gray to greenish gray
Cretaceous	Upper Cretaceous	Montana group	Horsethief sandstone	250–400	Chiefly massive gray to buff and greenish-gray coarse-grained sandstone with slabby sandstone and shale in lower half. Contains one or more shell beds
			Bearpaw shale	0–500	Dark-gray shale with a few thin beds of gray sandstone. Marine shells of Pierre types. Present only in northern part of area. To south grades into brackish and fresh water clays and sandstones
			Two Medicine formation	1,800–2,200	Gray, greenish-gray, and red clay and clay shale with subordinate irregular sandstones, mainly in lower half. Bones of reptiles of Judith River types and fragments of wood are abundant. Thin beds of coal near base
			Virgelle sandstone	200–380	Upper part, massive coarse gray sandstone, much cross-bedded, and with heavy, irregular beds of magnetite sandstone at top. Lower part, interbedded sandstone and shale. Contains gas at Medicine Hat and elsewhere in Alberta and at Havre, Montana
		Colorado shale with Blackleaf sandy member at base		1,800+	Upper part, dark shale with bituminous shale and thin, maltha-bearing limestones near base. Blackleaf sandy member, coarse sandstones locally conglomeratic in beds 20 to 75 feet thick, alternating with dark marine shale; thickness 610 to 700 feet
	Lower Cretaceous	Kootenai formation		890–920	Red and green shales and clay shale with many beds of coarse gray sandstones. Contains a few fresh-water shells
Jurassic	Upper Jurassic	Ellis formation		240–310	Black to gray calcareous shale with thin limestone and sandstone. Many fossil shells. Marine
		—Unconformity—			
Carboniferous	Mississippian	Madison and later limestones		1,200+	Massive white limestone, cherty in middle and lower beds; coralline limestone in upper beds

GEOLOGIC SECTION, SWEETGRASS ARCH, MONTANA

(After Romine, Collier, Perry and others)

System	Series	Group or formation	Thickness, feet	Character of rocks
Quaternary	Recent	Alluvium		Sand, gravel, and silt along larger drainage courses
	Pleistocene	Glacial drift	0–200	Clay, gravel, boulders, and silt
		Unconformity		
Cretaceous	Upper	*Montana* — Two Medicine formation	1,900+	Gray and greenish-gray clay and shales with irregular lenses of concretionary sandstone. Locally, lignite beds near base
		Montana — Eagle sandstone	200–385	Gray to buff massive sandstone containing iron concretions near top and locally a magnetite sandstone bed. Lower part, platy gray sandstone and sandy shale, Virgelle member at base
		Colorado — Colorado shale (Blackleaf member)	1,700–1,850	Gray to black marine shale with thin beds of calcareous concretions and a few thin sands in upper 1,000–1,100 feet. Lower 700–750 feet known as Blackleaf member; contains sandstones, interbedded with dark siliceous shales, clay, and bentonite. Locally, colored shales 400 feet above base
	Lower	Kootenai formation	300–500	Red, green, yellow, and dark gray sandy clay shales with irregular lime and sandstone lenses. Sunburst sandstone member near base. Some oil and gas at Kevin-Sunburst
Jurassic	Upper	Ellis formation	150–300	Gray to dark gray and green calcareous shale with locally 1–3 sand lenses near base. Basal part contains much pyrite and locally glauconite. Oil at Bannatyne; some oil at Kevin-Sunburst
		Unconformity		
Carboniferous	Lower Mississippian	Madison limestone	1,000 ±	Upper 700 feet chiefly white to cream-colored massive crystalline limestone, locally dolomitic and porous in upper 150 feet. Lower 300 feet thinner-bedded, gray and brown limestone with alternating beds of gray and dark gray shale. Main oil horizon at Kevin-Sunburst
Devonian	Upper	Three Forks formation	320 ±	Upper 100 feet very fine-grained calcareous sandstone, black organic shale, and gray calcareous shale, bearing pyrite. Lower 220 feet white to pinkish-colored massive anhydrite with thin laminae of black calcareous shale
	Middle and Lower	Jefferson limestone	540 ±	Granular, brown, magnesian limestone with varying amounts of white anhydrite. Locally, small flows of carbon dioxide gas under high pressure and slight showings of oil 350 feet below the top
		Unconformity		
Cambrian	Upper and Middle	?	1,400+	1. Upper 500 feet, dense gray to black limestone 2. Middle 700 feet, chiefly gray-green, brown, red, and blue shales with a few beds of limestone 3. Lower member, sandstone and quartzite
		Undetermined		

In 1929 Montana produced 3,183,000 barrels of oil valued at $5,700,-000. In 1928 Montana produced 6,277,000 thousand cubic feet of natural gas valued at $1,446,000.

Northern Montana.—The rocks of northwestern Montana[1] are shown in tables, pages 453 and 454. The Birch Creek-Sun River area lies between the Sweetgrass arch and the Lewis overthrust fault, and east of the front range of the Rocky Mountains. In this area Cretaceous rocks are found on structures and under cover.

Kevin-Sunburst.—The Kevin-Sunburst[2] oil field is 90 miles northwest of Great Falls, and 10 miles south of the Canadian boundary. The field was discovered in 1922 and has become one of the most productive fields of the Rocky Mountains region. The rocks (p. 454) are arched to form a great flat dome called the Sweetgrass arch, around the summit of which are smaller domes (Fig. 269). The rocks cropping out in the oil region are the Colorado shales and on the flanks of the dome the Virgelle (Eagle) sandstone appears. At many places the rocks are covered by surface debris and conditions for detailed mapping of the surface are difficult. Wells drilled near the top of the arch pass through about 800 feet of Colorado shales and 400 feet of the Kootenai formation, near the base of which is the Sunburst sand which yields much gas and some oil. Below the Kootenai is the Ellis formation about 250 feet thick, with sand lenses yielding oil, and below the Ellis is the Madison limestone, which is the main producing horizon of the field. There is an unconformity between the Madison limestone and the Ellis formation. The top of the Madison was subjected to erosion before the Ellis formation was laid down. The Quadrant quartzite of Pennsylvanian age is lacking as also are Permian, and Triassic rocks. Since the Quadrant quartzite (Pennsylvanian) is found at other places in the general region, it appears probable that the Sweetgrass arch was raised and the Quadrant eroded from an uplift

[1] STEBINGER, E., Anticlines in the Blackfeet Indian Reservation, Montana, U. S. Geol. Survey *Bull.* 641, pp. 281–305, 1917.

————, Possibilities of Oil and Gas in North-central Montana, U. S. Geol. Survey *Bull.* 641, pp. 49–91, 1917.

————, Geology and Coal Resources of North Teton County, Montana, U. S. Geol. Survey *Bull.* 621, pp. 117–156, 1916.

[2] PERRY, E. S., The Kevin-Sunburst and Other Oil and Gas Fields of the Sweetgrass Arch, Mont. State Bur. Mines *Mem.* 1, pp. 1–41, 1928.

COLLIER, A. J., The Kevin-Sunburst Oil Field and Other Possibilities of Oil and Gas in the Sweetgrass Arch, Montana, U. S. Geol. Survey *Bull.* 812, pp. 57–189, 1929.

PLATT, F. G., weekly issues of well records and large-scale structure contour map, Shelby, Montana.

PLATT, F. G., *Oil Gas Jour.*, pp. 80–105, Oct. 11, 1928.

ROMINE, T. B., Oil Fields and Structure of Sweetgrass Arch, Montana, Am. Assoc. Pet. Geol. *Bull.*, vol. 13, pp. 779–797, 1929.

HOWELL, W. F., Kevin-Sunburst Field, Toole County, Montana, "Structure of Typical American Oil Fields," vol. 2, pp. 254–268, 1929.

before the Ellis formation was laid down, and that the arch was raised at a later date to form a "reflected" buried ridge.   In the early days of

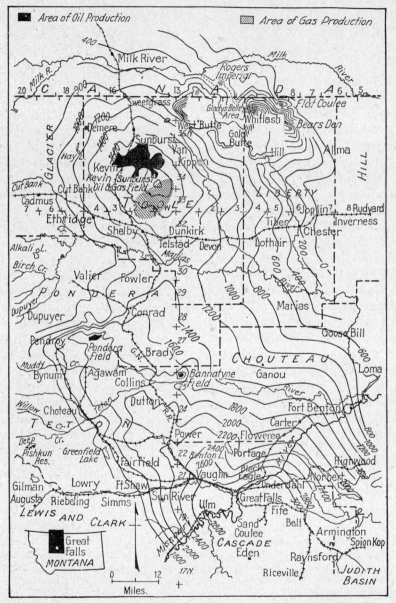

FIG. 269.—Map of Sweetgrass arch Montana; contours on top of Madison limestone.
(After Romine, with additions.)

development of the area the main oil sand was believed to be the basal beds of the Ellis formation, but, according to Perry, practically all of the oil below the Kootenai formation is from the Madison limestone, some of it being found 150 feet or more below the top of the limestone. The upper 150 feet of the Madison limestone is dolomitic and porous. This, according to Romine, is the result of weathering. The top of the dome is essentially barren, although most of the oil is found not far from the top of the arch on or near the tops of small subsidiary domes (Fig. 270). Many of the wells, however, appear to be independent of the domes. The localization of the oil pools is controlled very largely by the porosity of

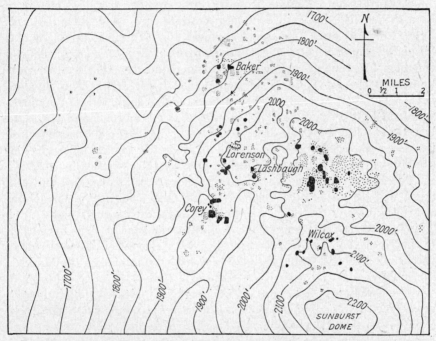

FIG. 270.—Map of Kevin-Sunburst dome, Sweetgrass arch, Montana. Black areas show regions of closely spaced wells. Stippled areas are regions of less closely spaced wells. Contours drawn on top of Madison limestone. Datum is sea level. (*Data from Collier, Platt, Perry, Romine, and others.*)

the top of the Madison limestone, which, as stated, is due to weathering at the ancient unconformity. The main oil-bearing horizon is from 2 to 50 feet thick. Certain investigators believe that the region has been extensively faulted by closely spaced faults of small throw which can not be seen at the surface, but which are discovered by comparison of records of wells. Most of the wells produce between 20 and 50 barrels a day or less, but some of them have large initial production and under strong gas pressure come in as gushers. The oil ranges in gravity from 31 to 34° Bé., most of it being 30 to 32° Bé. It has a mixed base and yields about 25 per cent gasoline and 14 per cent kerosene. Oil from the Sunburst sand has a gravity of about 36° Bé. and a little oil that is obtained from sands in the Colorado formation has a gravity of over 40° Bé. The original gas pressure in the Sunburst sand was about 380 pounds per square inch and some of the gas wells have had initial flows of 10,000,000 to 20,000,000 cubic feet per day. Gas is piped to Great Falls. Recently large amounts of gas have been developed in the Madison oil horizon, especially in the southeast part of the field. One well had an initial production estimated to be 77,000,000 cubic feet per day. This gas was found 63 feet below the top of the Madison limestone.

Subsurface data obtained from the large number of wells which have been drilled in the so-called Sweetgrass arch area has shown that this large Colorado shale area is not a single north-trending uplift, as was formerly supposed, but that it consists of two uplifts, *en echelon*, the axes of which are roughly parallel but do not coincide. These are locally known as the Kevin-Sunburst dome and South arch. The Pondera field, which is 60 miles northwest of Great Falls, is located on the northwest end of the South arch. The top of the Madison limestone is oil bearing and lies 2,038 feet deep. The wells yield 20 to 200 barrels of oil per day with considerable gas. The oil is similar to that of the Kevin-Sunburst field. Pondera produced nearly a million barrels in 1929.

The Bannatyne field 25 miles southeast of Pondera is located on a dome with about 100 feet of closure. A sand 1,450 feet deep not far above the base of the Ellis formation yields oil with a gravity of 27° Bé. This sand is probably equivalent to a stray sand in the Ellis formation, in the Kevin-Sunburst field, which, locally, yields oil on the east side of the Kevin-Sunburst field. Sulphur water is encountered in the Madison limestone.

The Sweetgrass hills (Fig. 269), about 20 miles east of Sunburst, are formed by a group of igneous intrusives around which the rocks locally are domed, possibly by laccolithic bodies. The domes and structural noses include Whitlash, Bear's Den, Flat Coulee, Erickson Coulee, and others. Several of the structures are drilled. In the Whitlash dome considerable gas is found in sands in the Colorado shales, probably at the horizon of the Bow Island sand of Alberta. Gas, said to be in the Kootenai sandstone, is found in the Bear's Den field, which is located on a plunging anticline. One well on this dome has produced oil (38° Bé.) at the base of the Cretaceous 2,470 ft. deep.

Bearpaw Mountains.—The Bearpaw Mountains are about 125 miles southeast of the Kevin-Sunburst field. In the plains surrounding the mountains for 30 to 40 miles on all sides, there are many folds and faults in the Cretaceous rocks. These are irregular in their trend and distribution and are probably related to the igneous intrusions in the mountains. The faults are of the thrust type, older formations having been carried upward beside younger rocks that lie for the most part undisturbed. Some of these faults are about 12 miles long. In this region the Colorado shale has been drilled for oil at many places, but no oil field is developed. Near Havre,[1] on the north side of the mountains, 100 miles east of the Kevin-Sunburst field, gas is found in the Eagle sandstone in the lower part of the Montana group. The gas occurs in domes and faulted anticlines. Gas is developed in the Bowes field east of Havre.

Two gas wells were drilled in 1923 south of the Bearpaw Mountains[2] east edge of Chouteau County, in a faulted dome. A well estimated to have an initial flow of 20,000,000 cubic feet was encountered in a sandstone which, according to Reeves, is probably the Eagle formation.

To the southeast of the Bearpaw Mountains, anticlines and domes are found on the west and south sides of the Little Rocky Mountains.[3]

Bowdoin Dome.—The Bowdoin dome[4] is on Milk River, in northeastern Montana, between Malta and Hinsdale. The sedimentary rocks range in age from Cambrian to Recent, but only the Claggett shale, Judith River formation, Bearpaw shale, and some of the more recent surficial deposits are exposed in the immediate vicinity of the dome. There are two or more structurally higher areas on top of the dome. One well recently encountered gas in a sandy shale in the Colorado and is estimated to have a capacity of 6,000,000 cubic feet per day.

Wolf Point and Poplar.—East of Bowdoin dome anticlines are found at Wolf Point and Poplar dome where, near the crests of the folds, the upper parts of the Cretaceous rocks are exposed. It is possible that these structures are continuations of the zone of the Glendive-Baker anticline Fig. 267. A well drilled 3,196 feet deep on the Poplar dome is bottomed in Colorado shale.

[1] STEBINGER, E., Possibilities of Oil and Gas in North-central Montana, U. S. Geol. Survey *Bull.* 641, pp. 49–91, 1917; The Montana Group of Northwestern Montana, U. S. Geol. Survey *Prof. Paper* 90, pp. 61–68, 1915.

FISHER, C. A., Geology of the Great Falls Coal Field, Montana, U. S. Geol. Survey *Bull.* 356, 1909; Geology and Water Resources of the Great Falls Region, Montana, U. S. Geol. Survey *Water Supply Paper* 221, 1909.

PEPPERBERG, L. J., The Milk River Coal Field, Montana, U. S. Geol. Survey *Bull.* 381, pp. 82–107, 1910; The Southern Extension of the Milk River Coal Field, Chouteau County, Montana, U. S. Geol. Survey *Bull.* 471, pp. 359–383, 1912.

BOWEN, C. F., The Cleveland Coal Field, Blaine County, Montana; The Big Sandy Coal Field, Chouteau County, Montana, U. S. Geol. Survey *Bull.* 541, pp. 338–378, 1914.

[2] REEVES, F., Geology and Possible Oil and Gas Resources of the Faulted Area South of the Bearpaw Mountains, U. S. Geol. Survey *Bull.* 751C, pp. 71–114, 1924.

[3] COLLIER, A. J., and S. H. CATHCART, Possibility of Finding Oil in Laccolithic Domes South of the Little Rocky Mountains, Montana, U. S. Geol. Survey *Bull.* 731, pp. 171–178, 1922.

CLAPP, C. H., ARTHUR BEVAN, and C. S. LAMBERT, Geology and Oil and Gas Prospects of Central and Eastern Montana, Mont. Univ. *Bull.* pp. 34–61, 1921.

[4] COLLIER, A. J., The Bowdoin Dome, Montana, a Possible Reservoir of Oil or Gas, U. S. Geol. Survey *Bull.* 661, pp. 193–209, 1918.

GENERAL SECTION OF THE ROCKS OF THE BOWDOIN DOME, MONTANA

(*After Collier*)

System	Series	Group	Formation	Thickness, feet	Character
Quaternary	Recent				Silts in the flood plains of streams
	Pleistocene				Scattered crystalline boulders; glacial moraines
					Silt, sand, and gravel deposited along the old channels of the Missouri, Musselshell, and other streams before the end of the glacial epoch
					Gravel interstratified with yellowish silt at an altitude of 300 feet above Milk River valley. May possibly be late Pliocene
Cretaceous	Upper Cretaceous	Montana	Bearpaw shale	800–1,000	Dark-gray shale; forms gumbo soil
			Judith River	400	Light-gray clay and irregular beds of gray and brown sandstone
			Claggett shale	750	Dark-gray shale; forms gumbo soil. About 500 feet exposed in Bowdoin dome
			Eagle (?) sandstone	100 ±	Light-gray sandstone; forms a low ridge; contains limestone concretions in its upper part
		Colorado		875	Bluish-gray to black shale; contains limestone concretions and marine fossils
				60 ±	Light-gray sandstone, capped by a thin limestone containing numerous gastropods
				485 ±	Bluish-gray to black shale
			Mowry shale	100 ±	Platy shale or sandstone, which is in places dark-colored but weathers white; contains numerous fish scales; yields traces of oil by distillation
	Lower Cretaceous		Kootenai (?)	825 ±	Mainly shale but includes some poorly defined sandstone. In lower part red and purple shales were noted. A bed of fresh-water sandstone and carbonaceous shale with fragments of woody stems near the base
Jurassic	Upper Jurassic		Ellis	200 ±	Massive white and yellow sandstone
				200 ±	Shale containing *Belemnites*
Carboniferous	Mississippian		Madison limestone		Massive limestone

Glendive-Baker.—A great fold known as the Glendive-Baker or Cedar Creek[1] anticline covers an area of 1,000 square miles in southeastern Montana, southwestern North Dakota, and northwestern South Dakota (p. 96). It extends from the Foothills region of the Black Hills northwest 100 miles to Glendive and the Yellowstone River. This anticline has been drilled at numerous places, and considerable gas has been developed on it, but thus far no oil has been encountered. There are more than 77 wells on the structure, two of which are over 4,000 feet deep. The gas deposits lie on domes along the crest of the anticline. From northwest to southeast these are the Gas City, Thirteen, Ash Creek, Cabin Creek, and Baker domes. The rocks exposed at the surface or encountered in the deep well of the Montana Yellowstone Oil Company near Glendive are shown on page 462.

In the Gas City dome, about 10 miles southwest of Glendive, a well drilled in 1913 found gas at 750 feet in the Judith River sand. Additional wells were drilled and supplied gas for Glendive. Wells on Ash Creek dome have produced gas, but some of the wells yielded water and rapidly declined. On the Cabin Creek dome, 20 miles northwest of Baker, wells yielding gas under about 500 pounds of pressure were drilled in 1926. In 1928 there were 14 wells operating on the structure. The gas is piped to Black Hills cities. In the Baker field gas was found in the Judith River sand in 1915. A group of wells about 820 feet deep supply the city from this formation and also a small carbon black plant which is operated there. The group of fields from Ash Creek to Little Beaver dome contains one of the greatest gas reserves in the Rocky Mountain region.

Central Montana.—In central Montana[2] there is a great area in which the Cretaceous rocks are thrown into anticlines and domes (Fig. 271). There are many raised structures in the area, but, as it is adjoined by high mountains, there is a vigorous artesian circulation, and it appears probable that at many places oil has been washed out of the reservoir rocks by underground water. At places the salt water once present in the beds has been greatly diluted or even replaced by fresh water. In certain domes the water circulation has been hampered by faulting, and this seems to have preserved the oil. The chief oil field in central Montana is the Cat Creek field of Fergus County.

[1] MOULTON, GAIL F., and N. W. BASS, U. S. Geol. Survey *Press Notes*, pp. 1–7 (with 2 maps showing structure), Jan. 11, 1922. MOULTON, GAIL F., *Black Hills Engineer*, vol. 16, pp. 254–264, 1928.

[2] BOWEN, C. F., Anticlines in a Part of the Musselshell Valley, Montana, U. S. Geol. Survey *Bull.* 691, pp. 185–209, 1919.

————, The Stratigraphy of the Montana Group, U. S. Geol. Survey *Prof. Paper* 90, pp. 95–153, 1915.

Section Showing Rocks Encountered on Glendive Anticline Montana
(After Moulton and Bass)

Arikaree (?) formation:

300 feet or less of calcareous sandstone, marl, clay, etc., probably Miocene.

White River formation:

100 feet or less, fresh-water Oligocene, consisting of limestone, clay, chert, volcanic ash.

Fort Union formation:

400 feet —.   Yellow to ash gray clays and sandstone; fresh water.   Basal Eocene.

Lance Formation:

Tertiary.   Underlies Fort Union unconformably.   Is made up of Ludlow lignitic member above, a middle "Somber" member, and Colgate sandstone below. The Ludlow is 350 feet thick and consists of sandstone, shale, and lignite.   The Somber member is 500 feet thick and consists of sandstone and lignite.   The Colgate is a sandstone of fresh-water origin and is 100 feet thick or less.

Fox Hills formation:

25 to 100 feet thick.   Upper Cretaceous; consists of soft sandstone with abundant fossil leaves and marine shells.   It outcrops conspicuously around the Cedar Creek anticline and around the Black Hills.   Grades into the Pierre formation below.

Pierre formation:

Consists of (1) an upper shale division 1,120 feet.   Dark marine shale with thick sandstone in the area southwest of Baker.   (2) A middle division including one or more gas sands which represent the Judith River formation farther west.   (3) A lower dark marine shale equivalent to Claggett formation.   The base of the Pierre is marked by a gas sand at Baker which may represent the Eagle sandstone.   If so, the Pierre is 1,850 feet thick at Baker.   It thins out toward the Black Hills.

Colorado shale:

Dark marine shale 2,150 feet thick.   Contains a 7-foot gas sand 1,070 feet below top and thin sandy beds in basal 75 feet.

Dakota sandstone:

120 feet.   Sandstone with some shale.

Fuson shale:

70 feet.   Red shale in Yellowstone well, probably belongs to the Fuson shale or to equivalent beds of the Kootenai formation.

Lakota:

25 to 90 feet.   Massive sandstone.

Morrison:

50 to 200 feet.   Red variegated clays and sandstones.

Sundance:

300 feet.   Sandy shale and thin sandstone; marine; petroliferous.

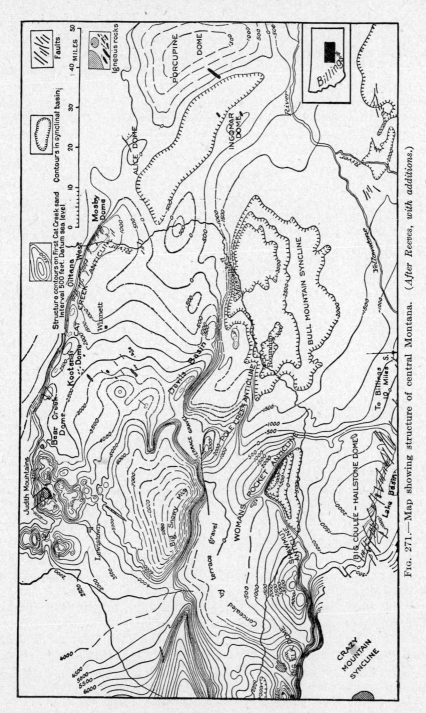

FIG. 271.—Map showing structure of central Montana. (*After Reeves, with additions.*)

Cat Creek.—The Cat Creek[1] district near Winnett, Montana, is about 75 miles east of Lewistown. The rocks of the district are shown in the table (p. 451), and the structural features of central Montana are indicated in Fig. 271. The uplifts of the Big Snowy and Judith Mountains merge eastward into the Cat Creek-Devil's Basin uplift. A series of anticlines are developed on both the north and south margins of this uplift. Oil was discovered on the Mosby dome of the Cat Creek field

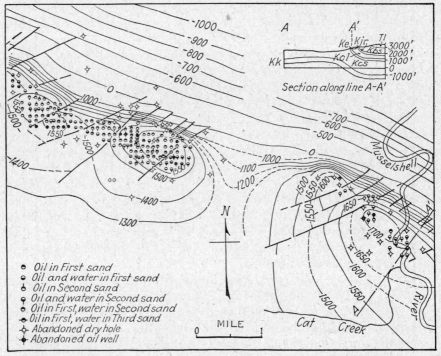

Fig. 272.—Map of Cat Creek oil field showing structure contoured on top of first Cat Creek sand. Numbers show elevations of sand above sea level. In cross-section *Kk*, Kootenai formation (Lower Cretaceous); *Kcs*, Colorado shale; *Ke*, Eagle sandstone; *Kcl*, Claggett shale; *Kjr*, Judith River formation; *Kbs*, Bearpaw shale; *Tl*, Lance formation (Eocene?). (*After Reeves.*)

(Fig. 272) in 1920, and to January 1, 1929, the field had produced 11,486,000 barrels of oil. The oil is high grade, 47 to 50° Bé., high in gasoline, low in sulphur, and has a mixed base.

Four sands are recognized: the Mosby, First, Second, and Third. The Mosby sand in the Colorado shale has yielded a little gas and water. Where not eroded it is 1,000 to 1,075 feet above the First sand. The First sand is at the base of the Colorado shale and, according to Reeves,

---

[1] REEVES, FRANK, Geology of the Cat Creek and Devil's Basin Oil Field and Adjacent Areas in Montana, U. S. Geol. Survey *Bull.* 786, pp. 39–95, 1927.

LUPTON, C. T. and W. LEE, Am. Assoc. Petrol. Geol. *Bull.*, vol. 5, pp. 252–275, 1927.

is probably equivalent to the Dakota sand. In the Cat Creek field it is 25 to 60 feet thick. It is overlain by sandy shale, and it is the chief oil producer of the region. The Second Cat Creek sand is 160 to 235 feet below the First sand and is in the Kootenai. It is about 40 feet thick and is overlain by red shale. The Third sand is 100 to 150 feet below the Second sand. It carries little oil. The sands yield large volumes of water under artesian head, where they do not carry oil. This water enters the outcrops on the mountain slopes farther west. The water carries little mineral matter, the analyses showing 351 to 2,524 parts per million, chiefly sodium chloride, carbonate, and sulphate. The sodium chloride water is believed to be a relic of sea water much diluted by surface water. It is noteworthy that the oil of the First sand is 2° Bé. lighter than the oil of the Second sand 160 to 235 feet deeper. According to Reeves, the oil of both sands is derived from the overlying Colorado shale and passed into the First sand during the period of compacting of the sediments. After faulting some of the oil migrated from the First to the Second sand. The faulted conditions of the beds also prevented the oil from being flushed out of the domes by the strong artesian-water circulation of the district. The production has come chiefly from the Mosby and West domes. To the northwest of these, other domes are found, among them Oiltana, Brush Creek, Kootenai, Wildhorse Lake, and Christenson. Most of these domes have been tested and are found to contain only large flows of fresh water. At Armells dome north of Judith Mountains gas is found in a Kootenai sand.

Devil's Basin.—The Devil's Basin field is about 40 miles southwest of the Cat Creek field and 60 miles north of Billings. A few small wells have yielded heavy oil from the Van Dusen sand of the Quadrant formation (table, p. 466), at depths of about 1,150 feet and 500 to 600 feet below the top of the Quadrant. In the Big Snowy Mountains to the west of the field, the Quadrant contains dark shale and petroliferous sandstones, and it is probably from the Quadrant that the oil is derived.

Alice Dome.—The Alice[1] dome is probably the east extension of the Cat Creek dome. The fold is faulted on the north side and the Judith River formation is exposed in its center. About 100 feet of this formation lies underground. Below the Judith River is the Claggett 700 feet, the Eagle 50 feet, the Colorado shale about 1,900 feet. This contains the Mosby sand and below it is the Cat Creek sand which produces oil at Cat Creek to the northwest. A well is drilled to the Ellis formation.

Porcupine Dome.—The Porcupine[2] dome lies north of Forsyth and is about 33 miles long and 27 miles wide. The rocks of the area are

[1] THOM, W. T., JR., and G. H. DOEBIN, U. S. Geol. Survey *Press Bull.*, pp. 1–3, July 22, 1921.

[2] BOWEN, C. F., Possibilities of Oil in the Porcupine Dome, Rosebud County, Montana, U. S. Geol. Survey *Bull.* 621, pp. 61–70, 1916.

shown in the table, page 467.   Along the east and north sides of the dome the Judith River dips away from the axis at angles of 1 to 8 degrees, the steeper dips being on the east side.   Near the center of the dome the

SEDIMENTARY FORMATIONS IN CENTRAL MONTANA
(After Reeves and others)

Geologic age		Group and formation		Thickness, feet	Character
Cenozoic	Recent	Alluvium		0–50 ±	Flood-plain and alluvial-fan deposits of clay, sand, and gravel
	Pleistocene	Glacial drift		1–10	Boulders and gravel of granite, other igneous rocks, and limestone
		Bench gravel		10–50	Deposits of gravel and sand forming flat-topped benches
	Eocene	Fort Union formation		1,850–1,950	A non-marine sandy formation containing massive sandstone, buff and gray shale, and coal beds
	Eocene (?)	Lance formation		820	A brackish to fresh water sandy formation containing brown and gray sandstone, shale, clay, and earthy lignite
Mesozoic	Upper Cretaceous	Montana group	Bearpaw shale	1,000–1,200	Steel-gray to black and greenish-black marine shale containing beds of bentonite and lumpy concretions
			Judith River formation	200–500	Beds of fresh and brackish water origin containing sandstone, sandy shale, and gypsiferous and lignitic clay. Gas at Baker
			Claggett shale	430–650	Dark-gray to brownish-black marine shale containing beds of bentonite and yellow calcareous concretions
			Eagle sandstone	120–220	Massive beds of white to buff sandstone and sandy shale; Virgelle sandstone member at base. Gas at Lake basin and Havre
		Colorado shale		1,740–2,080	Dark-blue to black marine shale containing beds of bentonite, calcareous concretions, sandy shale, and sandstone. Oil
		Dakota		?	Probably first oil sand at Cat Creek
	Lower Cretaceous	Kootenai formation		450–500	Non-marine red and green shale, sandstone, and nodular limestone. Second and Third Cat Creek sands
	Lower Cretaceous (?)	Morrison (?) formation		200–300	Variegated shales, lenses of sandstone, and thin limestone beds
	Upper Jurassic	Ellis formation		150–1,300	Marine sandy limestone, calcareous sandy shale, and sandstone. Oil at Kevin-Sunburst
Paleozoic	Pennsylvanian	Quadrant formation		1,288–1,670	Beds of marine and non-marine red and black shale, limestone, and sandstone. Oil at Devil's basin
	Mississippian	Madison limestone		1,950	Massive and thin-bedded marine limestone. Main oil at Kevin-Sunburst
	Cambrian			300	Conglomeratic limestone with flat pebbles
				750	Mainly greenish micaceous shale
				75	Coarse sandstone with layers of conglomerate
Proterozoic	Algonkian (Belt series)			300+	Dark limy shale

upper part of the Colorado shale is exposed. The crest of the dome is a network of small faults. Wells drilled in the dome have found no oil. The Quadrant quartzite is not yet tested.

In the Ingomar[1] dome, southwest of the Porcupine dome, the Judith River formation and Claggett shale crop out. A well has been drilled through the Third Cat Creek sand.

GEOLOGIC FORMATIONS EXPOSED IN THE PORCUPINE DOME, MONTANA
(After Bowen)

System	Group	Formation	Thickness, feet	Character
Quaternary				Alluvial sand, gravel, and silt along Yellowstone and Musselshell rivers and some of the smaller streams
Tertiary (?)		Lance		Brown, irregularly bedded sandstone, alternating with "somber" gray shale
Cretaceous	Montana	Bearpaw shale	900–1,000 ±	Dark, gray shale in which occur calcareous concretions containing marine invertebrate fossils
		Judith River	100–200 ±	Upper sandstone member, light-brown to light-gray massive sandstone. Middle member, light-gray to dark-gray shale. Lower member, sandstone which weathers brown and gives rise to large, boulder-like masses. The formation is of fresh-water origin in the western part of the field and of marine origin in the eastern part
		Claggett and Colorado shales	3,000	Dark gray to black shale; upper part highly plastic when wet, and contains fossils characteristic of the Claggett formations; lower part slightly darker in color, more fissile and less plastic when wet, and contains fossils of Colorado age

[1] HEALD, K. C., The Ingomar Anticline, Montana, U. S. Geol. Survey *Bull.* 786, pp. 1–37, 1927.

South-central Montana.—In south-central Montana near Billings (Fig. 273), the structure is dominated by the northwest end of the Big Horn Mountains and by the Beartooth Mountains. Northeast of Billings in the region of Huntley the Cretaceous rocks are found in folds under cover and certain structures were drilled but without finding oil. The area is highly faulted. The rocks of this field[1] are shown in the table

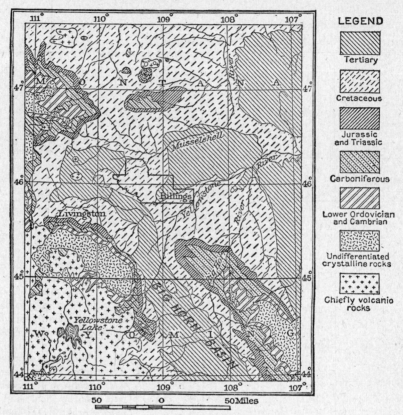

Fig. 273.—Geologic sketch or key map showing relation of Lake Basin field, Montana, to major structural features of the region. (*After Willis, Hancock, and others.*)

on page 470. In the Lake Basin area northwest of Billings there are two great folds, the northwest end of Big Horn Mountains and the Big Coulee-Hailstone dome. This dome has been drilled without discovery of oil. Faults are closely spaced, particularly in zones of regional shearing. Oil is found in the Big Lake field, 30 miles west of Billings, in the Soap Creek field, about 50 miles southeast of Billings, and in Elk basin south of Billings on the Wyoming line.

[1] HANCOCK, E. T., Geology and Oil and Gas Prospects of the Huntley Field, Montana, U. S. Geol. Survey *Bull.* 711G, pp. 105–148, 1920

Big Lake.—The Big Lake oil[1] field is 30 miles west of Billings in Stillwater County. It is a section of the Lake Basin area described by Hancock. Oil was found in 1924, and the field was outlined soon afterward (Fig. 274). The area containing oil seems to be confined to a small part of the top of a dome around which the oil sand contains salt water.

The Judith River formation lies at the surface upon the Big Lake dome. Gas in small amounts is found in the Claggett formation at a depth of 650 feet, in the Eagle at 1,200 feet, and in large amounts in the

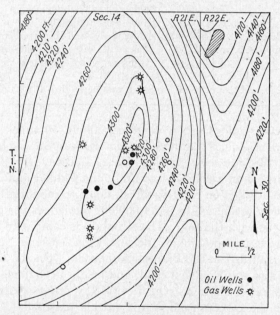

Fig. 274.—Contour map showing structure of Big Lake oil field, Montana. (*After Bauer.*)

Frontier sand at 2,980 feet. Oil with much gas is found in the Dakota sand at 3,824 feet. The oil has a gravity of 45° Bé., is high in gasoline, and yields a large proportion of lubricating oils. It congeals at 66° F. and requires special treatment for piping in cold weather. The gas in the sands above the oil horizon is used for making carbon black at a plant 5 miles east of the field. The field produced 195,000 barrels of oil to January 1, 1929.

The Broadview dome, northeast of Big Lake and northwest of Billings has been drilled. One well is sunk to the top of the Quadrant formation. Gas was found in the Frontier sands.

[1] HANCOCK, E. T., Geology and Oil and Gas Prospects of the Lake Basin Field, Montana, U. S. Geol. Survey *Bull.* 691, pp. 101–147, 1918.

BAUER, C. M., Lake Basin Oil Field, *Mining Met.*, vol. 6, pp. 22–25, 1925.

SECTION OF THE LAKE BASIN FIELD

(*After Bauer*)

Formation	Thickness, feet	Description
Montana:		
Lennep................	15–25	Sandstone, light gray, well bedded, marine
Bearpaw..............	380	Shale, gray, includes sand lenses, marine
Judith River..........	650	Sandstone, some shale and lignite
Claggett..............	550	Shale and sandstone, marine
Eagle.................	220	Sandstones and shales
Telegraph Creek.......	360–400	Sandy shales and thin sandstone
Colorado group..........	2,100	Shale with several sandstones, including the Frontier which produces much gas in Big Lake field
Dakota.................	50+	Sand, produces oil in Big Lake field.

In Stillwater and Carbon counties, about 50 miles southwest of Billings, there is a line of folding striking northwest on which the following domes (Fig. 268) are located: Nye, Dean, Roscoe, Dry Creek, Golden. To the southwest on a parallel fold are found Fiddler and McKay fields. In 1928 a well drilled on the Dry Creek dome to the Frontier sand developed a gas flow estimated to be 11,000,000 cubic feet per day, and light oil was sprayed with the gas. The structure is complexly faulted. The Golden dome is tested through the first Frontier sand. A well on the Dean dome is drilled to the Frontier formation. On the Roscoe dome a well is drilled to the Kootenai sand, and on the Nye dome one is drilled to the Quadrant formation. On the McKay dome a large flow of gas was found in the Dakota sand, but it quickly played out.

Soap Creek.—The Soap Creek[1] field is on the northeast slope of the Big Horn Mountains near the Wyoming line. It is a dome on the Soap Creek anticline which strikes northwest parallel to the mountains. Wells drilled in February, 1921, discovered a heavy black oil (20° Bé.) high in sulphur. The rocks of the district include Niobrara shale, Carlile shale, Frontier formation, Mowry shale, Thermopolis shale, and Cloverly formation, all of which are eroded from above the Soap Creek dome.

The Embar may be represented by the lower 125 feet of beds included in the Chugwater formation which contains gypsum and limestone. It carries oil in Wyoming but none in Soap Creek field.

[1] THOM, W. T., JR., and G. F. MOULTON, The Soap Creek Oil Field, Crow Indian Reservation, Montana, U. S. Geol. Survey *Press Bull.*, pp. 1–15, 1921.

THOM, W. T., JR., Oil and Gas Prospects in and Near Crow Indian Reservation, Montana, U. S. Geol. Survey *Bull.* 736, pp. 35–54, 1923.

SECTION OF SOAP CREEK AREA MONTANA
(After Thom and Moulton)

Group	Thickness, feet	Description
Morrison........	250+	Upper Jurassic or Lower Cretaceous; variegated clays, etc.
Unconformity (?)		
Sundance........	650–680	Upper Jurassic; Ellis in part; green sandstone, white and pink limestone, green and pink shale
Chugwater......	590–610	Triassic; shales, sandstones, gypsum, a little limestone
Tensleep........	60	Pennsylvanian; yellow sandstone. Oil in Soap Creek district
Amsden.........	275	Pennsylvanian; thin white and red limestone, quartzitic sandstone, and red shale equivalent to Quadrant; yields oil at Soap Creek
Unconformity		
Madison........		Limestone, Mississippian; upper part contains oil. Probably source of oil at Soap Creek

A well at 1,534 feet obtained some oil from the Tensleep sandstone, and at 1,642 feet it obtained between 200 and 400 barrels daily from the Amsden. Another well obtained an estimated production of 1,500 barrels a day from the Amsden. A third well obtained a little oil from the lower Amsden at 1,710 feet. This well penetrated the upper part of the Madison at 1,738 feet and was sunk to a depth of 1,810 feet when the well flowed a small stream of oil. Its capacity was estimated to be 200 barrels a day. The oil is believed to have originated in the Madison and to have migrated through faults and fractures into the Amsden and Tensleep formations. Gas pressures are low. The South Soap Creek and Rotten Grass domes are on the Soap Creek anticline to the south of Soap Creek. The Reed dome is 4 miles west of Rotten Grass dome (p. 452).

WYOMING

General Features.—Wyoming is made up of lofty mountain ranges and intermontane basins. In the northern part of the state there are three great anticlinal ranges, between which lie two great synclinal basins. The Black Hills, in the northeast corner, extend into Wyoming from South Dakota; west of them is the Big Horn Range, and west of it the Shoshone Range of Yellowstone Park. Southwest of the Big Horn Mountains and nearly parallel to them is the Wind River Range. The Front Range, known in Wyoming as the Laramie Range, occupies a large area in the southeast quarter of the state. In the southwest corner is the Wyoming Range, about parallel to the Wasatch Range of northern Utah. The Owl Creek Mountains lie southeast of the Shoshone Mountains.   In the central and southern part of the state are the Rattlesnake and Sweetwater Mountains.

The mountains are, in the main, anticlinal folds, the tops of which are eroded, so that in some of them the strata from the pre-Cambrian to the Tertiary are exposed (Fig. 275).   On the flanks of the mountain folds and in the interiors of the basins there are many subordinate folds, and on these are the principal oil fields.   There are altogether about 150 anticlines and domes.   Many of these have been drilled without yielding oil or gas.   About 30 produced oil and gas in considerable quantities.

A considerable part of Wyoming is underlain by Cretaceous beds, and these have supplied nearly all the oil produced.   The principal productive strata of the Cretaceous are in the Colorado group, which

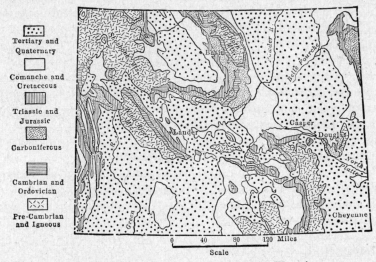

Tertiary and Quaternary

Comanche and Cretaceous

Triassic and Jurassic

Carboniferous

Cambrian and Ordovician

Pre-Cambrian and Igneous

Scale 0 40 80 120 Miles

FIG. 275.—Sketch showing Big Horn basin, Wyoming.

includes the chief oil-producing sands in central Wyoming and in the Big Horn basin, and the Cloverly group of sands which include the "Muddy" sands.   These were once classed as Lower Cretaceous, but W. T. Lee has included the "Muddy" sands in the Rock Creek region in the Dakota formation (base of Upper Cretaceous).

At places in the Big Horn and Wind River basins the sands of the Chugwater formation of Triassic age carry heavy oil.   In north-central Wyoming the Embar limestone of Permian age carries a heavy black oil in many fields.   The Tensleep formation of Pennsylvanian age also produces black oil.   This oil could probably be produced in large amounts, but it is not in great demand on account of the expense of refining it. The Amsden formation is oil bearing at North Sunshine and Four Bear fields.   The Madison limestone yields oil at Frannie.

Nearly all of the oil fields of Wyoming are located on domes. Shannon pool is on a plunging anticline sealed by a fault and Osage field is located on two structural terraces. A number of monoclines, terraces, and monoclines of low dip have been drilled, however, without finding oil. The oil of the Douglas field has probably accumulated at or near an unconformity between steeply tilted Cretaceous rocks and flat-lying Tertiary beds.

In 1929 Wyoming produced 19,190,000 barrels of oil valued at $25,-700,000 and 44,700,000 gallons of natural gas gasoline, valued at $3,250,-000. In 1928 the state produced 47,490,000,000 cubic feet of natural gas valued at $3,527,000.

Big Horn Basin.—The Big Horn basin[1] is a depression nearly surrounded by high mountain ranges. On the east lie the Big Horn Mountains, on the south the Owl Creek and Bridger ranges, and on the west the Shoshone Mountains (Fig. 276). The rocks dip from the mountains toward the center of the basin, where the older formations are deeply buried. The Big Horn basin may be separated into two parts—an inner or central part, in which the surface rocks belonging to the Wasatch and younger formations are almost horizontal, and an outer or border part adjacent to the mountains, in which the beds older than the Wasatch are thrown into small folds. The Wasatch and younger beds of the central part are not quite horizontal, however, for they dip slightly toward the middle trough, which trends about N.40° W.

Near the mountains there are two or more rudely circular chains of anticlines and domes, one inside the other (Fig. 277). All of the producing folds are elongated domes, or anticlines plunging at both ends. Their axes are rudely parallel to the axes of the mountain ranges, which almost encircle the basin. The domes and anticlines have large closures; that of the Grass Creek anticline, the most productive in the basin, is

[1] HEWETT, D. F., and C. T. LUPTON, Anticlines in the Southern Part of the Big Horn Basin, Wyoming, U. S. Geol. Survey *Bull.* 656, 1917.

————, The Shoshone River Section, Wyoming, U. S. Geol. Survey *Bull.* 541, pp. 89–113, 1912.

HINTZE, F. F., JR., The Basin and Greybull Oil and Gas Fields, Wyoming, Wyo. State Geologist's Office *Bull.* 10, 1914.

DARTON, N. H., Mineral Resources of the Big Horn Mountain Region, U. S. Geol. Survey *Bull.* 285, pp. 303–310, 1906.

FISHER, C. A., Geology and Water Resources of the Big Horn Basin, Wyoming, U. S. Geol. Survey *Prof. Paper* 53, 1906.

WASHBURNE, C. W., Gas Fields of the Big Horn Basin, Wyoming, U. S. Geol. Survey *Bull.* 340, pp. 348–363, 1908.

SCHULTZ, A. R., Geology and Geography of a Portion of Lincoln County, Wyoming, U. S. Geol. Survey *Bull.* 543, 1914.

HEALD, K. C., The Oil-bearing Horizon of Wyoming, Am. Assoc. Pet. Geol. *Bull.*, vol. 5, pp. 186–211, 1921.

LUPTON, C. T., Results and Prospects of Deeper Drilling in the Rocky Mountains Field, Am. Assoc. Pet. Geol. *Bull.*, vol. 7, pp. 400–411, 1923.

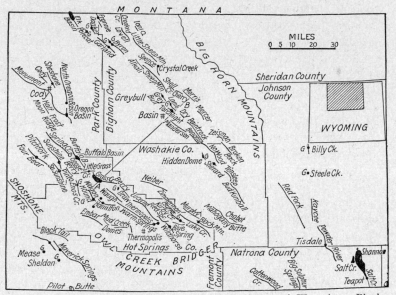

Fig. 276.—Map showing anticlines (lines) of north-central Wyoming. Black areas indicate oil except where lettered *G*, which indicates gas. (*After Hewitt, Lupton, Collier, Richardson, Heald, and others.*)   For section *AB*, see Fig. 277.

WYOMING OIL PRODUCTION
(Barrels)

Field	1928	Total to Dec. 31, 1928	Field	1928	Total to Dec. 31, 1928
Alkali Butte....	5,670	5,670	Mule Creek....	122,377	1,005,994
Ant Hills.......	8,719	8,719	Notches........	Shut in	167,114
Big Muddy.....	980,021	19,603,323	Oregon Basin...	838,665	838,665
Bolton Creek...	Shut in	24,392	Osage..........	149,846	1,115,269
Byron..........	12,525	293,640	Pilot Butte.....	17,724	467,098
Dallas-Derby...	86,518	975,777	Poison Spider...	350,393	1,329,291
Dutton Creek..	13,852	21,242	Rex Lake.......	17,676	161,361
Elk Basin......	358,415	8,164,021*	Rock River.....	921,622	11,596,728
Ferris.........	19,202	393,173	Salt Creek......	14,046,081	206,340,268
Frannie........	28,027	28,027	Shannon.......	Abandoned	55,441
Grass Creek....	859,765	20,922,164	Simpson Ridge.	24,223	123,149
Greybull.......	4,126	338,947	Spring Valley...		97,290
Hamilton.......	293,379	1,894,655	Teapot N. R....	Shut in	3,618,803
Hudson........	107,609	808,845	Teapot Outside.	6,544	9,019
Labarge........	450,022	689,231	Torchlight......	2,288	252,376
Lance Creek....	200,872	3,911,165	Warm Springs..		170,443
Lost Soldier....	1,429,294	11,235,344	Wertz..........		3,423
			Total.........	21,355,455	296,670,067

* Elk basin production Wyoming side of field only.

over 2,000 feet. Many of the oil-bearing folds are faulted, but faulting seems to influence accumulation favorably. For a productive region that is so much faulted, surface indications of oil are not numerous, although oil seeps have been found on or near the Bonanza, Sherard, and Lysite Mountains anticlines, and near the base of the Chugwater formation on the Red Spring anticline. The oil-bearing strata are all or nearly all marine. Salt water is found in many of the folds, but in some of them it is not very salty. The water below the oil on both limbs of the Grass Creek anticline is neither sulphurous nor very salty but is somewhat alkaline. The surface water has probably entered the oil-bearing strata and, moving down the dip, has either diluted the water that was once stored in the sands or carried it out.

The chief productive horizons of the Big Horn basin are the Frontier sands which yield large amounts of oil at Grass Creek and Elk basin, a sand in the Mowry which yields oil at Torchlight and Greybull, and the Cloverly which produces oil at Greybull. These strata yield light oils that are readily salable. Lower strata include the Morrison which contains heavy oil at Grass Creek; the Chugwater which contains heavy oil at Grass Creek and Hamilton; the Embar which contains heavy oil at Warm Springs, Grass Creek, Oregon basin and at many other places; Tensleep which carries heavy oil at Grass Creek and Oregon basin; and the Amsden formation which produces oil at Sunshine and Four Bear; and the Madison limestone which produces oil at Frannie.

In 1917 Hewett and Lupton noted that practically all of the oil and gas produced in the Big Horn basin had come from the inner group of folds—the ones nearest the center of the basin. Twelve years of development work has shown that this relation is still essentially true as regards the production of oil in the Frontier group, although the Enos Creek and Kirby Creek anticlines, which are mountainward folds, carry some oil and gas in the Frontier formation. In rocks below the Frontier this relation is not so clearly evident. Black oil is found in the Chugwater, Embar, and lower strata in folds of the outer as well as the inner group. The inner folds are more productive than the outer folds, because they are situated in positions where they gather oil from larger areas, and their oil deposits are more generally protected from losses by leakage and movements of ground water. In an outer dome containing oils in the

Fig. 277.—Section across the southern part of Big Horn Basin, Wyoming, on line *AB*, Fig. 276. (After Hewett and Lupton.)

State Teachers College Library
Willimantic, Conn.

FORMATIONS OF BIG HORN BASIN, WYOMING
(*After Hewett and Lupton*)

System	Formation			Thickness, feet	Character of rocks
Quaternary	Alluvium			0–50	Valley and flood-plain deposits along streams
	Hot-spring deposits			. . . . . .	Local deposits of calcareous tufa
	Terrace gravels			0–30	Gravels and boulders washed from adjacent mountains
Tertiary	Volcanic rock			(?)	Andesitic tuffs and flows on west side of basin
	Wasatch			1,300+	Red and drab clay; buff and white sandstone with gravel lenses. Many areas of badlands around border of basin
	—Unconformity—				
	Fort Union			2,000–5,600	Buff and white gritty sandstone, with drab, red, and green clay; lenses of gravel and lenticular beds of coal
Tertiary (?)	—Unconformity—				
	Lance			840–1,800	Buff and drab sandstone with drab and green shale. No red shale or coal beds
Cretaceous	Montana	Meeteetse		250–1,400	Soft gray and brown shale; gray and buff sandstone and lenticular beds of coal
		Mesaverde		1,120–1,410	Buff and white sandstone, gray and brown shale and lenticular beds of coal near base
	Colorado	Cody		1,900–3,400	Gray, green, and black shale, with calcareous concretions near base, merging with buff sandstone at top. No persistent sharply marked beds
		Frontier		494–648	West side; seven or more beds of gray and buff sandstone with gray and brown shale and bentonite
					East side; two to six or more beds of sandstone
		Mowry		160–375	Hard gray shale containing fish scales with lenses of gravel-bearing sandstone
		Thermopolis		400–800	Gray to black shale with one persistent sandstone, the Muddy sand of the drillers
	Cloverly			110–300	Two beds of massive buff sandstone separated by gray or variegated shale. Upper sand is the Greybull
Cretaceous (?)	Morrison			150–580	Purplish and pale greenish-gray shales with sandstones interbedded
Jurassic	Sundance			250–530	Greenish-gray sandstones and shales with a little limestone interbedded
Triassic	Chugwater			700–1,100	Red Beds. Red sandstones and shales with a thick bed of gypsum near top
Carboniferous	Embar			250–480	Gray limestone, with gray and red sandy shale and gypsum interbedded. Limestone very thin on east side of basin
	Tensleep			30–230	Massive gray sandstone, containing thin layers of limestone
	Amsden			150–200	Red sandy shales and sandstones, with layers of limestone and chert
	Madison			600–1,000	Gray massive limestones
Ordovician	Big Horn			150–300	Siliceous gray limestone, very hard and massive
Cambrian	Deadwood			700–900	Sandstone, shale, conglomerate, and limestone

deeper beds, the deposits in the lower strata would in general be less likely to suffer loss. Many of the deposits in the lower beds have not yet been exploited, because the demand for heavy oil is limited and the price is low; the distribution of the larger deposits of black oil is known only in a general way.

In most of the oil fields that are extensively developed, the basinward side of the dome is gentler than the mountainward side; consequently, the productive areas are greater on the basinward side of the axis. Moreover, the oil blanket generally descends to lower depths on the gentler side. In the Grass Creek pool it lies 200 to 300 feet lower on the basinward side. This distribution is due to the position of the larger gathering areas, which in general are on the basinward sides of the folds.

Northeast Side of Big Horn Basin.—Elk Basin field is in the northeast part of Big Horn basin on the boundary between Wyoming and Montana. The field is on a dome extending northwest. The rocks dip about 10 to 20 degrees or more, and the dome is outlined by the Eagle sandstone and by a sandstone in the Mesaverde. It is cut by many faults[1] that strike northeast and by other faults that strike northwest. The oil and gas are found in two sands of the Frontier formation (Colorado group) at depths about 1,100 feet or more in the center of the field. The Second sand is highly productive and the field, to January 1, 1929, had yielded 8,164,021 barrels of oil from the Wyoming end and 867,991 barrels from the Montana end of the dome. The gravity of the oil is about 40° Bé. The oil in the First sand extends downward 150 feet below the top of the dome and in the Second sand it extends downward about 350 feet. Gas[2] is found in the Greybull sand of the Cloverly (Dakota) at 2,400 feet. This gas is under a pressure of 925 pounds per square inch which is nearly a normal hydrostatic pressure. Notwithstanding the extensive faulting, the field shows no oil or gas seeps. Danker, or Big Polecat dome, is about 10 miles southeast of Elk basin, on the extension of the Garland anticline. Gas is found in the Frontier formation. On the Frannie fold, east of Elk basin, black oil is found in the Embar and Madison limestones in considerable amounts. In the Garland[3] field, 20 miles southeast of Elk basin, oil is found in the Frontier formation, and gas in the Cloverly, Morrison, Embar, and Tensleep formations.

Greybull is 35 miles southeast of Garland (Fig. 276). The Frontier formation is exposed on the axis of a dome (Fig. 278). A high-grade

[1] Estabrook, E. L., Faulting in Wyoming Oil Fields, Am. Assoc. Pet. Geol. *Bull.*, vol. 7, pp. 95–102, 1923.

Bartram, J. G., "Structure of Typical American Oil Fields," vol. 2, pp. 577–588, 1929.

[2] Bartlett, A. B., Wyo. Geol. Survey, *Thirteenth Ann. Rept.*, Table 4, 1926.

[3] Ziegler, V., The Byron Oil and Gas Fields, Big Horn County, Wyoming, Wyo. Geol. Survey *Bull.* 14, pp. 181–207, 1917.

paraffin oil and much gas are found in the Greybull sand of the Cloverly formation. The gas is at the top, and the oil is mainly on the west and north sides of the dome. At Crystal Creek, 15 miles north of Greybull, a dome exposes the Chugwater (Triassic). Some oil is found in the Tensleep formation.

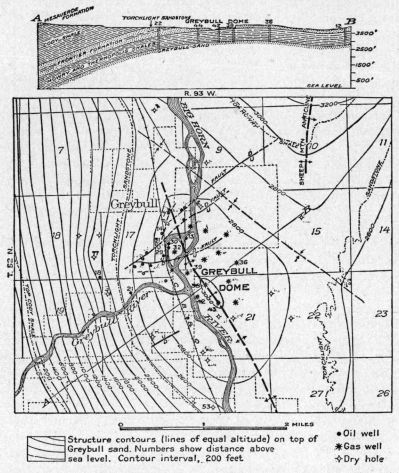

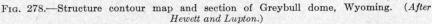

FIG. 278.—Structure contour map and section of Greybull dome, Wyoming. (*After Hewett and Lupton.*)

Southeast Side of Big Horn Basin.—Torchlight dome, 10 miles southeast of Greybull and 2 miles east of Basin, is outlined by the Torchlight sand of the upper part of the Frontier formation. At depths of 225 to 450 feet the Octh Louie and Kimball sands of the Mowry formation yield light oil. The Lamb anticline to the east of Greybull (Fig. 279) found gas in the Peay and Greybull sands. At the crest of the Bonanza dome, 18 miles southeast of Basin, an oil seep is found in a sand of the Mowry shale. The oil was used by early settlers. At Hidden dome, 22 miles southeast of Basin, gas is found in the Frontier sand.

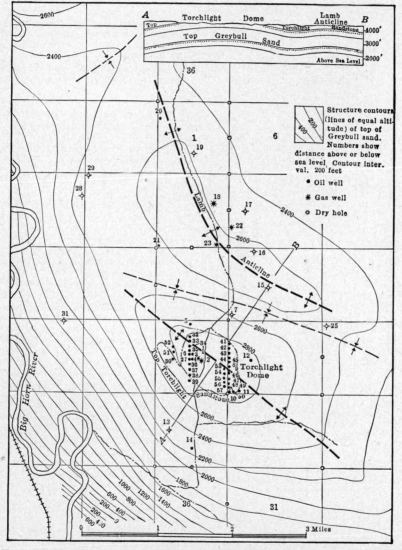

FIG. 279.—Contour map and cross-section of Lamb anticline and Torchlight dome, Bighorn Basin, Wyoming. Numbers with symbols refer to descriptions in U. S. Geol. Survey *Bull*. 656. (*After Lupton.*)

South Side of Big Horn Basin.—At Black Mountain, 30 miles south of Hidden dome on a narrow anticline, black oil is found in the Embar and Tensleep formations. On the Lake Creek anticline, which is about

GEOLOGIC FORMATIONS EXPOSED NEAR THERMOPOLIS, WYOMING
(*After Collier*)

System	Group or formation	Thickness, feet	Character of the rocks
Cretaceous	Frontier formation	390	Seven or more beds of gray and buff sandstones with interbedded gray and brown shales and bentonite. Marine deposits
Cretaceous	Mowry shale	266	Hard gray shale containing fish scales and having a few interbedded lenses of sandstone. A marine deposit
Cretaceous	Thermopolis shale	589	Gray to black shale with one persistent sandstone, called the Muddy sand by drillers, near its base. A marine deposit
Cretaceous	Cloverly formation	248	Two beds of massive buff sandstone separated by variegated shale. Upper bed is known as the Greybull sand. In part at least a fresh-water deposit
Cretaceous (?)	Morrison formation	145	Purplish and pale greenish-gray shales with sandstone interbedded. A fresh-water deposit
Jurassic	Sundance formation	240	Greenish-gray sandstone, shale, and limestone containing many oyster, *Gryphaea*, and belemnite shells. Marine deposits
Triassic	Chugwater formation	1,200	"Red Beds." Red sandstone and shale containing beds of gypsum, the largest having a thickness of more than 60 feet near the top of the formation, and at least one bed of limestone near the middle. Largely a fresh-water formation. Oil in Hamilton dome
Carboniferous	Embar group	270	About 60 feet of the upper part consists of calcareous shale, sandstone, and gypsum, which represent the Triassic Dinwoody formation. Below this about 60 feet of limestone and about 150 feet of thin-bedded sandstone, reddish shale, and limestone, including the "Embar sand" of drillers, represent the Park City formation. Oil in Warm Springs Hamilton and Black Mountain dome
Carboniferous	Tensleep sandstone	250	Gray cross-bedded sandstone. Probably marine. Oil at Black Mountain
Carboniferous	Amsden formation	300	Red sandy shale and sandstone with layers of limestone and chert. Marine
Carboniferous	Madison limestone	600–1,000	Gray massive limestone. Marine
Ordovician	Big Horn dolomite	150–300	Siliceous gray limestone. Marine
Cambrian	Deadwood formation	700–900	Sandstone, shale, conglomerate, and limestone. Marine
Pre-Cambrian	Metamorphic complex		A complex of schists, gneiss, etc.

a mile west of the Black Mountain anticline, a little oil was found in the Embar formation, and at Kirby Creek, 8 miles west of Black Mountain, on a small dome oil and gas are found in the Frontier sands.

A mile or two north of Thermopolis the Warm Springs anticline strikes nearly east. On it several domes are developed. The West dome is 4 miles east of Thermopolis Hot Springs and the East dome is 7 miles east of Thermopolis Hot Springs. Both domes have yielded heavy black oil from the Embar limestone, which is encountered at a depth of about 1,000 feet.

At the Hamilton[1] dome, 20 miles northwest of Thermopolis on the Cotton Wood anticline, oil has been produced from a sand in the red beds (Chugwater) 440 feet below the top of the formation. This is a fresh-water formation and is generally barren of oil in this region, and, according to Collier, the oil probably leaked into it from a lower formation. Oil is developed also in the Embar limestone.

Grass Creek.—The Grass Creek[2] oil field, 28 miles northwest of Thermopolis, is one of the most productive oil fields in Wyoming. Oil was discovered in 1914 in the Frontier formation and in 1916 there were 129 wells producing oil. The peak of production was reached in March, 1918, when 292,887 barrels of oil were produced from 240 wells. To January 1, 1929, the total production amounted to 20,922,164 barrels. Although some of the wells flowed at an early stage, most of the oil is pumped. It is light, about 44° Bé. and is high in gasoline. There is also a considerable production of gasoline from the compression of gas which yields 3.5 gallons of gasoline per 1,000 cubic feet. The oil from the Frontier sands is met at depths of 365 feet to 1,000 feet. Deeper tests discovered a heavy black oil in the Morrison, Chugwater, Embar, and Tensleep formations and there has been a small production of black oil.

The Grass Creek anticline is a broad basinward fold with a large closure. The lowest formation cropping out on the Grass Creek anticline is the Cody shale which is exposed at a horizon 300 feet above the base. The Frontier formation is between 494 and 648 feet thick. It contains nine oil sands which are separated by shale and bentonite. A map is shown by Fig. 280, page 482 and a section of the oil field by Fig. 281, page 482. The east slope of the dome is gentler and broader than the west slope and is more productive. Edge water is 300 feet

[1] COLLIER, A. J., Oil in the Warm Springs and Hamilton Domes, Near Thermopolis, Wyoming, U. S. Geol. Survey *Bull.* 711, pp. 61–73, 1920.

HEWETT, D. F., Map of Grass Creek Quadrangle in U. S. Geol. Survey *Prof. Paper* 145, 1926.

[2] HEWETT, D. F., Geology and Oil and Coal Resources of the Oregon Basin, Meeteetse, and Grass Creek Basin Quadrangle, Wyoming, U. S. Geol. Survey *Prof. Paper* 145, pp. 1–111, 1926.

HARRISON, T. S., "Structure of Typical American Oil Fields," vol. 2, pp. 623–635, 1929.

lower on the east side than on the west side, the total productive area being 1,300 acres.

The Mayfield pool on the east extension of the Grass Creek axis produced a small amount of oil. On the Little Grass Creek dome, on

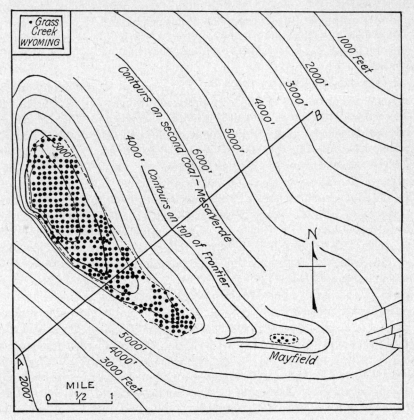

Fig. 280.—Map of Grass Creek oil field, Wyoming. (*After Hewett.*)

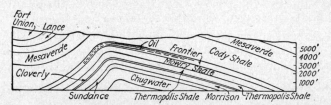

Fig. 281.—Section of Grass Creek oil field on line *AB*, Fig. 280. (*After Hewett.*)

the northwest side of the Grass Creek dome, wells to the Frontier formation encountered large amounts of gas. One well is estimated to have had an initial daily capacity of 40,000,000 cubic feet. Gas is found also on Golden Eagle dome 10 miles east-southeast of Grass Creek in the Mesa

Verde formation. At Enos Creek field, 6 miles west of Grass Creek, gas is found in the Frontier sands.

Buffalo basin is 12 miles northwest of Grass Creek. A broad dome brings up the Cody shale which is surrounded by the Mesaverde formation. Gas is developed in the Frontier sands. A pipe line extends to Greybull. In the Sunshine field oil is found in the Amsden formation and in the South Sunshine field in the Embar limestone. In the Four Bear structure, west of Buffalo basin, black oil is found in the Amsden formation.

Oregon Basin.—South Oregon basin is 30 miles northwest of Grass Creek on a broad dome on which the Frontier formation crops out. North Oregon basin is 6 miles north of South Oregon basin, and the same formation crops out on a broad dome. In both fields large flows of gas are found in the Cloverly formation. The Oregon Basin fields[1] were drilled for oil, but edge water was found below the gas without discovering

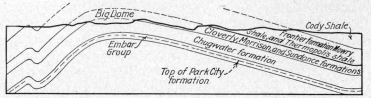

Fig. 282.—Section of Big Dome (Maverick Springs) anticline, Fremont County, Wyoming (*After Collier.*) Embar formation is oil bearing. (*After Collier.*)

oil. Deep tests in 1927 found large amounts of black oil in the Embar limestone at 3,360 feet and in the Tensleep formation. Later tests found oil in the Madison limestone. Oil is found in a well 3 miles northeast of Cody, which is sunk on the Shoshone anticline on which the Colorado, probably the Frontier formation, crops out. A little oil is found in Frontier and Muddy sands and in the Embar limestone.

Maverick Springs.—Maverick Springs[2] anticline is in the Wind River basin 35 miles southwest of Thermopolis. Three domes are developed on the anticline: Circle Ridge, Big Dome, and Little Dome. In the Circle Ridge dome the top of the Embar formation is exposed and wells drilled about 300 feet deep encounter heavy oil. At Big Dome (Maverick Springs) the Chugwater crops out in the center of the dome (Fig. 282). This dome has large closure and is capable of producing considerable heavy oil from the Embar and Tensleep formations. At Mease, 8 miles west of Maverick Springs dome, a well encountered gas. On Sheldon anticline, 5 miles south of Maverick Springs, gas is found in Frontier sands.

[1] Hewett, D. F., *op. cit.*

Ziegler, V., The Oregon Basin Oil and Gas Field, Park County, Wyo. Geol. Survey *Bull.* 15, pp. 209–242, 1917.

[2] Collier, A. J., Anticlines near Maverick Springs, Fremont County, Wyoming. U. S. Geol. Survey *Bull.* 711, pp. 149–171, 1920.

Pilot Butte.—The Pilot Butte[1] oil field is 27 miles northwest of Riverton and 6 miles northeast of the Winkleman gas field, which is on the

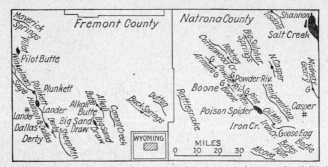

Fig. 283.—Map of parts of Fremont and Natrona counties, south of Bighorn basin, Wyoming, showing oil fields (black), gas fields (black with letter *G*) and anticlines. (*After Woodruff, Collier, Richardson, Heald, and others.*)

Shoshone anticline (Fig. 283). Pilot Butte field is a dome (Fig. 284) which brings the Pierre shale to the surface. The rocks dip steeply away from the axis and on the northwest side of the dome are nearly on edge.

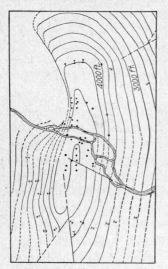

Several faults cut the rocks near the crest of the dome. The field was drilled between 1916 and 1920 and has produced about 467,098 barrels of oil. In December, 1927, 12 wells were being pumped, yielding a total of about 55 barrels of oil per day. The oil is high-grade paraffin oil with a gravity of 37° Bé. and is piped to Riverton for shipment to Casper refineries. The oil is found in sandy shales of the Pierre about the horizon of the Shannon sands, but there are several productive horizons. These are met at depths from 300 to 1,000 feet. Certain wells produce from fractures. A deep test found much gas and some high-gravity oil near the Mowry-Thermopolis contact at a depth of 2,970 feet.

Fig. 284.—Contour map of Pilot Butte oil field, Wyoming. (*After Fisher and Lowrie.*)

Big Sand Draw.—At Big Sand Draw,[2] 20 miles southeast of Riverton and 28 miles east of Lander, a sharp elongated dome striking northwest brings up beds of the Steele formation, below which is the Niobrara and below that are Carlile and Frontier formations (Figs. 283, 285). Tertiary

[1] ZIEGLER, V., The Pilot Butte Oil Field, Fremont County, Wyoming, Wyo. Geol. Survey *Bull.* 13, pp. 139–178, 1916.

[2] COLLIER, A. J., Gas in the Big Sand Draw Anticline, Fremont County, Wyoming, U. S. Geol. Survey *Bull.* 711, pp. 75–83, 1920.

RAE, C. E., Big Sand Draw Field, Fremont County, Wyoming, Am. Assoc. Pet. Geol. *Bull.* 12, pp. 1137–1146, 1928.

beds rest unconformably on the Cretaceous formations and obscure the structure. In 1918 a well 2,531 feet deep encountered a great flow of gas in the upper sand of the Frontier formation under a pressure of about 1,200 pounds per square inch. Other wells developed much gas, and the field now supplies Riverton and Lander with gas and also part of the needs of Casper. In December, 1928, the field had produced 20,000,000,000 cubic feet of gas from the upper Frontier formation and rock pressure was then more than 1,000 pounds per square inch. Oil showings are found at edge wells, but the field has not produced oil. The formations below the Upper Frontier are not tested on the dome. A delivery of gas amounting to 7,500,000,000 cubic feet between December, 1925, and December, 1927, caused the pressure to decline from 1,100 to 1,043 pounds. This indicates about 131,500,000,000 cubic feet down to 100 pounds which is the working pressure.

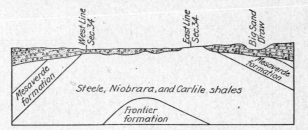

Fig. 285.—Cross-section of Big Sand Draw gas field, Wyoming. (*After Collier, U. S. Geol. Survey.*)

At Alkali Butte, 10 miles north of Big Sand Draw, the Steele shale crops out on an anticline. A little oil and gas are found in the Shannon sand. A deep well found oil in the "Muddy" sand. The well had an initial production of 550 barrels a day but quickly declined. In the Dakota and Lakota formations some oil was found. In the Buck Springs or Muskrat field east of Big Sand Draw a large gas well was drilled to the Upper Frontier sand in 1928 at a depth of 4,340 feet.

Lander.—Near Lander, about 18 miles southwest of Riverton and striking northwest, east of and nearly parallel to the Wind River Range, there is a great belt of deformation traced 45 miles on strike, which is called the Shoshone or Lander anticline (Fig. 283). On this fold are located from northwest to southeast seven oil or gas fields or domes. These are Winkleman, Sage Creek, Plunkett, Lander, Dallas, Derby, and Sheep Mountain. Oil seeps are found at several places along this axis. At Winkleman the Mowry shale crops out. A well 900 feet deep finds gas said to be in the Lakota sand. At Sage Creek[1] the Chugwater crops out at the top of the dome. The Embar is found at a depth of 900 feet and

[1] WOODRUFF E. G., The Lander Oil Field, Fremont County, Wyoming, U. S. Geol. Survey *Bull.* 452, pp. 1–36, 1911.

is said to contain black oil. At Plunkett anticline, 6 miles southeast of Sage Creek, a little oil was found in sands of the Mowry shale. At the

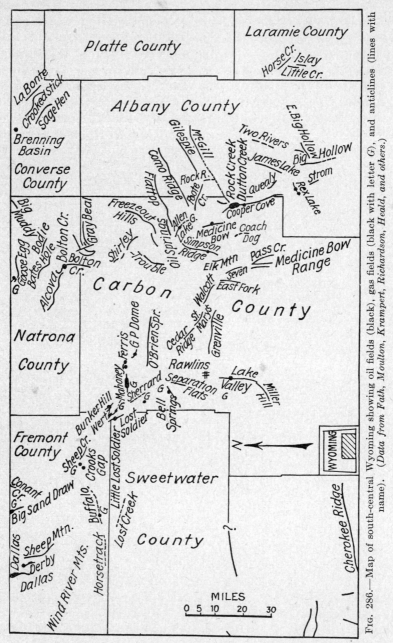

Fig. 286.—Map of south-central Wyoming showing oil fields (black), gas fields (black with letter *G*), and anticlines (lines with name). (*Data from Fath, Moulton, Krampert, Richardson, Heald, and others.*)

Lander (Hudson) dome, northeast of Lander, oil is found in the Embar about 800 feet deep and larger amounts in the Tensleep formation. At

Dallas dome, 8 miles southeast of Lander, and at Derby southeast of Dallas, oil is found in the Embar. The oil is from the Chugwater and Embar formations and is black and heavy. The fields near Lander supply fuel oil to the Chicago and Northwestern Railway, the Hudson, Dallas, and Derby fields producing about 500 barrels per day.

South-central Wyoming.—In south-central Wyoming[1] the Rawlins uplift extends northwest from Rawlins (Fig. 286) and is an anticlinal area about 50 miles long and 20 miles wide. A great fault zone striking northeast cuts across the uplift and faults down the northwest end, and in this downthrown block are located the oil fields of the Lost Soldier district which include the Little Lost Soldier, Wertz, Mahoney, Ferris, G. P., and other oil pools. Southeast of this field on the east side of the

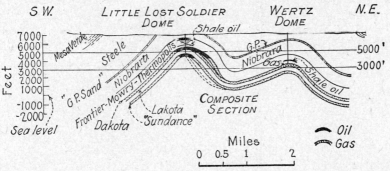

Fig. 287.—Section through Little Lost Soldier and Wertz domes, Wyoming. (*After Irwin.*)

Medicine Bow Range is an area of Cretaceous rocks that are thrown into strong folds. In this southeast belt are found the Simpson Ridge, Rock Creek, Rex Lake, and other oil and gas fields. There is a considerable production of oil in this region derived chiefly from Little Lost Soldier, Ferris, G. P., and Rock Creek (Rock River) fields. Pipe lines extend from Lost Soldier to Casper and Rawlins, and from Rock Creek to Lander.

Lost Soldier Region.—The Little Lost Soldier field (Fig. 287) is on a steep dome with a closure of 3,500 feet that brings the Niobrara formation to the surface. The north part of the dome is highly faulted. The sands of the Frontier, Mowry, Cloverly (Dakota), and Sundance are productive.[2] Wells drilled in 1916 found oil at a depth of 265 feet in a sand at the top of the Frontier. Wells having initial daily flows of 700 barrels were drilled to this sand, and an oil blanket of 160 acres was

[1] FATH, A. E., and G. F. MOULTON, Oil and Gas Fields of the Lost Soldier-Ferris District, Wyoming, U. S. Geol. Survey *Bull.* 756, pp. 1–57, 1924.

[2] KRAMPERT, E. W., The Oil Fields of the Rawlins-Lost Soldier District, Am. Assoc. Pet. Geol. *Bull.*, vol. 7, pp. 131–146, 1923.

IRWIN, J. S., Oil and Gas Fields of Lost Soldier District, Wyoming, "Structure of Typical American Oil Fields, vol. 2, pp. 636–666, 1929.

outlined in the Frontier formation. The Mowry carries oil over a small area. The Cloverly formation (Dakota) is encountered at a depth of 1,200 feet at the top of the dome. The Dakota sand and the Lakota sand, which some include with the Dakota formation, together form the chief reservoirs. Wells in the Dakota sand produced from 300 to 4,000 barrels a day. Oil is found also in the Sundance formation. The oil in the Frontier has a gravity of 31° Bé., that of the Dakota 33° Bé. Both are paraffin oils, that of the Dakota being particularly high in paraffin.

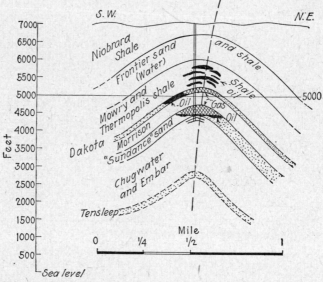

Fig. 288.—Section through Ferris dome, Wyoming. (*After Irwin.*)

In the Wertz dome, 2 miles east of Lost Soldier, the sands lie deeper than in the Little Lost Soldier dome. Oil is found in the Mowry formation, and a great gas well with an initial production of 40,000,000 cubic feet was drilled to the Dakota, which was met at a depth of 3,400 feet. This gas had an initial pressure of 1,840 pounds per square inch. It is high in gasoline and as much as 100 barrels a day have been obtained from drippings of the gas pipe line to Casper.

The Mahoney pool, 12 miles southeast of Little Lost Soldier dome, is a gas field located along the crests of two domes. The gas is derived from the Dakota and Sundance. The Ferris dome (Fig. 288) is 8 miles east of Mahoney and on the same anticlinal axis. Oil is produced from the Mowry, Dakota, Sundance, and Chugwater (?) formations. The G. P. pool is about 4 miles southeast of Ferris dome and on a parallel anticline. Oil is found at a depth of 1,585 feet in a horizon, which, according to Krampert, is a lenticular sand near the base of the Steele shale. The productive area is 160 acres. No dome is recognized.

On the O'Brien Springs anticline, which lies about 8 miles south of Ferris, a well found gas in the Frontier. On the Sherrard dome, 5 miles southwest of Mahoney, gas is found in both the Frontier and Dakota sands. The Bell Springs[1] district is about 20 miles southeast of Lost Soldier and 16 miles northwest of Rawlins. A dome trending northeast is faulted on the east side. Gas is found in a sand of the Dakota formation at a depth of 1,924 feet. One well is estimated to have had an initial capacity of 15,000,000 cubic feet per day.[2] The pressure of the gas is 860 pounds to the square inch.

In the Crooks Gap field, northwest of Lost Soldier, some oil has been found in the Frontier formation. In the Buffalo Basin field southwest of Crooks Gap, gas is found in a Frontier sand on a nose that plunges southeast. The oil sand is probably sealed up dip by dried petroleum.

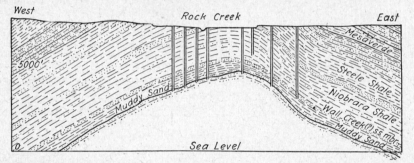

Fig. 289.—Section across Rock Creek oil field, Wyoming. (*After Hancock, Dobbin, Hoots, Dane, and Torrey.*)

Rock Creek.—The Rock Creek[3] oil field, 10 miles southwest of the town of Rock River and 40 miles northwest of Laramie, was opened in 1918 and to January 1, 1925, had produced about 10,000,000 barrels of oil having a gravity of about 36° Bé. The field is located on a structural dome (Fig. 289) and the rocks cropping out include the Mesaverde and Steele formations. The oil is found chiefly in basal beds of the Cloverly (Dakota), although oil is found also in the upper sands of the Cloverly, and small yields are obtained from the Wall Creek(?) sand. The Cloverly lies about 2,600 feet deep on top of the dome.[4] In the Dutton Creek dome, 5 miles south of Rock Creek, a little oil is found in the Muddy sand at a depth of 4,876 feet.

[1] Dobbin, C. E., H. W. Hoots, and C. H. Dane, Geology and Oil and Gas Possibilities of the Bell Springs District, Carbon County, Wyoming, U. S. Geol. Survey *Bull.* 796, pp. 171–198, 1928.

[2] Bartlett, A. B., Wyo. Geol. Survey *Thirteenth Ann. Rept.*, Table 11, 1926.

[3] Dobbin, C. E., H. W. Hoots, C. H. Dane, and E. T. Hancock, Geology of the Rock Creek Oil Field and Adjacent Areas in Carbon and Albany Counties, Wyoming, U. S. Geol. Survey *Bull.* 806D, pp. 131–153, 1929.

[4] Emery, W. B., Rock River Oil Field, Carbon County, Wyoming, "Structure of Typical American Oil Fields," vol. 2, pp. 614–623, 1929. Emery groups the 3 oil sands, first and second Muddy and Dakota in the Dakota formation.

GENERAL SECTION OF FORMATIONS, ROCK CREEK DISTRICT, WYOMING

(After Dobbin, Hoots, Dane, and Hancock)

Age	Group	Formation	Thickness, feet	General characteristics
Recent		Alluvium	Variable	Fine silt, clay, and loam
Pliocene and later		Terrace gravel	Variable	Fine to coarse gravel and moderate-sized boulders in places firmly cemented
Eocene		Hanna Unconformity	(?)	Yellowish-green sandy shale, massive yellowish-brown sandstone, carbonaceous shale, coarse conglomerate, and coal
		Lewis shale	2,500 ±	Dark marine shale containing several yellowish-brown fossiliferous sandstones
	Montana	Mesaverde	1,250	Chiefly massive to slabby and concretionary brown sandstone and zones of sandy material containing shale and thin beds of coal alternating with sandy shale. Top marked by grayish-white Pine Ridge sandstone member, which contains coal. Alternating marine and continental beds occur throughout the formation
		Steele shale	3,300 ±	Dark-gray to black shale containing several soft brown sandstones in its upper part
Upper Cretaceous		Niobrara shale	700	Dark-gray calcareous shale containing thin beds of sand and layers of impure chalk
		Carlile shale	460	Soft dark shale containing many ironstone concretions
	Colorado	Frontier	665	Dark shale about 625 feet thick, overlain by a brownish sandstone about 40 feet thick herein called the Wall Creek (?) sandstone member
		Mowry shale	120	Hard fissile dark-gray shale, weathering light gray, which contains numerous fossil fish scales
		Thermopolis shale	130	Soft dark shale containing near its middle a sandstone locally called the First Muddy sand
		Cloverly	125 ±	An upper sandstone 30 to 85 feet thick and a lower one about 60 feet thick, separated by about 30 feet of shale. Principal oil-producing formation
Cretaceous (?)		Morrison	225	Maroon, pink, and olive-green shale and a few thin sandstones. Yields dinosaurian fauna
Upper Jurassic		Sundance	350	Green and gray fossiliferous shale in upper part and massive to cross-bedded gray sandstone and gray shale in lower part
Triassic		Chugwater	1,350	Red shale, sandy shale, and gypsum, with beds of gray sandstone in upper part and thin beds of limestone
Permian		Forelle limestone	3	Lavender-colored limestone
		Satanka shale	140 ±	Red and green shale, gray limestone, gray sandstone, and gypsum
Pennsylvanian and Mississippian		Casper	1,000	About 300 feet of massive to cross-bedded sandstone merging downward into limestones, dolomite, and sandstones
Pre-Cambrian				

Medicine Bow oil field 10 miles northwest of Rock Creek is located on a dome in which the Steele shale crops out. A well found oil in the Frontier formation at a depth of 4,033 feet, but the oil soon played out. At Simpson Ridge, 10 miles west of Medicine Bow, the Mesaverde crops out on a long anticline and oil is won from the basal Mesaverde. A well drilled to the Frontier formation is 6,941 feet deep and is said to be the deepest well in the state. At Allen Lake, north of Medicine Bow, gas is found in the Dakota sand. The Niobrara formation crops out on a small dome surrounded by Steele shale. A gas well said to have daily capacity of 15,000,000 cubic feet is developed. At Rex Lake, 24 miles south of Rock Creek the Mesaverde formation crops out on an anticline that strikes northeast. Sands encountered at 3,800 and at 3,850 feet, said to be Dakota and Lakota, have encountered oil and gas. According to Bartlett,[1] the wells are estimated to have had initial productions of 400 barrels per day.

Salt Creek.—The Salt Creek[2] oil field is southeast of the Big Horn Mountains and about 40 miles north of Casper. It is located on a great dome which rises on an anticline that strikes west of north and is about 20 miles long. The Shannon pool lies on the north end of this anticline and the Teapot dome is on the same anticline south of the Salt Creek dome. The Shannon pool, Salt Creek dome, and Teapot dome are commonly included in the Salt Creek field. The Shannon pool was discovered in 1889 and the Salt Creek field proper in 1908. The first pipe line was laid from the field to the railroad at Casper in 1911. The total production of the field to the end of 1928 amounted to 206,340,268 barrels of oil.

The structure of Salt Creek dome (p. 90) is outlined by the Shannon and Parkman sandstones, which are displaced by many faults which die out on the flanks of the dome. The Steele shale crops out on the center of

[1] BARTLETT, A. B., Wyo. Geol. Survey *Thirteenth Ann. Rept.*, Table 14, 1926.

[2] WEGEMANN, C. H., The Salt Creek Oil Field, Wyoming, U. S. Geol. Survey *Bull.* 670, pp. 1–52, 1917.

———, Notes on Oil Fields of Wyoming, Am. Assoc. Pet. Geol. *Bull.*, vol. 4, pp. 37–42, 1920.

CLAPP, C. H., Report on the Teapot Dome Naval Reserve 3, Wyoming, before the United States Senate Commission on Public Lands and Surveys, *Rept.* 138, Oct. 22, 1923.

NOWELS, K. B., Preliminary Report on Water Conditions in the First Wall Creek Sand, Salt Creek Wyoming, Am. Assoc. Pet. Geol. *Bull.*, vol. 8, pp. 492–505, 1924.

ESTABROOK, E. L., and C. M. RADER, History of Production of Salt Creek Oil Field, Wyoming, "Petroleum Development and Technology in 1925," pp. 199–254, 1926.

YOUNG, H. W., and E. L. ESTABROOK, Waters of Salt Creek Field, Wyoming, "Petroleum Development and Technology in 1925," pp. 255–277, 1926.

BECK, E., "Structure of Typical American Oil Fields," vol. 2, pp. 589–603, 1929.

STRATIGRAPHIC SEQUENCE, SALT CREEK ANTICLINE

(After Wegemann, Beck, and others)

Age	Formation		Thickness, feet	Remarks	No. of producing wells
Tertiary	Wasatch		2,500+		
	Fort Union		2,000+		
——?——	Lance		3,200		
	Lewis		1,400		
	Mesaverde		850	Includes Parkman and Teapot sandstone	
	Steele		2,300	Includes Shannon sandstone	
	Oil at Shannon				
	Niobrara and Carlile shale		1,000		
Cretaceous	Fron-tier	First Wall Creek sandstone, oil	120	4,350 acres productive	308
		Shale	260		
		Second Wall Creek sandstone, oil	70	22,000 acres productive	1,627
		Shale	165		
		Third Wall Creek sandstone, oil	15	12 acres productive	21
		Shale	270		
	Mowry and Thermopolis		250		
	Da-kota group	Muddy sandstone oil	7		10
		Shale	175		
		Dakota, oil	0–15	10 acres productive	1
		——Hiatus——			
		Fuson	60		
		Lakota, oil	50	2,135 acres productive	96
	——Unconformity——				
	Morrison		315		
Jurassic	Sundance, oil		250	2,000 acres productive (est.)	15
Triassic	Chugwater		700		
Permian	Embar		220		
Pennsyl-vanian	Tensleep		270		1 water well
	Amsden		210	Not penetrated	
Mississip-pian	Madison		400		

the dome. Oil is found in large amounts in the First Wall Creek sand, which, on the top of the dome, lies about 900 to 1,000 feet deep, and in the Second Wall Creek sand which lies about 1,300 feet deep on the top of the dome. A little oil is found in the Third Wall Creek sand which lies about 1,650 feet deep. Oil is found also in the Dakota, Lakota, and Sundance formations, but as yet the developments in these formations are not extensive. In addition to the oil in the sands, light oil is found in considerable amounts in shale above the Salt Creek and Teapot domes and also in wells in the syncline on the west side of the field. Some of the wells in shale have large flows of oil, but most of them are small. In general the oil in shale comes from crevices in the shale, and the behavior of the wells shows that the crevices are in general isolated rather than in connected systems. Most of the oil derived from crevices comes from the shale above the First Wall Creek sand, but some on top of the Salt Creek dome is derived from crevices between the First and Second sands, and in places oil in crevices is found between the Second and Third sands and below the Third sand.

The First Wall Creek sand was productive over an area of 4,400 acres. The sand is about 136 feet thick. The upper part of the sand is a porous "bench" 80 to 100 feet thick, below which is about 20 feet of relatively impervious strata consisting either of shale or hard calcareous sand; below the latter is a sand about 20 feet thick. The lower sand member is more porous and contains water under greater pressure than the upper sand member. In the lower member the oil deposit does not extend so far from the center of the dome as in the upper one. As development progressed edge water encroached on the field, so that the area covered by the oil gradually decreased. This is shown by Fig. 101 where the positions of edge water in 1915 and 1923 are shown. Originally, the oil in the First Wall Creek sand, as stated, covered an area of about 4,400 acres, but in 1923 the area had decreased to about 3,600 acres.

The Second Wall Creek sand is productive over an area of about 22,000 acres. It lies about 400 feet below the top of first sand and is from 20 to 100 feet thick. It contains layers of shale and bentonite which separate the sand members or "benches." The best production is found in the lower half of the sand, and the northern part of the field is the most productive area. In the southern part of the field many of the wells are unprofitable. The main production of the Salt Creek field has come from the Second Wall Creek sand. The Third sand has produced relatively little oil.

The Salt Creek oil has an intermediate base and yields 25 to 40 per cent gasoline and naphtha. It deposits paraffin on cooling and tends to seal up the wells and sands. In cold weather it becomes waxy which causes difficulties in pumping it. Estabrook and Rader give the following gravities; shale oil 0.810, First sand 0.8323, Second sand 0.835, Third sand

0.839. The slight increase in gravity with depth is noteworthy. In the Second Wall Creek sand the oil within 100 feet, structurally, of edge water is 6° Bé. heavier than the average oil of the sand.

Nearly all of the gas found on the Salt Creek dome is associated with oil. In the Second sand there is very little gas near the oil-water contact. The zone of "dead" oil or oil without gas does not extend more than 50 to 100 feet, structurally, above the oil-water contact. The original gas pressure in the First sand was about 550 and that of the Second sand was somewhat higher. Estabrook and Rader estimate that the Salt Creek field has produced 224,331,800,000 cubic feet of gas to 1924, which is equivalent to 1,620 cubic feet of gas produced with each barrel of oil to 1924. Some of the gas is utilized in natural gasoline plants, the average recovery of gasoline being 2.17 gallons per 1,000 cubic feet.

The porosity of the sand varies considerably, tests showing pore space of 7.6 per cent in the "shells" and as high as 25.8 per cent in more open sands. These differences in the character of the sand and included shale cause the oil to lie in pay streaks. Owing to the thickness of the sand and its high saturation, some part of the sand carries oil in practically all holes sunk within the oil pool. The waters of the First sand are alkaline and are more concentrated near the oil than they are away from the oil deposit. The waters of the Second sand are similar to the waters of the First sand but are more concentrated. The waters of the Salt Creek field are discussed on page 43.

In the Teapot dome, south of the Salt Creek dome, water was found in the First Wall Creek sand and dry gas in the Second sand, except in the north part of the dome where oil was found in the sand. The oil occupied the saddle between the domes and, according to Estabrook and Rader, the oil-water line is 2,135 feet above sea level; the oil-producing area across the saddle is about ½ mile wide.

Shannon.—North of Salt Creek field the axis of the Salt Creek anticline passes through the Shannon pool. The oil is accumulated in the Shannon sand where it lies against a fault with a downthrow to the north, which throws the faulted edge of the Shannon sand against shale that effectively seals it. The Shannon wells were small, producing about 5 to 15 barrels of high-grade paraffin oil per day, and the field occupied about 160 acres. The field is now abandoned.

South Casper Creek and Poison Spider.—South Casper Creek and Poison Spider[1] are adjoining oil fields about 22 miles west of Casper (Fig. 283). These fields are located on a long anticline where the Frontier formation crops out along the axis. The anticline plunges away from the oil field at both ends, forming an elongated dome. The Sundance, which is found at a depth of 1,400 feet, yields oil and gas and the Tensleep contains

[1] HARES, C. J., Anticlines in Central Wyoming, U. S. Geol. Survey *Bull.* 641, pp. 233–279, 1917.

black oil. The waters of the field which issue from the Dakota, Morrison, Sundance, and Tensleep are the subject of a special study by Parks.[1] At Iron Creek, 8 miles southeast of Poison Spider in a dome on the same zone of folding, gas is developed in the Lakota formation. On Pine Mountain, 10 miles northwest of Poison Spider, a little oil and gas are found in the Tensleep and Amsden formations. On Boone dome 10 miles northwest of Pine Mountain dome the Mesaverde formation crops out. Gas is developed in the Shannon and higher sands. At Powder River field, 5 miles northeast of Boone and 3 miles north of Powder River station, a dome drilled to the Frontier found gas. At Notches dome, 12 miles north of Powder River station, the Benton shale crops out. Wells drilled on an anticline have produced oil from the Tensleep at a depth of 2,775 feet. The North Casper Creek dome is 23 miles northwest of Casper and 17 miles northeast of Pine Mountain, on an anticline that strikes northwest. Gas is found at a depth of 1,050 feet and a little black oil in the Tensleep at a depth of 3,220 feet. Warm water, somewhat salty, rises with the oil.

The Emigrant Gap anticline, east of Poison Spider, is part of a structural ridge that lies between the Big Horn Mountains and the Laramie Mountains separating the Wind River and Powder River basins. Three domes on this fold have been drilled without finding commercial supplies of oil. On the Midway-Geary anticline northeast of Casper two domes are tested, one contained oil in the top of the Frontier sand and the other, gas in the Shannon sand.

Big Muddy.—At Big Muddy[2] field (Fig. 291) near Glenrock and 18 miles east of Casper, the Pierre shale crops out on a broad low dome outlined by the Parkman sandstone. Oil is obtained from the Shannon sand at a depth of about 1,000 feet and from the Wall Creek sands of the Frontier at about 3,100 feet. Oil is found also in the Dakota and Lakota formations. The field is probably faulted on the southwest side.

Douglas.—The Douglas[3] oil field (Brenning basin) (Fig. 291) is 10 miles west of Douglas and 18 miles southeast of Big Muddy (Glenrock). Oil seeps are numerous and oil is found at depths that are between 300 and 400 feet. The field is on a monocline in which Cretaceous and older rocks dip steeply away from the pre-Cambrian granite that crops out 5 miles southwest of the oil field. The truncated edges of the Cretaceous rocks are overlain by the White River formation. According to Hewett, the oil of the Cretaceous sands moves upward and lodges in the porous

---

[1] PARKS, E. M., Water Analysis in Oil Production and Some Analyses from Poison Spider, Wyoming, Am. Assoc. Pet. Geol. *Bull.*, vol. 9, pp. 927–946, 1925.

[2] BARNETT, V. H., Possibilities of Oil in the Big Muddy Dome, Converse and Natrona Counties, Wyoming, U. S. Geol. Survey *Bull.* 581, pp. 105–117, 1915.

[3] BARNETT, V. H., The Douglas Oil and Gas Field, Wyoming, U. S. Geol. Survey *Bull.* 541, pp. 49–88, 1915.

material of the White River near the unconformity or in faults that cut the White River.

Bolton Creek.—At the Bolton Creek district, 25 miles southwest of Casper, a dome lies on an anticline that strikes northwest. The Mowry

GENERALIZED SECTION OF FORMATIONS INVOLVED IN THE BIG MUDDY DOME, WYOMING

(After Barnett)

System	Series	Group	Formation and member	Character	Type of topography and soil	Thickness, feet
Quaternary				Alluvium, gravel, and sand	Sand dunes, gravel-topped hills, and valley flats	25+
			—Unconformity—			
Tertiary	Oligocene		White River formation	Clay, conglomerate, and sandstone	Flat-topped hills and gentle slopes; thin soil	1,000
			—Unconformity—			
Tertiary (?)	Eocene (?)		Lance formation	Friable sandstone and shale, with local beds of coal	Rolling hills and broad gentle slopes; thin, sandy soil and alkali flats	200+
Cretaceous	Upper Cretaceous	Montana	Fox Hills formation, base uncertain	Friable sandstone and shale with local coal beds near top	Ridges of sandstone and valleys in shale; sandy soil	860
			Pierre formation — Sandy shale	Sandy shale	Valleys; thin clay soil	400
			Pierre formation — Teapot sandstone member	Gray and buff sandstone and carbonaceous shale	Low ridges, barren rock slopes, and pine-clad hills	160
			Pierre formation — Sandy shale	Sandy shale	Valleys; thin clay soil	320
			Pierre formation — Parkman sandstone member	Friable sandstone and beds of shale and coal	Ridges of some prominence and broad, grassy slopes	330
			Pierre formation — Dark shale	Dark shale	Broad valleys; thin soil	2,000
		Colorado	Niobrara shale	Gray to buff calcareous shale	Low rounded ridges and brown slopes	100–650
			Benton shale — Dark shale	Dark shale	Narrow valleys; thin soil	200
			Benton shale — Wall Creek sandstone member	Gray and buff sandstone and beds of shale	Ledges and hogback ridges covered with small pines	100–200
			Benton shale — Dark shale including Mowry shale member	Dark shale including Mowry shale member	Broad valley with low, rounded pineclad ridge of Mowry shale. Thin soil	1,200
	Lower Cretaceous		Cloverly formation	Buff sandstone and shale with conglomerate in lower part	Ledges, hogback ridges, and barren slopes of rock; thin sandy soil	140
Jurassic	Jurassic or Cretaceous		Morrison formation	Green, buff gray, and maroon shale and thin beds of sandstone	Gentle slopes below ridges of Cloverly rocks	700
	Upper Jurassic		Sundance formation	Greenish-gray limestone and sandstone		

formation crops out at the center of the dome. Oil is found in the Sundance formation at 1,050 feet and is produced from a sand in the Embar formation at a depth of 2,050 feet. The productive area is 1 square mile. On the Spindletop dome, 2 miles northwest of Bolton Creek, the Sundance sand produces small amounts of oil.

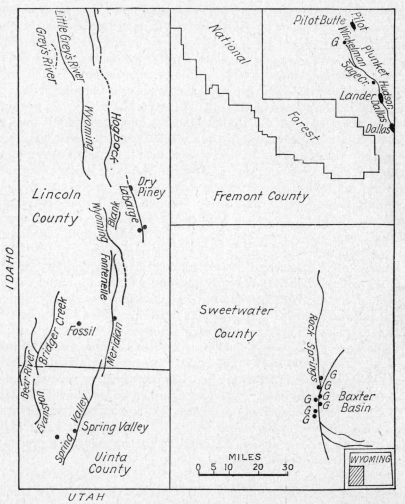

Fig. 290.—Map of southwestern Wyoming showing oil fields and oil seepages (black), gas fields (black with letter *G*), and anticlines (lines). (*After Schultz, Veatch, Sears.*)

Baxter Basin.—In the Baxter basin[1] (Fig. 290), about 12 miles from Rock Springs, gas is discovered in three domes located on the Rock

[1] SCHULTZ, A. R., Oil Possibilities in and Around Baxter Basin, Sweetwater County, Wyoming, U. S. Geol. Survey *Bull.* 702, pp. 1–107, 1920.

SEARS, J. D., Geology of the Baxter Basin Gas Field, Sweetwater County, Wyoming, U. S. Geol. Survey *Bull.* 781B, pp. 13–27, 1926.

Springs anticline. The top of the North dome is 7 miles north of the South dome. At both domes the Baxter shale of the Upper Cretaceous crops out. Both domes are faulted by many faults that strike northeast. At depths of about 2,000 feet gas is found in the Frontier sand and about 500 feet deeper in the Dakota sand. Some of the wells have flows estimated to be 35,000,000 cubic feet per day and one well is rated at twice that amount. Between the North and South domes gas is found in a half dome, probably closed by a fault, which is called the Middle dome. In the domes the gas descends down dip 300 feet below the axes of the domes. At greater depths water under pressure is found. The water wells lie so near the lower gas wells that it appears improbable that gas sands contain large oil deposits. At the north end of the field gas and a showing of oil occur in the Lakota sand. A pipe line is built from the field to supply Salt Lake, Ogden, and neighboring cities with gas.

Spring Valley.—The Spring Valley field,[1] Uinta County, southwestern Wyoming, is an area of Mesozoic and later sedimentary rocks deformed by faulting and folding. The Aspen tunnel of the Union Pacific Railroad, which was driven through the Cretaceous Frontier formation, crossed a secondary fault in the Absaroka fault zone, and at the fault there was a considerable seep of oil. Many wells put down in this region found some oil but not in paying quantities.

Fossil.—The Fossil field 35 miles north of Spring Valley is located near the contact between Wasatch and Green River formations near a faulted anticline. Wells 250 feet deep have encountered a heavy lubricating oil and wells 450 feet deep a paraffin base oil. These oils are believed to have migrated upward from the Cretaceous.[2]

Labarge.—The Labarge[3] field is in Lincoln County, about 40 miles northeast of the Fossil field. The country is an area of faulted and folded strata of Cretaceous and Tertiary age. The dominant structural feature is the Labarge thrust fault. The oil is found on an anticline in the Almy or Wasatch beds immediately overlying the thick black organic Hilliard shale which is possibly the source of the oil. The deepest well, at 4,800 feet, is in the Hilliard shale. In 1929 the Labarge field was producing about 2,150 barrels of oil per day.

At Dry Piney, 12 miles north of Labarge, near the contact of the Adaville and Wasatch formations, oil is found in wells sunk to the Hilliard formation.

Black Hills.—The Black Hills of South Dakota constitute a great mountain uplift from which the strata dip in all directions. In the area

[1] VEATCH, A. C., Geography and Geology of Southwestern Wyoming, U. S. Geol. Survey *Prof. Paper* 56, p. 138, 1907.

[2] MORGAN, G. B., Wyo. Geol. Survey *Press Bull.* 11, Aug. 16, 1921.

[3] VEATCH, A. C., *op. cit.*, p. 139.

SCHULTZ, A. R., The Labarge Oil Field, Central Uinta County, Wyoming, U. S. Geol. Survey *Bull.* 340, p. 364–373, 1907.

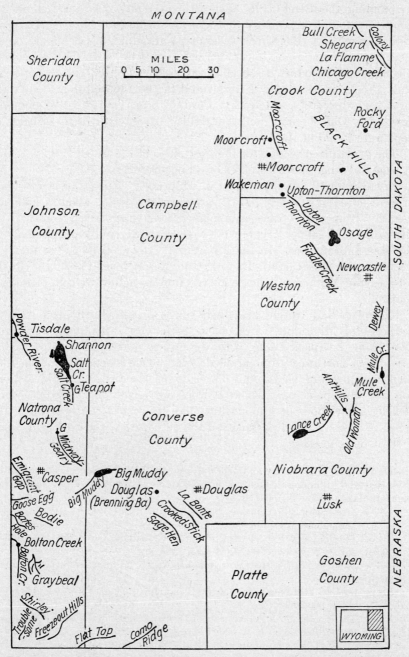

FIG. 291.—Outline map of northeastern Wyoming showing oil fields (black), gas fields (black with letter *G*), and anticlines. (*Data from Wegemann, Collier, Hancock, Richardson, Heald, and other sources.*)

surrounding the Black Hills (Fig. 291) at many places anticlines and domes are found, and many of these are drilled for oil. North of the uplift along the Cedar Creek (Glendive) anticline, gas fields are developed, but oil is not found in commercial quantities. On the west side oil in commercial amounts has been discovered at Osage, Lance Creek, and Mule Creek, and some oil is discovered in the Moorcroft field, 12 miles north of Moorcroft, at Rocky Ford, Upton-Thornton (Wakeman), Newcastle, Old Woman, and Ant Hills. At several of these fields oil seeps were found at the surface.

The generalized section for the west slope of the Black Hills[1] is shown on page 501, together with notes of oil occurrences.

In the field 12 miles northeast of Moorcroft seepages of heavy black oil were noted at an early date. Several wells drilled about a half mile down dip from the seepages are reported to have produced from 1 to 150 barrels of heavy oil per day, but the wells declined rapidly and the exploration was unprofitable. In the Moorcroft[2] region oil seeps are found in the Graneros (Newcastle), Dakota, and Fuson formations. At Rocky Ford, east of Moorcroft, a heavy oil is found in shallow wells in Minnelusa sandstone.

Thornton and Upton[3] are small towns on the Burlington Railway southeast of Moorcroft. Cretaceous rocks crop out dipping southwest away from the Black Hills. Two domes are developed on an anticline that strikes northwest through the district. One is near Upton, the other a mile southwest of Thornton. These domes are drilled, but the exploration was disappointing. About 3 miles northwest of Thornton a small oil field is developed on a monocline that lies east of the anticline. The wells are on a structural terrace and the oil occurs in the Carlile members of the Colorado shale.

[1] DARTON, N. H., Geology and Water Resources of the Northern Portion of the Black Hills and Adjoining Regions in South Dakota and Wyoming, U. S. Geol. Survey *Prof. Paper* 65, pp. 1–105, 1909.

———, Newcastle, Wyoming, U. S. Geol. Survey *Folio* 107.

———, Sundance, Wyoming-South Dakota, U. S. Geol. Survey *Folio* 127.

———, Preliminary Report on Underground Waters of Central Great Plains, U. S. Geol. Survey *Prof. Paper* 32, pp. 1–433, 1905.

———, and W. S. T. SMITH, Edgemont, North Dakota, U. S. Geol. Survey *Folio* 108.

SINCLAIR, E. G., Oil Possibilities of the Black Hills Region, Am. Assoc. Pet. Geol. *Bull.*, vol. 10, pp. 800–809, 1926.

LUPTON, C. T., Results and Prospects of Deeper Drilling in the Rocky Mountains Fields, Am. Assoc. Pet. Geol. *Bull.*, vol. 7, pp. 400–410, 1923.

[2] BARNETT, V. H., The Moorcroft Oil Field, Crook County, Wyoming, U. S. Geol. Survey *Bull.* 581C, pp. 83–105, 1915.

[3] HANCOCK, E. T., The Upton-Thornton Oil Field, Wyoming, U. S. Geol. Survey *Bull.* 716B, pp. 17–34, 1921.

GENERALIZED GEOLOGIC SECTION WEST SLOPE BLACK HILLS, WYOMING

(*Mainly from Darton*)

Formation	Thickness, feet	Description
Tertiary:		
Eocene(?):		
Lance............		(Laramie) cross-bedded sandstone and sandy shale, concretions, fragments of dinosaurs and turtles, non-marine
Upper Cretaceous:		
Montana:		
Fox Hills..........	50±	Light gray sandstone and sandy shale, thin bedded, calcareous concretions, marine
Pierre............	1,250±	Dark clay shale, calcareous concretions, marine. Oil at Shannon and Pilot Butte, Wyoming, gas at Pierre, South Dakota
Colorado:		
Niobrara..........	200	Light-yellow calcareous shale, some sandstone and chalk
Carlile...........	610	Upper part dark shale with bands of concretion. In lower part are 80 feet of shaly sandstone (Wall Creek sands). Oil at Upton Thornton, some at Osage field
Greenhorn.........	100	Fossiliferous shaly limestone at top, shaly below with calcareous concretions and some limestone. Oil show at Osage
Graneros:		
Belle Fourche......	560	Dark shale with calcareous concretions; bentonite near base. Oil shows at Osage
Mowry............	150	Siliceous shale, fish scales, bentonite. Oil shows at Osage field
Nefsy............	25–50	Soft dark shale, thin sand lenses
Newcastle........	40–60	One to four layers of sand separated by shale, bentonite, impure coal, called "Muddy" sand. Chief oil sand at Osage
Skull Creek........	200	Dark shale with calcareous concretions, represents basal part of Thermopolis shale, marine. Oil shows at Osage
Dakota............	50–100	Light reddish sand and sandy shale usually water bearing. Oil at Lance Creek, Moorcroft, and Osage
Lower Cretaceous:		
Fuson..............	30	Gray or red shale and thin sandstone
Lakota.............	200	Massive coarse sandstone and shale. Chief oil sand at Mule Creek; probably oil bearing at Lance Creek
Morrison...........	150	Massive buff, green, and maroon sandy shale
Jurassic:		
Sundance...........	350	Green and dark shale, thin limestone, and sandstone
Triassic:		
Spearfish...........	500	Red beds, shale, sandstone, and gypsum "Chugwater"
Minnekahta.........	40	Thin-bedded gray limestone
Opeche.............	75	Red sandy shale and shaly limestone
Pennsylvanian:		
Minnelusa..........	600±	White sandstone and calcareous sandstone, thin beds limestone and gypsum
Mississippian:		
Pahasapa...........	700	Massive gray limestone, equivalent of Madison

The Osage[1] oil field (Fig. 291) is a few miles southeast of Upton and about 14 miles northwest of Newcastle. In 1910 an oil seep was discovered within the field, but the area was not drilled until 1919 when a shallow well was brought in. The field was rapidly developed, about 700 wells were drilled, and several refineries were built near Osage. The

[1] COLLIER, A. J., The Osage Oil Field, Weston County, Wyoming, U. S. Geol. Survey *Bull.* 736, pp. 71–110, 1923.

wells have small production, but on account of the high grade of the oil they are operated to supply the local needs of the region. The rocks dip southwest away from the Black Hills (Fig. 85) at angles from 3 to 10 degrees or more. The geologic section is shown on page 501. The oil is found in small amounts in several formations, as shown in the section, but nearly all of the producing wells derive their oil from the Newcastle sand member of the Graneros shale (Colorado, Cretaceous). Most of the wells are on two structural terraces, but in 1925 small wells were being brought in in the belt where the rocks dip more steeply in the area between the terraces. The Newcastle sand crops out just east of the town of Osage, but the outcrop is not marked by oil springs. The sand is thin and impure at the outcrop and, according to Collier, is faulted by small faults. It is probably due, in part at least, to faulting that the reservoir is sealed. The wells on the upper terrace are 200 to 600 feet deep, and those on the lower one are from 800 to 1,500 feet deep. The latter wells are more productive, although the average production for the field of all except three or four of the wells is less than a barrel a day (1926). The oil is light olive green, has a gravity of 39.1 to 40.3° Bé., and carries about 50 per cent gasoline and kerosene. It is essentially free from sulphur. Gas pressure in the field is low. The oil, according to Collier, is derived from the Graneros shale. It accumulated in the Newcastle which includes one to four sandy layers between sandy shale beds. It also contains bentonite and impure coal which has a carbon ratio of 54.9. In 1930 a well drilled in the Muddy sand (Dakota), was reported to have an estimated initial daily production of 500 barrels of oil.

Newcastle.—In Newcastle field,[1] 14 miles southeast of Osage, a heavy paraffin oil exudes from the Newcastle sandstone. A small production was obtained by drilling, but the wells rapidly declined.

Mule Creek and Lance Creek.—Between the Black Hills and the Rocky Mountains Front there is a great anticline on which, at the Hartville uplift, Rawhide Butte, and elsewhere, the pre-Cambrian rocks are brought to the surface. The anticlines of Mule Creek and Lance Creek[2] are in this belt of deformation. The Old Woman anticline is in the same belt, and on it the Sundance formation is brought to the surface.

The Lance Creek field is on a great anticline that lies west of the Old Woman anticline, from which it is separated by a shallow syncline. The Lance Creek anticline strikes east and bends to the north. On it

[1] KNIGHT, W. C., and E. E. SLOSSON, The Newcastle Oil Field, Wyo. Univ. School Mines, Petroleum Series, *Bull.* 5, 1902.

[2] HANCOCK, E. T., The Lance Creek Oil and Gas Field, Niobrara County, Wyoming, U. S. Geol. Survey *Bull.* 716E, pp. 91–122, 1920.

EMERY, W. B., "Structure of Typical American Oil Fields," vol. 2, pp. 604–613, 1929.

Rock Formations in the Mule Creek Field, Wyoming
(*After Hancock*)

System	Series	Group, formation, and member	Character	Thickness, feet
Cretaceous	Upper Cretaceous	Colorado group — Niobrara formation	Soft shaly limestone or impure chalk, including some clay and sand	200
		Colorado group — Carlile shale	Dark shale with thin beds of soft sandstone (Wall Creek sandstone member) near the base	700
		Colorado group — Greenhorn limestone	Impure slabby limestone	50
		Colorado group — Graneros shale	Dark-gray to black shale, including many large calcareous concretions, especially in the upper part	575
		Colorado group — Graneros shale — Mowry shale member	Hard light-gray sandy shales containing numerous fish scales. Contains bentonite beds near the top and to some extent near the base	100
		Colorado group — Graneros shale	Dark sandy shale grading upward into typical Mowry shale	25
		Colorado group — Graneros shale — Newcastle sandstone member	Reddish to light-yellow sandstone associated with black carbonaceous shale	3–15
		Colorado group — Graneros shale	Dark-gray to black shale	175
		Dakota sandstone	Thin-bedded to massive hard buff sandstone	60
	Lower Cretaceous	Fuson formation	Shale and thin-bedded sandstone	20
		Lakota sandstone	Sandstone, in part conglomeratic, with some coal beds near the base. Oil	199
Cretaceous (?)	(?)	Morrison formation	Light-gray to pinkish shale	130
Jurassic	Upper Jurassic	Sundance formation	Light-gray to dark greenish-gray and pinkish sandy shale, with a 25-foot sandstone near the base	346
Triassic (?)		Spearfish formation	Gypsum and red clay beds in alternating succession ("Red Beds")	492
	Permian (?)	Minnekahta limestone	Light-gray to pinkish or purplish limestone	34
Carboniferous	Pennsylvanian	Opeche formation	Red sandy clay, purplish at the top	74
		Minnelusa sandstone	Light-gray to buff calcareous sandstone	851
	Mississippian	Pahasapa limestone	White, pale-buff, pinkish, and gray limestone	398

the beds dip steeply northwest and more gently southeast, and a dome is situated on the crest of the fold. Most of the wells are begun in the Pierre shale at about the horizon of the Shannon sand. The oil has a gravity of about 42° Bé., and it is associated with wet gas. Wells with initial productions as high as 2,900 barrels of oil per day were brought in, but the production has been irregular and water trouble common, so that the total production of the field to January 1, 1929, is something less than 4,000,000 barrels. The oil is found in the Muddy sands near the crest of the dome about 3,460 feet deep. There are three sands in the Dakota. The first carries gas, the second gas on the crest of the dome and oil on its flanks, and it is the source of most of the oil in the field. The third sand carries oil and gas, and oil and gas are found also in the Lakota sand.

The Mule Creek[1] field is about 35 miles south of Newcastle, 4 miles from the state line, and 18 miles west of Edgemont, South Dakota. The field is marked by two anticlines that strike north with axes about $1\frac{1}{2}$ miles apart. On the western anticline the Graneros shale is brought to the surface, and on the eastern anticline the Carlile shale crops out. The rocks of the area are shown in the table (p. 503). The chief oil developments are on the eastern axis where oil was found in 1919, the wells yielding 125 to 1,250 barrels of oil per day. The oil is low-grade asphaltic oil, testing about 31° Bé. and derived chiefly from the Lakota formation.

On the Old Woman Creek dome, as already stated, the Sundance formation crops out. Wells drilled to the Minnelusa formation had good showings of oil but did not produce commercially. On the Ant Hills anticline southwest of Mule Creek a well drilled to the Muddy sand at a depth of 3,900 feet had an initial production of about 100 barrels a day. It produced a total of 8,719 barrels in 1928. Drilling to the Dakota and Lakota sands has not increased production.

COLORADO

The oil-bearing structures of Colorado resemble those of Wyoming. A great series of Cretaceous rocks is exposed along the Rocky Mountains Front and anticlines are developed east of the mountains with relations similar to those around the mountain uplifts of Wyoming.[2] In Colorado (Fig. 292) the oil and gas fields developed along the Rocky Mountains Front are Fort Collins, Boulder, and Florence. In the intermontane area farther west are Walden, Moffat dome, and Iles fields which are being actively drilled. The chief oil and gas deposits are found in the Cretaceous, Morrison, and Sundance, but gas is found in the northwest

[1] HANCOCK, E. T., The Mule Creek Oil Field, Wyoming, U. S. Geol. Survey *Bull.* 716E, pp. 35–51, 1921.

[2] GEORGE, R. D., Geologic map of Colorado, *Colo. Geol. Survey*, Boulder, 1913.

part of the state in Tertiary rocks.   In 1929 Colorado produced 2,298,000 barrels of oil valued at $2,300,000.

Fort Collins.—The Fort Collins[1] oil field is near Fort Collins, Colorado, about 60 miles north of Denver.   Gas was discovered in the field on November 11, 1923, in a well drilled on the Wellington structure about 6 miles north and 2 miles west of Wellington and 14 miles north and 3 miles east of Fort Collins.   At 4,283 feet the well touched the oil sand and made 3,000,000 cubic feet of wet gas.   A day later the well began to spray oil and the same day it blew in as a large gas well.   The well got out of control, and, 49 days later, when it was brought under control

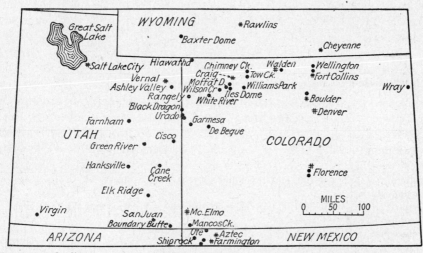

FIG. 292.—Outline map of parts of Colorado, Utah, and New Mexico, showing locations of oil fields and prospects.

and gaged, it was estimated to have a flow of 82,000,000 cubic feet of gas per day.   Later, the well began to spray oil and the amount increased until the well was estimated to be capable of yielding 400 barrels a day.

The well is located on an anticlinal axis that lies 3 miles east of Fort Collins and extends north about 15 miles.   The rocks on the sides of the fold dip 5 to 15 degrees.   On this axis are two crests, one northeast of Fort Collins and the other northwest of Wellington.   Each crest or dome is about 5 miles long and 1 to 1½ miles wide.   West of the saddle between the two crests there is a small dome, called the Douglas Lake structure,

[1] MATHER, K. F., J. GILLULY, and R. G. LUSK, Geology and Oil and Gas Prospects in Northeastern Colorado, U. S. Geol. Survey *Bull.* 796B, pp. 65–124, 1928.

HENDERSON, J., The Foothills Formations of North-central Colorado, Colo. Geol. Survey *Bull.* 19, pp. 58–98 (map of region adjoining gas field on west), 1920.

LEE, W. T., Correlation of Geologic Formations between East-central Colorado, Central Wyoming, and Southern Montana, U. S. Geol. Survey *Prof. Paper* 149, p. 37, 1927.

COLORADO OIL PRODUCTION
(Barrels)

Field	1928	Total to Dec. 31, 1928
Boulder.........................	9,175	569,395
Canyon City....................	246,939	396,063
Florence........................	182,550	11,850,063
Fort Collins....................	241,429	1,472,028
Iles............................	621,960	923,567
Moffat[1].......................	463,647	3,210,329
Rangely........................	23,790	221,328
Tow Creek.....................	189,962	639,373
Walden.........................	5,951	53,810
Wellington.....................	794,847	2,491,130
Total.......................	2,780,250	21,827,086

[1] 1928 Moffat production includes 65,380 barrels Sundance production.

GEOLOGIC FORMATIONS OF NORTHEAST COLORADO
(*After Mather, Gilluly, and Lusk*)

Formation	Thickness, feet	Description
Quaternary ...	0–100	Gravel and silt
Unconformity .		
Tertiary	10–300	Gravel, sand, and clay (Arikaree and White River)
Unconformity .		
Cretaceous:		
Laramie	200–800	Sandstone, shale, coal
Fox Hills. ...	400–2,000	Sandstone, sandy shale
Pierre.......	4,500–10,000	Shale with many sandstone members
Niobrara ...	330–410	Limestone and limy shale
Benton	583–640	Dark shale, limestone, bentonite. Cadell ("Nio-benton sand") 3 to 20 feet at top
Dakota.....	285–425	Sandstone, shale, conglomerate at base, oil and gas at Wellington
Unconformity .		
Cretaceous (?):		
Morrison ...	200–300	Marl, sandstone, limestone
Unconformity .		
Jurassic:		
Sundance...	0–100	Massive sandstone
Triassic (?):		
Lykins......	400–800	Red shale, sandstone, limestone bands
Permian:		
Lyons.......	50–200	Cream-colored sandstone
Pennsylvanian:		
Fountain ...	300–800	Sandstone and conglomerate
Unconformity .		
Pre-Cambrian .		Granite, schist, etc.

2 miles long and ½ mile wide. Other wells drilled on the Fort Collins-Wellington anticline have found oil and large flows of gas. Drilling on the Douglas Lake dome has proved disappointing. Accumulation on the mountainward fold may have been originally low, or possibly oil and gas have been swept out by ground water. The rock section of the region is shown on page 506. On the Wellington dome the wells are begun in the Pierre shale near the horizon of the Larimer sandstone member. The gas, as stated, is found at a depth of about 4,300 feet. The productive horizon is the "Muddy" sand of the Dakota group. Oil is found near Berthoud south-east Larimer County. Near Wray (Fig. 292) two or more wells encountered gas, probably in the Dakota sandstone.[1]

In the foothill region west of Fort Collins oil field the Dakota formation is subdivided by Lee as follows:

	Feet
Upper sandstone, "Muddy sand" of drillers	0–80
Upper shale, bituminous, marine	110–240
Middle sandstone	10–15
Lower shale with hard thin sandstone beds	25–65
Lower sandstone, conglomerate at base	35–75

Boulder.—The Boulder oil district[2] lies a few miles north of Boulder, east of the Front Range. The rocks dip eastward, away from the mountains. The beds from which the oil is obtained are sands or sandstones in the Pierre. Such beds may be encountered at any depth, but there is no depth at which they are certain to be found. Some of the wells are dry, others yield salt water. The productive wells are on an anticline and derive their oil from a sandstone in the Pierre shale 2,000 to 2,500 feet deep. The wells sunk near the crest of the anticline produce gas and a light oil of about 42° Bé. The wells farther down the limbs of the anticline produce heavier oil (40° Bé.) mixed with water. Gas wells which once supplied the city of Boulder are now closed. The oil production for 1928 was 9,175 barrels, and the total production December 31, 1928, was 569,395 barrels.

Florence.—The Florence field,[3] in south-central Colorado, is in a synclinal reentrant of the Rocky Mountains front, between the fold made by the Front Range on the northeast and the Wet Mountains on the southwest. This reentrant is commonly called Cañon City embayment. The rocks are Paleozoic and Mesozoic sediments. Solid bitumen is found in the Dakota sandstone near Cañon City, and about 7 miles

[1] BASS, N. W., Geologic Investigations in Western Kansas, Kan. Geol. Survey *Bull.* 11, pp. 1–96, 1926.

[2] FENNEMAN, N. M., Geology of the Boulder District, Colorado, U. S. Geol. Survey *Bull.* 265, 1905.

[3] WASHBURNE, C. W., The Florence Oil Field, Colorado, U. S. Geol. Survey *Bull.* 381, pp. 517–544, 1910.

northeast of Cañon City there is an oil spring, running less than 20 gallons of oil a day. It issues from Pleistocene gravel but probably rises from the Morrison beds. The Florence[1] field (Fig. 293) is the most productive oil field in Colorado, having yielded 11,850,063 barrels of oil to December 31, 1928. Production reached its peak of 824,000 barrels in 1892 and declined steadily to 59,000 barrels in 1924, when it increased again, reaching 430,000 barrels in 1928, the increase being due largely

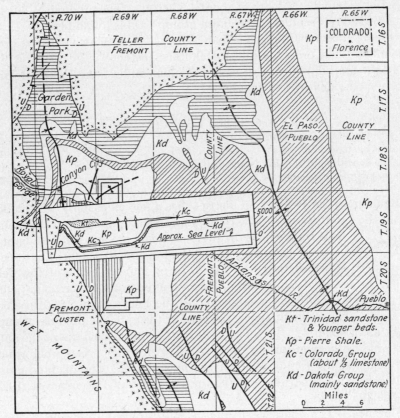

Fig. 293.—Generalized map and section through Florence oil field, Colorado. (*After de Ford.*)

to the extension of the field to the south. The main oil field now extends about 8 miles south of the town of Florence. The field occupies a syncline and the oil is found in fissures in the Pierre shale which is remarkably uniform. There are no oil sands. The Pierre, which crops out in the region of the wells, is productive through a zone 2,500 feet thick. It carries marine fossils. The oil is rather light (30° Bé.), has a paraffin base, and is free from sulphur. It is associated with gas, and the deep

[1] DeFord, R. K., Surface Structure Florence Field, Fremont County, Colorado, "Structure of Typical American Oil Fields," vol. 2, pp. 75–92, 1929.

wells encounter salt water. As a rule, however, water does not follow the oil when the well is pumped dry.

In the Cañon City field, 2 miles east of Cañon City, the oil is found in fissures in the Pierre shale. An anticlinal nose plunges southward through the field and the oil seems to follow its trend.

A well at Thatcher 60 miles southeast of Pueblo has an open flow of 3,000,000 cu. ft. of gas daily. This gas comes from a depth of 900 ft. and contains 7 per cent helium.

DeBeque.—The DeBeque field[1] is on the Grand River in Mesa County. The country is a high plateau deeply dissected. The rocks are nearly flat lying, and the formations exposed are the Wasatch and Green River. Below the Wasatch is the Mesaverde formation. Structurally the region is a saucer-like basin that extends from the Uncompahgre Plateau on the southwest to the Grand Hogback on the northeast. Due west of DeBeque there is an anticline which extends westward for 8 miles or more. Oil is encountered in wells on the anticline not far from its crest. Most of the wells found small quantities of oil and gas but no clearly defined oil sand was encountered.

Walden.—Near Walden in Jackson County, about 70 miles northeast of Craig is located the McCallum anticline with a closure of 1,400 feet. On it are two domes called the North and the South domes. A well 5,110 feet deep, drilled to the top sand of the Dakota formation in 1927, encountered oil associated with carbon dioxide under pressure. Due to rapid expansion at the surface, the carbon dioxide formed "snow" which included the oil. On warming, the carbon dioxide passed off as gas, leaving a light amber colored oil with a gravity of 50° A.P.I. The well yields 30,000,000 cubic feet of gas per day. The gas carries 83 per cent CO_2 and 17 per cent N. The well has produced as high as 500 barrels oil per day. A well on the South dome was brought in with about the same amount of oil and a larger flow of similar gas.

Northwest Colorado.—In northwest Colorado oil is produced from the Hamilton or Moffat dome about 13 miles south of Craig, on the Denver and Salt Lake Railway (Moffat Line). The rocks in this region, which are shown in the table, pages 511 and 512, are thrown into strong folds, and the oil and gas accumulate in the domes. The Moffat[2] dome has a closure of about 500 feet and, in the center of the dome, shale of the Mancos formation that lies 1,300 feet below the top of the Mancos is exposed. In 1923 a well drilled 3,800 feet to the Dakota sandstone discovered a light green oil which flowed from the well at a rate of 1,000

[1] WOODRUFF, E. G., Geology and Petroleum Resources of the DeBeque Oil Field, Colorado, U. S. Geol. Survey *Bull.* 531, pp. 54–68, 1913.

[2] SEARS, J. D., Oil and Gas in Part of Moffat County, Colorado, and Southern Sweetwater County, Wyoming, U. S. Geol. Survey *Bull.* 751, pp. 269–319, 1924.

COFFIN, R. E., V. C. PERINI, JR., and M. J. COLLINS, Some Anticlines in Western Colorado, Colo. Geol. Survey *Bull.* 24, pp. 1–59, 1920.

barrels and soon increased to 4,560 barrels a day. A well drilled below the Dakota sandstone shut off oil in the Morrison formation and was sunk to the Sundance formation, where it encountered oil.   This well has been producing over 200 barrels a day.   The oil pool in the Dakota sandstone covers about 160 acres.   On the Iles dome, 6 miles southwest of Moffat dome, several wells found small amounts of oil in the shale above the Dakota sand, and wells drilled to the Morrison and Jurassic (Nugget-Sundance) formations have found considerable oil in both of the sands. The Thornburg or Morapos dome, 6 miles southeast of Iles, has a closure of 900 feet.   In this field two wells found large flows of gas in the Dakota sandstone, but found only a little oil.   On the Tow Creek anticline, 25 miles east of Craig, a dome cut by a porphyry intrusion, and, near the crest of the dome, a fractured zone in Mancos shale produced oil.[1]   On the Wilson Creek dome, Devil's Hole district, a well 5,913 feet deep found gas in the shale above the Dakota sandstone and water in the Dakota.

In Chimney Creek dome northeast of Craig, a well discovered gas, probably from the lower part of the Mancos shale.   Large flows of gas and some oil are discovered in the Mancos on the Williams Park anticline, southeast of Craig.   Wells in this field found also considerable gas and some oil in the Dakota sand.

The White River field, about 50 miles southwest of Craig, is located on a dome that brings up to the surface the horizon of the Wasatch beds about 1,000 feet below the top of the formation.   The Wasatch consists of clay, shales, and sandstones and is 4,000 feet thick.   Wells less than 1,000 feet deep found large flows of gas in sands in the Wasatch together with a little oil.   The gas has probably migrated from the underlying Mancos.

The Rangely[2] field is located on a dome about 40 miles west of the White River field and 33 miles northeast of Dragon, Utah.   Attention was drawn to the field as the result of the discovery of an oil seep, and for many years the field produced about 1,500 barrels a month of high-grade yellow oil of about 44° Bé.   The oil is from wells about 500 feet deep drilled in Mancos shale, and the productive horizon is about 1,900 feet below the top of the formation.   It is said that the producing beds are shales that are not sandy.   Wells drilled to the Dakota discovered large flows of gas.[3]

About 8 miles south of Dragon station, Utah, on the Uintah Railway, 1½ miles east of the Utah line, an oil well and small refinery have been operated producing a high-grade lubricating oil. A well 505 feet deep is sunk near the base of the Green River formation which rests upon the

[1] HEATON, R. V., Structure of Typical American Oil Fields," vol. 2, pp. 93–114, 1929.

[2] GALE, H. S., Geology of the Rangely District, Rio Blanco County, Colorado, U. S. Geol. Survey Bull. 350, pp. 1–61, 1908.

[3] SEARS, J. D. op. cit., 313.

GEOLOGIC FORMATIONS IN MOFFAT COUNTY, COLORADO, AND SWEETWATER COUNTY, WYOMING

(*After Sears,* with additions)

System	Series	Group or formation	Thickness, feet	Character
Quaternary		Alluvium; terrace gravels		Sandy clay along streams and in valley bottoms; terrace gravel on benches along rivers
Tertiary	Miocene (?)	—Unconformity— Browns Park formation / Bishop conglomerate	Browns Park, 1,200+; Bishop, 0–200	Browns Park soft sandstone; chert; conglomerate at base. Oil seeps
	Eocene	—Unconformity— Bridger formation		Gray and green clay shale; gray, buff, and green sandstone; marl, limestone, and chert; conglomerate
		—Unconformity locally— Green River formation (including Laney shale member and Tipton tongue)	1,500±	Gray fissile shale and oil shale; gray clay shale; gray and buff sandstone and limestone; oil seeps
		Wasatch formation (including Cathedral Bluffs tongue)	3,000–5,600	Variegated clay shales; gray, buff, and pink sandstone, grit, and conglomerate; coal beds
Tertiary (?)	Eocene (?)	Unconformity Post-"Laramie" formation	0–800	Sandstone; shale; coal beds; conglomerate at base
Cretaceous	Upper Cretaceous	—Unconformity— "Laramie" formation	1,020–2,350 (?)	Sandstone, shale, and some coal
		Lewis shale	900–1,600	Gray shale and sandstones
		Mesaverde group: Williams Fork formation	1,600–3,400	Gray, white, and brown sandstone; shale; coal beds
		Mesaverde group: Iles formation	1,350	Gray, white, and brown sandstone predominant; gray shale; some coal beds
		Mancos shale	5,085–5,370	Gray marine shale; thick lenticular beds of sandstone in upper 1,000 feet, and one thick sandstone near base. Gas and oil at Rangely and Tow Creek

GEOLOGIC FORMATIONS IN MOFFAT COUNTY, COLORADO, AND SWEETWATER COUNTY, WYOMING.—(*Continued*)

System	Series	Group or formation	Thickness, feet	Character
Cretaceous—*Continued*	Upper Cretaceous—*Continued*	Dakota sandstone	155–250	Gray sandstone, at places quartzitic; gray and greenish clay shale; conglomerate of black chert pebbles. Oil at Moffat dome
		–Unconformity–		
Cretaceous (?)	Lower Cretaceous (?)	Morrison formation	500	Variegated clay shale; thin lenticular sandstones, conglomeratic. Oil at Moffat and Iles; gas at Rangely
		Twin Creek limestone	125	Gray thin-bedded limestone above; gray shale below
Jurassic		Nugget sandstone (Sundance)	950	White and gray cross-bedded sandstone; some red sandy shale in upper part. Oil at Moffat and Iles
Triassic (?)		Ankareh (?) shale	200	Red and gray sandy shale; sandstone and grit
		–Unconformity–		
Triassic		Thaynes (?) formation and Woodside shale	760	Mostly gray and drab shale; thin beds of limestone and sandstone
	Permian and Pennsylvanian	Park City formation	115	White and gray limestone; chert; sandstone and shale; phosphate beds
Carboniferous	Pennsylvanian	Weber quartzite	900	White and buff sandstone
			525	Limestone, shale, sandstone, and thin coal beds
	Mississippian		600	Gray cherty limestone; white quartzose sandstone and conglomerate at base
		–Unconformity–		
Devonian (?) to later Cambrian			0–200	Red and green shale; red, green, and white sandstone; pink limestone; conglomerate
		–Unconformity–		
Earlier Cambrian and pre-Cambrian			12,000+	Red quartzite and sandstone

Wasatch beds.   Drilling was suggested by the presence of an oil spring, and a little oil was found in three sands in a series that dips 2 or 3 degrees northwest.   A tunnel 375 feet long is run on the upper sand and in 1917 there was a flow of about 5 or 10 barrels a day.   The tunnel is bulkheaded near the portal.   There is little or no gas.

In the Hiawatha field, or Vermilion Creek area, northwestern Colorado, gas in considerable amounts has been recently discovered and the field is connected with the Baxter basin line to Salt Lake, Utah.   There are three domes, namely, Hiawatha, Alkali Creek and Cañon Creek, each of which has about 300 or 400 feet of closure.   In the Hiawatha dome three gas wells are drilled to depths of 2,000 to 2,200 feet, the aggregate volume of gas being about 90,000,000 cubic feet per day.   Wells with smaller flows are drilled in Alkali Creek and Cañon Creek domes, and a well is being drilled on the Powder Wash dome to the southeast of this area.   The age of the producing horizon is uncertain, some regarding it as Wasatch and others as Lewis formation.

The Garmessa field west of DeBeque, is on a long anticline that strikes northwest and three domes are found on it.   One well has encountered gas, probably in the Dakota formation.   The flow is estimated to be 47,000,000 cubic feet per day.   Another well drilled to the Dakota has a flow of 20,000,000 cubic feet.

Southwest Colorado.—On the McElmo dome in southwestern Colorado, 25 miles north of the New Mexico line, a well 4,458 feet deep is drilled into Pennsylvanian strata.   This well found gas and showings of oil but no commercial supplies.   In Paradox Valley,[1] 70 miles to the north, several wells have found great thicknesses of salt.

NORTHWEST NEW MEXICO

The Shiprock district[2] is in northwestern New Mexico about 25 miles west of Farmington.   The area was drilled as a result of explorations

[1] COFFIN, R. C., Radium, Uranium and Vanadium Deposits of Southwestern Colorado, Colo. Geol. Survey *Bull.* 16, pp. 1–230, 1921.

[2] NOWELS, K. B., Development and Relation of Oil Accumulation to Structure in the Shiprock District of the Navajo Indian Reservation, New Mexico, Am. Assoc. Pet. Geol. *Bull.*, vol. 13, pp. 117–151, 1929.

GREGORY, H. E., Geology of the Navajo Country; a Reconnaissance of Parts of Arizona, New Mexico, and Utah, U. S. Geol. Survey *Prof. Paper* 93, pp. 1–161, 1917.

BAUER, C. M., and J. B. REEDSIDE, JR., Coal in the Middle and Eastern Parts of San Juan County, Utah, U. S. Geol. Survey *Bull.* 716, pp. 155–237, 1921.

ELLIS, R. W., The Oil Situation in New Mexico, Univ. N. M. *Bull.* 101, pp. 1–48, 1920.

———, Oil and Gas in New Mexico, Univ. N. M. *Bull.* 112, pp. 1–27, 1923.

EMERY, W. B., Natural Gas in the Rocky Mountains Area, *Oil Gas Jour.*, pp. G182–G197, June 16, 1927.

WINCHESTER, D. E., Geology of Alamosa Creek Valley, Socorro County, New Mexico, U. S. Geol. Survey *Bull.* 716, pp. 1–15, 1921.

at McElmo, Colorado, where a well 4,458 feet deep found a little oil in Pennsylvanian strata in 1922, and at Ute dome, 24 miles northeast of

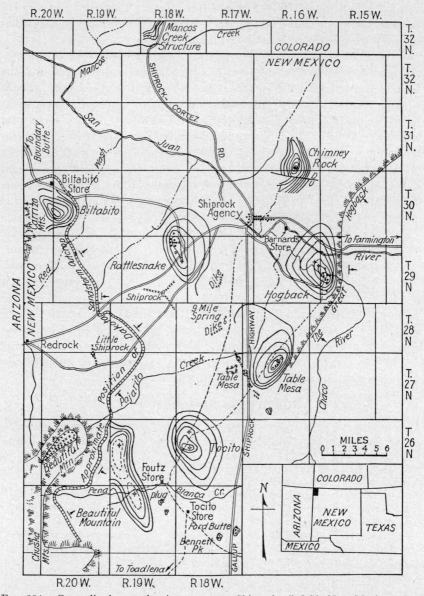

FIG. 294.—Generalized map showing structure, Shiprock oil field, New Mexico. (*After Nowels.*)

Shiprock, where three large gas wells were drilled in 1922.   In the Hogback structure, southeast of Shiprock village, oil was found in 1922.   Subsequently, oil was found at Table Mesa southwest of Hogback and at

Rattlesnake dome west of Hogback (Fig. 294). The gravity of the oil of the Hogback field is 63° A.P.I. and that of the Rattlesnake field is 74° A.P.I., while that of Table Mesa is 57° A.P.I.

Nearly all of the oil has come from the Dakota sandstone. The Tocito and Beautiful Mountain domes were tested and were found to carry water in the Dakota sandstone. These domes are near outcrops of the Dakota sandstone, and, according to Nowels, have probably lost their oil through flushing by water under artesian head. In the Hogback field the oil horizon is about 700 feet deep. This field produces oil without gas; the pressure is 182 pounds to the square inch. Sulphur water is found below the oil. In Table Mesa field, also, sulphur water is found below the oil. The very high gravity of the oil is probably due to the effect of the intrusions of igneous rocks found within the area. The highest gravity oil, that of Rattlesnake dome, is found near Shiprock, a considerable intrusive body 11 miles southwest of Shiprock postoffice. A well drilled on Rattlesnake dome in 1921 found oil in Pennsylvanian strata 6,750 feet deep.

NEW MEXICO OIL PRODUCTION

(Barrels)

Field	1928	Total to Dec. 31, 1928
Artesia	403,244	2,739,444
Bloomfield	6,163	13,717
Cap Rock-Maljamar	69,252	108,912
Hobbs	40,705	40,705
Hogback	165,709	792,997
Hospah		5,980
Jal	930	930
Rattlesnake	239,073	1,062,850
Sand Simeon	12,424	12,424
Table Mesa	52,388	178,192
Twin Hills	6,835	6,835
Total	996,723	4,962,986

UTAH

In Utah there are large areas of folded Paleozoic and later sedimentary rocks and numerous attempts have been made to discover oil in them, but these attempts in general have been unprofitable. In the northeast part of the state south of the Uinta Mountains, there are many gilsonite[1] dikes which are the residue of petroleum. These dikes are exposed at the surface and attracted attention at an early date. One of them, the

[1] ELDRIDGE, G. H., The Asphalts and Bituminous Rocks of the United States, *Twenty-second Ann. Rept.*, pt. 1, pp. 209–452, 1901.

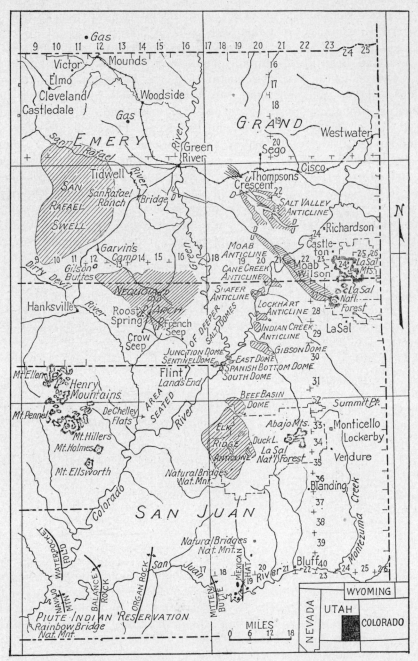

FIG. 295.—Map of southeast Utah.   (*From Prommel and Crum, with additions.*)

Black Dragon, has been mined for many years. Wells drilled in this area have found little oil. Bituminous sands occur in Asphalt Ridge a few miles west of Vernal. In the Ashley Valley field, a few miles from Vernal, gas is found in the Dakota sand and in the McElmo formation. A well in the McElmo is estimated to have a daily capacity of 20,000,000 cubic feet. At Cisco in east-central Utah (Fig. 292), gas is found in the Dakota and McElmo formations.

The chief area in southeastern Utah now being prospected is an intermontane basin[1] with the La Sal and Abajo Mountains on the east and the Henry Mountains and San Rafael swell on the west (Fig. 295). The geologic section of this area is shown on page 518. The intermontane area was subject to repeated uplift and erosion during Mesozoic time, while the surrounding area was little disturbed. The surrounding mountains were raised in Tertiary time.

In Emery County a well on the Woodside dome in 1922 obtained from a sand at a depth of 3,120 to 3,165 feet a flow of non-inflammable gas, high in helium, estimated to be 20,000,000 cubic feet per day, the rock pressure being 900 pounds per square inch. A carbon dioxide gas was found in a well near Farnham,[2] Carbon County.

In the Green River district near the Green River, petroliferous sandstones crop out, and a little oil is found in several wells in the McElmo formation.[3] The region is a gentle monocline dipping northeast on which there is a low anticline broken by faults. According to Lupton, the McElmo contains no persistent oil sand. Six miles southeast of Green River, a fault structure has been drilled to a depth of 2,935 feet, about 325 feet in the Hermosa formation (Carboniferous). Showings of oil and gas were found in the Shinarump, Moenkopi, and Cococino formations. About 40 miles south of Green River on the Nequoia arch, which practically connects San Rafael swell on the northwest with the

[1] LONGWELL, C. R., H. D. MISER, R. C. MOORE, K. BRYAN, and S. PAIGE, Rock Formations in the Colorado Plateau of Southeastern Utah and Northern Arizona, U. S. Geol. Survey *Prof. Paper* 132, pp. 1–24, 1924.

HARRISON, T. S., Colorado-Utah Salt Domes, Am. Assoc. Pet. Geol. *Bull.*, vol. 11, pp. 111–134, 1927.

BAKER, A. A., C. E. DOBBIN, E. T. McKNIGHT, and J. B. REESIDE, Notes on the Stratigraphy of the Moab Region, Utah Am. Assoc. Pet. Geol. *Bull.*, vol. 11, pp. 785–808, 1927.

PROMMEL, H. W. C., and H. E. CRUM, Salt Domes of Permian and Pennsylvanian Age in Southeastern Utah and Their Influence on Oil Accumulation, Am. Assoc. Pet. Geol. *Bull.*, vol. 11, pp. 373–394, 1927.

————, and ————, Structural History of Parts of Southeastern Utah from Interpretation of Geologic Sections, Am. Assoc. Pet. Geol. *Bull.*, vol. 11, pp. 809–820, 1927.

[2] EMERY, W. B., *Oil Gas Jour.*, vol. 26, p. G197, June 16, 1927.

[3] LUPTON, C. T., Oil and Gas near Green River, Grand County, Utah, U. S. Geol Survey *Bull.* 541, pp. 115–133, 1914.

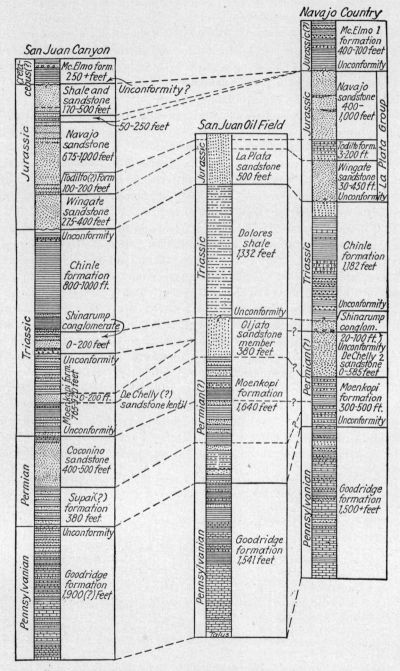

Fig. 296.—Generalized geologic section in San Juan Canyon, Utah, and in the Navajo country, Arizona.   (After Miser, Woodruff, and Gregory.)

anticlines southwest of Moab, a well on the Sweetwater dome was drilled 2,885 feet deep and abandoned.

On Cane Creek dome, about 8 miles southwest of Moab, a well drilled December, 1925, at a depth of 2,028 feet encountered oil and made 250 barrels of light oil per day, flowing by heads. The well was drilled to 5,000 feet, encountering thick beds of salt. On the Elk Ridge[1] dome south of Cane Creek, a well was drilled to crystalline rock.

The San Juan oil field[2] is in southeastern Utah about 18 miles southwest of Bluff, where several oil seeps occur along the San Juan River. The strata of this region are indicated on Fig. 296. The rocks are thrown into gentle folds whose axes trend nearly north. The principal structural feature is a broad gentle syncline flanked by anticlines. There are several oil sands, all near the top of the Goodridge formation. Several wells from 263 to 625 feet deep have produced small amounts of oil from sands near the top of the Goodridge. Most of the producing wells are near the axis of the Mexican Hat[3] syncline which crosses San Juan River 16 miles southwest of Bluff. The oil has a gravity of about 40° Bé. On the east anticline, east of the syncline, wells passed through the Pennsylvanian strata and encountered metamorphic rocks. Gas was found in Pennsylvanian strata. On the west anticline, Cedar Mesa dome, north of the San Juan River, and Hulkito dome, south of the river, are partially tested. The Gypsum Creek dome on the Utah-Arizona state line is possibly on the southern extension of this axis. This dome also is partially tested. On the Boundary Butte anticline in the southeastern corner of Utah, a well encountered gas flowing about 6,000,000 cubic feet a day at a horizon about 1,500 feet below the top of the Pennsylvanian system.

Virgin City is on Virgin River in the southwest corner of Utah.[4] It is underlain by almost flat-lying strata which range in age from Carboniferous to Eocene. Carboniferous limestone crops out a few miles west of Virgin City, and the town is underlain by the Permian (?) red beds. Small wells find oil in a sand lens in the Moenkopi formation at depths of 600 or 700 feet.

[1] INGRAM, T. R., *Oil Gas Jour.*, vol. 26, p. 63, Nov. 17, 1927.

[2] WOODRUFF, E. G., Geology of the San Juan Oil Field, Utah, U. S. Geol. Survey *Bull.* 471, pp. 76–104, 1912.

GREGORY, H. E., The San Juan Oil Field, U. S. Geol. Survey *Bull.* 431, pp. 11–25, 1911.

[3] MISER, H. D., Geologic Structure of the San Juan Cañon and Adjacent Country, Utah, U. S. Geol. Survey *Bull.* 751, pp. 115–155, 1924.

[4] RICHARDSON, G. B., Petroleum in Southern Utah, U. S. Geol. Survey *Bull.* 340, pp. 343–347, 1908.

CHAPTER XVI

PACIFIC COAST

CALIFORNIA

General Features.—Petroleum is found in California in a belt about 400 miles long extending from San Francisco Bay southward to Orange County. This belt is one of the most prolific oil-bearing areas in the world. Impressive showings of asphaltic sands and oil seepages are common in California. Asphaltic deposits are found in Sunset-Midway, Santa Maria, Santa Clara Valley, Los Angeles, Puente Hills, and other areas. The oil was used by the Indians for medicinal purposes before the country was settled by the Spanish. The first wells were drilled in 1866 near Ventura in the Santa Clara Valley region where asphaltic deposits and oil seepages abound. These wells were small and were not commercially successful. Other wells were drilled in this region, and in 1876 a small refinery was built at Newhall.[1] The first big well in California was the gusher, in Adams Cañon, Ventura County, which, in 1892, was brought in with an initial flow of 1,500 barrels per day. In 1898 and 1899 large gushers were developed in the Coalinga field, and in 1904 the Hartnell No. 1 well with an initial flow of 12,000 barrels a day was drilled in the Santa Maria field. This well produced 3,000,000 barrels of oil before it was put on the pump. In 1910 the Lakeview No. 1 well in the Sunset district was brought in with an initial flow of 15,000 barrels, which soon increased to 68,000 barrels per day and yielded 9,000,000 barrels in 18 months.

In the Los Angeles basin oil was known in the Puente Hills region at an early date. The Los Angeles field was developed in 1893. The early developments of the basin were chiefly on the east side near the Puente Hills. The Santa Fe Springs field was discovered in 1919. The Beverly Hills field at the north end of the Beverly Hills-Newport anticline was discovered in 1907, the Huntington Beach field on the same uplift in 1920, and Long Beach field in 1921. These and other developments resulted in a great expansion of the oil industry in California. In 1899 the production of the state was 2,677,000 barrels; in 1902 it was 14,387,000 barrels; and by January 1, 1926, the total production of California was 2,327,438,-000 barrels. The total production to date is more than 3,000,000,000 barrels. In 1929 California produced 292,037,000 barrels of petroleum

[1] ORCUTT, W. W., Early Oil Development in California, Am. Assoc. Pet. Geol. *Bull.*, vol. 8, pp. 61–72, 1924.

valued at $289,000,000 and 804,200,000 gallons of natural gas gasoline valued at $69,000,000. In 1928 California produced 246,215,000,000 cubic feet of natural gas valued at $56,695,000.

The rocks containing the oil are for the most part unconsolidated or poorly consolidated beds and are highly folded or faulted so that they dip at high angles. In some of the districts they are overturned. Oil seeps are numerous. At no other place in the United States is oil found in commercial amounts where the deformation is so extensive and surface

Fig. 297.—Map showing oil fields of California.

indications so abundant. In most respects the California oil fields resemble those of Europe and Asia more closely than they resemble other fields in North America.

In California oil is found in all the main geologic divisions from Upper Cretaceous to Pleistocene. The greater part of the oil, however, is in the Miocene and Pliocene formations. It is almost everywhere in sands or sandstones, although a little is found in fractured shales or other rocks in the Casmalia, Conejo, and Placerita (Newhall) districts. The oil sands are remarkable for their great thickness, and in some fields the oil-bearing zones consisting of sands and interbedded shales or clays are 300 to 600 feet thick. In a few fields, such as Long Beach and Huntington Beach, the oil-bearing series are 3,000 feet thick or more. The oil sands in the series not including clays, shales, and water sands in several fields aggregate 1,000 feet.   The oil-bearing strata are sealed with overlying clay or shale cappings.   Most of the oil fields lie in topographic basins which are also structural basins.   Of these the largest is the San Joaquin Valley, although the most productive in recent years is the Los Angeles basin.

The distribution of the oil fields is shown by Fig. 297.   The generalized sections of the principal fields are shown in the table[1] (p. 523).   All of the important fields are on anticlines and sealed monoclines.   The anticlines in general have undulating axes, and the oil is accumulated at the high places on the axes in domes formed at the crests of the folds.   In many of the fields the oil sands are numerous and lenticular, and it is difficult to contour such fields accurately because the sands play out and overlap.   Many of the great fields in the Los Angeles basin (Long Beach, Santa Fe Springs, Dominguez and others) are on rather regular domes, and in general the greater fields on the anticlines have large closures. Several prolific fields, however, are on plunging anticlines that are not known to be closed by folding.   These include Torrance and East Coyote Hills in the Los Angeles basin and Thirty-five anticline in the Sunset district.   Of the fields on monoclines in the Coalinga and Sunset-Midway fields, the oil sand is sealed by drying out of oil and formation of tar, and also by sands being overlapped by younger clays at an unconformity. The Mount Pozo, Brea Cañon, Olinda, Los Angeles, Salt Lake, and other fields on monoclines are sealed by faults.   In Casmalia and Conejo fields the oil is accumulated in fractured zones.

In many fields the oil becomes gradually lighter with depth.   This feature is noted in more than a score of fields in California.   At the surface the oil hardens to asphalt.   Near the surface, tar and heavy oils from 8 to 14° Bé. are common; at greater depths oils between 12 and 44° Bé. are found often in large amounts.   This relation is brought about in part by evaporation and loss of lighter constituents of the oils near the surface.   The change from heavy to light oil is not invariable, however, for in the Ventura Avenue field a heavy oil is found below a lighter one.

The main sources of the oil of the California fields are probably the Tertiary shales: Eocene, Oligocene, Miocene, and Pliocene.   Of these the Miocene[2] shales (Monterey and other formations) have been regarded as chief sources.   As was pointed out long ago by Arnold and associates, the organic shales are present in all of the oil-bearing regions, and

---

[1] This table published by Arnold and Anderson in the early history of developments of the fields is essentially correct today.   Gester states that fossils recently discovered show that the shale series regarded by Arnold and Anderson as Miocene in the Santa Maria district is in part of Pliocene age.

[2] ARNOLD, R., and V. R. GARFIAS, Am. Inst. Min. Eng. *Bull.* 87, p. 405, 1914.
GESTER, G. C., Am. Assoc. Pet. Geol. *Bull.* 10, p. 899, 1926.

TENTATIVE CORRELATION OF FORMATIONS OF COALINGA DISTRICT WITH THE STANDARD CALIFORNIA COAST RANGE SECTION AND THOSE OF OTHER LOCALITIES IN CALIFORNIA

(After Arnold and Anderson)

Era	System	Series	Standard Coast Range section	Coalinga district section	Santa Maria district section	Santa Clara Valley (Ventura Co.) section	Los Angeles and Puente Hills section
Cenozoic	Quaternary	Recent	Alluvium	Stream conglomerate and alluvium	Alluvium	Alluvium	Alluvium
		Pleistocene	San Perdo —Unc.	Stream deposits, valley fillings, and raised beach —Unconformity	Terrace deposits and dune sand —Unconformity	Terrace deposits, sand, and gravel —Unconformity	Terrace deposits, sand, and gravel —Unconformity
			Merced				
	Tertiary	Pliocene	San Diego	Tulare			
			San Pablo	—Unconformity— Etchegoin[1] —Unconformity—	Fernando	Fernando	Fernando
				Jacalitos —Unconformity—			
		Miocene	—Unconformity (?)— Santa Margarita —Unconformity—	Santa Margarita (?) —Unconformity—	—Unconformity—	—Unconformity— Shale, Upper sandstone, Shale, Lower sandstone (Modelo)	—Unconformity— Upper shale, Sandstone, Lower shale (Puente[2])
			Monterey	Lacking (with possible exception of a small part)	Monterey		
			—Unconformity— Vaqueros —Unconformity—	Vaqueros —Unconformity—	Vaqueros	Vaqueros	—Unconformity—
		Oligocene	San Lorenzo —Unconformity (?)—	Wanting (?)	Sespe and Tejon undifferentiated	Upper beds, Red beds, Lower beds (Sespe) Topatopa	
		Eocene	Tejon Martinez —Unconformity—	Tejon —Unconformity—			
	Cretaceous		Chico —Unconformity— Horsetown	Chico —Unconformity—	(?)		
Mesozoic			Knoxville —Unconformity— Franciscan —Unconformity—	Knoxville —Unconformity— Franciscan	Knoxville —Unconformity— Franciscan	—Unconformity—	—Unconformity—
	Jurassic (?)		Granitic rocks, schist, etc. —Unconformity—			Granitic rocks, gneiss, etc.	Granitic rocks, gneiss, etc. —Unconformity—
	(?)		Schist; limestone				Black schist

[1] Most of Jacalitos and Etchegoin now classed as Pliocene.
[2] Lower part probably Vaqueros in Los Angeles field.

in most of the oil-bearing regions the shales are from 1,000 to 5,000 feet or more thick. Diatoms and foraminifera are found in large amounts in many of the shale beds, and, according to Gester, radiolaria are abundant and in certain shales predominate. Gester tested many samples of the shales for oil and found that the light-colored shales rarely showed more than traces of oil but the chocolate-colored and other dark shales yielded oil to distillation in quantities varying from traces to nearly 30 gallons per ton of shale.

Petrolia.—In northwestern California, about 35 miles south of Eureka (Fig. 297 index inset) in Humboldt County near Petrolia,[1] oil and gas seeps are found, and a little light oil has been recovered from wells. The oil is found in folded and faulted Cretaceous rocks.

Petaluma.—Near Petaluma, some 30 miles north of San Francisco (Fig. 297 inset), a well 994 feet deep was drilled in 1926. This well found oil in upper Miocene beds and was estimated to have a settled production of 30 barrels of oil per day.

Santa Clara and Sargent.— South of San Francisco[2] small oil fields are developed at Purisima, Moody Gulch, and Sargent. In the Purisima field, 15 miles west of Palo Alto, small amounts of light oil are found in sands of the Monterey. The country is folded and extensively faulted. In the Moody Gulch field, some 20 miles southeast of Palo Alto, oil probably originating in the Monterey shales has accumulated in the Vaqueros and San Lorenzo (Oligocene) formations. Wells about 1,200 feet deep have produced small quantities of light oil with gravity of about 45° Bé.

In the Sargent field, 30 miles southeast of Moody Gulch and 3 miles west of Sargent station, oil probably originating in the shales of the Monterey has collected in sandstones of the Monterey. The beds dip 45 degrees south and the oil which has a gravity of 18° Bé., is found at a depth of about 1,500 feet. In Santa Cruz County, about 6 miles northwest of Santa Cruz city, the Monterey formation has been extensively quarried for asphalt.[3] South of Sargent in the San Joaquin Valley[4] there are large areas that are regarded as promising territory for oil prospecting.

[1] Hoots, H. W., U. S. Geol. Survey *Press Bull.* review in *Oil Weekly*, vol. 49, pp. 54–58, 1928.

[2] Branner, J. C., J. F. Newsome, and R. Arnold, Geology Atlas of the United States, U. S. Geol. Survey, Santa Cruz *Folio* 163.

Leck, L. V., Petroleum Resources of California, Calif. Min. Bur. *Bull.* 89, pp. 63–66, 1921.

[3] Eldridge, G. H., U. S. Geol. Survey *Twenty-second Ann. Rept.* pt. 1, pp. 381–417, 1911.

[4] Anderson, R., and R. W. Pack, Geology and Oil Resources of the West Border of the San Joaquin Valley North of Coalinga, California, U. S. Geol. Survey *Bull.* 603, pp. 1–220, 1915.

Coalinga.—The Coalinga district on the east side of the Diablo Mountains is 15 miles long and 8 miles wide. It is an area of slightly consolidated folded Tertiary strata (Figs. 298 to 301). The dominant structural feature is the monocline that dips eastward from the Coast Range to the valley.[1] On this is developed the Coalinga anticline, and bordering it the Coalinga syncline and a great monoclinal area that forms the west limb of the syncline. The oil is found principally near the top of the anticline and on the monocline. The geologic formations are shown in Fig. 299.

The oil is found (1) in sandy zones of the purple shale of the Chico; (2) in the porous sandstone of the Tejon, which consists mainly of diatomaceous and foraminiferal shale; (3) in three zones in the Vaqueros, which is the most productive formation in the area; (4) in the sandstone above the Tejon in the Santa Margarita; and (5) in the Jacalitos, particularly where it rests on or is near the Tejon.

The oil is found mainly along the Coalinga anticline and in the monocline in the west part of the area (Fig. 298). On this monocline tar springs or oil seeps occur mainly in the Tejon and Vaqueros and especially along an unconformity between these two formations. The bituminous matter on oxidation and drying has sealed up the beds. Where water is present with the oil, the oil rises to crests of anticlines or to the higher parts of the monocline.

In the Coalinga district it has been found that the areas of Miocene sediments, where underlain by the Tejon, are oil bearing. The productiveness is greatest where the Tejon occupies a position of angular unconformity with the Miocene sands or is more or less disturbed, as near the axis of an anticline, such as the Coalinga anticline.

The few small faults are so situated as not to affect the oil zones greatly, and they are not marked by the presence of escaping hydrocarbons. There are two types of oil, a paraffin oil, which appears to have originated in foraminiferal shales in the Upper Cretaceous, and an asphalt oil, which is believed to have its original source in diatomaceous and foraminiferal shales of upper Eocene age. The former is accumulated in sandy zones interbedded with the shales that are supposed to have given rise to it; the latter, which is the chief product of the district, is accumulated to some extent in the Tejon formation but chiefly in sands of the Vaqueros (lower Miocene), Santa Margarita (?) (upper middle Miocene), and Jacalitos (upper Miocene) formations. The Vaqueros is the principal producer of the district. The oil wells range in depth

---

[1] ARNOLD, RALPH, and ROBERT ANDERSON, Geology and Oil Resources of the Coalinga District, California, with a Report on the Chemical and Physical Properties of the Oils by Irving C. Allen, U. S. Geol. Survey *Bull.* 398, 1910.

———, and ———, Preliminary Report, U. S. Geol. Survey *Bull.* 357, 1908.

STEVENS, J. B., Amer. Assoc. Pet. Geol. *Bull.*, vol. 8, pp. 29–40, 1924.

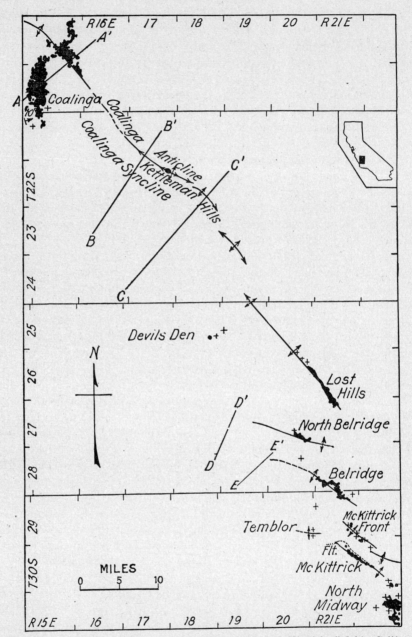

FIG. 298.—Map of Coalinga, Lost Hills, Belridge, and McKittrick oil fields, California. For geologic cross-sections, see Figs. 299 and 300.   (*Data from Arnold, Anderson, English, and others.*)

from 600 to more than 4,000 feet and penetrate from 20 to over 200 feet of productive sands. The product ranges from a black oil of 14 or 15° Bé. to a greenish oil of 35° Bé. or lighter.

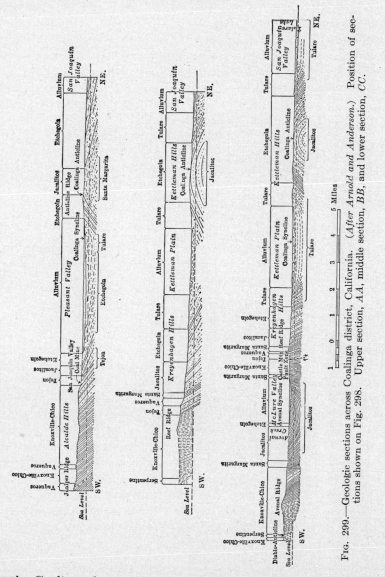

Fig. 299.—Geologic sections across Coalinga district, California. (*After Arnold and Anderson.*) Position of sections shown on Fig. 298. Upper section, *AA*, middle section, *BB*, and lower section, *CC*.

In the Coalinga district the gas pressure was high in the early stages of development, but in 1921 it was about 2 pounds per square inch, and in the east side of the field it was practically nothing. In 1921, during a strike, and in 1923, during a period of overproduction, certain groups of wells were shut in while others near by were pumped. The results of closing certain wells were studied by Wilhelm[1] who shows that a considerable flush production is obtained on reopening, due to resaturation of sands during the period of shutdown. This flush production averages 30 to 60 per cent above normal production. As a rule the flush production of water is as great as that of oil, and certain wells that produced all water before being shut produced all oil when opened. Many wells when opened produced increased amounts of sand. An irregular edge-water line tends to become straight during periods of shutdown, and in edge-water regions the flush production is small and a shutdown may result in loss of oil to certain wells. The ultimate oil recovered from the field, according to Wilhelm, is not decreased.

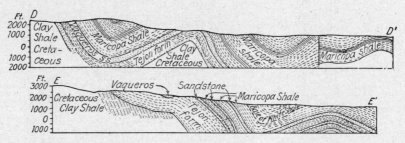

Fig. 300.—Cross-sections west of Belridge, Kern County, California. (*After English, U. S. Geol. Survey.*) Positions of sections are shown on Fig. 298.

Kettleman Hills.—Kettleman Hills[2] occupy an area about 30 miles long and 4 miles wide between Coalinga and Lost Hills. The first well to discover oil is the Milham well, 22 miles southeast of Coalinga, completed November 7, 1928, which was soon producing 3,670 barrels of oil having a gravity of 60° Bé. This well was drilled 7,236 feet deep and was believed to produce from a sand 7,100 feet deep, but wells subsequently drilled were productive at depths of 6,400 feet. Large amounts of gas high in gasoline are associated with the oil. The Kettleman Hills district is on a series of overlapping elongated domes approximately on the strike of the Coalinga anticline. The Etchegoin formation crops out in the center of the domes and the wells generally are started in it. The production is probably from the Vaqueros (Lower Miocene) in which beds of productive sands are probably present for its entire thickness of 900 feet. The field is under active development and very large amounts of oil and gas are discovered.

[1] WILHELM, V. H., Effect of Closing in Production in the Coalinga Field, Summary of Operations California Oil Fields, Calif. Min. Bur., vol. 11, No. 6, pp. 5–16, December, 1925.

CASE, J. B., Summary of Operations California Oil Fields, Calif. Min. Bur. vol. 5 No. 4, pp. 9–13, October, 1919.

[2] MUSSER, E. H., Preliminary Report on the Kettleman Hills Oil Field, Summary of Operations California Oil Fields, Calif. Min. Bur., vol. 14, No. 5, pp. 5–17, 1928.

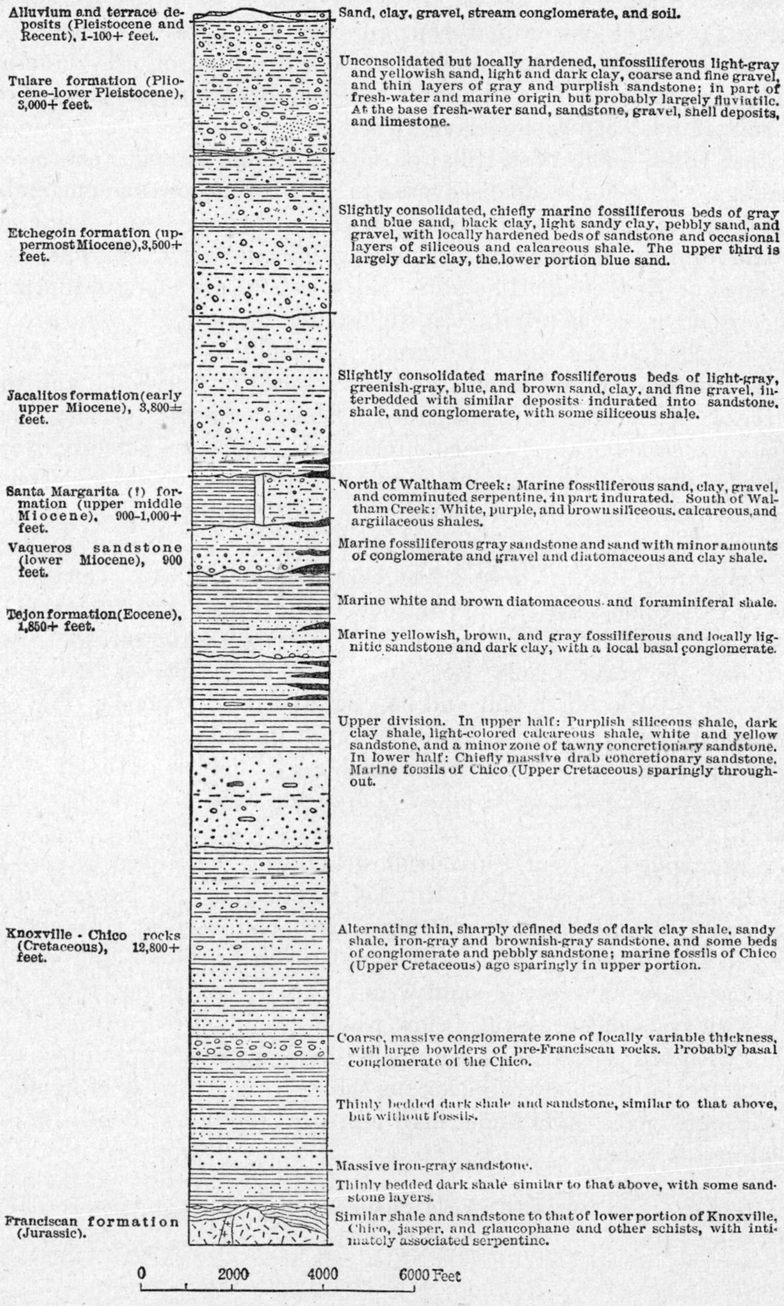

Alluvium and terrace deposits (Pleistocene and Recent), 1-100+ feet.	Sand, clay, gravel, stream conglomerate, and soil.
Tulare formation (Pliocene–lower Pleistocene), 3,000+ feet.	Unconsolidated but locally hardened, unfossiliferous light-gray and yellowish sand, light and dark clay, coarse and fine gravel, and thin layers of gray and purplish sandstone; in part of fresh-water and marine origin but probably largely fluviatile. At the base fresh-water sand, sandstone, gravel, shell deposits, and limestone.
Etchegoin formation (uppermost Miocene), 3,500+ feet.	Slightly consolidated, chiefly marine fossiliferous beds of gray and blue sand, black clay, light sandy clay, pebbly sand, and gravel, with locally hardened beds of sandstone and occasional layers of siliceous and calcareous shale. The upper third is largely dark clay, the lower portion blue sand.
Jacalitos formation (early upper Miocene), 3,800± feet.	Slightly consolidated marine fossiliferous beds of light-gray, greenish-gray, blue, and brown sand, clay, and fine gravel, interbedded with similar deposits indurated into sandstone, shale, and conglomerate, with some siliceous shale.
Santa Margarita (?) formation (upper middle Miocene), 900–1,000+ feet.	North of Waltham Creek: Marine fossiliferous sand, clay, gravel, and comminuted serpentine, in part indurated. South of Waltham Creek: White, purple, and brown siliceous, calcareous, and argillaceous shales.
Vaqueros sandstone (lower Miocene), 900 feet.	Marine fossiliferous gray sandstone and sand with minor amounts of conglomerate and gravel and diatomaceous and clay shale.
Tejon formation (Eocene), 1,850+ feet.	Marine white and brown diatomaceous and foraminiferal shale.
	Marine yellowish, brown, and gray fossiliferous and locally lignitic sandstone and dark clay, with a local basal conglomerate.
	Upper division. In upper half: Purplish siliceous shale, dark clay shale, light-colored calcareous shale, white and yellow sandstone, and a minor zone of tawny concretionary sandstone. In lower half: Chiefly massive drab concretionary sandstone. Marine fossils of Chico (Upper Cretaceous) sparingly throughout.
Knoxville - Chico rocks (Cretaceous), 12,800+ feet.	Alternating thin, sharply defined beds of dark clay shale, sandy shale, iron-gray and brownish-gray sandstone, and some beds of conglomerate and pebbly sandstone; marine fossils of Chico (Upper Cretaceous) age sparingly in upper portion.
	Coarse, massive conglomerate zone of locally variable thickness, with large bowlders of pre-Franciscan rocks. Probably basal conglomerate of the Chico.
	Thinly bedded dark shale and sandstone, similar to that above, but without fossils.
	Massive iron-gray sandstone.
	Thinly bedded dark shale similar to that above, with some sandstone layers.
Franciscan formation (Jurassic).	Similar shale and sandstone to that of lower portion of Knoxville, Chico, jasper, and glaucophane and other schists, with intimately associated serpentine.

0 2000 4000 6000 Feet

FIG. 301.—Generalized section of Coalinga district, California. (*After Arnold and Anderson.*)

Devil's Den.—The Devil's Den[1] oil field is 35 miles southeast of Coalinga. The rocks cropping out are Oligocene beds, Temblor, Vaqueros, and Maricopa shale. Small quantities of heavy oil are found in all the formations named, and some oil was produced from the Oligocene beds or from alluvial deposits overlying them.

Lost Hills.—The Lost Hills[2] oil field is about 45 miles southeast of Coalinga. The field was discovered in 1910, when oil was encountered at a depth of 472 feet. The country is an alluvial plain. A low ridge of alluvium trends northwest. These hills lie near the line of the Coalinga or Kettleman Hills anticlinal zone and are along a sharp anticline which is developed in the underlying rocks. The strata on the flanks of the fold dip 10 to 15 degrees. A dome occupies part of the top of the anticline and oil wells are closely spaced on the dome and to the southeast of it, where the anticline plunges steeply southeast. The oil is found in sands of the Etchegoin formation, which lies directly over the Maricopa brown shale from which the oil is probably derived. The area is about 500 feet above sea level. On the high part of the structure the oil is found at depths of about 300 feet; at the south end of the field the wells are 2,400 feet deep. The oil sands lie in 2 zones separated by 200 feet of shale. In the upper zone the oil has a gravity of 11° Bé. at the north end of the field, where the sands lie near the surface. At the south end the gravity is 28° Bé. In the lower zone the oil has a gravity of 19° Bé. at the north end and 38° Bé. at the south end. The oil on the crest of the anticline is lighter than on its flanks. The upper sand plays out at the south end of the field. The field is outlined by edge water on its sides and at its ends. · Large gas wells are developed in the field.

Buttonwillow.—Near Buttonwillow,[3] 20 miles southeast of Lost Hills and 12 miles northeast of McKittrick, the surface of the ground rises slightly in the strike of the extension of the Coalinga-Lost Hills anticline. Several wells in this region have found much gas and some oil. The wells encounter 600 feet of sand with clay partings; about 1,400 feet of clay with beds of hard sand below which are 1,200 feet of lignitic blue shales with brown shale beds, probably upper Etchegoin; and below that are 900 feet or more of carbonaceous shales with thin beds of lignite also of Etchegoin age. Gas under high pressure is found at depths of about 4,000 to 4,400 feet.

[1] HUGUENIN, E., Devil's Den Field, Summary of Operations California Oil Fields, Calif. Min. Bur., vol. 9, No. 12, pp. 5–11, June, 1924.

[2] McCABE, R. E., Lost Hills Oil Field, Summary of Operations California Oil Fields, Calif. Min. Bur., vol. 10, No. 1, pp. 5–10, 1924.

ENGLISH, W. A., U. S. Geol. Survey *Bull.* 721, p. 37, 1921.

[3] FERGUSON, R. N., Summary of Operations California Oil Fields, Calif. Min. Bur., vol. 7, No. 3, pp. 7–13, September, 1921.

North Belridge.—The North Belridge[1] oil field (Fig. 300) is about 6 miles southwest of the Lost Hills field on a southeast spur of the Antelope Hills. The area is covered with alluvium. The field is probably developed on an anticline that strikes northwest. The oil is in sands that lie in two zones about 1,500 feet apart and are separated by shales and clays.

Belridge.—The Belridge field is 10 miles northwest of McKittrick and 12 miles south of the Lost Hills field. Oil was discovered in 1911 in a well completed at a depth of 782 feet and having an initial production of 100 barrels per day. The field occupies a dome that is elongated northwest and plunges steeply southeast. Wells pass through the McKittrick group consisting of the Paso Robles (Upper Pliocene and Pleistocene?) and the Etchegoin (Lower Pliocene or Upper Miocene), and the deeper wells penetrate the Maricopa shale (Monterey). The oil occurs near the top of the dome and on its southeast side (1) in the lower sands of the Etchegoin, (2) in basal sands of the Etchegoin which rest on the Maricopa, and (3) in sands of the Maricopa. The Maricopa brown shale is believed to be the source of the oil. The oil in the Maricopa is found at depths between 2,100 and 4,000 feet and has a gravity of 29° Bé. The oil at higher elevations is heavier.

In the Temblor Ranch field, 6 miles southwest of Belridge field, oil is discovered near an anticline in Maricopa shale.

McKittrick, Sunset, and Midway.—The McKittrick, Sunset, and Midway fields[2] are in Kern County, some 40 miles west of Bakersfield (Figs. 302, 303). The oil fields lie on the east slope of the Temblor Range, which rises some 4,000 feet above the sea. The San Emigdio Range lies to the south on the border of the Sunset field. The country is an area of hills and plains east and north of the mountain ranges.

The Temblor Range, which trends northwest, is a great monocline dipping northeast on which are developed many minor folds, the axes of which make small angles with the major range. In general they strike a few degrees more to the west than the major monocline. On the southwest the Temblor Range is bordered by the great San Andreas fault zone, which has been traced from Point Arena, on the Pacific Coast north of San Francisco, for over 600 miles, nearly to Salton Sea.[3] The faulting and folding on the sides of the range give in effect a huge anticli-

---

[1] BOEZINGER, H., Belridge and North Belridge Oil Fields, Summary of Operations California Oil Fields, Calif. Min. Bur., vol. 10, No. 1, pp. 11–19, July, 1924.

[2] ARNOLD, RALPH, and H. R. JOHNSON, Preliminary Report on the McKittrick-Sunset Oil Region, U. S. Geol. Survey *Bull.* 406, 1910.

ARNOLD, RALPH, and V. R. GARFIAS, Geology and Technology of the California Oil Fields, Am. Inst. Min. Eng. *Bull.* 87, pp. 383–470, 1914.

[3] LAWSON, A. C., Report of the Earthquake Investigation Committee on the California Earthquake of Apr. 18, 1906, Carnegie Inst., Washington, *Pub.* 87, 1908.

norium.   There are also several smaller faults in the region, some of them thrust faults.

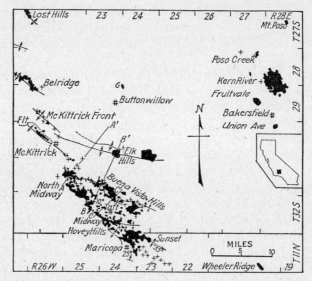

FIG. 302.—Map showing Kern River, Sunset, Midway and other fields, California. Black areas are oil fields, except those marked *G* which are gas fields.   Crosses indicate areas where small amounts of oil are found.   Cross-sections of area on lines indicated. (*Based on various reports of U. S. Geol. Survey by Arnold, Johnson, Pack, English, and others, and reports of California State Mining Bureau by Huguenin, McCabe, Balzinger, Goode, Keyes, Saunders, Rogers, and others.*)

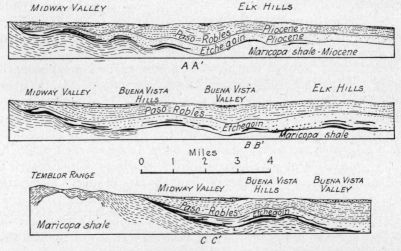

FIG. 303.—Cross-sections of McKittrick, Midway, and Sunset oil fields.   Positions of sections are shown on Fig. 302.   (*After Pack Arnold, Johnson, English, and Davies.*)

The McKittrick field lies on the flanks of three more or less local and highly complex folds subsidiary to the great northeastward dipping monocline of the Temblor Range. Thrust faulting and overturning have so complicated the folding as to place the older beds above the younger (Fig. 304).

The oil is believed to have originated in the diatomaceous shales of the Monterey and Santa Margarita formations and to have migrated to the porous layers intercalated with them or to the sands and gravels of the unconformably overlying Etchegoin formation. Most of it is heavy oil with gravity between 12 and 20° Bé.

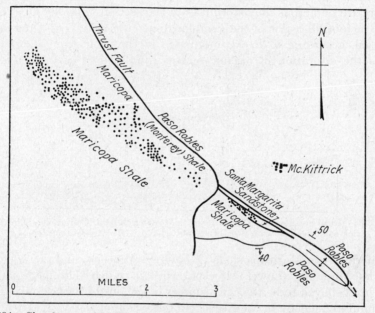

FIG. 304. —Sketch map of McKittrick oil field California. (*After English*.) Heavy lines are faults, light lines are normal contacts, and dots are wells.

There are two productive zones in the McKittrick district. In the northern part of the district one zone, the lower, lies nearly horizontal and is usually between 100 and 240 feet thick; in the southern part the zone is overturned and stands nearly vertical. The upper zone is only moderately productive. Where the oil sand reaches the surface, west of the town of McKittrick, enormous deposits of asphalt have formed. The structure of this area is complicated (Fig. 305). The main producing belt is 4 miles long and from a few hundred feet to a half mile wide.[1] Owing to the overthrust the oil-bearing strata of the Etchegoin are overlain and also underlain by the Maricopa shales. At the south end of the area the oil comes from an uncovered in-lying area of the Santa

[1] ENGLISH, W. A., Notes on the McKittrick, California, Oil Field, Am. Assoc. Pet. Geol. *Bull.*, vol. 11, pp. 617–620, 1927.

Margarita. Tar sands and brea deposits with bone beds are found, similar to those of Los Angeles.

The Sunset-Midway field has been described by Pack[1] and Rogers.[2] The area covered in their reports overlaps the area mapped by Arnold and Johnson, and extends farther southeast.

The Tertiary formations range in age from Eocene to Pliocene and are altogether 18,000 feet thick. They consist of sands, gravels, and clays, poorly consolidated, and in the central part of the section are 4,800 feet of material of Miocene age that consists largely of remnants of diatoms. There are numerous unconformities in the section (Fig. 306).

The foothill region of the Temblor Range is closely folded and faulted. The oil, according to Pack,[3] originated in the shale formations, chiefly from the alteration of organic matter contained in diatoms and fora-

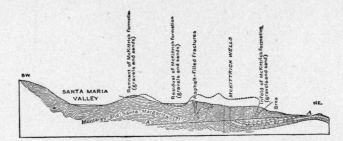

FIG. 305.—Ideal cross-section of north end of McKittrick field, California. The McKittrick sand lies below an overthrust fault *AA*. (*After Arnold and Johnson.*)

minifera. The Maricopa shale (Monterey, Miocene) and the upper part of the Vaqueros (Lower Miocene) contain much diatomaceous shale and are believed to be the chief sources of the oils of the region. The oil accumulated chiefly in the Etchegoin formation of the McKittrick group of Pliocene age, although some of the oil is found in sands in the Maricopa and Vaqueros formations. Beds of sandy strata overlying the Maricopa shales unconformably are in favorable positions for accumulation.

The oil-bearing beds in the late Tertiary sequence are coarse and fine sands that range in thickness from a few feet to a few hundred feet. These beds crop out in the foothills of the Temblor Range, and their line of outcrop marks the western limit of the main productive field. Toward the east the productive oil sands are buried progressively deeper beneath the surface. In the eastern part of the field the productive sands, which are usually 10 to 50 feet thick, are interspersed with barren beds

[1] PACK, R. W., The Sunset-Midway Oil Field, California, U. S. Geol. Survey *Prof. Paper* 116, pt. 1; Geology and Oil Resources, pp. 1–179, 1920.

[2] ROGERS, G. S., The Sunset-Midway Oil Field, California, U. S. Geol. Survey *Prof. Paper* 116, pt. 2; Geochemical Relations of the Oil, Gas, and Water, pp. 1–103, 1919.

[3] PACK, R. W., *op. cit.*, p. 70.

of equal thickness through a section 600 to 800 feet thick. Near the outcrop the total thickness of the zone containing oil sands is rarely more

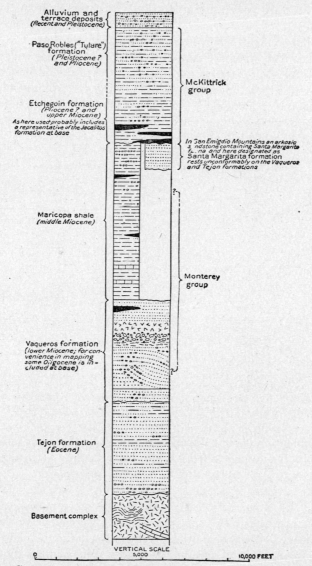

Fig. 306.—Generalized columnar section of the rocks in the Sunset-Midway oil field and in the north flank of San Emigdio Mountains. Position of oil-bearing beds indicated by solid black. (*After Pack*.)

than 200 or 300 feet, but the portion of it composed of oil sand is greater there than in the parts of the field where the sands lie deeper.

The richest sands lie close to the contact with the diatomaceous shale. These oil-bearing beds are, however, not of the same age throughout the field, for the formation of which they are a part rests unconformably on the shale, and younger beds that abut against the shale in the western part of the field are younger than those against the shale in the eastern part.

The oil has evidently moved chiefly through the lowest part of the formation that rests upon the diatomaceous shale, as these beds are fairly porous and offer less resistance to the movement of the oil than the shale. The movement is therefore chiefly parallel to the plane of unconformity— that is, to the top of the shale. Near the outcrop, either by fractionation or by reaction with alkaline water, the oil becomes very viscous and seals the beds through which the oil is moving.

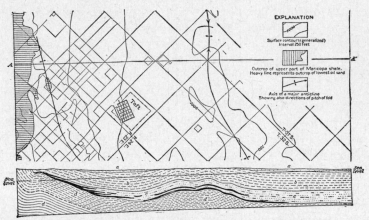

FIG. 307.—Upper figure is a plan of part of Sunset-Midway field, near Taft, California. Each large square is one square mile. Contour interval is 250 feet. The lower figure is a section on line AA.' a, Alluvium; b, Paso Robles ("Tulare") formation; c, Etchegoin formation (contains chief petroleum reservoirs of the district); d, Maricopa shale. (After Pack.)

The tarrification of the oil is caused chiefly by the addition of sulphur derived from the sulphate-bearing surface waters. At places a similar process has caused the formation of deposits of sulphur.

When the avenue of escape to the surface is closed, the oil moves out from the plane of unconformity through the more porous of the beds in the formation that rests upon the shale. Movement in this manner is rendered easy by the fact that the younger formation was laid down in a transgressing sea and the different beds in it abut against the shale just as horizontal layers of sand held in a huge bowl would rest against the sides of the bowl (Fig. 307). The distance that the sands which extend out from the unconformity are filled with oil is variable, but each sand beyond the point at which it contains oil, according to Pack, is filled with water.

Along the anticlines that are separated by synclines from the outcrop of the oil sands, the oil has collected in sands that lie some distance above the plane of unconformity (Fig. 303). This oil has evidently moved vertically through the lenticular sands. In any sand that contains oil and gas in these outer anticlines there is a notable tendency for the gas to occupy the higher parts of the fold and the oil the lower parts or saddles of the same fold. In the outer anticlines the gas has collected 200 or 300 feet above the oil.

In some parts of the field where the oil is buried more than 2,000 feet a zone of tar-filled sand lies less than 1,000 feet below the surface. This zone is believed to mark the place where the upward-moving hydrocarbons have met and been oxidized by surface waters. The evidence indicates that these hydrocarbons have moved more or less vertically through the intervening beds.

The gravity of the oil varies with the grain of the sand, the oil being lighter in the fine-grained beds; with the distance from the outcrop; with the relation of the oil to mineralized water, the oil in contact with water of certain types being tarry; and with the position on the fold, the oil being lighter on the higher parts of the anticline.

The oil ranges in gravity from less than 11° Bé. near the outcrop to 31 or 32° Bé. in the part of the field where the oil comes from great depths. The average gravity of the oil obtained from the sands near the outcrop is between 14 and 18° Bé.; that of the oil obtained in the Buena Vista Hills and other parts of the field where the sands lie deep is 21 to 28° Bé. or lighter. The oil normally carries but little gasoline, the proportion distilling at a temperature of less than 150° C. being usually less than 4 per cent.

Buena Vista Hills.—The Buena Vista Hills,[1] about 2 miles northeast of Taft, are a long low group of hills that trend northwest. This group of hills is structurally a small anticlinorium on the top of which are developed elongated narrow domes on which gas is found in Pliocene beds near the crests of the domes and oil lower on the flanks. In this area wells encounter about 700 feet of sands and soft shale; 900 to 1,200 feet of clay and shale; about 500 feet of sand and sandy shale which is the main gas zone of the field; about 400 feet of shale with streaks of sand which constitutes the upper oil zone; shale and sands of a water-bearing zone of undetermined thickness; a lower oil zone, also of undetermined thickness. The oil (27° A.P.I.) is in the Etchegoin formation (Fig. 303). The gas of the field is under high pressure and is present in large amounts. It is delivered to a pipe line and forms part of the gas supply of Los Angeles. The gas is high in gasoline vapor.

---

[1] Thoms, C. C., Gas Conservation in Buena Vista Hills, Summary of Operations California Oil Fields, Calif. Min. Bur., vol. 8, No. 2, pp. 5–14, August, 1922.

Goode, H. A., and R. L. Keyes, Report on the Northeastern Flank of the Buena Vista Hills, Midway Oil Field, Kern County, California, Summary of Operations California Oil Fields, Calif. Min. Bur., vol. 12, No. 1, pp. 5–12, July, 1926.

Elk Hills.—The Elk Hills[1] oil field, about 10 miles north of Taft, to July 1, 1928, produced 96,199,914 barrels of oil. The field is located on an anticline which trends east, and the crest of the hills corresponds closely with the high part of the anticline. The surface strata are sands, shales, and conglomerates of the Paso Robles (Tulare) formation, below which are the strata of the Etchegoin of undetermined thickness. Faults strike northeast across the area. The wells pass through about 3,000 to 3,400 feet of shale, sandy shale, and some sand into the oil measures. The oil is found chiefly in a zone of sands and shales in the Etchegoin formation (Fig. 303). The main production comes from low domes on the anticline.

In the Hovey Hills[2] field, 3 or 4 miles south of Taft, important deposits of oil were discovered in 1921. The rocks cropping out are McKittrick

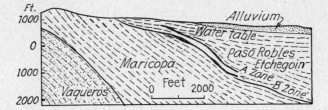

Fig. 308.—Cross-section of Sunset Extension field, Sunset district, California; oil zones in black. (*After Rogers.*)

and Maricopa beds. The main part of the field is on a gentle monocline that dips northeast. Tar beds with viscous oils are found at the base of the Paso Robles and top of the Maricopa series. The sands and shales of this zone constitute a wedge from 50 to 700 feet thick and the beds have been classed as probably Etchegoin. The oil of the contact zone has a gravity of 13 to 16° Bé. The brown shales of the Maricopa below the unconformity dip about 60 degrees northeast. Sand lenses in this series produce oil with a gravity of about 18° Bé.

The Sunset Extension[3] field is in the Sunset district southeast of Maricopa. Brea deposits have long been known in this field. The earliest developments were wells operated by hoist and barrel, which derived a very heavy oil from depths of 130 feet. This oil was used for

[1] SAUNDERS, L. W., Recent Developments in Elk Hills, *Oil Gas Jour.*, vol. 23, p. 60, Oct. 29, 1925.

——, Summary of Operations California Oil Fields, Calif. Min. Bur., vol. 10, No. 11, pp. 5–12, May, 1925.

PEMBERTON, J. R., Elk Hills, Kern County, California, "Structure of Typical American Oil Fields," vol. 2, pp. 44–61, 1929.

[2] SAUNDERS, L. W., Summary of Operations California Oil Fields, Calif. Min. Bur., vol. 9, No. 12, pp. 11–18, June, 1924.

[3] ROGERS, R. G., Sunset Extension Field, Summary of Operations California Oil Fields, Calif. Min. Bur., vol. 9, No. 12, pp. 18–24, June, 1924.

making a high-grade asphalt. In 1922 a lighter oil (13° Bé.) was found at a depth of 915 feet. The Maricopa shale dips northeast at high angles and is overlain unconformably by the Etchegoin strata, which dip northeast at much lower angles (Fig. 308). The oil is found at the unconformity between the Etchegoin beds and the Maricopa beds in a zone of shales and sands and also in a zone of sands above the latter and separated from it by about 130 feet of blue shale.

The Thirty-five anticline[1] lies about 8 miles south of Buena Vista Lake at the southeast edge of the Sunset district. This anticline strikes southeast and plunges steeply southeast. The Etchegoin formation becomes thicker to the southeast, and, due to its unconformable relation and its overlap of the Maricopa shales, the beds that rest upon the Maricopa to the southeast are older than those which rest upon the Maricopa to the northwest. Thus new oil sands progressively appear in lower sands to the southeast, and oil in the higher sands gives way to edge water down the dip of the sands. Deep drilling has encountered deposits of oil in the sands in the upper 400 feet of the Maricopa shale. The production from these sands is somewhat erratic and appears to be controlled in part by fracturing. The bulk of the oil from the Thirty-five anticline is from the Etchegoin above the Maricopa shale. The oil has gravities between 19 and 30° A.P.I.

Kern River.—The Kern River field is in Kern County, about 4 miles north of Bakersfield, near the southeastern extremity of San Joaquin Valley.[2] It was discovered in 1900 and produced large amounts of heavy oil. Its production is due to the great thickness of its sands, which ranges from 200 to 600 feet. The long axis of the field extends northwest. The beds dip southwest. The depth to the productive oil sands ranges from 400 feet on the northeast part of the fold to 1,200 feet or more on the south and west borders. The gravity of the oil averages about 14° Bé.

The formations of the Kern River district consist of a basement of granitic rocks overlain by a series of Tertiary strata which attain a thickness of about 5,000 feet in the oil field. The granite of the Sierra Nevada is continuous around the south end of San Joaquin Valley, and in the vicinity of Kern River the escarpment of the mountain front is believed to mark a normal fault along which the granite on the east has been raised and the Miocene beds on the west depressed.

Tertiary formations include an upper and a lower division. The upper division is made up of coarse, unconsolidated sands, gravels, and

[1] COPP, W. W., and H. A. GODDE, Summary of Operations California Oil Fields, Calif. Min. Bur., vol. 9, No. 5, pp. 5–33, November, 1923.

GODDE, H. A. and E. H. MUSSER, Summary of Operations California Oil Fields, Calif. Min. Bur., vol. 12, No. 11, pp. 5–17, May, 1927.

[2] ARNOLD, RALPH, and V. R. GARFIAS, Geology and Technology of the California Oil Fields, Am. Inst. Min. Eng. *Bull.* 87, p. 436, 1914.

boulders. These beds are supposed to correspond to portions of the Tulare, Etchegoin, and possibly Santa Margarita formations of the west side of the valley. The lower division, composed mostly of clays and soft diatomaceous shales grading up from a basal sandstone, represents the Monterey. The lower division is regarded as the source of the oil, and the upper is the main zone of accumulation.

A part of the southeastern portion of the Kern River oil field has been mapped by Ferguson.[1] In this area the rocks dip southwest. The wells pass through 300 to 700 feet of clays, gravels, and water sands. Immediately below this series is zone A consisting of 50 feet of water sands with heavy oil at many places. Below zone A is 40 feet of clay. This caps zone B, which is about 600 feet thick and is the main oil-bearing zone. This zone contains shaly layers and also two sands in which water occurs at relatively high levels. Below zone B is a sand 80 feet thick, which is a water sand or flooded oil sand. Below the latter sand is the Kern water sand 20 feet thick, and below the latter are 200 feet of tar sands which at places contain oil. Oil is found at Fruitvale 2 miles west of Bakersfield in Etchegoin beds in large amounts.

The Pozo Creek[2] oil field, 4 miles northwest of Kern River field, was discovered in 1912. Several wells have had production of heavy oil but have had much trouble with water. The oil is found in a zone of sands 50 feet thick at a depth between 1,580 and 2,500 feet. The oil probably originated in the Miocene shale and rose to overlying Pliocene or later beds. Between discovery and 1924 this field produced 1,024,114 barrels of oil.

The Mount Pozo[3] oil field 16 miles north of Bakersfield (Fig. 302), was discovered in 1926. The rocks exposed at the surface are fresh-water sands and clays of the Kern River beds of Pliocene age. They dip 5 to 6 degrees to the southwest and lie unconformably above the sandy zone of the Temblor formation. The tilted beds are sealed by a fault that dips 50 degrees northeast. The productive area is 700 acres. In 1927 the field (p. 111) had a daily production of 5,000 barrels. The oil is found about 1,900 feet deep; its gravity is about 16° Bé.

In the Round Mountain[4] field, 10 miles northeast of Bakersfield, oil is found in the "Jewett" zone at a depth of 1,218 feet. This zone lies above

[1] Ferguson, R. N., Summary of Operations California Oil Fields, Calif. Min. Bur., vol. 5, No. 3, pp. 5–52, September, 1919.

[2] Kaiser, C. L., Pozo Creek Field, Summary of Operations California Oil Fields, Calif. Min. Bur., vol. 10, No. 1, pp. 19–22, July, 1924.

[3] Wilhelm, V. H., and L. W. Saunders, Report on the Mount Pozo Oil Field, Summary of Operations California Oil Fields, Calif. Min. Bur., vol. 12, No. 7, pp. 5–12, January, 1927.

Godde, H. A., Summary of Operations California Oil Fields, Calif. Min. Bur., vol. 14, No. 1, pp. 7–8, 1928.

[4] Op. cit., pp. 8–10.

that producing at Mount Pozo. Accumulation is governed chiefly by faulting.

The Wheeler Ridge oil field, 26 miles south of Bakersfield (Fig. 302), was discovered in 1922 when oil was found at a depth of about 2,000 feet. The field[1] is located on an anticline that strikes N.10° W. and has steep dips, particularly on the north side. The anticline is closed to form a dome. The rocks exposed at the surface are of the Paso Robles formation. Wells drilled on the top of the anticline (Fig. 309) pass through 1,000 feet of sandy beds of the Paso Robles formation, below which are 1,000 to 1,200 feet of clay and sands of the Etchegoin, near the base of which are located the upper oil sands of Miocene age. Below the

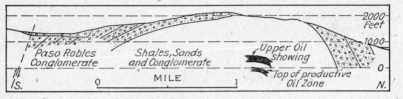

FIG. 309.—Cross-section of Wheeler Ridge oil field, California. (*After Cunningham.*)

Etchegoin wells penetrate 2,000 feet of sandy brown shale and sands of the Maricopa (?) formation, which constitute the deeper oil-bearing zone.

Arroyo Grande.—In the Arroyo Grande[2] oil field in southwest San Luis Obispo County small wells about 3 miles northeast of Pismo produce heavy oil, about 14° Bé. The wells are located in a syncline and the oil is found in the basal beds of the Pismo formation (Fernando) which consist mainly of loose sands with lenses of shale.

Santa Maria.—The Santa Maria[3] oil district in western Santa Barbara County includes the Santa Maria, Casmalia, Cat Cañon, and Lompoc

[1] CUNNINGHAM, G. M., The Wheeler Ridge Oil Field, Am. Assoc. Pet. Geol. *Bull.*, vol. 10, pp. 495–501, 1926.

GODDE, H. A., *op. cit.*, p. 13.

[2] FAIRBANKS, H. W., U. S. Geol. Survey, San Luis *Folio* 101.

ELDRIDGE, G. H., Asphalt and Bituminous Rock Deposits, U. S. Geol. Survey, *Twenty-second Ann. Rept.* 1, pp. 412–424, 1900.

LECK, L. V., Petroleum Resources of California, Calif. Min. Bur., *Bull.* 89, pp. 95–96, 1921.

[3] ARNOLD, R., and R. ANDERSON, Preliminary Report on the Santa Maria Oil District, U. S. Geol. Survey *Bull.* 317, pp. 1–69, 1907.

———, and ———, Geology and Oil Resources of the Santa Maria Oil District, Santa Barbara County, California, U. S. Geol. Survey *Bull.* 322, pp. 1–157, 1907.

GORE, F. D., Oil Shale in Santa Barbara County, California, Am. Assoc. Pet. Geol. *Bull.*, vol. 8, pp. 459–472, 1924.

COLLOM, R. E., "Structure of Typical American Oil Fields," vol. 2, pp 18–22, 1929.

oil fields (Fig. 310).   The area is occupied chiefly by Tertiary sedimentary
rocks that are thrown into moderately steep folds that strike northwest
and west.   Faults trend nearly parallel to the folds.

The rocks present in the petroliferous region include the Monterey
(Miocene-Pliocene) diatomaceous and clay shale, limestone, and volcanic
ash; Fernando (Pliocene) conglomerate, sandstone, and shale; and
Quaternary gravel, sand, clay, and alluvium.   At the surface there are
oil and tar seeps, asphalt, and bituminous shale.   The asphalt occurs as a
mixture of bituminous material with sand resulting from the absorption

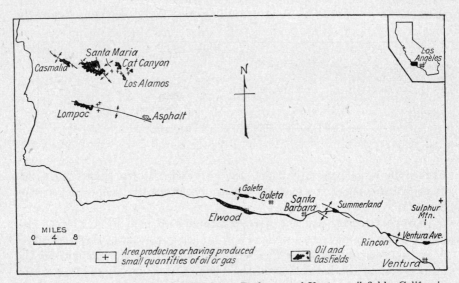

Fig. 310.—Map showing Santa Maria, Santa Barbara, and Ventura oil fields, California.

by overlying sand deposits of seeps from the shale, as hardened fillings
of asphalt in cavities along joints, and as saturated shale.   Burnt shale
which is a rose-colored or slaglike rock observed within the Monterey
shale is found at many places.   It is the result of the burning of the
hydrocarbons that have impregnated the shale.   The Monterey formation is highly fractured and faulted, the overlying Fernando is less
fractured but is faulted along Pre-Fernando zones of deformation.

In the Casmalia[1] oil field (Fig. 310) a heavy oil is produced from
wells sunk on the Schuman anticline.   The oil is obtained at depths
averaging about 1,800 feet from the Monterey formation.   Its gravity
is about 9.5° Bé. and the fluid carries 18 per cent of oil and 82 per cent
of water.   The water has a temperature of 145° F. and aids the flow of the

[1] Gore, F. D., Summary of Operations California Oil Fields, Calif. Min. Bur.,
vol. 8, No. 6, pp. 5–9, December, 1922.

oil which is pumped from the wells. The Pan-American Company operates a large group of wells in this district that produce from fractured shales. To dehydrate the oil it is mixed with distillate, warmed to 170° F. and passed through Cottrell electric dehydrators. This causes the water to collect in globules which separate from the oil.

The Santa Maria field proper, sometimes called the "Old field," is in Santa Barbara County about 8 miles south of the town of Santa Maria. Over most of this area the Fernando sands, clays, and conglomerates crop out, but at places the Monterey shales rise to the surface. The Monterey is faulted and fractured. In this area there are several anticlines some of them striking northwest and others northeast and the general result is a structure that is a broad and relatively short dome. Most of the wells pass through the Fernando sands and clays, and in some of the wells there are 650 feet or more of the Fernando. Below the latter they pass into the "shale" series (Monterey) which is the oil-bearing formation. This series was first mapped and has long been regarded as Miocene in age, but, according to Gester,[1] a part of the shale has recently been identified as Pliocene in the Santa Maria and Lompoc areas. The upper portion of the Monterey shale series contains the sands of the zone which contains heavy oil and beneath it are thick beds of blue shale which cap the second oil zone near the base of the Monterey. In this zone oil is found in fractured flinty shale. This zone is an important producing horizon and yields oil with a gravity of 20 to 38° Bé. The third zone which is also an important one is, according to Leck, a group of sands probably at the top of the Vaqueros.[2]

In the Cat Canyon[3] field east of the Santa Maria field, the oil is found in sands in the Monterey shale that lie near the crest of an anticline that strikes northwest. This fold, however, does not show at the surface but is covered unconformably by the Fernando beds. The oil is found at depths at 1,600 to 2,300 feet below sea level. Above the main zone is a thick brown shale series at the base of which is found a tar sand. The upper oil sand is 80 feet thick and produces oil ranging in gravity from 8.8 to 12° Bé. The lower oil sand is 120 feet thick and produces oil with a gravity of about 16° Bé.

The Lompoc field is northeast of Lompoc in the Purisima Hills that are formed by a broad anticline that strikes south of east. The Monterey shales crop out along the top of the fold and dip from 15 to 20 degrees

[1] GESTER, G. C., Am. Assoc. Pet. Geol. *Bull.*, vol. 10, p. 898, 1926.

[2] LECK, L. V., Petroleum Resources of California, Calif. Min. Bur., *Bull.* 89, p. 104, 1921.

[3] COLLOM, R. E., Geology of Cat Canyon Oil Formation, Calif. Min. Bur., *Bull.* 83, pp. 210–219, 1918.

GORE, F. D., Water Conditions in the Northwesterly Part of Cat Canyon Oil Field, Summary of Operations California Oil Fields, Calif. Min. Bur., vol. 7, No. 9, pp. 12–17, March, 1922.

along its flanks.   The steeper dips are on the north side of the anticline, and along a fault that lies south of the west part of the crest there are numerous deposits of asphalt.   The oil is found in the fractured Monterey strata which dip away from the crest of the anticline.

Goleta.—At Goleta field,[1] 12 miles west of Santa Barbara and 2 miles from the coast, a high-gravity paraffin oil is found in the Sespe formation.   The field is developed on an east-west anticline which is probably 10 miles long and plunges at each end.   North of the anticline ½ mile from the crest is the Hollister fault.   The limbs of the anticline dip 25 to 38 degrees.   A well brought in February, 1927, made 450 barrels of oil a day and also large amounts of gas containing 1.2 gallons of gasoline per 1,000 cubic feet.   This well encountered the oil at a depth of 1,339 feet and penetrated 19 feet of sand.

Elwood.—Since the discovery of Goleta, deep wells have been drilled along the coast to the south of Goleta and large deposits of oil are developed.   Some of the wells are located on wharves built out into the sea.   The field extends 8 miles west of Elwood.

Summerland.—The Summerland district is in Santa Barbara County about 6 miles east of Santa Barbara.   The field is of no great importance economically, although in 1899 it produced 208,000 barrels of oil.   The oil is dark brown or black and ranges in gravity from 9 to 18° Bé., the average being about 14° Bé.   The district is in an area of complexly folded Tertiary sediments.   The beds in the vicinity of Summerland[2] dip south from the Arroyo Parida fault, which is also the crest of an anticline.   Small folds are developed on the south limb of this anticline in the region of the oil wells.   The Monterey has been eroded from the top of the anticline.   Resting unconformably on the truncated edges of the Monterey are the Fernando beds which are steeply tilted.

The oil wells are put down on the terrace on which the town is situated, on the beach in front of this terrace, and on wharves that extend out into the ocean.   The oil is obtained from sands alternating with clay beds in the Fernando formation.   In 1929 a well drilled on the west edge of the field found oil.

In the Rincon-Seacliff field on the coast about 8 miles west and a little north of Ventura Avenue field, oil was discovered in November, 1927, in a well 3,220 feet deep which had an initial production of 1,000 barrels a day, the oil having a gravity of 29.9° Bé.   Soon afterward four other wells were drilled about 2,600 feet deep, these producing 600 to 1,000 barrels a day.   The field is on the northwest extension of the Ventura anticline, the production coming from the Fernando formation.

    [1] VICKERY, F. P., and R. H. GARRISON, The Goleta Field, *Mining Met.*, vol. 8, pp. 429–433, 1927.
    [2] ARNOLD, RALPH, Geology and Oil Resources of the Summerland District, California, U. S. Geol. Survey *Bull.* 321, pp. 1–93, 1907.

Santa Clara Valley.—The Santa Clara Valley[1] region in Ventura and Los Angeles counties (Fig. 311) is the oldest oil-producing area in Cali-

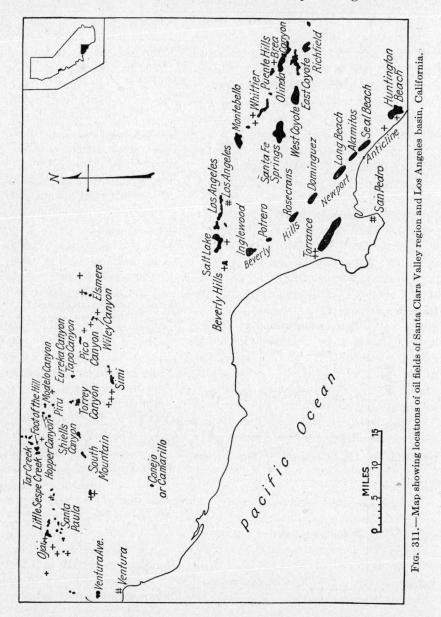

FIG. 311.—Map showing locations of oil fields of Santa Clara Valley region and Los Angeles basin, California.

[1] ELDRIDGE, G. H., and R. ARNOLD, The Santa Clara Valley Oil District, Southern California, U. S. Geol. Survey *Bull.* 309, pp. 1–266, 1907.

KEW, W. S. W., Geology and Oil Resources of a Part of Los Angeles and Ventura Counties, California, U. S. Geol. Survey *Bull.* 753, pp. 1–202, 1924.

GEOLOGICAL FORMATIONS IN PART OF LOS ANGELES AND VENTURA COUNTIES, CALIFORNIA

(*After Kew*)

Series	Generalized section		Thickness, feet	Character
Recent	Alluvium			Sand, gravel, and silt
Pleistocene	Terrace deposits		250 ±	Gravel and sand
Pliocene	Fernando group	Saugus formation	2,000 ±	Conglomerate and sandstone, some shale; mainly terrestrial
		Pico formation (restricted)	4,000 ±	Sandstone, and conglomerate. Sandy shale and fine sandstone with lenses of diatomaceous shale; upper strata largely sandstone with conglomerate. Marine. Oil, Ventura Avenue
Miocene	Modelo formation		9,000 ±	Clay, diatomaceous shale, fine sandstone and cherty beds; lenses of coarse brown sandstone. Marine. Oil bearing
	Mint Cañon formation		4,000 ±	Non-marine conglomerate, sandstone, and clay, red in lower part, gray in upper part
	Topanga formation		6,000 ±	Coarse sandstone and conglomerate with zone of medium-grained greenish-brown fossiliferous sandstone
	Vaqueros formation		100–1,800 ±	On Little Sespe Creek and Oak Ridge, mainly gray to buff sandy shale with limy beds. In Simi Valley brown conglomerate and sandstone. Marine. Oil, Sespe Cañon
Oligocene (?)	Sespe formation		3,500–4,000 ±	Conglomerate and sandstone with shale. Oil, South Mountain, Shiells Cañon, etc.
Eocene	Tejon formation		2.000 ±	In Simi Valley brown sandstone with interbedded conglomerate. At Sespe Creek greenish-brown sandstone and shale; at top 500 feet of light-gray sandstone with shale. Marine. Oil, Sespe Cañon
	Meganos formation		2,000–3,500 ±	Brown to rusty-colored conglomerate, brown and gray sandstone, and gray shale with calcareous concretions. Marine. Oil, Simi
	Martinez formation		1,500–3,500 ±	Massive conglomerate overlain by shale and sandstone. Marine

fornia. It is a mountainous country made up chiefly of Tertiary and Quaternary rocks, except in the southeastern part of the area where granites and gneisses are found. The region is highly faulted and folded and is marked by many oil springs and asphalt deposits. The rocks of the area are shown in the table on page 546. The oil is found in the Meganos, Tejon, Sespe, Vaqueros, Modelo (Monterey), and Fernando formations, the largest deposits being in the Fernando and Sespe. It is generally believed that the oil originated chiefly in the Meganos from which it migrated to the Sespe formation and in the Modelo (Monterey) shale from which it migrated to the Fernando group.

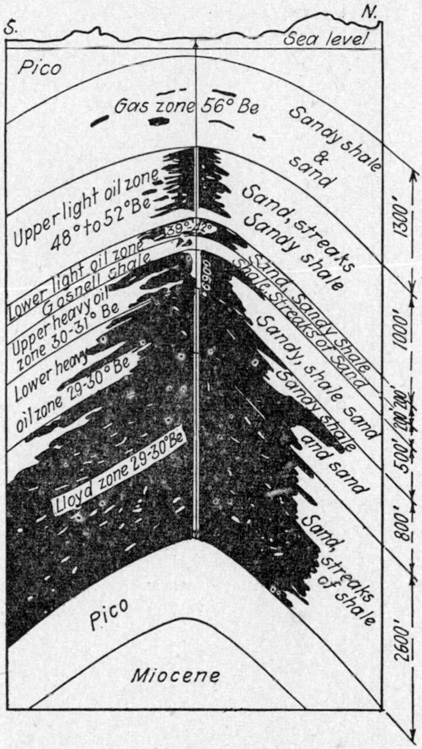

The Ventura Avenue[1] field is 3 miles north of Ventura City. Gas seepages coming up through the water of a ditch were noted in 1903, and the field was first developed for gas, the most prolific sands lying 300 to 400 feet deep, although considerable gas is found in the first 2,000 feet of the section. Light oil with a gravity of 50° Bé. was found at a depth of 2,250 feet in 1915, and later heavier oil was found at greater depths. This oil has a gravity of 28 to 39° Bé.

The field is on the structural summit of the Ventura anticline (Figs. 310, 311) that strikes east.

Fig. 312.—Sketch showing oil zones in Ventura Avenue field, California. (*After Hertel.*)

The beds on the flanks dip 30 to 45 degrees and at the surface the Pico formation is exposed. Below the gas zone mentioned are zones containing light oil, and below these are several zones with heavy oil. These zones are noted on Fig. 312 after Hertel. The heavy gas pressure in the upper sands and the large amount of salt water in the oil sands have made operations difficult in the field, although the total yield to January 1, 1928,

[1] TALIAFERRO, N. L., F. S. HUDSON, and W. N., CRADDOCK, The Oil Fields of Ventura County, California, Am. Assoc. Pet. Geol. *Bull.*, vol. 8, pp. 789–829, 1924.

THOMAS, C. C., Production and Utilization of Gas from the Ventura Field, Summary of Operations California Oil Fields, Calif. Min. Bur., vol. 11, No. 10, pp. 4–10, April, 1926; also vol. 10, No. 5, pp. 6–9.

HERTEL, F. W., Ventura Avenue Oil Field, Ventura County, California, "Structure of Typical American Oil Fields," vol. 2, pp. 23–43, 1929.

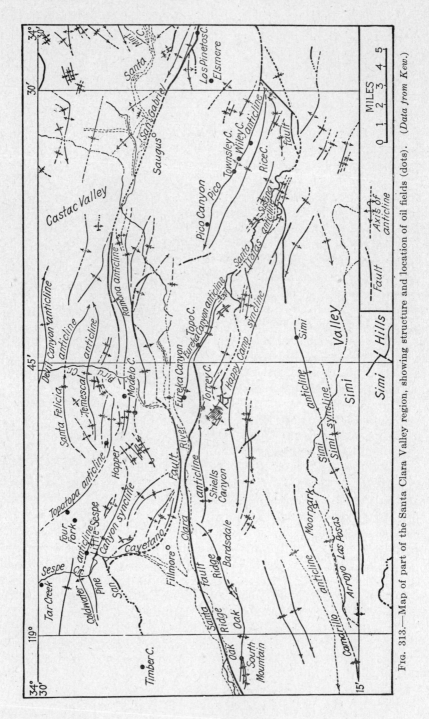

FIG. 313.—Map of part of the Santa Clara Valley region, showing structure and location of oil fields (dots). (Data from Kew.)

was 44,000,000 barrels of oil and 130,000,000,000 cubic feet of gas. To January 1, 1929, the production was about 63,000,000 barrels of oil. The gas is now piped to Los Angeles basin and to Santa Barbara. It yields about 1 gallon of gasoline per 1,000 cubic feet. The gas, light oil, and heavy oil zones are all in the Pico formation of the Fernando group (Pliocene).

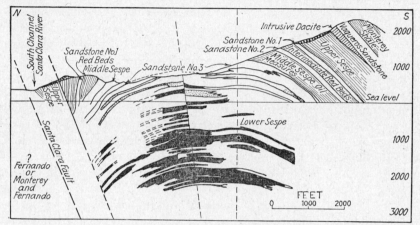

Fig. 314.—Cross-section South Mountain oil field California; oil zones are black, water is stippled. (*Data from Hudson.*)

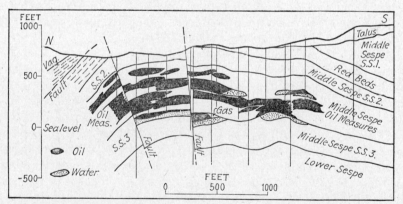

Fig. 315.—Cross-section through dome showing shallow oil zone in Shiells Cañon oil field, Ventura County, California. Oil measures are black. (*After Hudson.*)

Sulphur Mountain[1] field is about 8 miles north of Ventura. Oil is found in the Fernando and Monterey sands near a great fault. At Timber Canyon, 15 miles northeast of Ventura, and in the Ojai Valley and Sisar Creek district near Santa Paula, oil probably originating in the Monterey shale has accumulated in the Sespe formation near an overthrust fault.

[1] GODDE, H. A., Oil Fields of Ventura County, Summary of Operations California Oil Fields, Calif. Min. Bur., vol. 10, No. 5, pp. 5–24, November, 1924.

The South Mountain[1] oil field, 16 miles northeast of Ventura, was discovered in 1916 and in 1922 had reached an annual production of 1,432,000 barrels of oil. The field lies on the north side of South Mountain and has an elevation above sea level of about 900 feet. It is located on a dome (Figs. 313, 314) elongated east-west that lies on the Oak Ridge anticline. Near the center of the dome the Sespe series is exposed. This formation in this region is over 6,000 feet thick and consists of sandstone, shaly sandstone, and shale. It is made up largely of red beds and is believed to be non-marine. The Eocene beds consisting of marine shales and sands, which in this region are found below the Sespe, are believed to be the source of oil in the Sespe. The oil-bearing zone consists of a series of alternating oil sands and barren layers in which the oil-bearing portion constitutes between 30 and 100 per cent of the whole. The oil sands are not continuous, yet certain groups of sands are rather persistent throughout the field. The entire productive zone developed is about 3,000 feet thick, and the area of the beds carrying oil is greater in depth than in beds near the surface. The gravity of the oil is about 27° Bé.

Bardsdale,[2] 6 miles east of South Mountain field, is also on the Oak Ridge anticline. The rocks exposed at the surface are sandstones and marls of the Sespe formation. The field occupies an elongated dome on the anticline, and the main oil zone is found in sand lenses of the Sespe at a depth of between 600 and 1,000 feet. The oil is found near the apex of the fold and is of low gravity, about 27° Bé.

Shiells Cañon oil field, located about 3 miles east of Bardsdale, is also located on the Oak Ridge anticline. A dome is found on the top of the anticline and the oil wells are located near the top of the dome (Fig. 315). On the north limb of the anticline the beds dip about 50 degrees to the south and on the south limb they dip about 15 to 30 degrees. The dome is crossed by faults. The oil is found in a shallow zone in the Sespe formation, at depths within 700 feet of the surface, which produces oil having a gravity of about 31° Bé., and in deeper zones between 800 and 3,500 feet deep which yield oil of higher gravity. The oil in the Shiells Cañon oil field was discovered in 1911 and at one time the field was the most productive in Ventura County.

At Torrey Cañon, 5 miles east of Shiells Cañon, there is a domelike uplift on the Oak Ridge anticline with a nearly vertical dip to the north and a dip to the south of about 30 degrees. The Sespe crops out over a

[1] TALIAFERRO, N. L., F. S. HUDSON, and W. N. CRADDOCK, The Oil Fields of Ventura County, California, Am. Assoc. Pet. Geol. *Bull.*, vol. 8, pp. 810–820, 1924.

[2] GODDE, H. A., Oil Fields of Ventura County, Summary of Operations California Oil Fields, Calif. Min. Bur., vol. 10, No. 5, pp. 5–24, November, 1924.

KEW, W. S. W., U. S. Geol. Survey *Bull.* 753, pp. 168–178, 1924.

AUGUR, I. V., Calif. Min. Bur. *Bull.* 84, p. 323, 1918.

small area in the top of the dome and oil is found in the Sespe formation at depths between 75 and 1,965 feet. The gravity of the oil is 28 to 30° Bé.

In Sespe Cañon, 8 miles north of Bardsdale field, oil is found near the crests of the Topatopa and other anticlines. This area contains many oil fields, but the wells have had small yields. The oil is found in a sandstone at the top of the Tejon and unconformably below the Sespe formation and in sands in the Sespe. The Vaqueros also carries oil. Subdistricts of this region include Foot of the Hills, Four Fork, Tar Cañon, and Little Sespe fields. Southeast of Sespe Cañon in and near Hopper Cañon and in Modelo Cañon, several wells derive their oil from near the top of the Topatopa anticline.

The Pico Cañon field is on the north slope of the Santa Susana Mountains on the Pico anticline. Oil is found in the Modelo formation. The main production is on the north flank of the anticline which is the steepest side. In the Towsley Cañon field southeast of Pico County and in the Wiley Cañon field, southeast of Towsley Cañon oil is found in small areas on the crest of the Pico anticline. The Elsmere field, on a small fold northeast of the Pico anticline, produces oil from the Pico and Saugus formations of the Fernando group of the Pliocene. Most of the wells are located near the crest of an anticline that plunges north. In the Los Pinetos field a little oil is found in schist.

The Simi[1] oil field, 7 miles southeast of Torrey Cañon field, is located on the Simi anticline which strikes north of east and is followed 13 miles. The rocks at the surface are clays, sandstones, and conglomerates of the Sespe formation in which oil seeps and brea deposits are found. Wells drilled near the top of the anticline encounter the Meganos (Middle Eocene) formation about 500 feet deep. The oil has a gravity of 38° Bé. and is found in sand lenses included in shales of the Meganos formation. The Brea Cañon or Scarab district is 5 miles west of Simi field on the strike of the Simi anticline. Oil is found in the sands of the Sespe formation. In the Conejo district southwest of Simi oil has probably accumulated in Miocene beds and in a basalt agglomerate.

Los Angeles Basin.—The Los Angeles basin[2] (Fig. 311) is an area of about 1,000 square miles which lies between the Pacific Ocean and San

---

[1] KEW, W. S. W., Structure and Oil Resources of the Simi Valley, Southern California, U. S. Geol. Survey *Bull.* 691, pp. 323–347, 1919.

[2] ARNOLD, R., and W. LOEL, New Oil Fields of the Los Angeles Basin, California, Am. Assoc. Pet. Geol. *Bull.*, vol. 6, pp. 303–316, 1922.

KEW, S. W., Geologic Formations of a Part of Southern California and Their Correlation, Am. Assoc. Pet. Geol. *Bull.*, vol. 7, pp. 411–420, 1923.

EATON, J. E., Divisions and Duration of the Pleistocene in Southern California, Am. Assoc. Pet. Geol. *Bull.*, vol. 12, pp. 111–141, 1928.

———, A Contribution to the Geology of the Los Angeles Basin, California, Am. Assoc. Pet. Geol. *Bull.*, vol. 10, pp. 753–767, 1926.

Pedro Hills on the southwest, the Santa Monica and San Gabriel Mountains on the north, and the Santa Ana Mountains and San Joaquin Hills on the southeast. Most of the basin is nearly flat, but here and there low

STRATIGRAPHIC COLUMN, LOS ANGELES BASIN
(After Eaton)

Age	Formation		Thickness, feet	Lithology
Recent				Alluvium and terrace materials
				————Unconformity————
Pleistocene	San Pedro group		500 ±	Sands and gravels (partly marine)
				————Unconformity————
Pliocene	Fernando group	Saugus	1,400 ±	Conglomerates, sands, and blue clays (partly marine)
				————Unconformity————
		Pico	5,600 ±	Sands and blue, brown and gray sandy shales. Locally conglomeratic (chiefly marine)
				————Unconformity————
Miocene	Monterey group	Puente	3,200 ±	Diatomaceous shales with local sandstones and thin, calcareous layers (marine). Igneous intrusives. Heavy-bedded sandstones with sandy and diatomaceous shales, and locally a basal argillaceous lens (marine)
		Vaqueros	1,000 +	Coarse, massive sandstones; locally conglomeratic (chiefly marine)
Oligocene (?)				
				————Unconformity————
Pre-Cretaceous				Dark, micaceous schist

hills rise above the plain. The rocks that are exposed within the basin are chiefly of Pliocene, Pleistocene, and Recent age. It is a structural basin as well as a topographic one, and older rocks are found around the rims. Folding and faulting have taken place within very late geologic

FERGUSON, R. N., and C. G. WILLIS, Dynamics of Oil-field Structure in Southern California, Am. Assoc. Pet. Geol. *Bull.*, vol. 8, pp. 576–583, 1924.

JENSEN, J., and G. D. ROBERTSON, Developments in Southern California, *Oil Gas Jour.*, vol. 26, pp. 152–154, Apr. 12, 1928.

GESTER, G. C., Observations Relating to the Origin and Accumulation of Oil in California, Am. Assoc. Pet. Geol. *Bull.*, vol. 10, pp. 892–900, 1926.

VICKERY, F. P., The Interpretation of the Physiography of the Los Angeles Coastal Belt, Am. Assoc. Pet. Geol. *Bull.*, vol. 11, pp. 417–424, 1927.

times and many of the hills within the basin are domes or anticlines that have not yet been eroded to the general level of the plain.

Most of the oil produced in the Los Angeles basin has been derived from the sands and sandstones of the Pliocene formations. Los Angeles City field, the Salt Lake field, and the Old Puente field have produced oil from the Miocene beds, and, recently, large deep deposits have been opened probably in Miocene beds below the productive Pliocene beds in the Long Beach and neighboring fields along the west side of the basin and also in the Santa Fe Springs and Richland fields on the east side. The oil-bearing strata consist of sands and sandstones closely spaced and interbedded with clays and shales. The oil-bearing horizons in many of the fields are over 400 feet thick, and in several of them they aggregate more than 2,000 feet. In the Long Beach field the productive strata of the Pliocene and Miocene are probably about 6,000 feet thick. Most of the fields lie in two belts, one striking east-southeast from Salt Lake to Richland, and another striking southeast from Beverly Hills to Newport. Nearly all of the oil fields are located on domes. Los Angeles City field, Brea-Olinda, Whittier, and Newport are on monoclines, and East Coyote Hills and Salt Lake are on plunging anticlines. The oils of the Los Angeles basin range in gravity from 8 to 42° Bé. In nearly all of the fields the oils become progressively lighter with depth. The oil is associated with gas, generally under considerable pressure, and in most of the fields the oil deposits are outlined by salt water.

The oil fields first to be developed in the Los Angeles basin were those on the east side of the basin in and near the Puente Hills, and the Los Angeles and Salt Lake fields on the north side of the basin. Later, the Santa Fe Springs field and the great fields south of Los Angeles were developed. This group of fields is now one of the most productive oil-bearing areas of the world.

The Beverly Hills-Newport uplift is traced from the Beverly Hills oil field southeast to Newport, a distance of 45 miles. It is a long anticline with an undulating crest marked by domes, some of which are expressed at the surface in low hills. At places the anticline is faulted near the crest by one or more faults that follow the strike of the uplift and by cross-faults. The fields located along the uplift from northwest to southeast are Beverly Hills, Inglewood, Potrero, Athens-Rosecrans, Dominguez, Long Beach, Alamitos, Seal Beach, Huntington Beach, and Newport.

The Beverly Hills,[1] at the northwest end of the uplift, is a small field yielding heavy oil from 12 to 16° Bé. It is located on a dome and derives its oil from Pliocene beds at depths between 2,450 and 2,700 feet.

[1] JENSEN, J., and G. D. ROBERTSON, *Oil Gas Jour.*, vol. 26, pp. 152–154, Apr. 12, 1928.

The Inglewood[1] district (Fig. 316) is about 4 miles southeast of the Beverly Hills field. The first commercial well was completed in September, 1924, and to August 31, 1925, the field had produced 8,953,900 barrels of oil. The oil has a gravity of 14 to 22° Bé. It is similar to the Beverly Hills oil. The Baldwin Hills rise 513 feet above sea level and about 300 feet above the surrounding plain. The rocks exposed at the surface are sandstones, shales, clays, sands, and gravels of Pliocene, Pleistocene, and Recent age. The Pliocene rocks are thrown upward to form a dome elongated northwest that is faulted up on the east side. The top of the oil zone is found at a depth of 1,000 feet on the crest of the dome, and the oil zone is 1,300 feet thick or more. Around the rim of

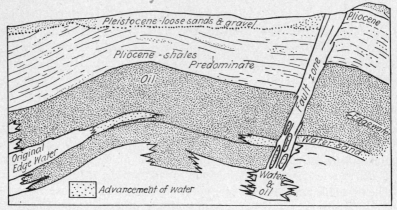

Fig. 316.—Cross-section of Inglewood oil field, Los Angeles basin, California. (*Data from Robertson and Jensen.*)

the field edge water appears about 600 to 1,200 feet from the top of the dome. As oil was withdrawn, the water rose up dip, until in certain beds it reached the top of the dome. At Potrero, southeast of Inglewood, oil was found in 1927 at a depth of 4,717 feet.

The Rosecrans[2] field, southeast of Potrero, is on a group of three small domes (Figs. 317, 318) in a line that strikes northwest and that are probably separated by faults. The first important oil deposits were found in 1924. The oil is very high gravity, from 36 to 42° Bé., and the main productive sands lie at depths from 4,000 to 5,100 feet. In the Athens dome considerable deposits of high-grade oil have recently been developed

[1] ROBERTSON, G. D., and J. JENSEN, Baldwin Hills and Inglewood Field, *Oil Gas Jour.*, vol. 24, pp. 104–106, Jan. 14, 1925.

TIEJE, A. J., The Pliocene and Pleistocene History of the Baldwin Hills, California, Am. Assoc. Pet. Geol. *Bull.*, vol. 10, pp. 502–512, 1926.

HUGUENIN, E., Inglewood Oil Field, Summary of Operations California Oil Fields, Calif. Min. Bur., vol. 11, No. 12, pp. 5–18, June, 1926.

[2] MUSSER, E. H., The Rosecrans Oil Field, Summary of Operations California Oil Fields, Calif. Min. Bur.. vol. 11, No. 5, pp. 5–21, November, 1925.

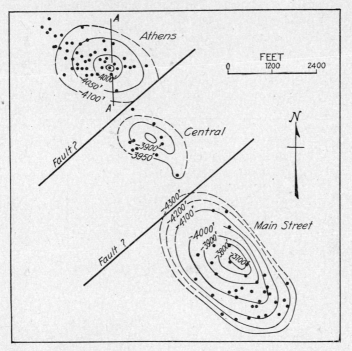

FIG. 317.—Map showing structure of Rosecrans oil field, Los Angeles basin, California, contoured on top of upper Athens oil zone; datum is sea level. (*After Musser.*)

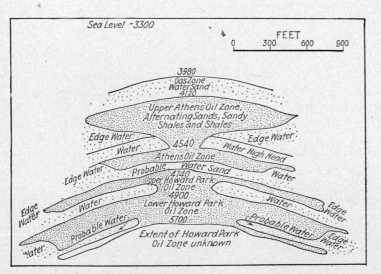

FIG. 318.—Cross-section of Rosecrans oil field on line *AA*, Fig. 317. Elevations are below surface. Rosecrans is about 180 feet above sea level. (*After Musser.*)

between 4,900 and 5,100 feet.   Drilling in the Rosecrans field has shown that there is present about 7,000 feet of Pliocene (Fernando) strata, and oil-bearing strata are found at that depth.

The Dominguez field 4 miles southeast of the Rosecrans field is located on a dome elongated northwest and marked by hills.   The surface rocks are of upper Pleistocene and Recent age.   The field was opened in 1923, yielding oil with gravity from 22 to 32° Bé. and high in gasoline.

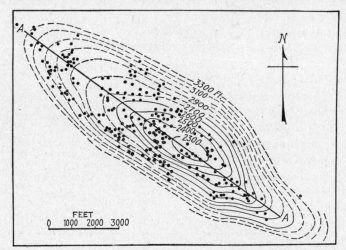

Fig. 319.—Map showing structure of Long Beach oil field, California.   Contours are on Alamitos zone.   (*After Schwennesen, Overbeck, and Dubendorf.*)

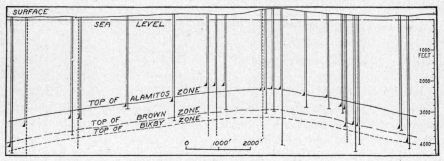

Fig. 320.—Cross-section of Long Beach oil field on line *AA*, Fig. 319.   (*After Schwennesen, Overbeck, and Dubendorf.*)

The main oil-bearing zone is 400 feet thick or more and lies 3,500 to 4,300 feet below the surface.   In 1927 a deeper oil-bearing zone[1] with light oil was penetrated.   It is believed by some that this deep oil is derived from Miocene strata.   Between its discovery, September, 1923, and October, 1926, the field produced 26,454,373 barrels of oil.

[1] Dodd, H. V., Dominguez Oil Field, Summary of Operations California Oil Fields, Calif. Min. Bur., vol. 12, No 4, pp. 7–20, 1926.

Vickery, F. P., Am. Assoc. Pet. Geol. *Bull.*, vol. 11, pp. 417–424, 1927.

The Long Beach[1] oil field is located at the north city limits of Long Beach, 2 miles from the coast and 15 miles south of Los Angeles. The discovery well was drilled in 1921 and to July 1, 1929, the field had produced 352,000,000 barrels of oil. The Long Beach field includes Signal Hill, 364 feet above sea, and Reservoir Hill, 213 feet above sea. These rise above the surrounding area and are surface expressions of a great elongated dome (Figs. 319, 320, 321) on which the oil field is located. On Signal Hill the dips of the San Pedro (Pleistocene) formation, which are as high as 35 degrees, outline a dome, and in depth this dome is shown to have about 1,200 feet of closure. A cross-section is shown in Fig. 321. The San Pedro group is probably 1,000 feet deep. Below the San Pedro, probably unconformably, is the Fernando group 4,000 feet thick or more, consisting of blue and brown shale, sandy shale, and sands, and containing four groups of oil sands. The sands of the Wilbur zone yield much gas and some heavy oil. The Alamitos group 670 feet thick yields oil with gravity 21 to 23° Bé. The Brown zone 250 feet thick yields oil with gravity 27 to 30° Bé., and the oil of the Bixby zone is somewhat lighter. In 1928 large amounts of high-gravity oil were encountered below the Bixby zone.

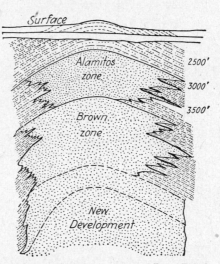

Fig. 321.—Cross-section of Long Beach oil field, showing recent development of deep oil-bearing zone. (*After Jensen and Robertson.*)

Seal Beach[2] field is about 3 miles southeast of Long Beach field on the Beverly Hills-Newport anticline. The field is situated on two domes about one mile apart, both faulted on the northeast sides. The fault dips slightly east and the oil is found on its footwall side. The north dome is at Alamitos Heights and the south dome at Seal Beach. The surface rocks are San Pedro (Pleistocene) sands and gravel which constitute a series 1,000 feet thick. Below the San Pedro are the Fernando series, probably 6,000 feet thick, consisting of sandstones and shales.

[1] SCHWENNESEN, A. T., R. M. OVERBECK, and H. H. DUBENDORF, The Long Beach Oil Field and Its Problems, Am. Assoc. Pet. Geol. *Bull.*, vol. 8, pp. 403–423, 1924.

ROBERTS, C. D., Long Beach Oil Field, Los Angeles County, California, Structure of Typical American Oil Fields, vol. 2, pp. 62–74, 1929.

[2] CUNNINGHAM, C. M., and N. HARDY, Notes on Seal Beach and Alamitos Areas, California, Am. Assoc. Pet. Geol. *Bull.*, vol. 11, pp. 870–873, 1927.

COPP, W. W., and G. H. BOWES, Seal Beach Oil Field, Summary of Operations California Oil Fields, vol. 12, No. 3, pp. 5–16, September, 1927.

In both domes the oil is found in the Fernando sands at depths of 4,000 feet or more. The oil-bearing strata are in a group about 700 feet thick and are divided into three zones separated by water-bearing sands. These zones from the top down are the Bixby, Selover, and Wasom zones.

Huntington Beach[1] field is 15 miles southeast of Long Beach and 30 miles south of Los Angeles. The field was discovered about 1920 and to August 31, 1925, had produced over 75,000,000 barrels of oil. It is located on a slight elevation about 126 feet above sea. The rocks exposed are the San Pedro beds, below which is found the Fernando group. Oil is found at depths from 2,100 to 5,200 feet and the productive area is

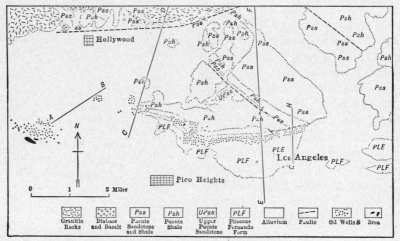

Fig. 322.—Sketch of part of Los Angeles oil field, California, showing position of certain wells and of sections shown in Fig. 323. (*After Eldridge and Arnold.*)

2,750 acres or more. The structure is a monocline that is extensively faulted. The oil is derived from sands in the Fernando group and occurs in two oil zones, which are separated by a zone 75 feet thick which carries water. The upper zone is the Bolza, 600 to 800 feet thick, and the lower zone is the Ashton, 1,200 to 2,000 feet thick. The latter extends downward to near the Puente formation. The lower 800 feet of the Ashton zone particularly is productive, and the oil ranges in gravity from 24 to 29° Bé., which is considerably lighter than the oils found at shallower depths. In one fault block the oil is said to come from Miocene strata. The Huntington Beach oil is high in sulphur.

[1] GESTER, S. H., Huntington Beach Oil Field, Orange County, California, Am. Assoc. Pet. Geol. *Bull.*, vol. 8, pp. 41–46, 1924.

GRASER, F. A., Recent Developments in the Huntington Beach Oil Field, Summary of Operations California Oil Fields, Calif. Min. Bur., vol. 12, No. 12, pp. 5–16, June, 1927.

CASE, J. B., and V. H. WILHELM, Report on Huntington Beach Oil Field, Summary of Operations California Oil Fields, Calif. Min. Bur., vol. 9, No. 6, pp. 5–28, December, 1923.

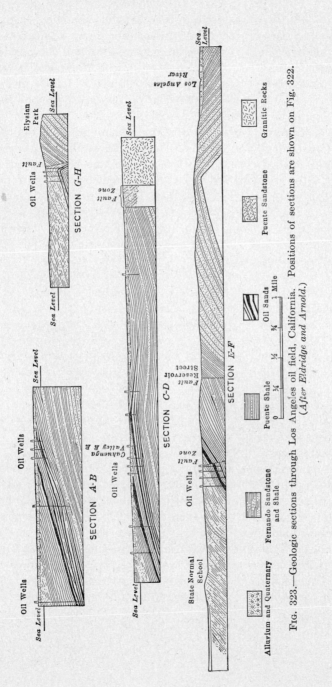

FIG. 323.—Geologic sections through Los Angeles oil field, California. Positions of sections are shown on Fig. 322. (*After Eldridge and Arnold.*)

About 4 miles southeast of the Huntington field the Fernando beds are exposed, dipping west and southwest from 18 to 25 degrees. These beds rest unconformably on the Puente formation and the basal sands of the Fernando carry tar. The monocline near Newport has produced a little heavy oil from 8 to 12° Bé. from wells 800 to 1,400 feet deep.

In the Playa del Rey—Venice field on the coast west of Inglewood large production of oil was attained in 1930.

The Torrance[1] field lies west of Long Beach and faces the San Pedro Hills. It is southwest of the Beverly Hills-Newport uplift on a narrow anticline that plunges sharply southeast. Oil was discovered in 1922 and an area of 4,400 acres proved to be oil bearing. The peak of production was reached in 1924, when the total daily yield was 75,000 barrels. The oil is 12 to 27° Bé. gravity and is derived from 2,700 to 3,900 feet below the surface in sands of the Fernando (Pliocene), which are interbedded with blue and brown shales and sandy shales. The oil zone is in general about 600 feet thick.

The Los Angeles[2] city field (Fig. 322) extends westward for 6 miles from a point about 2 miles north of the business center of Los Angeles. It was discovered in 1892 when a shaft was sunk near a brea deposit. The wells are 500 to 1,200 feet deep or more and the gravity of oil from 12 to 19° Bé. The wells are small producers and are pumped. The Salt Lake field is a few miles west of the city field. The wells are between 1,200 and 3,000 feet deep, and the average gravity of the oil is between 16 and 18° Bé. Enormous deposits of brea or impure asphalt have formed along the outcrop of the upper Puente sand and in the wash above the oil sand. Some of the oil has apparently risen through cracks in the shaly beds above the oil sand and has escaped to the surface.

The formations, in the order of age, comprise more than 2,000 feet of indurated sandstone, believed to be largely of Vaqueros (lower Miocene) age;[3] about 2,000 feet of shale and soft thin-bedded sandstone of Monterey (Puente), also of lower Miocene age; pre-Fernando basalt and diabase intrusions cutting the Monterey; 3,000 feet or more of soft thin- and thick-bedded sandstone, thin-bedded shale, and heavy-bedded conglomerate composing the Fernando formation of Pliocene age; and a capping of Pleistocene gravels and sands of variable thickness. The oil in the Los Angeles district is derived largely from the upper 500 feet of the Puente or Monterey and the basal beds of the Fernando.

[1] MUSSER, E. H., Report on the Torrance Oil Field, Summary of Operations California Oil Fields, Calif. Min. Bur., vol. 11, No. 3, pp. 5–19, September, 1925.

[2] ELDRIDGE, G. H., and RALPH ARNOLD, The Santa Clara Valley, Puente Hills, and Los Angeles Oil Districts, California, U. S. Geol. Survey Bull. 309, p. 138, 1907.

ARNOLD, RALPH, and V. R. GARFIAS, Geology and Technology of the Oil Fields of California, Am. Inst. Min. Eng. Bull. 87, pp. 455–458, 1914.

[3] Possibly in part Oligocene.

The most prominent structural feature in the district is the great flexure which trends N. 60° W. This fold is known as the Elysian Park anticline. This anticline (Fig. 323) is almost an elliptical structural dome, as it appears to plunge at both its northwest and southeast ends. Not far from the northwest extremity of the anticline, where it approaches the fault zone lying along the southern base of the Santa Monica Mountains, the fold develops into a fault. The City field is developed in strata at the top of the Monterey and, possibly, the base of the Fernando formation on the south limb of the Elysian Park anticline. The trend of the productive belt, however, instead of conforming to the axis of the main fold, follows the strike of the formations on the south side of a divergent subordinate line of disturbance and hence has a direction about east. The oil appears to have accumulated in the sands of the southern limb of the anticline.

The Montebello[1] field is in the Merced Hills 8 miles east of Los Angeles on a dome approximately in line with the west extension of the Whittier fault. The field has a productive area of about 1,200 acres and produces oil at depths between 2,100 and 4,700 feet, from Fernando strata. The gravity of the oil is 11 to 28° Bé. To August 31, 1925, the field had produced 61,484,082 barrels of oil. The oil is derived from sands in the lower part of the Fernando and possibly from the upper beds of the Puente.

The Puente Hills[2] oil-bearing region is on the southwest part of the Puente Hills on the east side of the Los Angeles basin and about 20 miles southeast of Los Angeles (Figs. 324, 325). In this region there are exposed great thicknesses of Miocene and Pliocene strata, including the Puente of the Miocene and the Fernando group of the Pliocene. These rocks are thrown into steep folds and are extensively faulted. The Whittier fault strikes northwest across the area and along the fault there are developed Rideau, Whittier, Brea, and Olinda fields, all deriving the oil from the Fernando and in some of the fields possibly from the top of the Puente. In the old Puente field north of the fault the oil is in the Puente. To the south of the fault are the Sante Fe Springs, West Coyote, East Coyote, Richfield, and Santa Ana Cañon or Kramer fields. In all of these fields, except the old Puente field, oil is found in sands of the Fernando group or possibly in the top of the Puente formation near its unconformity with the Fernando. In the old Puente field the

[1] McLaughlin, R. P., Am. Assoc. Pet. Geol. *Bull.*, vol. 5, p. 624, 1921.

[2] Eldridge, G. H., and R. Arnold, The Puente Hills Oil District, Southern California, U. S. Geol. Survey *Bull.* 309, pp. 1–103, 1907.

English, W. A., and P. W. Prötzman, Geology and Oil Resources of the Puente Hills Region, Southern California, U. S. Geol. Survey *Bull.* 768, pp. 1–110, 1926.

Eaton, J. E., A Contribution to the Geology of Los Angeles Basin, Am. Assoc. Pet. Geol. *Bull.*, vol. 10, pp. 753–767, 1926.

oil is found in sands well within the Puente group of strata.   The age
of the deep beds in the Santa Fe Springs area is, probably, Miocene.

The Whittier[1] field, 1 mile east of Whittier, was opened about 1900
and to August 31, 1925, had produced 11,247,323 barrels of oil.   Clays,
shales, and sandstones of the Fernando group dip south at angles from

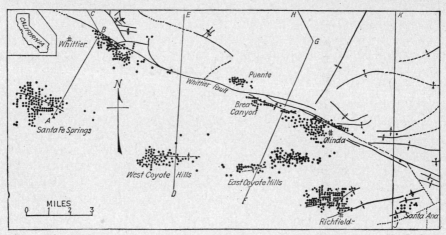

Fig. 324.—Map of Puente Hills oil fields. (*After English and Prutzman, U. S. Geol.
Survey.*)

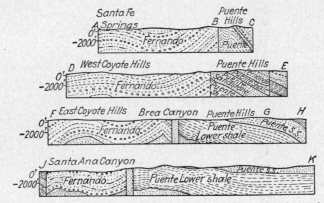

Fig. 325.—Geologic cross-sections of Puente Hills oil fields. Locations of section are
shown on Fig. 324. (*After English and Prutzman.*)

20 to 60 degrees and lie against the Whittier fault.   The oil is found in
the monocline near the fault and from 600 to 3,300 feet deep.   The productive area is about 603 acres.   The oil is found at five horizons in the
lower part of the Fernando.   The gravity of the oil is 15 to 28° Bé.   On
the north side of the fault a few wells have found oil of higher grade than
that found on the south side of the fault.

[1] ENGLISH, W. A., Geology and Oil Resources of the Puente Hills Region, Southern
California, U. S. Geol. Survey *Bull.* 768, pp. 77–78, 1926.

In Brea Cañon, 8 miles east of Whittier on the south side of the Whittier fault, a steep anticline strikes south of east parallel to the fault. The Olinda field is southeast of the Brea Cañon field and is continuous with it. In the Olinda field the Fernando strata dip south away from the Whittier fault, but possibly the Brea anticline extends into this field also. In these fields the chief oil deposits are found from 900 to 4,450 feet deep and occur in three main zones, two of which are in the Fernando. The third zone is the most productive and is either near the base of the Fernando formation or in the Puente formation just below the Fernando. Near the crest of the Brea anticline the top rises to near the surface and oil seeps are numerous. It is from these that the Brea Cañon derived its name. The oil is found in beds below the top of the first sand through a thickness of 2,500 feet of strata consisting of oil sands and shales. The Brea and Olinda fields together with the old Puente field produced 107,504,132 barrels of oil to August 31, 1925.

The Old Puente field is a mile or two northwest of the Brea Cañon field on the north side of the Whittier fault. It was one of the first fields opened in California, but its production has been small. The oil is derived from sands well down in the Puente formation in a distorted zone on a north-dipping monocline. According to English, the field does not show anticlinal structure. The wells are mainly 1,000 to 2,000 feet deep.

The Santa Fe Springs[1] oil field, 3 miles south of Whittier and 12 miles southeast of Los Angeles (Figs. 311, 326) came into prominence in 1921, when a well with an initial yield of 4,000 barrels a day was drilled. The field was developed rapidly and to July 1, 1929, had produced 218,000,000 barrels of oil. The surface is nearly flat and is covered with alluvium, below which is found the beds of the Fernando group of the Pliocene, consisting of shales, siltstones, sandstone, and conglomerate. This group is over 4,000 feet deep and includes the Foix and Bell oil sand groups and probably also the Meyer oil sands, although the latter are included by some in the Puente formation.

The field is located on a dome which has a closure of probably 600 feet with a long axis that strikes west-northwest. The Foix sand zone is found at a depth of about 3,450 feet on the top of the dome, and the oil in it covers a relatively small area. At a depth of 3,650 feet the Bell sand is found. This sand is tapped by many wells with initial daily yields of over 3,000 barrels of oil. The sand produces over a much greater area than that of the Foix sand.

The Meyer zone[2] is 200 feet below the top of the Bell and below it are the Nordstrom, Buckbee, O'Connell, Upper Clark, Second Clark, and Third Clark zones. The latter is encountered over 8,000 feet deep.

[1] TEMPLETON, R. R., and C. R. McCOLLOM, Santa Fe Springs Field, California, Am. Assoc. Pet. Geol. *Bull.*, vol. 8, pp. 178–194, 1924.

[2] WALLING, R. W., *Oil Gas Jour.*, vol. 28, No. 12, p. 98, Aug. 8, 1929.

In June, 1929, a well 8,006 feet deep was producing from the Second Clark zone 4,200 barrels of oil, including considerable water. The oil of the Clark zone is of medium gravity and contains about 35 per cent gasoline. The temperature of the water at 7,802 feet in the Lower Clark zone is 206° F. In 1930 oil production from the deep sands was steadily increasing. The deeper oils are the lighter. Oil from the Foix sand has a gravity of 29° Bé., that from the Bell from 30 to 32° Bé., and that from the Meyer 34 to 35° Bé. In the central part of the field, at

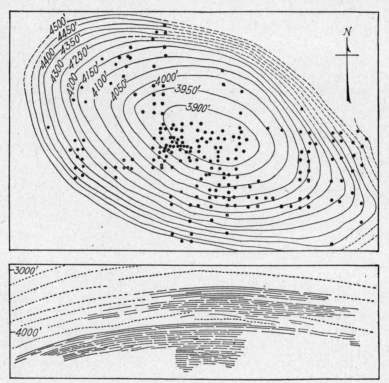

Fig. 326.—Map and section of Santa Fe Springs oil field California. (*Data from Templeton and McCollom.*) Vertical equals horizontal scale.

a depth of 2,000 feet, the top of a shaly formation containing gas under great pressure is encountered. The shale extends downward 1,500 feet deeper to the top of the Foix sand. The gas from this zone has caused destructive blowouts of wells.

The West Coyote Hills field is about 5 miles southeast of Santa Fe Springs. The surface is marked by a group of hills formed of the Fernando strata which rise to an elevation of about 600 feet. Structurally these hills are a dome with a long axis which strikes east. Oil is found in the Fernando sands at depths between 2,800 and 4,450 feet. One important producing sand is found at a depth of about 3,200 feet and a second sand

300 feet deeper. This sand found at depths between 3,500 and 4,000 feet is highly productive, and several wells drilled to it have each produced about 3,000,000 barrels of oil. The gravity of the oil in the upper zone is 24° Bé. and that in the lower zone is 27 to 30° Bé. Oil from the same sand is commonly 1 to 3° Bé. lighter in the center than on the sides of the dome.

The East Coyote Hills field is 2 miles east of the West Coyote Hills field. The structure of these hills is an anticline that strikes a few degrees north of east. Two low domes with a low saddle between them are developed on this anticline. The anticline plunges irregularly to the west and shows steep dips on the north and south sides. The oil is not confined to the domes but occupies most of the crest of the plunging anticline. Beds of the Fernando group crop out on the hills, and the oil is found in sands of the Fernando group at depths between 2,700 and 4,000 feet. The oil in the main producing zone has a gravity from 17 to 25° Bé. and that of the upper zone 800 feet higher is 17 to 20° Bé. The East Coyote Hills field and the West Coyote Hills field together produced 97,873,916 barrels of oil to August 31, 1925, the larger amount coming from the West Coyote Hills.

The Richfield[1] oil field is 3 miles southeast of the East Coyote Hills field. The discovery well was completed in 1919 with an initial yield of 5,000 barrels of oil a day, and by October 1, 1926, the field had produced 38,359,592 barrels. The surface is nearly flat and is covered with alluvium, below which the strata of the Fernando group are found. The field is located on two anticlines with axes closely spaced and nearly parallel. The oil sands occur in two groups 250 feet apart and lie at depths from 2,700 to about 4,500 feet. The oil from the upper sand has a gravity of 19 to 22° Bé. and that from the lower group from 25 to 29° Bé. The oil zone is found at a depth of 1,800 feet at its highest point, and it has a total thickness of about 1,100 feet.

The Santa Ana Cañon field, 3 miles east of Richfield, is situated on a series of small anticlines that are found in a group of low hills made up of the Fernando formation. The oil sands are encountered at depths of 1,900 to 2,500 feet.

ALASKA

The oil fields of Alaska (Fig. 327) are located along the south coast and include Katalla, Yakataga, Iniskin and Cold Bay. The Katalla[2] field is located on Controller Bay just west of Bering glacier. Oil seepages are prominent. The field was drilled in 1902, when a well 366

---

[1] MUSSER, E. H., The Richfield Oil Field, Summary of Operations in California Oil Fields, Calif. Min. Bur., vol. 12, No. 6, pp. 5–18, December, 1926.

[2] MARTIN, G. C., Preliminary Report on Petroleum in Alaska, U. S. Geol. Survey *Bull.* 719, pp. 11–34, 1921.

feet deep brought in a flow of oil. Production has never been large and between 1904 and 1919 totaled about 56,000 barrels. The oil has a gravity of 43° Bé. and contains 63 per cent gasoline and distillate and is associated with gas which is used locally. A small refinery has been operated near Katalla.

The country is an area of Tertiary shales, which are faulted against metamorphosed and igneous rocks of pre-Tertiary age. Oil seepages are numerous in the Tertiary rocks (Miocene?) and all of the producing wells are sunk in the Tertiary rocks. These rocks are strongly folded and faulted. The folds strike northeast, but the strike of the zone of seepages is nearly due east. The oil is like that which comes from Jurassic rocks elsewhere in Alaska, and Martin suggests that the oil of Katalla may be derived from underlying Jurassic beds.

The Yakataga field is on the coast 60 miles east of Katalla field. A series of Tertiary shales, sandstones, and conglomerate, is thrown into

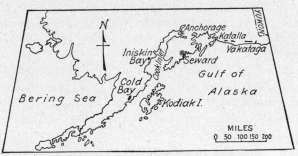

Fig. 327.— Map showing oil fields of Alaska.

sharp folds. An anticline extends along the coast and marks a minor valley along the south of a ridge. Along this anticline numerous oil seeps are found.[1] The oil is probably derived from Oligocene beds.

The Iniskin Bay[2] district is on the west side of Cook Inlet. The country is an area of sandstones, conglomerates, and shales of Jurassic age, which rest on sheared igneous rocks and are thrown into folds that strike northeast. Oil seepages are numerous, and in 1903 a well found oil, gas, and salt water, probably at a depth of about 600 feet. A year later a well yielding 10 barrels of oil a day was drilled 900 feet deep. The oil comes from the Tuxedni sandstone of Jurassic age.

Cold Bay is about 165 miles southwest of Iniskin Bay. Oil seepages occur in upper Jurassic strata which consist of sandstone, shale, and a little limestone. These rocks are underlain by Jurassic and Triassic

[1] MADDREN, A. G., Mineral Deposits of the Yakataga District, U. S. Geol. Survey *Bull.* 592, pp. 119–153, 1914.

MARTIN, C. G., *op. cit.*, pp. 34–38.

[2] MOFFIT, F. H., The Iniskin Bay District, U. S. Geol. Survey *Bull.* 739, pp. 117–132, 1922.

General Section of Rocks of the Controller Bay Region
(*After Martin*)

Age	Formation	Character of rocks	Thickness, feet
Quaternary		Stream deposits, probably in part underlain by marine sediments	0–500 ±
		Sediments and abandoned beaches of glacial lakes	0–200 ±
		Morainal deposits	0–100 ±
		Marine silt and clay	100
Tertiary or later		Diabase and basalt dikes	
Tertiary	Tokun	Sandstone	500
		Shale	2,000 +
	Kushtaka	Arkose with many coal beds	2,500 ±
	Stillwater	Shale and sandstone	1,000 ±
	Katalla	Conglomerates, and sandstones and shales, some of which are conglomeratic	2,500
		Sandstone	500
		Shale, concretionary and with a glauconitic bed at the base	2,000
		Sandstone	1,000
		Shale	500 +
Pre-Tertiary		Graywacke, slates, and igneous rocks	

sandstone. Wells drilled near the crests of anticlines have found paraffin saturated beds and some oil. The strata are thrown into broad open folds that strike parallel to the coast. At a spring 5 miles west of Cold Bay oil and gas issue. The oil[1] flow amounts to $\frac{1}{2}$ barrel a day and the gas flows by small heads.

Oil seeps are found a mile southwest of Anchorage,[2] 150 miles north of Iniskin Bay field.

On the Arctic Coast on the west side of Smith Bay, 50 miles east of Point Barrow,[3] petroleum residue is found.

[1] MATHER, K. F., W. R. SMITH, and G. C. MARTIN, Petroleum in Alaska Peninsula, U. S. Geol. Survey *Bull.* 773, pp. 159–213, 1925.

CAPPS, S. R., The Cold Bay District, U. S. Geol. Survey *Bull.* 739, pp. 76–116, 1922.

[2] BROOKS, A. H., U. S. Geol. Survey *Bull.* 739C, pp. 133–135, 1922.

[3] LEFFINGWELL, E. deK, U. S., Geol. Survey *Prof. Paper*, 109, p. 178, 1919.

CHAPTER XVII

NORTH AMERICA AND WEST INDIES, EXCEPT UNITED STATES

CANADA

In Canada (Fig. 328) oil is found in Quebec, New Brunswick, Ontario, Alberta, and Northwest Territory. To January 1, 1928, Canada produced 26,980,699 barrels of oil. Of this amount Ontario produced 26,105,407 barrels, Alberta 783,840 barrels, and New Brunswick 91,452

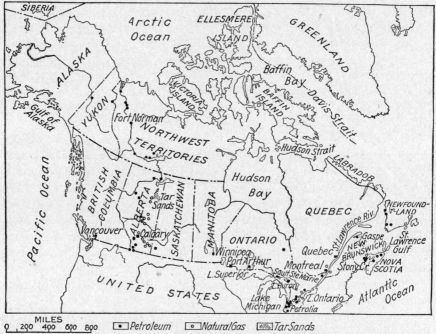

Fig. 328.—Map showing oil fields of Canada.

barrels. Considerable amounts of gas are produced in Alberta and Ontario and smaller amounts in New Brunswick.

Quebec.—On Gaspe Peninsula, Quebec, Paleozoic limestones, sandstones, and shales are steeply folded and faulted and cut by igneous intrusions. Oil seeps are numerous, but deep drilling has not revealed commercial deposits of oil, the entire production being about 2,000 barrels. The oil is found in Devonian and also in Silurian beds. The production was from synclines; anticlines are barren.[1] The intense deformation of the area has probably caused leakage of oil.

New Brunswick.—In New Brunswick oil seepages are found in the Alberta shales, and albertite, which occurs in dikes, has been mined in large amounts. In central New Brunswick the Paleozoic rocks are only gently folded, and on anticlines that trend northeast near Stony Creek, 9 miles south of Moncton, a wet gas has been exploited since 1905, the production in 1927 being 630,755,000 cubic feet. Many wells are sunk for oil developing only small supplies. The gravity of the oil is 39° .A.P.I. The productive beds are shales and sands of the Albert series of Lower Mississippian age. The gas is found in anticlines. Water is said to be absent.

Ontario.—The main oil-bearing area of Canada lies in Ontario[2] between Lake Erie and Lake Huron. This field was opened in 1860 and produced 26,105,407 barrels of oil to 1928. In 1927 it produced 139,606 barrels. Nearly all of the oil has come from Devonian limestone, although a small amount has come from several horizons of the Silurian system. As already noted, one branch of the Cincinnati anticline extends to northeastern Ohio. It is not well defined near Lake St. Clair, but the same general zone of folding extends into south Ontario where there is an axis of gentle folding near Port Lambton that probably extends to Petrolia (Fig. 329). The general attitude of the beds is shown by sections (Figs. 330, 331) which, in part, are drawn on Fig. 329.

The chief producing fields are on structural domes and include Petrolia (Fig. 37), Oil Springs in Lambton County, Mosa Township field near Shields in Middlesex County. A section through the Petrolia and Oil Springs fields is shown on Fig. 38. The oil is found in what is called the "Big Lime" or "Corniferous Limestone" of the Devonian. This limestone is divided into the upper, or Delaware, limestone and the lower, or Onondaga, limestone. The limestone is very porous and at places contains solution cavities, so that the drill has been known to drop several inches in the holes. At Petrolia connection of open channels is shown, since the pumping of one well affects the other wells near by. This field is an elongated dome and the wells are about 480 feet deep.

[1] ELLS, R. W., The Oil Fields of Gaspe, Can. Geol. Survey *Fifteenth Ann. Rept.*, new ser., pp. 340–363, 1903.

[2] BRUMELL, H. P. H., Natural Gas and Petroleum in Ontario, Can. Geol. Survey *Ann. Rept.*, vol. 5, pt. Q, pp. 1–94, 1892.

STAUFFER, C. R., The Devonian of Southwestern Ontario, Can. Geol. Survey *Mem.* 34, pp. 1–341, 1915.

CLAPP, F. G., and others, Petroleum and Natural Gas Resources of Canada, Can. Dept. Mines, Mines Branch, *Pub.* 291, vol. 2, pp. 172–185, 1915.

WILLIAMS, M. Y., Oil Fields of Southwestern Ontario, Can. Dept. Mines *Summary Rept.* 1918, pt. E, pp. 30–42, 1919.

Oil springs supplied a fine lubricating oil from surface "gum beds." When the field was opened large gushers were brought in fed from a "mud vein" or crevice 7 to 12 feet below the top of the Delaware limestone. Later, the production came from a zone 100 to 120 feet below the top of the Delaware.

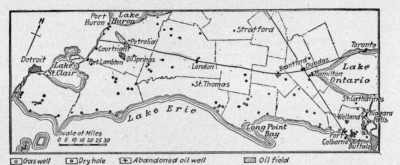

Fig. 329.—Sketch showing location of oil fields and wells in South Ontario. (*After Clapp.*) The heavy lines indicate lines of sections in Figs. 330 and 331.

In the Mosa oil pool, about 4 miles west of Glencoe, Middlesex County, the main oil production comes from the crest of the dome and very few wells produce from terraces or structurally lower portions. The porous oil stratum of the older fields appears to be absent in the Mosa field. The oil is obtained mainly from the crevices or shattered zones in the Delaware formation.

WELL LOG, CENTER OF THE MOSA FIELD

	Thickness, feet	Depth, feet
Surface..	77	77
Petrolia shale.... { "Soap"......................	58	135
Limestone.....................	6	141
"Soap" with streaks...........	73	214
Widder beds or middle limestone....................	19	233
Olentangy shale.. { "Lower soap"..................	20	253
Streaks of limestone............	4	257
Streaks of "soap"..............	2	259
Delaware and Onondaga limestone penetrated.......	55	314
Oil at 264 feet		

Oil in this field generally occurs in the upper 20 feet of the Delaware limestone, but it occurs also in a few wells in the "middle lime" or Widder beds. Figure 332 shows a model of this field.

As the Silurian produces gas from the Medina sand ("Clinton") in Ohio, and as oil is obtained from the Trenton in Ohio and Indiana,

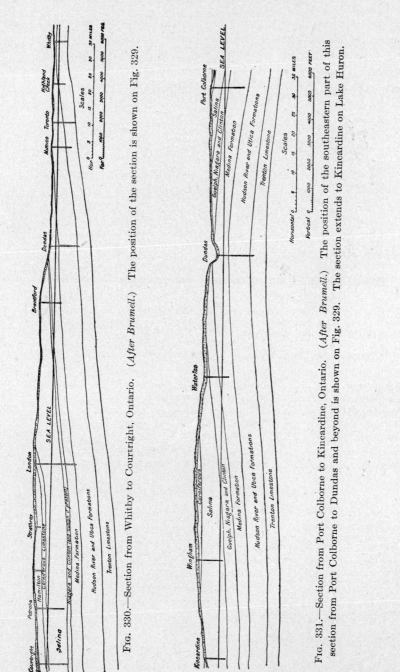

Fig. 330.—Section from Whitby to Courtright, Ontario. (*After Brumell.*) The position of the section is shown on Fig. 329.

Fig. 331.—Section from Port Colborne to Kincardine, Ontario. (*After Brumell.*) The position of the southeastern part of this section from Port Colborne to Dundas and beyond is shown on Fig. 329. The section extends to Kincardine on Lake Huron.

the rocks below the Devonian have naturally been regarded as possible sources of oil and gas below the domes in Lambton County. A well drilled on the Petrolia dome to a depth of 3,770 feet has failed to reach a productive stratum. At Oil Springs, according to report, some oil has been obtained from the Trenton. Ontario oils range from 28 to 40° A.P.I.

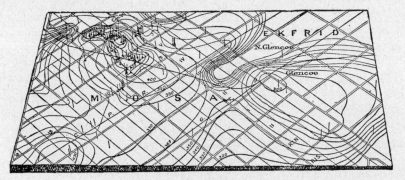

Fig. 332.—Model of Mosa oil field, Ontario, representing the top of the Delaware (Corniferous) limestone. The edges of the cardboards used in making the model may be considered as lines of equal elevation or contour lines. The wells are marked by pins and beads represent producing oil wells. (*After Williams.*)

RECORD OF DEEP WELL ON R. I. BRADLEY ESTATE, PETROLIA POOL

		Feet
Pleistocene..............	Surface..............................	0–90
Hamilton...............	Streaks of limestone and shale..........	90–330
Onondaga[1]..............	Limestones...........................	330–520
Salina..................	Streaks of brown, gray, and black dolomite...........................	520–1,210
	Salt strata and streaks of dolomite......	1,210–1,640
	Salt strata and streaks of dolomitic limestone..........................	1,640–1,747
	Salt strata and gray dolomitic lime and shale..............................	1,747–2,105
Guelph and Niagara......	Guelph and Niagara dolomitic limestone.	2,105–2,380
	Niagara shale, red and dark............	2,380–2,440
Clinton.................	Clinton..............................	2,440–2,530
Medina.................	Red Medina..........................	2,530–2,805
Utica..................	Lorraine shales, light..................	2,805–3,010
	Utica shales, dark.....................	3,010–3,175
Trenton................	Trenton.............................	3,175–3,345
	Birdeye..............................	3,345–3,460
	Chazy, Canadian.....................	3,460–3,770

[1] Probably includes Delaware formation.

Wells about 40 miles southwest of Petrolia, in Kent County, Dover West, obtained oil from the Trenton.

East of the Mosa field there is a broad shallow syncline, and still farther east the rocks rise to the northeast on a broad low anticline that plunges southwest. On the flank of the anticline near Port Colborne (Fig. 329) gas is obtained in the "Clinton" sand, and gas wells are found at several other places between Lake Ontario and Lake Erie.

Western Canada.—The Great Plains of western Canada[1] lie west of the Canadian Shield and east of the Rocky Mountains front. In the western part of the Great Plains there is a great structural trough known as the Alberta geosyncline in which the rocks dip away from the mountains. In this trough Cretaceous and later rocks have been folded down and protected from erosion. At places these rocks are folded upward, where smaller anticlines are superimposed on the geosyncline, and on these the chief oil and gas fields of western Canada are developed.

Oil is found in considerable amounts at Turner Valley and in smaller amounts in other fields. Gas is found at Turner Valley, Viking, Battle River, Medicine Hat, Bow Island, Foremost, and in smaller amounts elsewhere. The main oil and gas deposits of Turner Valley are found in the Madison limestone of Mississippian age, but most of the gas in the other fields is in sands in the lower part of the Benton shale, in the Milk River sandstone above the Benton shale, and from the Lower Cretaceous beds. The oil fields are in an area in which coals are extensively developed. In general, according to Jones, there is no close relation between the carbon ratios of the coals and the character of oil developed. In 1928 Alberta produced 489,531 barrels of oil. Of this amount 410,623 barrels was naphtha from Turner Valley. In 1929 Alberta produced 997,359 barrels of oil. The locations of the oil fields of Alberta are shown on Fig. 333. Correlations of the beds of Turner Valley, southern Alberta, and the Wainwright region are shown on Fig. 334.

[1] HUME, G. S., Oil and Gas in Western Canada, Can. Geol. Survey, *Econ. Geol.* ser. 5, pp. 1–152, 1928.

———, Notes on Development during 1925 in the Wainwright Field, Alberta, Can. Geol. Survey *Summary Rept.* 1925, pt. B, pp. 14–15, 1926.

———, Oil Prospects in the Vicinity of Battle River at the Alberta-Saskatchewan Boundary, Can. Geol. Survey *Summary Rept.* 1925, pp. 1–14, 1926; also *Summary Rept.* 1922, pt. B, pp. 47–64, 1923.

JONES, I. W., Carbon Ratios as an Index of Oil and Gas in Western Canada, *Econ. Geol.*, vol. 23, pp. 353–380, 1928.

DYER, W. S., Geologic Structure in the Western End of the Cypress Hills, Alberta, Can. Geol. Survey *Summary Rept.* 1926, pp. 15–29, 1927.

———, Oil and Gas Prospects in Southern Saskatchewan, Can. Geol. Survey *Summary Rept.* 1926, pp. 30–38, 1927.

WARREN, P. S., Geology and Oil Prospects in the Vicinity of Riverhurst, Saskatchewan, Can. Geol. Survey *Summary Rept.* 1926, pp. 39–42, 1927.

Ross, C. C., Petroleum and Natural Gas Development in Alberta, *Trans.* Can. Inst. Min. and Met., vol. 29, pp. 317–346, 1926.

MADGWICK, T. G., The Oil and Gas Situation in the Prairie Provinces, *Trans.* Can. Inst. Min. and Met., separate Winnipeg meeting, 1929, pp. 1–23.

. Turner Valley[1] or Sheep River oil field is located at Turner Valley post office, about 25 miles southwest of Calgary. Drilling in this field began in 1913, and oil was found in Cretaceous sandstone at a depth of

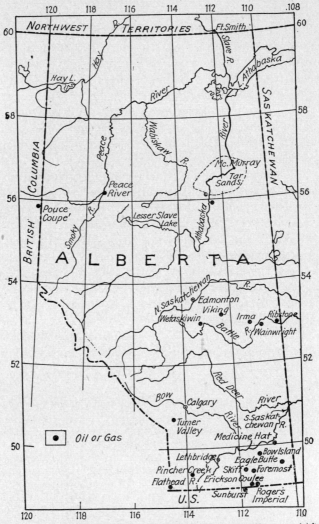

FIG. 333.—Sketch showing locations of oil and gas fields in Alberta. (*After Madgwick and others.*)

2,718 feet in 1914. A few years later a well, Royalite 4, entered an oil-bearing stratum about 3,740 feet deep and encountered gas, under heavy

[1] SLIPPER, S. E., Sheep River Gas and Oil Field, Alberta, Can. Geol. Survey *Mem.* 122, pp. 1–46, 1921.

HUME, G. S., Turner Valley Oil Area, Alberta, Can. Geol. Survey *Summary Rept.* 1926, pt. B, pp. 1–14, 1927.

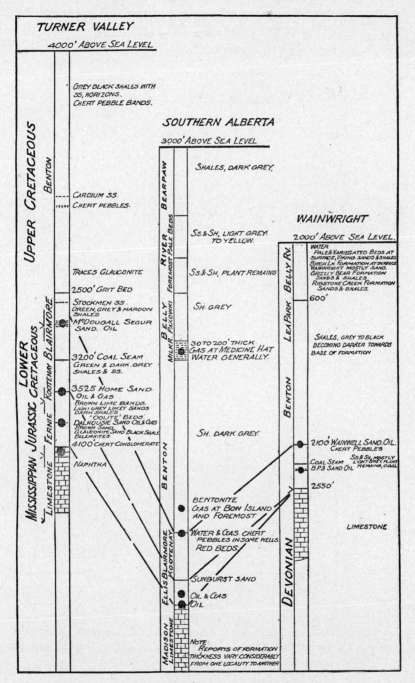

Fig. 334.—Geologic sections of oil- and gas-bearing areas in Alberta. (*After Madgwick*.)
Black dots show wells containing oil or gas.

State Teachers College Library
Willimantic, Conn.

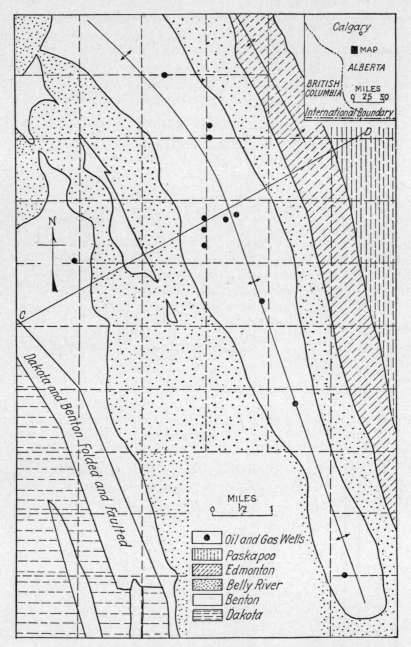

MILES
0   25   50

MILES
0   ½   1

● Oil and Gas Wells
Paskapoo
Edmonton
Belly River
Benton
Dakota

Dakota and Benton Folded and Faulted

FIG. 335.—Sketch of Turner Valley (Sheep River) oil field, Alberta.   Many wells are not
shown.   (*After Slipper.*)   "Dakota" is now considered Blairmore.

pressure, carrying naphtha. This well yielded about 500 barrels a day of oil with a gravity of 73° Bé. and has produced steadily for several years, the oil being recovered from the gas.

At Turner Valley the crest of a sharp anticline (Fig. 335) is eroded to form a long narrow basin. At the crest the Benton formation crops

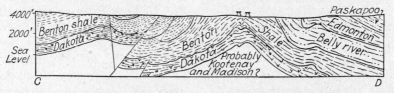

Fig. 336.—Geologic section on line *CD*, Fig. 335. (*After Slipper.*) Formation mapped Dakota now mapped Blairmore of Lower Cretaceous Age.

out in a belt 2 miles wide and on the flanks of this belt the Belly River formation forms two parallel ridges. As shown by Fig. 336, there is a narrow syncline at the top of the anticline making, in effect, two anticlines. The oil found in Royalite 4 well, at a depth of 3,740, feet is

SECTION OF TURNER VALLEY REGION

(*After Slipper, Hume, and others*)

Series	Thickness, feet	Description
Tertiary: Paskapoo.........	4,000 ±	Massive ash-colored sandstone and green shales and clays of fresh-water origin. Conglomerate at base, fresh water
Cretaceous: Edmonton........	1,300	Green clay and green sandstone, carbonaceous horizon at base, brackish water
Montana: Bearpaw.......	?	Black shales, locally carbonaceous, not certainly present at Turner Valley
Belly River....	1,850	Green shales, green sandstone, coal at top; brackish water. Gas at Medicine Hat
Colorado: Benton.........	2,500–3,000	Dark shales and thin sandstone, marine; gas at Bow Island and Foremost
Lower Cretaceous: Blairmore ⎱ Kootenay ⎰	1,050	Thin-bedded shale, green and gray sandstone, conglomerate at base. Coal, black shale, and sandstone. Oil sand in Blairmore
Jurassic: Fernie...........	400–500	Dark shales, marine; oil and gas
Paleozoic: Madison.........		Dolomitic limestone, Turner Valley oil

in the Madison limestone.   This limestone is covered unconformably by the Fernie formation.

The area producing at Turner Valley (1930) is 15 miles long and $1\frac{1}{4}$ miles wide.   Thirty wells produce oil from the upper strata or gas from the Madison limestone.   The daily yield is about 2,700 barrels of naphtha from gas and 300 barrels of crude oil.   The daily flow of gas is 250,000,-000 cubic feet.   Gas pressures as high as 1,700 pounds per square inch are recorded.   No edge water is discovered at the edge of the gas-bearing area.   The field is noteworthy for its extensive thrust faulting.

The Bow Island[1] gas field (Fig. 333) is a few miles northwest of Bow Island on the Canadian Pacific Railway.   It occupies a small dome on the flank of the north extension of the Sweet Grass arch.   Wells sunk 1,849 to 2,100 feet deep have encountered large flows of gas, some as high as 29,000,000 cubic feet per day, the original gas pressure being about 700 to 800 pounds per square inch.   The field was opened in 1911 and gas was piped to neighboring cities.   In 1920 the gas pressure had declined to 210 pounds and since then the line has been supplied to a considerable extent by other fields.   Edge water has appeared in several of the gas wells.   The gas is derived from a sandstone member near the base of the Benton shale.

Medicine Hat is about 30 miles northeast of Bow Island.   Gas was found in 1908 in the Milk River sandstone above the Benton shale.   The wells encountered gas at a depth of about 1,187 feet, the original pressure being about 550 pounds per square inch.   The wells had initial flows of nearly 5,000,000 cubic feet per day.   The rock pressure had declined to 425 pounds per square inch in 1925.

The Foremost gas field is 30 miles south of Bow Island and about 40 miles north of the Kevin-Sunburst field, Montana.   Gas is encountered in sandstone lenses in the Benton shale of the Colorado (Cretaceous) formation at depths between 2,070 and 2,250 feet.   Some of these wells had initial daily production of 10,000,000 to 25,000,000 cubic feet of gas. In 1924 the field was connected with the Bow Island gas distributing lines which supply Calgary, Lethbridge, and other cities.

Near Coutts wells have encountered the Sunburst sand (Kootenai) 2,505 feet deep, and have found shows of oil; the Madison limestone is found 2,695 feet deep.

In the Flathead River[2] area in the southeast corner of British Columbia, oil and gas seepages are found in rocks regarded as Cambrian sediments.   It is probable that the older sediments are thrust over Cretaceous rocks.   Wells are sunk in this area but no oil field is dis-

---

[1] WILLIAMS, M. Y., and W. S. DYER, Can. Geol. Survey, *Econ. Geol.*, ser. 5, pp. 42–62, 1928.

[2] INGALL, E. D., Deep Borings in British Columbia and the Yukon, Can. Geol. Survey *Summary Rept.* 1924. pt. A, pp. 145–146, 1925.

covered. In Cameron Brook area, Alberta, east of Flathead area, a well is sunk on an anticline in Beltian strata (pre-Cambrian), which probably are thrust over Cretaceous beds, and has found a little oil, probably in Cretaceous beds.

The Viking[1] gas field is about 75 miles southeast of Edmonton in a flat area covered with drift. The field, according to Hume, lies on a local fold on the flank of the Alberta syncline. The gas is found at depths of about 2,100 to 2,400 feet and the gas pressure was about 800 pounds to the square inch. The gas is mainly methane and ethane and contains no gasoline vapor. It is piped to Edmonton and neighboring cities. The gas is probably from sandy beds near the base of the Benton shale.

The Battle River area lies southeast of Viking and extends east from Irma to the Saskatchewan boundary.[2] A series of anticlines strike northwest through this area and oil and gas are found in several wells.

Oil is found at two horizons, one near the base of the Colorado shale, which yields oil with a gravity of about 13° Bé., and another probably in Lower Cretaceous beds, which yields oil with a gravity of about 20° Bé.

In northern Alberta, along Athabaska River, there is one of the largest deposits of asphaltic material known. For 100 miles along the river and over an area estimated to be 2,000 square miles or more, tar sands are found impregnating sandstone. These sands are at the base of the Cretaceous and rest unconformably on Devonian strata. They lie on an irregular floor and are from 13 to 200 feet thick. At some places they are incoherent; at others they are cemented by a calcareous matrix. The tar sand[3] formation grades upward into a light green sandstone with which are stratified bands of light-green shale. The shale covers the sand where it has not been eroded. The sands are saturated with asphaltum and heavy oil and are said to contain 14 gallons of oil to the ton. The Devonian limestone below the sands contains pitch in joints and cracks, and it has been stated that the oil came from the Devonian limestone.[4] The area containing the tar sands recently has been described

[1] SLIPPER, S. E., Viking Gas Field, Can. Geol. Survey *Summary Rept.* 1917, pt. C, pp. 6–9, 1919.

ELSWORTHY, R. T., Gas in Alberta, Dept. Mines, Mines Branch, *Pub.* 616A, p. 17, 1924; Investigations of Mining Resources for 1924, pp. 103–115, 1925.

[2] HUME, G. S., Oil and Gas Prospects of the Wainwright Vermilion area, Alberta, Can. Geol. Survey *Summary Rept.* 1924, pt. B, pp. 1–22, 1925; also Can. Geol. Survey, *Econ. Geol.*, ser. 205, pp. 79–90, 1928.

[3] McCONNELL, R. G., Report on an Exploration in the Yukon and Mackenzie Basins, Can. Geol. Survey *Rept.*, new ser., vol. 4D, pp. 1–163, 1889; Report on a Portion of the District of Athabaska, Comprising the Country between Peace River and Athabaska River North of Lesser Slave Lake, Can. Geol. Survey *Rept.*, new ser., vol. 5D, pp. 1–67, 1891.

[4] BELL, ROBERT, The Tar Sands of the Athabaska River, Canada, Am. Inst. Min. Eng. *Trans.*, vol. 38, p. 838, 1907

by Hume[1] who concludes that the origin of the petroleum in the sands is probably the Lower Cretaceous strata rather than the underlying Devonian sandstone. Many wells are sunk along the Athabaska River, but no commercial supplies of oil are found.

On Peace River, north of the town of Peace River and about 175 miles west of the area containing the tar sands, wells drilled on a broad uplift have found a little heavy oil in strata near the base of the Lower Cretaceous system. In the western Peace River[2] area near the border of Alberta, west of the town of Peace River, wells have found a little oil, probably at the same horizon.

The Norman[3] oil field is 50 miles northwest of Norman, which is at the junction of Great Bear and Mackenzie rivers (Fig. 328). The oil field lies along the Mackenzie river in a low area between the Norman Range and Carcajou Mountains. In 1920 a well drilled near an oil seepage of the Bosworth formation (Upper Devonian) encountered oil in the Fort Creek shales (Upper Devonian), the well yielding about 100 barrels of high-gravity oil a day.

NEWFOUNDLAND

The west coast of Newfoundland (Fig. 328) from Cape Bay to Cape Norman consists of closely folded Paleozoic strata which at places are overturned. Oil and gas seeps are found in many places, and wells sunk near Parson's Pond in Ordovician rocks found a little high-gravity oil. One or two barrels a day were bailed from three wells. The Ordovician rocks consist of shales, sandstones, and some limy layers which are highly faulted, folded, and at places on edge.[4]

MEXICO

Mexico stands third in the world in total production of oil, to the end of 1927 having yielded 1,465,096,121 barrels or 9.3 per cent of the world's total. The production has recently declined, however, and in 1927 amounted to 64,168,824 barrels and in 1928 to 50,178,061 barrels. The producing districts (Fig. 337) are Tuxpam, or southern district of

[1] HUME, G. S., The McMurray Athabaska Area, Oil and Gas in Western Canada, Can. Geol. Survey, *Econ. Geol.*, ser. 5, pp. 90–96, 1924.

ELLS, S. C., Bituminous Sands of Northern Alberta, Can. Dept. Mines, Mines Branch *Pub.* 632, 1926.

[2] MCLEARN, F. H., Can. Geol. Survey *Summary Rept.* 1917, pt. C, pp. 14–21, 1918.

[3] HUME, G. S., Geology of the Norman Oil Field and a Reconnaissance of a Part of Liard River, Can. Geol. Surv. *Summary Rept.* 1922, pt. B, pp. 47–64, 1923.

———, Mackenzie River Basin, Oil and Gas in Western Canada, Can. Geol. Survey, *Econ. Geol.*, ser. 5, pp. 113–121, 1928.

BOSWORTH, T. O., *Jour. Inst. Pet. Tech.*, vol. 7, pp. 276–297, 1921.

[4] HOWLEY, J. P., Report upon the Petroliferous Region Situate on the Northwest Coast of Newfoundland, Newfoundland Geol. Survey, St. Johns, pp. 35–46, 1918.

the east coast, which from 1914 to 1927 yielded 866,707,237 barrels; Tampico, or north district, which during the same period yielded 591,-928,482 barrels; the Isthmian district, which in the same period yielded 6,460,402 barrels. These three districts account for practically the entire production of Mexico.

The chief oil fields of Mexico[1] (Fig. 338), occupy an area 150 miles long and 30 miles wide in the states of Vera Cruz and Tamaulipas. The chief cities of this area are Tampico and Tuxpam. Oil seeps are numerous within the area and attracted attention at an early date. A small production of oil was developed at Furbero in 1868, but the first comprehensive development was begun near Ebano in 1901 by the Mexican Oil Company, an organization of California men who brought in a small well in 1903 at a depth of 425 feet. In 1904 a few miles south of Ebano this company brought in a well which flowed for 9 years and yielded 3,500,000 barrels

[1] REDFIELD, A. H., Federal Oil Conservation Board *Rept.* 3, Appendix C, pp. 61–69, 1929.

TRAGER, E. A., The Geologic History of the Panuco River Valley and Its Relation to the Origin and Accumulation of Oil in Mexico, Am. Assoc. Pet. Geol. *Bull.*, vol. 10, pp. 667–696, 1926.

BAKER, C. L., Panuco Oil Fields, Mexico, Am. Assoc. Pet. Geol. *Bull.*, vol. 12, pp. 395–441, 1928.

STAUB, W., Der Unterbau des Erdoelgebietes von Nordost-Mexiko, *Z. prakt. Geol.*, vol. 34, pp. 120–125, 1926.

Ver Wiebe, W. A., Geology of Southern Mexico Oil Fields, *Pan-American Geologist*, vol. 44, pp. 121–130, 1925.

CUSHMAN, J. A., The Foraminifera of the Velasco Shale of the Tampico Embayment, Am. Assoc. Pet, Geol. *Bull.*, vol. 10, pp. 581–612, 1926.

DeGOLYER, E. L., The Effect of Igneous Intrusions on the Accumulation of Oil in the Tampico-Tuxpam Region, Mexico, *Econ. Geol.*, vol. 10, pp. 651–662, 1915.

DUMBLE, E. T., Tertiary Deposits of Eastern Mexico, *Science*, vol. 35, pp. 906–908, 1912.

———, Geology of the Northern End of the Tampico Embayment Area, Calif. Acad. Sci. *Proc.*, ser. 4, pp. 113–156, map, 1918.

GARFIAS, V. R., The Oil Region of Northeastern Mexico, *Econ. Geol.*, vol. 10, pp. 195–224, 1915.

———, Effect of Igneous Intrusions on the Accumulation of Oil in Northeastern Mexico, *Jour. Geol.*, vol. 20, pp. 666–672, 1912.

HUNTLEY, L. G., The Mexican Oil Fields, Am. Inst. Min. Eng. *Bull.* 105, pp. 2067–2106, 1915; also, *Trans.*, vol. 52, pp. 281–322, 1915.

ORDOÑEZ, EZEQUIEL, Occurrence and Prospects of Oil in Mexico, *Eng. Mining Jour.*, vol. 89, p. 1020, May 14, 1910.

———, The Oil Fields of Mexico, Am. Inst. Min. Eng. *Trans.*, vol. 50, pp. 859–869, 1914.

SEMMES, D. R., Petroliferous Formations of the Tampico Embayment, Mexico, Am. Assoc. Pet. Geol. *Bull.*, vol. 5, p. 101, 1921.

VILLARELLO, J. D., Algunas Regiones Petroliferas de Mexico, Inst. Geol. Mexico *Bol.* 26, pp. 1–120, 3 pl., 1908.

WHITE, I. C., Petroleum Fields, of Northeastern Mexico between the Tamesi and Tuxpam Rivers, Geol. Soc. Am. *Bull.*, vol. 24, pp. 253–274, 1913.

of oil. Other companies leased lands to the east and south of Ebano and the region was rapidly developed. The chief production has come from the north region, including the Ebano and Panuco fields, and the south region, including the fields from Dos Bocas to Alamo. The bulk of the oil has been obtained from a few wells which have large flows. As a rule the wells flow when brought in and continue to flow until the oil is exhausted and salt water issues. A single well has yielded more than a hundred million barrels of oil. Some of the wells near the ends of their periods of production yield emulsions of oil and water that are very difficult to treat profitably, and that are not saved.

Fig. 337.—Map showing oil fields and prospects in Mexico and Central America.

The country is an area of Cretaceous and later sedimentary rocks that dip eastward away from the Sierra, forming a gentle monocline that extends to the coast. A generalized section of the rocks is shown in the table that follows, and a cross-section after Palmer is shown by Fig. 338. Drilling has discovered great unconformities in the section, and buried hills and ridges which in part have localized the areas of accumulation. The country is cut by many stocks and dikes of igneous rocks and the Cretaceous beds are highly fractured and faulted. Nearly all of the oil is in limestone of Cretaceous age and most of the deposits are on anticlines and domes, although some seem to be independent of such structural features and are controlled by fracturing.

Geologic Section of Mexico Oil Field

(*After Trager, Belt, Palmer, Powers, Baker, Small, and others*)

	Thickness, Feet
Pleistocene.　Sand, gravel, etc.	
Miocene:	
Tuxpam.　Gray shales with beds of sandstone and limestone......	1,000
Oligocene:	
Meson.　Sandy clays, sandstones and limestones................	1,000 ±
Alazan.　Shales, blue, gray; thin sandstone.　Some place the Alazan in the Eocene...	2,000 ±
Unconformity.	
Eocene:	
Guayabal.　Shale..	0–500
Tantoyuca.　Conglomerate, grit and limestone at base passing up into shale...	3,000 ±
Tempoal.　Shale, dark blue or brown..........................	0–2,000
Chicontepec.　Shale, sandstone, chert, gravels..................	4,000 ±
Unconformity.	
Upper Cretaceous:	
Valasco.　Globigerina ooze, red beds, light gray to green limy clays, muds, shales (also called Tamesi)............................	950–1,100
Mendez.　Shale, purple, red, gray, green, limy at base, oil bearing.	1,000 ±
San Filipe:	
Upper.　Limestone, gray, green, shaly; oil bearing.............	500
Lower.　Limestone, pink or light gray; oil bearing.............	300
Unconformity.	
Lower Cretaceous:	
Tamaulipas:[1]　Limestone, light gray, dense, hard, thin bedded, oil bearing in north field; formerly called Tamasopo..............	1,200 ±
Unconformity.	
El Abra:[1]　Massive limestone porous at top; oil-bearing horizon in south field (called Tamasopo)...............................	0–3,500
Jurassic.　Limestone, white, fine grained	

[1] Middle Cretaceous according to Redfield.

Tampico.—The Panuco region, or north area, lies west of Tampico and includes the Panuco, Topila, Ebano, Cacalilao, and Corcovado oil fields. Ebano became an important producing field in 1904 and Panuco field in 1910. From 1914 to 1927 the north area yielded about 591,928,482 barrels of oil and it is now the chief producing part of the Tampico-Tuxpam region.

The Panuco field is on the great monocline that dips east from the mountains to the sea. The field is in the strike line of the Tamaulipas Mountains, an anticlinal range that strikes south and plunges south. The Panuco anticline or "high" is a narrow elevated block, probably faulted on both sides, that lies in the general direction of the mountains. The Topila field is located on a dome and the Ebano field, according to Garfias, is on a dome where an igneous mass has raised the beds, but later, on cooling, the beds near the intrusive were drawn down near the

contact and an anticlinal "ring and funnel" structure was formed.   In
general the oil is accumulated at high places on the structures but is not
confined to such places, nor is it greatly concentrated at summits.   In
all of the north group of fields the openings in the limestone are important.
These openings are largely due to fissuring and to fracturing.   Although

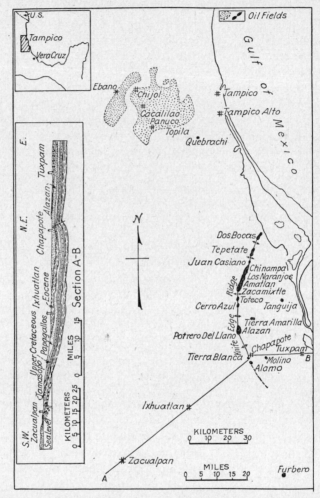

Fig. 338.—Map of oil fields of Tampico and Tuxpam, Mexico, (*Section from Palmer.*)

porosity due to weathering may be of some importance in certain fields,
the fracturing and fissuring are believed to be controlling features.   The
chief production of oil is from the upper part of the Tamaulipas limestone
("Tamasopo") and the lower part of the San Felipe limestone, and most
of the oil is derived from beds that lie within 300 feet of the contact,
although there is considerable production in the Ebano field from the

upper part of the San Felipe. The Ebano oil is heavy, ranging in gravity from 10.6 to 12.9° Bé. The oil of the Panuco field ranges from 12.5 to 12.9° Bé. That of Topila has a gravity of 15 to 17.2° Bé. in the main, but in the Mendez marl a higher grade oil with gravity as light as 48° Bé. is encountered in small amounts. The heavy oils are high in sulphur. The temperature of the Panuco oil is from 90 to 120° F. and generally rises a few degrees as salt water appears. The Panuco oil carries sulphur as the element, and in certain wells the oil is a saturated solution. The gas of Panuco commonly contains from 50 to 98 per cent carbon dioxide and much of it will not burn. According to Baker, the carbon dioxide has resulted in part from the action of hot intrusive rocks on the limestone. The gas contains also hydrogen sulphide which has reacted with the oil, making it heavy. The waters of the oil field have a total salinity of 2.8 to 7.2 per cent and are in the main alkali chloride waters, high in bicarbonate. One would suppose from the analyses reported by Baker that some of the waters would justify an investigation with a view to recovering potassium chloride. The sulphate radical in some of the waters is less than 1 per cent of the total solids. Baker states that the water is under sufficiently great pressure to cause it to flow, although gas is an important agent in causing both oil and water to flow. The source of the oil is uncertain. It is commonly supposed to be derived from the Tamaulipas limestone or from the San Felipe limestone, that is, from approximately the producing horizons. Trager, however, considers the Valasco shale that lies above the producing horizon as a possible source and Baker regards the Jurassic shales that are found below the producing beds as the probable chief source beds.

Tuxpam.—The south part of the Tampico-Tuxpam field in Mexico extends southward from Dos Bocas to Alamo; the oil is concentrated along a narrow belt[1] about a mile wide which is called the "Golden Lane" and also the "Knife Edge," on account of its narrow width. Drilling has revealed below an anticline a buried limestone ridge, which DeGolyer and Powers have compared to the Nemaha Ridge of Kansas. This ridge has been called the "Tamasopo Ridge" and its core is formed by the El Abra limestone of Lower Cretaceous age.[2] The ridge in the main has a steep western slope and a gentle east slope, as illustrated by the contour map (Fig. 339) of part of the ridge. A section of the ridge in the Cerro Azul field, after Small, is shown as Fig. 340. The El Abra

[1] DeGolyer, E., Zacamixtle Pool, Mexico, Am. Assoc. Pet. Geol. *Bull.*, vol. 5, p. 85, 1921.

Powers, S., Reflected Buried Hills in the Oil Fields of Persia, Egypt, and Mexico, Am. Assoc. Pet. Geol. *Bull.*, vol. 10, pp. 439–442, 1926.

Palmer, R. H., Geology of Eastern Hidalgo and Adjacent Parts of Vera Cruz, Am. Assoc. Pet. Geol. *Bull.*, vol. 11, pp. 1173–1220, 1927.

[2] The limestone in Tamasopo Cañon, commonly called the Tamasopo limestone, is of Upper Cretaceous age.

limestone was folded to form an anticline. Its surface was made porous by weathering. After the San Felipe formation was deposited there were folding and faulting and downwarping of the basin to the west. This was followed by the deposition of the Mendez and Valasco formations of the Upper Cretaceous and in post-Valasco time the major period of folding and faulting occurred. The Cretaceous shale was removed from the top of the ridge and during Eocene time the Chicontepec formation was deposited west of the area, followed by the deposition of the Tempoal, Tantoyuca and Guayabal (?) formations. Another period of uplift and erosion followed, and finally the Alazan and later formations were deposited. The period of post-Oligocene folding followed and the gentle structures which now mark the ridge were developed. Numerous oil fields are located on domes along the ridge; these are separated from each other by faulting and folding.

The Dos Bocas field at San Geronimo is on the north end of the ridge near the coast. The Dos Bocas well was brought in July, 1908. At a depth of 1,811 feet the well "drilled itself in" and the casing was hurled from the hole. It caught fire soon after its eruption and could not be extinguished. The fire raged for about 2 months and burned with such fierceness that a pillar of flame and smoke could be seen 50 miles away. The reservoir was apparently exhausted and salt water followed the oil and extinguished the flame in the fall of 1908. A crater of several acres was formed at the head of the well and salt water continued to flow from the crater.

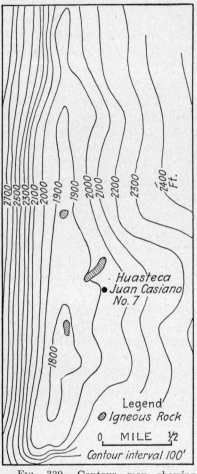

Fig. 339.—Contour map showing structure of top of El Abra limestone, Casiano oil field, Mexico. (*After De Golyer.*)

The Tepetate[1] field, 8 miles southwest of Dos Bocas was drilled in 1915. It is probably connected with the Juan Casiano field to the south,

[1] Huntley, L. C., A Graphic Model of the Tepetate-Chinampa Pool in the Mexican Fields, Am. Assoc. Pet. Geol. *Bull.*, vol. 5, pp. 677–679, 1921.

since the wells in both fields began to yield salt water at the same time. The Juan Casiano field was opened in 1910. Both fields had large wells. The Chinampa field was opened in 1918. It has been regarded as a north extension of the Los Naranjos field, which was opened in 1913 and was one of the most prolific fields in Mexico. In 1920 the Los Naranjos field yielded 95,000,000 barrels of oil.

The Amatlan field is essentially a southern continuation of Los Naranjos. To the south and on the same buried ridge is the Zacamixtle[1] pool which was opened in 1920. Toteca to the south of Zacamixtle was opened soon after the Zacamixtle pool. Two enormous gas wells were

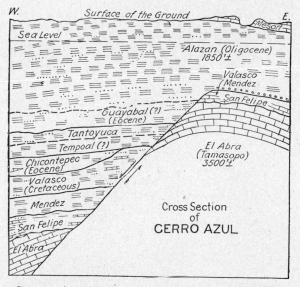

Fig. 340.—Cross-section of Cerro Azul oil field, Mexico. (*After W. M. Small.*)

drilled in and these soon began to yield oil. Cerro Azul was opened in 1916. Well No. 4 of the field was rated as the largest oil well in the world, its production being estimated at 200,000 barrels or more a day.

Alazan and Potrero del Llano fields are probably developed on the same fold. The Potrero 4 was the chief producing well in this field, and yielded about 115,000,000 barrels of oil before it was closed. The well was drilled through shales and encountered the top of the oil-bearing limestone at a depth of 1,911 feet in December, 1910. It ran wild[2] 2 months and was brought under control in March, 1911. It flowed 4 years and developed large seepage areas near its head early in 1914; it

[1] DeGolyer, E., Zacamixtle Pool, Mexico, Am. Assoc. Pet. Geol. *Bull.*, vol. 5, p. 85, 1921.

[2] Chambers, A. E., A History of One of Mexico's Earliest and Largest Wells, *Jour. Inst. Pet. Tech.*, vol. 9, pp. 141–164, 1923.

caught fire in August, 1914. The fire was extinguished about 6 months later and the well produced under partial control for 4 years. It began to yield an emulsion of oil and water December, 1918. In April, 1919, it was closed in. The Potrero oil has a gravity of 21° Bé. and is desirable for refining.

The Terra Blanca pool is southeast of Potrero del Llano and the Alamo pool is a short distance farther south, both pools being on the buried limestone ridge. The Alamo was opened in 1913 and has been

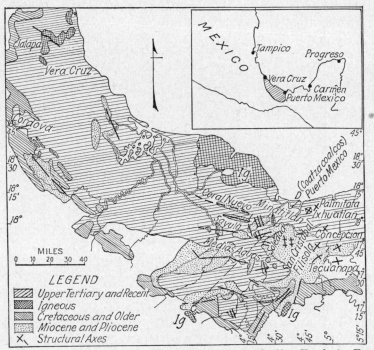

Fig. 341.—Map of Tehuantepec oil field, Mexico. (*After Sterling Huntley.*) For cross-section, line *CD*, see Fig. 342.

drowned by salt water.[1] In 1928 a well was brought in about 22 miles south of San Isidro.[2]

East of the "Knife Edge" fold there are several pools, among them the Tanguija which produces oil from Tertiary formations, the Tierra Amarilla which has produced some oil with much salt water, and the Molino, northeast of Alamo. The Molino well was drilled to a depth of 2,713 feet which was deeper than the wells in the other districts mentioned. It yielded a very heavy oil with a gravity of 11° Bé. Hartley states that

[1] HARTLEY, B., The Oil Fields of Mexico, Am. Assoc. Pet. Geol. *Bull.*, vol. 5, pp. 504–507, 1921.

[2] REDFIELD, A. H., Federal Oil Conservation Board *Rept.* 3, Appendix C, p. 66, 1929.

there is a fold east of and parallel to the main field and in line with Molino and Tierra Amarilla.

Furbero.—The Furbero[1] field, about 35 miles south of Alamo and 50 miles southwest of Tuxpam, is in an area of Mendez shales intruded by basalts and other igneous rocks. A ridge of hardened fractured shale crops out and lies above a dome of igneous rock that rises from a great intruding sill. Oil seeps attracted attention to the area, and the field was one of the first to be explored in Mexico. The oil is found in the fractured shale and in the fractured igneous rock. The sedimentary rocks are raised to form a dome but the main oil reservoirs are not at the top of the dome. The production of the field is small.

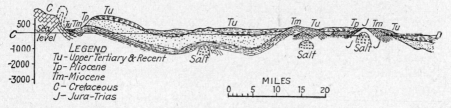

Fig. 342.—Geologic section of Tehuantepec oil field, Mexico, on line *CD*, Fig. 341. (*After Sterling Huntley.*)

Isthmus of Tehuantepec.—On the Atlantic Coast between Vera Cruz and Puerto Mexico on the Isthmus of Tehuantepec,[2] oil fields are developed above and on the flanks of salt domes (Figs. 341, 342). The region was opened in 1902 and in 1914 the production was 228,761 barrels. The chief production was from the salt domes Concepcion, Soledad, Ixhuatlan, San Cristobal, and Tecuanapa. The production decreased until 1918 when it was only 321 barrels. Attempts were made to increase the yield without much success until 1923, when the Filisola dome was discovered. In 1927 the production, which came mainly from this dome, amounted to 2,761,175 barrels. Between 1914 and 1917 the Isthmian district yielded 6,460,402 barrels.

[1] DeGolyer, E. L., The Furbero Oil Field, Mexico, Am. Inst. Min. Eng. *Trans.*, vol. 52, pp. 268–280, 1915.

[2] Hartley, B., Petroleum Geology of the Isthmus of Tehuantepec, *Econ. Geol.*, vol. 12, pp. 581–588, 1917.

Huntley, S., Oil Development on the Isthmus of Tehuantepec, Am. Inst. Min. Eng. *Trans.*, vol. 69, pp. 1150–1166, 1923.

Redfield, A. B., Isthmian Oil Fields of Mexico, *Eng. Mining Jour.*, vol. 111, pp. 510–514, 1921.

DeGolyer, E., Theory of Volcanic Origin of Salt Domes, Am. Inst. Min. Eng. *Trans.*, vol. 61, pp. 467–468, 1919.

VerWiebe, W. A., Oil Fields of the State of Tabasco, *Pan-American Geologist*, vol. 44, pp. 273–284, 1925; Tectonics of the Tehuantepec Isthmus, vol. 45, pp. 15–28, 1926; Oil fields of the Isthmus of Tehuantepec, vol. 45, pp. 189–200, 1926; Salt Domes of the Isthmus of Tehuantepec, vol. 45, pp. 349–358, 1926.

GEOLOGIC SECTION TEHUANTEPEC OIL FIELD

Series	Thickness, feet	Description
Quaternary and Upper Tertiary:	0–1,000	Gravel, sand, volcanic ash, clays, conglomerate; red and gray predominate
Unconformity Pliocene..............	0–2,500	Sandy shales and sandstones, blue, yellow, red; ash, conglomerate
Unconformity Miocene..............	0–3,000	Blue shales, white shales, with limestone and gypsum, sandstones
Unconformity Cretaceous...........	3,000+	White massive limestone grading downward into dark calcareous shales and the latter downward into white limestone
Unconformity	1,100+	Red and yellow conglomerate, red tuff, pink limestone with chert

On the Isthmian plain Tertiary and older rocks are found. These are crossed by two systems of folds (Fig. 341) one trending northeast and another northwest. Domes are found where the axes cross. At many places salt masses are thrust up from below and above the salt cores there are caps of dolomite. The oil is produced from the dolomite caps, which are porous, and from the Tertiary beds that dip away from the sides of the domes. Oil seepages are numerous, many of them have an odor of sulphur, and sulphur springs are common. The gravity of the oil is from 23 to 33.5 A.P.I. On the flanks of the domes the oil is found in Miocene or Pliocene beds and is believed to have originated in the beds, although some suppose that it has migrated from underlying Cretaceous rocks. Most of the wells drilled to the dolomite caps are shallow. The bulk of the production on the sides of the domes comes from wells about 2,900 feet deep. Many of the wells, on failing, produce salt water. The water contains appreciable magnesium sulphate, and, unlike the water of Tampico wells, it is not hot.

Other Districts.—Sarbat, northeast of Macuspana, Tabasco, in the east part of the Isthmian region (Fig. 337) has yielded small amounts of light oil. At Caimba, 12 miles south of Pichucalco, in Chiapas, a well drilled on a dome found a little oil. At Xilitla, southeast San Luis Potosi, some thick oil seeps from upper Cretaceous rocks. Near Arteaga, 20 miles east of Saltillo, oil seeps from Jurassic beds. At Guadalupe Hidalgo, near Mexico City, shallow wells found gas and shows of oil. Near Camargo, about 5 miles south of Rio Grande, Texas, a well 3,605 feet deep encountered a small flow of oil and gas. Near La Angostura, southeast of Guadalajara, oil seeps are found in Cretaceous limestone. Near Purisima[1] in Lower California, a heavy oil was found in folded Miocene beds.

CENTRAL AMERICA

In Central America at many places Tertiary rocks are thrown into folds and in the northern part of Central America Cretaceous limestones underlie the Tertiary rocks.[2]   Oil seepages are found at places and a few wells have been drilled.   Thus far no oil field is developed.

In Guatemala[3] oil seeps are found in the Department of El Peten in the northeastern part of the republic where Cretaceous and Tertiary rocks lie in folds that strike east.

In British Honduras[4] near the north border oil seepages are found near Orange Walk in folded Tertiary beds and in southern British Honduras, where Cretaceous beds are folded.

In Honduras in the Guare Mountains, 21 miles north of Comayagua, seepages of oil are found in Cretaceous strata, and near Jutigalpa, in Lower Cretaceous rocks, gilsonite veins are found.

In southeastern Panama,[5] near Garachine, oil seepages are found in Tertiary rocks (Fig. 346).

CARIBBEAN ISLANDS

Cuba.—Asphalt, pitch, and oil seeps have been known in Cuba[6] for many years, but little petroleum has been recovered.

[1] REDFIELD, A. H., Federal Oil Conservation Board *Rept.* 3, Appendix C, pp. 61–69, 1929.

[2] REDFIELD, A. H., The Petroliferous Systems of South America, Central America, and the West Indies, *Proc.* Pan-Pacific Sci. Cong., 1923, vol. 2, pp. 1207–1244, Melbourne, 1926.

[3] REDFIELD, A. H., Petroleum Possibilities of Guatemala, *Eng. Mining Jour.*, vol. 112, pp. 540–544, bibliography, 1921.

———, The Petroleum Possibilities of Honduras, *Econ. Geol.*, vol. 18, pp. 474–493, bibliography, 1923.

POWERS, S., Notes on the Geology of Eastern Guatemala and Northwest Spanish Honduras, *Jour. Geol.*, vol. 26, pp. 507–523, 1918.

[4] REDFIELD, A. H., Federal Oil Conservation Board *Rept.* 3, p. 59, 1929.

[5] McDONALD, D. F., Geology of the Isthmus, Canal *Rec.* 6, pp. 213–215, 1913; also Geol. Soc. Am. *Bull.* 24, pp. 707–715, 1913.

[6] DeGOLYER, E., The Geology of Cuban Petroleum Deposits, Am. Assoc. Pet. Geol. *Bull.*, vol. 2, pp. 133–167, 1917.

VAUGHAN, T. W., Bitumen in Cuba, *Eng. Mining Jour.*, vol. 73, p. 344, 1902.

HAYES, C. W., T. W. VAUGHAN, and A. C. SPENCER, Report on a Geological Reconnaissance of Cuba.   Made under the direction of Gen. Leonard Wood, Military Governor, 123 pages, 17 figures and maps, Washington, 1901.   Chapter on asphalt and petroleum same as Vaughan's work cited above.

PECKMAN, H. E., Bituminous Deposits of Cuba, *Am. Jour. Sci.*, ser. 4, vol. 12 pp. 33–41, 1901.

The rocks of Cuba may be divided into five series, as follows:

1. Quaternary and Recent deposits, including coral limestones, terrace gravels, soils, and sands.

2. Tertiary rocks, igneous in part.

3. Upper Cretaceous marls, shales, sandstones, conglomerates, and some limestone.

4. Triassic and Jurassic limestones and associated rocks.

5. The basement complex, consisting of granites, schists, slates, and limestone. Of unknown age, most of them probably Paleozoic or older. Includes probably also some serpentines of Cretaceous age. Serpentine is said to crop out in every province in Cuba.

The basement rocks and the Triassic rocks are in general intensely folded and are overlain by the Cretaceous and later rocks, which as a rule have comparatively low dips. The Cretaceous and older rocks are

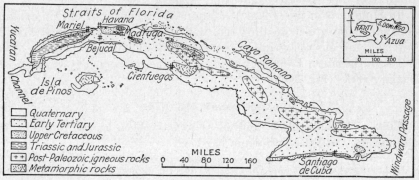

Fig. 343.—Geologic sketch map of Cuba.

intruded by igneous rocks. The Quaternary and Recent deposits are laid down upon the older rocks and are now forming near the sea shore (Fig. 343).

The structure in general is anticlinal, the older rocks forming the central axis and younger rocks cropping out on either side. The folding was probably accomplished in the Tertiary or in a later period. Subordinate folds occur away from the central axis.

Asphalt, oil seeps, and gas seeps have been reported from every province in Cuba and extend over a distance of 475 miles. They are most common on the north coast, in a zone some 20 miles wide between Esperanza and the eastern boundary of Santa Clara Province. The scattered wells that have been drilled here have not yielded important supplies, though several of them have encountered oil or gas. Most of the occurrences are in fractured serpentines. De Golyer believes that the oil was derived from the Jurassic limestones or other sedimentary rocks, that the igneous rocks from which the serpentines are derived were intruded, for the most part, into the Cretaceous rocks that overlie the Jurassic, and that the asphalt deposits and oil seeps found in the serpentine and other igneous rocks are the result of oil seeping from the underlying sedimentary rocks or from patches of the sedimentary rocks which have been caught up in the serpentine. It is believed by some, however, that the Cretaceous beds are unconformable with some of the serpentine bodies and that the oil has accumulated near the unconformity. About 12 miles East of Havana a little medium grade oil is recovered from serpentine. A dome at Bejucal, 19 miles south of Havana, was drilled in 1924 and found a large flow of gas in Cretaceous beds. At Mariel, on Mariel Bay 25 miles west of Havana, asphaltic beds are found, and, according to Wright and Sweet,[1] the oxidation of over 20,000,000 barrels of oil would be required to form the residue. These writers believe that the source of the oil of Cuba is chiefly the Jurassic limestone. A live oil spring is found 2 miles northwest of Madruga, which is 36 miles southeast of Havana.

Haiti.—Near Azua, Dominican Republic,[2] about 60 miles west of Santo Domingo (Fig. 343, inset) oil seeps from Miocene beds. Wells drilled 590 to 950 feet discovered a heavy oil which was drowned out by salt water which rose from deeper beds.

Barbados.—The island of Barbados[3] is a British colony located about 600 miles southeast of Porto Rico and 200 miles north of Trinidad. Oil and tar are found at many places on the island and have been exploited from shallow wells. Manjak, a partly dried out oil, has been exported since an early date. In 1922 a well drilled at Turner's Hall encountered oil, flowing 100 barrels or more a day from sands of the St. Andrews beds of the Scotland series. About 10,000 barrels of oil are produced annually.

The rocks exposed on the island include:

Recent. Coral limestone and detrital deposits, forms terraces. 400 feet thick.
Unconformity.
Upper Tertiary:
  Oceanic. Marine marls and chalks, limestone near base, volcanic ash and infusorial
    earth. 2,000 feet thick.

[1] Wright, A. Jr., and P. W. K. Sweet, Am. Assoc. Pet. Geol. *Bull.*, vol. 8, pp. 517–519, 1924.

[2] Woodring, W. P., Stratigraphy, Structures, and Possible Oil Resources of the Miocene Rocks of the Central Plain, Haiti, Dept. Public Works, Washington, 1922.

———, John A. Brown, and W. S. Burbank, Geology of the Republic of Haiti, *Rept.* Haiti Dept. Pub. Works, Port au Prince, 1924.

[3] Harrison, J. B., The Coral Rocks of Barbados, *Quart. Jour. Geol.* Soc., vol. 63, pp. 318–337, 1907.

———, and A. J. Jukes-Brown, "The Geology of Barbados, London," 1890.

Craig, E. H. C., The Prospective Oil Fields of Barbados, *Jour. Inst. Pet. Tech.*, vol. 4, pp. 68–78, 1918.

Thompson, A. B., "Oil-field Exploration and Development," p. 398, 1925.

Unconformity.
  Joe's River.   Clays, sands, limestone breccia; only locally developed.   Thickness
    varies greatly.
Unconformity.
Lower Tertiary (Eocene):
  Scotland series.   Highly folded.
    Chalky Mountain beds.   Sands, clays, conglomerate at base.
    St. Andrews beds.   Sands, clays, thin limestone; oil bearing.

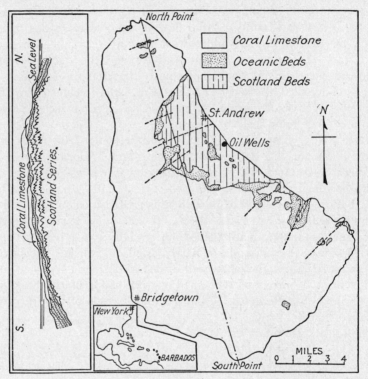

Fig. 344.—Map and section of Barbados Island.   (*After Craig.*)

The Scotland series is highly folded and the axes of the folds strike
northeast.   The Upper Tertiary beds which are unconformable above the
Scotland strata are folded less closely, the axes of the folds striking a
little north of east (Fig. 344).   Since most of the island is covered by
the Coral limestone, the structure of the oil-bearing rock is generally
concealed.

  Trinidad.—The island of Trinidad[1] which lies off the coast of Venezuela is about 50 miles long and 30 miles wide (Fig. 345).   It is divided

  [1] WALL, G. P., and J. G. SAWKINS, Report on the Geology of Trinidad, West
Indian Geol. Survey, pt. 1, pp. 1–211, 1860.
  ILLING, V. C., The Oil Fields of Trinidad, *Proc.* Geol. Soc., vol. 27, 1916.
  McREADY, G. A., Petroleum Industry of Trinidad, Am. Inst. Min. Eng. *Trans.*
vol. 65. pp. 58–68, 1921.

into five topographic provinces by three east-west ranges, namely, the Northern, Central, and Southern ranges. The Northern Range is 1,500 to 3,000 feet high and the Central and Southern ranges have maximum elevations of about 1,000 feet. The northern lowland zone is nearly flat and consists of detrital material from the mountains. The southern lowland zone is 200 to 300 feet above sea.

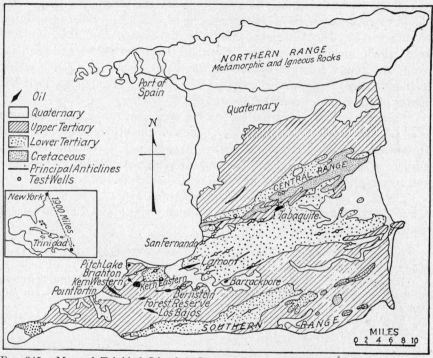

Fig. 345.—Map of Trinidad Island. (*Data mainly from Waring, Carlson, Liddle, and others.*)

In the Northern Range schists and crystalline limestones are found with a small area of basic igneous rocks on the northeast coast. The core of the Central Range consists of slates and limestone of Cretaceous age, flanked on both sides by Tertiary and later strata in which Lower Tertiary strata predominate. The summits of the Southern Range consist of Tertiary strata.

The southern half of the island is extensively folded and faulted. In the area of the Central Range close folds are locally overturned and

Waring, G. A., and C. G. Carlson, Geology and Oil Resources of Trinidad, British West Indies, Am. Assoc. Pet. Geol. *Bull.*, vol. 9, pp. 1000–1,008, 1923.

Milner, H., Trinidad, a Review of Its Geology and Oil Reserves, *Min. Mag.*, vol. 25, pp. 139–148, 205–213, 1921.

Liddle, R. A., "The Geology of Venezuela and Trinidad," pp. 1–552, J. P. Gowan, Ft. Worth, 1927.

cross-faults are noted. Away from the mountains low anticlines are found at many places. In the main the crests of the anticlines strike about N.60° E. to N.70° E., nearly parallel to the Central Range. Unconformities are noted between the Cretaceous and Eocene, between the Eocene and Oligocene, and overlaps are noted in the Miocene beds.

The oil fields are found in the south half of the island. They are associated with anticlines and produce from the Tertiary rocks. The island in 1927 produced 5,712,000 barrels of oil and its total production to 1928 was 39,108,563 barrels. The bulk of this came from the Bernstein field which includes the Apex, Fyzabad, and Oropuche subdistricts; from the Forest Reserve and from the Kern (eastern) district which includes Cruse, Parrykands, and Lots 1, 4, and 5. Tabaquite, near the center of the island, produced about 100,000 barrels.

There are three principal oil-bearing series including the Oligocene (and possibly Eocene), the lower Miocene and the upper Miocene strata. In southern Trinidad, where the geology is obscured by residual material, numerous bore holes, pits, and trenches are dug, and the heavy residuals and foraminifera[1] from them are studied to ascertain the structure.[1]

The chief asphalt deposits of Trinidad are at Pitch Lake, near Brighton in the southwest part of the island, which yields about 200,000 tons of asphalt annually.

[1] ILLING, V. C., Geology of the Naparima Region of Trinidad, *Quart. Jour.* Geol. Soc., vol. 84, No. 333, pt. 1, pp. 1–56, 1928.

HICKLING, H. C. B., Notes on the Control of Oil Wells and the Size of Screen on the Apex, Trinidad, Oil Field, *Trans.* Inst. Min. and Met., vol. 32, pp. 1–34, London, 1923.

CHAPTER XVIII

SOUTH AMERICA

COLOMBIA

In Colombia[1] the principal oil fields (Fig. 346) are situated in the Magdalena Valley which is a great structural trough that lies between the Sierra Central on the west and the Sierra Oriental on the east. The

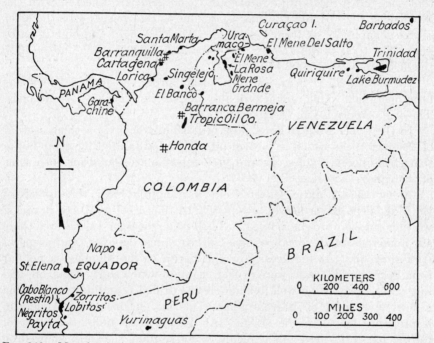

Fig. 346.—Map showing oil fields and prospects (black) in northern part of South America.

trough is about 600 miles long and is outlined in part by strike faults. The rocks consist of Cretaceous limestone and shale which are overlain

[1] Washburne, C. W., and K. D. White, Oil Possibilities in Colombia, Am. Inst. Min. Eng. *Trans.*, vol. 68, pp. 1023–1031, 1923.

Anderson, F. M., Original Source of Oil in Colombia, Am. Assoc. Pet. Geol. *Bull.*, vol. 10, pp. 382–404, 1926.

Huntley, L. G., and S. Mason, Colombian Oil Fields, Am. Inst. Min. Eng. *Trans.*, vol. 68, pp. 1014–1022, 1923.

Garner, A. H., General Oil Geology of Colombia, Am. Assoc. Pet. Geol. *Bull.*, vol. 11, pp. 151–156, 1927.

unconformably by Tertiary sandstone, cherts, clays, and shales.   Oil
seeps are numerous and are found at places in fractured zones from near
El Banco to near the head of the Magdalena river.

Near Barranca Bermeja about 350 miles above the mouth of the
Magdalena River and east of its tributary the Opon River, the Tropical
Oil Company, affiliated with the Standard Oil Company of New Jersey,
owns a concession.   A well 20 miles southeast of Barranca Bermeja
near Infantas, drilled in 1918, flowed between 3,500 and 5,000 barrels
of oil per day.   Since then many large wells were brought in.   These
wells are drilled on structural domes and probably derive their oil from
the Eocene rocks, although it has been stated by several investigators
that the source rocks are Cretaceous.   The field is connected with the
Magdalena river by rail and has a pipe line to the coast.   It is the chief
source of supply of oil from Colombia.   The oil is light and high in gasoline.   The total production to 1927 was 23,645,000 barrels and in 1927
the field produced 15,002,175 barrels.

Near Pomplona, near the Venezuela border, a small refinery has
been operated.   This region probably derives its oil from Eocene beds.
The chief supply is from seepages.

In the upper Magdalena Valley near Honda there is a thick section
of Tertiary rocks which is thrown into folds and faulted by great faults
that strike north.   Oil seeps and brea deposits are found on both sides
of the valley.

Along the Atlantic Coast from Barranquilla near the mouth of
the Magdalena River nearly to Panama, there is a belt of Tertiary rocks[1]
which is thrown into sharp folds and strikes northeast.   In this area there
are numerous mud volcanoes, gas springs, brea deposits, and seeps of
dark-green oil.   At Perdices, near the mouth of the Magdalena not far
from Barranquilla, wells were drilled, many of which showed gas, oil, and
salt water.   In 1922 a well flowing oil was drilled near Puerto Colombia
a few miles west of Barranquilla.   This oil, according to Anderson,
is probably from Eocene strata.   At Turbaco, 12 miles southeast of
Cartagena, tests made on a region of active mud volcanoes showed oil
and gas.   At Lorica a well sunk on an anticline showed oil, and in the
Sinu Valley, 40 miles south of Lorica, numerous tests were made.   In
1912 a 50-barrel well was brought in near San Sebastian, east of Sinu
River.

VENEZUELA

The great Andes chain, which forms the backbone of South America,
fingers out in Colombia and Venezuela, forming from west to east the

[1] BECK, E., Geology and Oil Resources of Colombia, the Coastal Plain, *Econ.
Geol.*, vol. 16, pp. 457–473, 1921.

Choco, Occidental, Central, and Oriental ranges. The Oriental Range itself branches, one branch forming the Sierra de Perija of the western border of Venezuela, and the northeast branch forming the Sierra de Merida or Venezuelan Andes which include the Sierra de Trujillo. Between these two latter groups of mountains is the Maracaibo basin, in which nearly all of the Venezuelan oil fields are found.

SECTION FOR WESTERN VENEZUELA
(After Jahn, Garner, Wasson, and others)

Series	Thickness, feet	Description
Quaternary: Alluvial.......		Sand and clay
Llanos........	250 ±	Clays, sandstone, and sand conglomerates
Tertiary: Pliocene.......		Clays and shales poorly consolidated, brown sandstone, a few limestone and lignite beds generally not recognized or wanting in western Venezuela
Miocene.......	0–9,000	Clays, white to red, sandstone, massive friable, poorly sorted, coarse lenticular, commonly micaceous. At places Miocene beds supply reservoir rocks for oil
Unconformity Oligocene......	0–3,000	Dark shale, locally slate. At places limestone beds are included, locally carries oil
Unconformity Eocene........	2,000–3,000	Hard, coarse, consolidated, massive sandstone, light colored, contains a little gray shale, locally quartzite. 1,000–2,000 feet carbonaceous brown and black shale, sandy shale, and thin-bedded sandstone. Locally contains thick coal beds. 500' ± dark shale, fossiliferous limestone, thin-bedded sandstone or quartzite. Lower Eocene carries oil
Unconformity Cretaceous......	6,000–10,000	Black bituminous limestone interbedded with black calcareous shale. Lower part contains calcareous concretions. The whole is fossiliferous and often impregnated with oil. 3,000 feet hard, gray, fossiliferous, crystalline limestone includes sandstone beds. 500 feet ± hard, coarse, even-grained quartzite sandstone
Unconformity Jurassic (?).....		Sandstone, shales, grits, conglomerates, chiefly red
Pre-Cretaceous...		Probably pre-Jurassic; igneous and metamorphic rocks

This basin (Fig. 347) is a synclinorium; the uppermost layers are composed of thick series of Cretaceous and Tertiary sediments.[1]	The axis

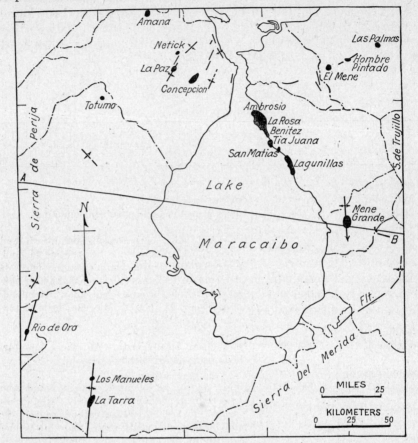

Fig. 347.—Map showing oil fields (black) of Maracaibo basin, Venezuela.	(*Data from Wasson, Hopkins, Liddle, and others.*)

[1] Wasson, H. J., Recent Oil Development in Venezuela, Min. and Met., vol. 8, pp. 414–418, 1927.

Liddle, R. A., Tectonics of the Maracaibo Basin, Am. Assoc. Pet. Geol. *Bull.*, vol. 11, pp. 177–186, 1927.

———, "The Geology of Venezuela and Trinidad," pp. 1–552, J. P. Gowan, Fort Worth, Texas, 1927.

Hunter, C. M., The Oil Fields of the Maracaibo Basin, *Jour. Inst. Pet. Tech.*, vol. 12, pp. 235–255, 1926.

Arnold, R., B. Bryan, and G. A. Macready, Petroleum Resources of Venezuela, Am. Inst. Min. Eng. *Trans.*, vol. 68, pp. 1052–1056, 1923.

Garner, A. H., Oil Geology of Northern Venezuela, Am. Inst. Min. Eng. *Trans.*, vol. 71, pp. 1358–1368, 1925.

Redfield, A. H., Federal Oil Conservation Board *Rept.* 3, Appendix C, pp. 86–89, 1929.

Williston, S. II., and C. R. Nichols, Review of Liddle's work in Am. Assoc. Pet. Geol. *Bull.*, vol. 12, pp. 445–451, 1928.

Hopkins, E. B., and H. J. Wasson, Geologic and Economic Notes on Venezuelan Oil Developments. Am. Assoc. Pet. Geol. *Bull.*, vol. 13, pp. 1187–1209. 1929.

of the trough passes approximately through the center of Lake Maracaibo. The basin (Fig. 348) is surrounded by mountains on all sides except the north. Strong faulting and folding is noted in the foothills of the mountains, diminishing toward the center of the basin. In the lowlands bordering the Lake, the formations appear to be relatively undisturbed, though the recent overburden for the most part obscures the structure.

A generalized section of the field is shown on page 599. This section at many places is not complete on account of the unconformities. The Miocene or Oligocene rocks, or both, at places were nearly all removed before deposition of later beds.

Oil seeps are numerous in the Maracaibo basin, particularly in the foothill belt, and small amounts of oil have been recovered from pits for many years. Commercial production was begun in 1917, and by the end of 1929 Venezuela had produced about 380,-791,000 barrels of oil. The production in 1928 was approximately 106,000,000 barrels, or about 8 per cent of the world's production. In 1929 the production was 135,953,000 barrels. About 95 per cent of the oil produced in Venezuela is heavy, between 17 and 25° A.P.I.; the remainder is lighter, ranging between 28 and 42° A.P.I. The oil is found principally in Tertiary rocks, though the Cretaceous may eventually become important producers. It is accumulated in sands interbedded with clays and shales. Unconformities and overlaps along gentle monoclines seem to have provided the combination of conditions suitable for widespread concentration of oil. There is an angular unconformity between the Eocene and Miocene beds and one also between the Oligocene and Miocene beds, and the top of the Oligocene and the base of the Miocene is an important reservoir. Valuable deposits are found also within the Eocene and Oligocene below the unconformities.

The most productive fields lie along the east shore of Lake Maracaibo and include Ambrosio, La Rosa, Punta Benitez, and Lagunillas, in which production is found under the lake bed as well as the adjoining land, and at Mene Grande, several miles inland from the shore. Developments in some of

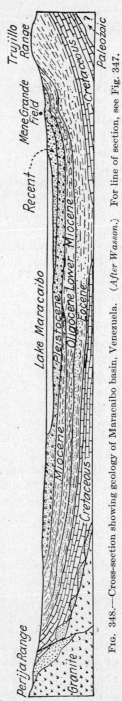

Fig. 348.—Cross-section showing geology of Maracaibo basin, Venezuela. (*After Wasson.*) For line of section, see Fig. 347.

these fields have followed the oil down the dip for over 1,500 feet vertically, and as yet no edge water has been found.

The La Rosa field, including Ambrosio, La Rosa, and Punta Benitez,
lies along a west-dipping monocline, the beds in the eastern part of the
field dipping about 10 degrees.   Some oil reservoir beds crop out at the
top of the monocline and are sealed by asphalt, imprisoning the oil down
the dip.   In others the sands play out toward the surface.   The chief
production is from the beds lower in the section and largely from the
beds near the plane of unconformity between the Miocene and Oligocene
beds.   A well drilled in 1922 produced 900,000 barrels of oil in 9 days
before sanding up.

The Lagunillas field is located 25 miles southeast of La Rosa, along the
shore of the lake.   Large wells have been found in a strip about 7 miles
long, with a maximum width of about 2 miles.   As yet the limits of the
field are undetermined in any direction, and the oil, which is of low
gravity, is found at depths ranging from 3,200 to 4,400 feet.   The oil
probably occurs near the plane of an unconformity at the base of the
Miocene and the top of the Oligocene series.   The structure at Lagunillas
appears to be a continuation of the same monocline found productive at
La Rosa and Ambrosio.

The Mene Grande field, the first commercial deposit developed in
Venezuela, lying 30 miles southeast of Lagunillas, is located on a well-
defined anticline that strikes and plunges to the south.   The oil occurs
in various beds from the Lower Tertiary, corresponding to the "Lower
Coal Horizon," to beds possibly as young as the Pleistocene.   The great
vertical distribution is due probably to migrations from more limited
source beds, and it is not entirely clear whether folding or overlapping
of beds has been the dominant factor which determined the locus of oil
accumulation.

The El Mene field, located 35 miles northeast of La Rosa, was discovered in 1924.   The oil, which is of 36° gravity, occurs in the upper
part of the Oligocene series where overlain by Miocene beds.   The field,
which is about 4 miles long, may be the result of minor folding accompanied by considerable faulting.   Here also, the effect of the structure as
an influence on the oil accumulation may, however, be subordinate to the
favorable reservoir conditions provided by the overlaps within the formations themselves.   At Hombre Pintado, 10 miles east of the El Mene field,
several wells with initial productions of 200 to 300 barrels have been
drilled.   The oil, which is of high gravity, occurs in Eocene rocks.

At Urumaco, in the state of Falcon, some 65 miles northeast of the El
Mene field, high-grade oil with a paraffin base has been found at a depth
of 3,400 feet.   Though not definitely known, it is believed that the oil
occurs in the Oligocene beds, and that it is closely related to a domal
structure clearly recognized at the surface.

The Concepcion field is located on the west side of the lake about 15 miles west of the city of Maracaibo, on a narrow sharply folded anticline which strikes N.45° E. The oil, which is of 38° Bé., occurs in upper Oligocene beds.

The La Paz field is located on the west side of the lake about 30 miles northwest of Maracaibo. The field is located on a long narrow structure which parallels that at Concepcion. The oil, which is 28 gravity, is also found in the Upper Oligocene.

La Tarra field, lying some 60 miles southwest of Lake Maracaibo, produces from the Lower Eocene, locally called the "Third Coal Horizon." Los Manueles, six miles to the north of the same structure, is a recent development where a small amount of high-grade oil has been found in the same horizons but at greater depths than in La Tarra field proper. La Tarra anticline striking south extends over 30 miles in the District of Colon and crosses the Venezuelan border into Colombia.

In the Rio de Oro field, lying 40 miles northwest of La Tarra field, oil has been found in the Lower Eocene, and possibly in the Upper Cretaceous beds. The Rio de Oro structure is nearly parallel to La Tarra anticline and of similar size.

At Totumo, in the District of Perija, several wells have been completed with initial productions ranging from 100 to 2,000 barrels. The oil, which is of low gravity, occurs in igneous formations, said to be of basaltic character, and evidently represents accumulation after migrations from the original source beds.

At El Mene del Salto, in eastern Falcon (Fig. 346), several wells have been completed with initial productions ranging from 100 to 400 barrels. The gravity of the oil is 40 degrees and the depths of the productive levels range from 700 to 2,000 feet. The oil occurs in the "Guayaval beds" of the Upper Eocene series.

In the vicinity of the Guanoco, Pitch Lake, in the northeastern part of Venezuela, oil of 10 degree gravity is being produced in small quantity for use in the asphalt industry. The producing horizon is not known but is probably either the Upper Cretaceous or the unconformably overlying Miocene.

In the Quiriquire area, about 16 miles north of Maturin, in the state of Monagas, several wells have encountered low gravity oil, and at the present time intensive drilling is being carried on in the hope of developing a commercial field. The oil occurs in the Upper Tertiary near its contact with the Upper Cretaceous, the Miocene-Eocene interval being locally missing.

ECUADOR

At Point Sta. Elena, Ecuador,[1] which lies on the Pacific Coast due west of Guayaquil, oil seeps are numerous, and oil has been recovered from shallow pits for centuries. The country is an area of Oligocene sandstones and shales, intruded by igneous dikes, which at places are highly silicified to form chert. The silicification, according to Sheppard, has resulted from the intrusion of the dikes. The country is highly faulted and the structure is uncertain. The oil seeps seem to be related to the intrusives as is suggested by Fig. 349. There are probably 2,000

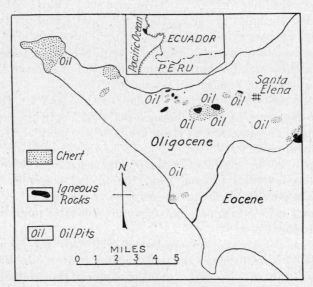

Fig. 349.—Map of part of Santa Elena Peninsula, Ecuador. (*After Sheppard.*)

pits in this region that were dug for oil. Although deep wells are drilled in the area, the results in the main are disappointing.

On the east slope of the Andes (Fig. 346) near the town of Napo[2] asphaltic oil and gas seeps are found along the Napo River. The rocks are shown in the table on page 605.

Near Napo these rocks form an anticline the crest of which strikes northeast along the Napo River. The oil is believed to have originated in the Napo limestone and shales and to have migrated to the Hollin sandstone.

---

[1] SHEPPARD, G., Observations on the Geology of the Santa Elena Peninsula, Ecuador, South America, *Jour. Inst. Pet. Tech.*, vol. 13, pp. 424–461, 1927; also *Econ. Geol.*, vol. 21, pp. 70–80, 1926.

REDFIELD, A. H., Federal Oil Conservation Board Rept. 3, p. 83, bibliography, p. 198, 1929.

[2] WASSON, T. and J. H. SINCLAIR, Geological Explorations East of the Andes in Ecuador, *Am. Assoc. Pet. Geol. Bull.*, vol. 11, pp. 1253–1281, map, p. 1265, 1927.

GEOLOGIC SECTION NEAR NAPO, ECUADOR
(*Data from Wasson and St. Clair*)

Formation	Thickness, feet	Description
Quaternary.......		Alluvium and volcanic agglomerate
Red Beds........	1,200	Red shale and ripple marked sandstone interstratified near bottom with red and green clays and tuffs, age not determined
Napo...........	1,500	Limestone and shale in part highly bituminous and fossiliferous (Cretaceous-Comanchean age)
Hollin..........	400	Massive fine-grained quartz, sand top saturated with oil
Misahualli.......		Tuffs and basalt

PERU

The oil fields of Peru[1] (Fig. 346) include the Tumbez-Paita field on the Pacific Coast of northern Peru; the Junin fields east of Lima; the Huancane and Islaicocha fields east of the Andes Range; the Mountain fields in which oil seeps are found along the Santiago and lower Ucayali and Huallaga rivers. The Tumbes-Paita field is in a desert area extending along the north coast of Peru for about 125 miles and is 30 miles wide. This field, which has yielded practically all of the oil of Peru, actively began production in 1884 and to 1927 had produced 82,720,437 barrels of oil. In 1927 the yield was 10,134,971 barrels. The field lies west of the Amatape Mountains, a foothill range of the Andes. The regional dip is northwest and the strata are strongly faulted and folded. Oil seepages are numerous. Oil is found in the Tertiary strata, the chief centers of production being Zorritos, Restin, Lobitos, and Negritos (Fig. 350). The oil has a mixed base, is low in sulphur, and has a gravity of about 38° Bé. A section of the rocks is shown on a following page. The Negritos, Salina, and Saman formations were developed on eroded surfaces, and faulting preceded erosion of the surfaces on which the Eocene beds and Saman formation were laid down. Unconformities are found also at the base of the lower Oligocene and at the base of the middle Oligocene.

[1] DEUSTUA, R. A., Explored Oil Fields of Peru, Pan-American Union *Bull.*, vol. 59, pp. 981–999, October, pp. 1120–1132, November, 1925.

IDDINGS, A., and A. A. OLSSON, Geology of Northwestern Peru, Am. Assoc. Pet. Geol. *Bull.*, vol. 12, pp. 1–40, 1928.

MARSTERS, V. F., Outline of the Geology and Development of the Petroleum Fields of Peru, Am. Assoc. Pet. Geol. *Bull.*, vol. 5, pp. 585–604, 1921.

BOSWORTH, T. O., Geology of the Tertiary and Quaternary Periods in the Northwest Part of Peru, pp. 1–434, 1922.

SPEIKER, E. M., Johns Hopkins Univ. Studies in Geology, Paleontology 3, pp. 1–196, 1922.

The Zorritos field is located on a narrow sharp fold or uplifted fault block that runs parallel to the coast and is developed several miles on strike. The beds dip east toward the mountains. The oil is found at depths from 300 feet to 1,700 feet and comes from the lower part of the Miocene and from sandy beds in the upper part of the Heath formation of the Upper Oligocene series. Most of the wells have initial production of less than 100 barrels a day. The total production of the Zorritos

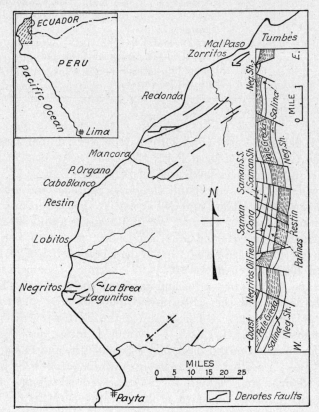

Fig. 350.—Map of oil fields of northwestern Peru and section of Negritos field. (*After Iddings, Olsson, and others.*)

field is about 3.5 per cent of that of Peru. A small field at Restin and Cabo Blanco is located on a faulted anticline. The crest of the anticline strikes northward and is very near the beach, part of the west flank of the fold lying below sea level. At Lobitos, south of Restin, there are several blocks of folded strata that are raised so as to expose the Eocene beds; the oldest formation cropping out is the Pale Greda formation. The oil is found in Eocene strata, particularly in the Negritos formation. The Lobitos, Restin, and Cabo Blanco districts together have produced about 20 per cent of the total yield of Peru.

GEOLOGICAL FORMATIONS OF NORTHWEST PERU
(Data mainly from Iddings and Olsson)

Formation	Thickness, feet	Description
Quaternary.............	400 ±	Sand, gravel, limestone, conglomerate, etc.
Tertiary:		
Pliocene.............	800 ±	Consisting of conglomerate, limestone, clays, diatomaceous earth, marls, gypsum (Sechura formation)
Miocene:		
Tumbez	700	Volcanic tuffs, shales, sandstone, conglomerate
Cardalitos	1,700	Shale, black with calcareous concretions, gypsum, thin sands in lower part
Zorritos..........	750	Sandstone, conglomerate, shales, fossiliferous, lower part contains oil at Zorritos
Oligocene............	7,000	
Heath.............	3,100 ±	Shales, black, bituminous; limestone concretions, sands in upper part; produce oil at Zorritos
Mancora.........	1,000–1,500	Sands and conglomerate grits, dark shales, locally gypsiferous shales; near Lagunitos conglomerates carry oil
Chira	1,500–2,000	Shales and sandstones
Verdun...........	2,000	Sandstones, gypsiferous shales. Some oil in Negritos field
Eocene:		
Upper............. (Saman formation).	2,900	Upper shale division 900 feet thick; middle sandstone division, sand and shale 800 feet thick, includes five oil sands; lower shale division 1,200 feet, locally conglomeratic at base; contains sand lenses and locally contains oil
Middle:		
Restin..........	400–1,100	Dark gray sandstone and shales, some conglomerate. Oil bearing
Parinas.........	900–1,000	Sandstone, medium to coarse grained, conglomerate, shale, three oil sands, produces much oil in Negritos field
Pale Greda	2,000–2,700	Shales, thin sandstones, thin limestones, conglomerates, contains a little oil
Salina...........	800	Sandstone, shale, pebble beds, oil sands
Lower:		
Negritos		Main oil production of Peru
Upper........	900	Shale, sandstone, oil sands
Lower	4,600	Shale containing oil sands
Cretaceous:		
Monte Grande...		Conglomerate and sandstone
Copa Sombrero..	3,000 ±	Shales, chert, sandstone, etc.
Pananga........		Limestones
Pennsylvanian:		
Amotape.........		Slates. etc., intruded by granite of Jurassic age

The Negritos field at the south end of the productive belt extends eastward to include Lagunitos and LaBrea.　It is the most extensively developed of all the Peruvian fields and has yielded about 76 per cent of the total production.　The wells range from 60 to 3,800 feet deep and the initial production is as high as 4,000 barrels per day, the average being about 300 barrels.　The field is on a great anticline that brings the Pale Greda formation to the surface.　High points located on this anticline include one at Negritos and another at LaBrea.　It is sliced by two or more systems of faults closely set, so that the area is essentially a fault mosaic.　These are normal faults and the three to the south have downthrows on the south side.　The one to the north throws the rocks down to the north so as to leave the high block of Lower Eocene strata exposed.　At Negritos the rocks dip east, but it is possible that they resume the regional west dip below the sea, section (Fig. 350).　If so, the Negritos field is a faulted structural dome.　The dip at Negritos is about 20 degrees and some of the oil sands crop out within the field.　It follows that the oil in such sands is accumulated in sealed beds or in lenses that play out up dip.　The bulk of the oil at Negritos has come from sands in the Lower Eocene strata, particularly from the Negritos formation, although the Salina formation of the Middle Eocene series also yields oil.　The Negritos is a highly fossiliferous marine series of shale and sandstone.　Highly productive sands are found near the base of the upper part of the formation and also at a horizon about 2,000 feet below the top of the formation, and minor sands are found throughout the entire series.

BOLIVIA

In Bolivia[1] oil seepages are found from the region near Lake Titicaca southeast to Santa Cruz de la Sierra (Fig. 351) and thence southward along the east slope of the Andes.　The oil is probably derived from Paleozoic beds.　The section of rocks that lies between the Devonian and Tertiary strata is much thinner to the north than it is to the south of Santa Cruz.　Near Santa Cruz oil is found in small amounts in sandy beds of Devonian shale, and this oil has been used for lighting in the city. Near Sapura, which is about 100 miles south of Santa Cruz, a well was drilled 2,240 feet deep, yielding about 60 barrels of oil per day.　Near

[1] HEALD, K. C., and K. F. MATHER, Reconnaissance of the Eastern Andes between Cochabamba and Santa Cruz, Bolivia, Geol. Soc. Am. *Bull.*, vol. 33, pp. 553–570, 1922.

MATHER, K. F., Front Ranges of the Andes between Santa Cruz, Bolivia, and Embarcacion, Argentina, Geol. Soc. Am. *Bull.*, pp. 703–764, 1922.

HERALD, S. C., Economic and Geologic Conditions Pertaining to the Occurrence of Oil in North Argentina-Bolivian Field of South America, Am. Inst. Min. Eng. *Trans.*, vol. 61, pp. 544–564, 1920.

ZUMELZU, R. R., El Petroleo en Bolivia, *Rev. Min. de Bolivia*, vol. 1, No. 4, pp. 112–124; vol. 1, No. 5, pp. 129–139, map, 1926.

Bermejo north-northwest of Oran, Argentina, wells were drilled in 1923 on a dome on which Jura-Triassic(?) sandstone crops out. One well had an initial production of 1,500 barrels of oil per day, probably from Carboniferous rocks. This field is now under development. The oil is of excellent grade.

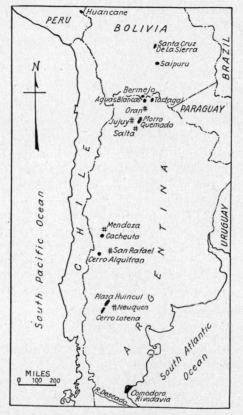

FIG. 351.—Map showing oil fields (black) in southern part of South America.

ARGENTINA

In Argentina east of the Andes from the Bolivia border south through Jujuy and Salta provinces there is a thick section of Paleozoic rocks.[1] The Devonian is 300 meters thick and consists of marine sandstone, limestone, and shales. It is impregnated with oil at many places. Above the Devonian are Permo-Carboniferous beds which, according to Mather, are of glacial origin. From these also oil exudes at several horizons. At the top of the Lower Sandstone is the Dolomitic limestone consisting of shale, sandstone, and dolomite. It is a marine formation possibly of Cretaceous age and at places in Jujuy it carries oil. Above the Lower

[1] ANDERSON, R., Observations on the Occurrence and Origin of Petroleum in Argentina and Bolivia, Am. Assoc. Pet. Geol. Bull., vol. 10, pp. 853–859, 1926.

Sandstone are non-marine Tertiary beds 3,000 meters thick and at a few places near the base of the series oil seeps are found. Anderson regards the Devonian and dolomitic limestone as the probable sources of oil in Bolivia and northern Argentina.

South of Tartagal (Fig. 351) and some 50 miles northeast of Oran heavy oil issues from both Mesozoic and Tertiary strata. At Quebrada de Galarza, near Tartagal, four wells have obtained a small production of oil. At Aquas Blancas, north of Oran and near Bermejo, Bolivia, 7,485 barrels of oil were produced in 1927. Near San Pedro, 25 miles east of Jujuy, a little oil was produced from Jurassic(?) limestone at a depth of 1,748 feet. Near Lomitas in the province of Salta, 10,504 barrels of oil were produced in 1927. Oil seepages and asphaltic (rafaelite) dikes are found at many places south of Salta, the belt in which they are found extending for hundreds of miles along the east front of the Andes.

In the Cacheuta district, 25 miles southwest of Mendoza, wells drilled in Tertiary and Cretaceous rocks produce a heavy oil which is used locally. At Cerro Alquitran in Mendoza,[1] about 60 miles west of San Rafael, there are oil seeps and rafaelite veins, the veins filling channels through which oil moved probably to the surface to feed oil springs. This region produced 12,580 barrels of oil in 1927. The rocks of the district are shown below.

SECTION OF CENTRAL MENDOZA
(After Lahee)

	Feet
Post-Tertiary:	
Alluvium, wind-blown sands, gravels, tuffs, etc.	
Tertiary:	
Ranch House conglomerate....................................	$6,000 \pm$
Probable Unconformity.	
Eocene or Upper Cretaceous (Danian):	
Ramadas series...	3,000–3,500
Cretaceous:	
Salas sandstone series......................................	1,500–1,800
Salas limestone group......................................	$200 \pm$
Lower Cretaceous (Neocomian):	
Diamante limestone......................................	40–800
Jurassic:	
Portlandian:	
Ammonite shale..	400–900
Blanca sandstone......................................	600–1,000
Oxfordian (?):	
Tabanos group...	800–1,000
Manga sandstone......................................	250–350
Probable unconformity. Chilca series........................	800–2,000
Liassic. Matilda series.....................................	1,400+
Triassic (?)	
Pre-Triassic. Gneiss, etc.	

[1] LAHEE, F. H., The Petroliferous Belt of Central-western Mendoza Province, Argentina, Am. Assoc. Pet. Geol. *Bull.*, vol. 11, pp. 261–278, 1927.

The Ammonite shale member, which overlies the Blanca sandstone conformably, is dark gray to black, carries lime concretions, and is highly fossiliferous and petroliferous. It contains cephalopods which, broken open, show[1] a residue of grahamite or rafaelite. The Diamante limestone, which rests on the Jurassic and also on the gneiss, carries shells of cephalopods two feet in diameter. At places the Diamante contains gypsum. Nearly all of the oil springs and rafaelite veins are in or above the Ammonite shale at the top of the Jurassic or on fault zones that probably involve the shale. It is probably the chief source of oil in the region.

The rocks are strongly folded, at places overturned and intruded by igneous rocks, but the Jurassic and younger beds are not greatly metamorphosed by pressure. The thin beds of coal in the Liassic show relatively low carbon ratios. According to Lahee, oil has probably accumulated along anticlines and in domes above intruded plugs and along beds tilted against strike faults and dikes. In the Cerro Alquitran district sands tilted up against an andesite plug yield a black viscous asphaltic oil of 14° Bé. gravity. Wells are drilled between 375 and 1,300 feet deep; seven yielded oil and two flowed for several years. In this field large seepages rise probably from both the Salas and Ramadas series.

The Neuquen oil district in central Neuquen, south of Mendoza, is in the eastern foothill belt of the Andes. Oil is produced at Plaza Huincul and Cerro Lotena fields. These fields are on strong folds with high dips. The oil is from fine clayey sands in the lower part of the Tithonian (Portlandian) division of the Upper Jurassic, which is near the horizon of the Ammonite shale of Mendoza.[2] The oil has a gravity of 34° Bé. and at Plaza Huincul comes from a depth of 1,800 feet. Between 1918 and 1927 the Plaza Huincul field produced 1,011,241 barrels of oil. About half of the amount was produced in 1927.

Comodoro Rivadavia[3] is located in the Territory of Chubut about 900 miles southwest of Buenos Aires. The oil field was discovered in 1907 by drilling for water. Production has increased steadily and in 1927 the field yielded 8,094,997 barrels of oil, the total production to the end of 1927 being 41,825,717 barrels. The deepest wells are about 3,000 feet deep. The oil is heavy, black, and viscous, the gravity being 16.4 to 24.5° A.P.I. Most of the wells yield from 50 to 100 barrels per day, but some of the wells have initial flows of 10,000 barrels. The oil is from

[1] LAHEE, F. H., Note on the Origin of Petroleum, Am. Assoc. Pet. Geol. *Bull*; vol. 8, pp. 669–671, 1924.

[2] HERMITTE, E., Annales del Ministerio de Agricultura de la Nacion, vol. 15, No. 3, pp. 99–108, Buenos Aires, 1924.

[3] WINDHAUSEN, ANSELMO, Cambios en el Concepto de las Condiciones Geologicas del Yacimiento Petrolifero de Comodoro Rivadavia (Communication Preliminar), *Bol.* Academia Nacional de Ciencas de Cordoba, vol. 27, Nos. 1 & 2, pp. 1–8, Cordoba, 1923; review by C. L. Baker, Am. Assoc. Pet. Geol. *Bull.*, vol. 9, p. 181, 1925.

three sands in the Upper Cretaceous system and comes from depth of
1,500 to 2,000 feet. Gas under pressure up to 200 atmospheres is
obtained at depths from 440 feet to 1,675 feet from both Tertiary and
Cretaceous beds. The gas is treated for the recovery of gasoline and
yields about 0.63 gallon per 1,000 cubic feet. The oil and gas are found
on domes, of which three are developed. One of these folds 3 miles north
of Comodoro Rivadavia has a maximum closure of nearly 150 feet.
These folds are very low in Tertiary rocks but are much sharper in the
Cretaceous beds. Outcropping beds show oil in the Rio Senguer and
Rio Chico districts to the west, and in the Deseado Valley to the southwest
of Comodoro Rivadavia.

SECTION AT COMODORO RIVADAVIA
(After Windhausen)

Formation	Thick-ness, meters	Description
Tertiary: Patagonian..........	....	Marine sandstone and shales, oyster beds, trace-able over large areas
Erosional unconformity Eocene...............	0–140	Shales and tuffs, continental origin
Angular unconformity Upper Cretaceous:	200	Clay shales, cross-bedded sandstone
Salamancian:........ (Danien)	120–130	Marine glauconite sandstone and shales, shale with oyster beds near base, contains oil-bearing glauconite sand
Senonian............	240 ±	Blue shales and sandstone; a sandstone 80 to 90 meters below the Salamancian is the second oil horizon. A third oil sand is found in certain wells

CHAPTER XIX

EUROPE EXCEPT RUSSIA

GREAT BRITAIN

Oil seepages, bitumen, and pitch are found at many places in England[1] and indications of oil of one kind or another occur in practically all formations from pre-Cambrian to Cretaceous (Fig. 352). The largest oil seepages are found in the coal measures of Carboniferous age, and at the Reddings Colliery the oil that seeped into the mine was utilized in the year about 1850. In 1870, or thereabouts, as much as 2 barrels a day was gathered in this colliery at a place where the oil flowed into the mine along a fault. An oil flow in a mine a few miles northeast of Sheffield is reported to have yielded considerable amounts of oil. During the World War, drilling was undertaken by the goverment, and as a result of this work a flowing well was drilled at Hardstoft, Derbyshire, in 1919. This well to January 1, 1928, yielded about 20,000 barrels of oil. Other wells found oil, but not in commercial quantities.

The wells in England are located in the Midlands, an important manufacturing region, occupying the heart of the country about 125 miles northwest of London. In this region the Pennine Chain, which has been called the backbone of England, extends northward to Scotland. It is an anticlinal ridge and along its axis the Mountain limestone crops out. This limestone is flanked on either side by the Yoredale formation which in turn is overlain by the Coal Measures. The carbon ratios of coals in this region range from 55 to 65 per cent. It is noteworthy that the fixed carbon ratio decreases[2] with depth.

[1] REDWOOD, B., "A Treatise on Petroleum," pp. 38–42, London, 1922.

THOMPSON, A. B., "Oil Field Exploration and Development," vol. 1, pp. 456–458, London, 1928.

FORBES-LESLIE, W., Occurrence of Petroleum in England, *Jour. Inst. Pet. Tech.*, vol. 3, pp. 152–190, 1916.

ICKES, E. L., Recent Exploration for Petroleum in the United Kingdom, Am. Inst. Min. Eng. *Trans.*, vol. 70 pp. 1053–1075, 1924.

WADE, A., The Oil Well and Later Developments at Hardstoft, Derbyshire, *Jour. Inst. Pet. Tech.*, vol. 14, pp. 357–387, 1928.

VEATCH, A. C., Petroleum Resources of Great Britain, Am. Inst. Min. Eng. *Trans.*, vol. 65, pp. 3–7, 1921.

BROMEHEAD, C. N., The Oil Horizons of England, *Geol. Mag.*, vol. 60, pp. 297–307, 1923.

[2] ICKES, E. L., *op. cit.*, p. 1071.

GENERALIZED SECTION OF ROCKS IN MIDLAND OIL-BEARING AREA, ENGLAND

Formation	Thickness, feet	Description
Productive Coal Measures	5,000 ±	Sandstone, clays, shales and coal
Millstone grit............	1,500 ±	Medium to coarse sandstone interbedded with shale, some coal
Yoredale...............	400 ±	Shale, black, fissile, impure limestone locally sandy beds; also called the Pendleside
Mountain limestone......	1,500 ±	Gray massive limestone locally dolomitic

FIG. 352.—Map of part of Europe, showing oil fields and certain prospects (dots).

FIG. 353.—Map of southern part of Europe and part of Africa, showing oil fields and prospects (dots).

The beds on the flanks of the Pennine fold dip away from its axis at angles of about 2 to 10 degrees or more. Normal faults with displacements of several hundred feet are common, and subsidiary faults are

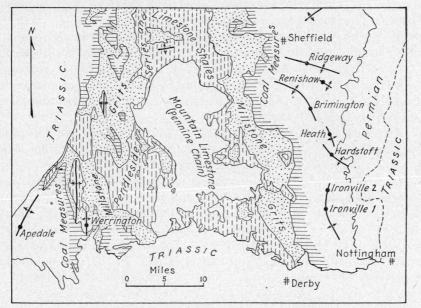

Fig. 354.—Map showing oil fields of Midlands, England. (*Data from British Geological Survey with additions from Forbes-Leslie, Ickes, Bromehead, and others.*)

developed in the flanks of the main anticline. These minor folds are drilled for oil (Fig. 354).

The Ironville No. 1 well, northeast of Derby, was drilled on a dome and found oil and salt water in the limestone at a depth of 2,031 feet.

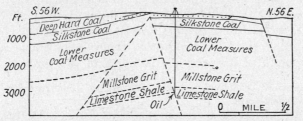

Fig. 355.—Section through Hardstoft well, Derbyshire, England. (*After Bromehead.*)

The Hardstoft well (Fig. 355), drilled on a dome, encountered oil at 3,150 feet in the Lower Carboniferous limestone. There was only a little gas with the oil, and it required 11 days for the 8-inch casing to fill and overflow. The oil has a gravity of 40° Bé., is high in lubricants, and resembles Pennsylvanian crude oil. The Heath well, north of Hardstoft well, developed gas near the base of the Coal Measures. This well found a little oil near the top of the limestone. The Brimington well further north found considerable gas near the top of the Millstone grits. The Ridgeway well, southeast of Sheffield, at a depth of 2,888 feet encountered hot sulphur water in the limestone. The temperature of the water when first met was 110° F., but in a day or two increased to 120° F. when the ascending water had heated the limestone. In general the waters of the wells are high in sodium chloride, and some of them are high in carbonates.

In Scotland, about 8 miles southeast of Edinburgh, the D'Arcy well, drilled on an anticline in Carboniferous limestone, encountered gas in a sand at a depth of 724 feet; at 1,810 feet some oil was found, and about 50 barrels was bailed out.

At Heathfield, Sussex (Fig. 352), in 1895 a well drilled for water encountered gas in the Portland sand of Upper Jurassic age. The small flow was used locally for lighting for several years.

In Scotland,[1] about 10 or 15 miles southeast of Edinburgh, oil shale of Lower Cretaceous age since 1857 has been mined and retorted to produce crude oil, gas, and ammonium sulphate. The shale mined formerly yielded as much as 130 gallons of oil per ton, but in 1925 the yield had declined to 21.4 gallons. The total production from 1872 to 1927 amounted to 86,114,740 barrels of oil. In 1927 the production was 1,183,309 barrels.

FRANCE

In France oil or asphalt is found at many places and in several systems of strata including the Jurassic (Lias), Lower Cretaceous (Urgonian), Upper Cretaceous, and Tertiary. Asphalt has been mined in several districts, but the only commercial oil fields are near Pechelbronn in Alsace and a small field recently developed near Gabian in Herault (Fig. 352). From 1880 to the close of 1927 Alsace produced 15,965,835 barrels. About 86,000 barrels were produced by the Gabian field from 1924 to the end of 1927. In 1928 France produced 520,000 barrels of oil.

The oil fields of Alsace[2] are in the Rhine Valley about 50 kilometers (30 miles) north of Strasbourg and north of the town of Haguenau.[3]

---

[1] BAILEY, E. M., Shale Oil Industry of Scotland, Jour. Inst. Pet. Tech., vol. 8, pp. 465–490, London, 1927.

REDFIELD, A. H., Federal Conservation Board Rept., p. 135, 1929.

[2] I wish to thank Dr. C. Hoffman and associates for many courtesies in connection with a visit to the Pechelbronn mines in 1922. (W. H. E.)

[3] GIGNOUX, M., and C. HOFFMAN, Le Bassin Pétrolifére de Péchelbronn, Serv. de la Carte d'Alsace et de Lorraine, pp. 1–46, Strasbourg, 1920.

DE CHAMBRIER, PAUL, Les Gisements de Pétrol d'Alsace, Bull. Soc. d'Encouragement pour l'Industrie Nationale, 15, Paris, January, February, 1920; also Jour. Inst. Pet. Geol., vol. 7, pp. 178–208, London, 1921.

VON WERVEKE, L., Vorkommen, Gewinnung und Entstehung des Erdöls im Unter-Elsass. Z. prakt. Geol., vol. 13, pp. 97–114, 1895; Die Entstehung der Unter-.

These fields were among the first in the world to be developed and were the first to be exploited by underground mining in a modern way. The fields have produced oil since 1742 and have been worked almost steadily for about 100 years.

The Rhine Valley is a great graben or down-faulted block about 20 kilometers wide, which lies between the Vosges Mountains on the west and the Black Forest on the east. In the valley Oligocene strata crop out flanked by the older strata in the mountains on either side. The oil fields are on the west side of the Valley. The Oligocene series in the Pechelbronn region is 1,550 meters thick. It consists of alternating marine and non-marine beds, chiefly marls, clays, and sands with some red marls and anhydrite. These beds are thrown into gentle folds, as is shown by Fig. 356, and are faulted. The field is limited on its west side by the Rhenish fault, lying parallel to the Rhine River, and is sliced by numerous parallel faults. The oil deposits lie at several horizons in the Oligocene rocks and are found in long narrow lenses that strike northeast. Some of these lenses are about 3,000 feet long, 600 feet wide, and 7 to 10 feet thick. The oil-bearing areas seem to have little if any relationship to the low folds that are found in the district (Fig. 356). The beds dip 3 to 8 degrees southeast and at places the oil deposits are limited to the northwest by faults which seal the oil sands up dip. The Pechel-bronn field produces three kinds of oil: a heavy thick asphalt oil (sp. gr 0.97) is found at depths of 50 to 60 meters; a heavy oil (sp. gr. 0.945) is found at depths of 70 to 100 meters; and a lighter oil (sp. gr. 0.880) is found at depths from 150 to 600 meters. The oil is believed to have originated in the series of beds in which it is now found.

In the earlier periods of the development of the field the oil sands were opened by shallow shafts, as is indicated by Fig. 357. Subsequently, the deeper sands were opened by drilling. After the production had declined, the field was again opened by deeper underground mines. This development was stimulated by the needs of Germany for petroleum during the war.

Conditions for underground mining are favorable in the district. The beds are soft and commonly may be mined without the use of explosives. The oil occurs in isolated sands; little water is present and the gas pressure is relatively low. The beds dip about 5 degrees east in the Clemenceau workings and the galleries are run either in the footwall

elsaessischen Erdoellager erlaeutert an der Schichtenfolge im Oligocaen. Philomat. Gesell. Elsass-Lothringen, Band 4, pp. 697–721, 1913; review by W. H. Bucher, *Econ. Geol.*, vol. 12, p. 203, 1917.

ANDREAE, A., Notiz ueber das Tertiär im Elsass, *Neues Jahrb.*, Band 2, pp. 287–294, 1882.

RICE, G. S., and J. A. DAVIS, Mining Petroleum in France and Germany, Am. Inst. Min. Eng. *Trans.*, vol. 74, pp. 857–893, 1926.

of the sand lens or more commonly in the oil sand itself.   At places holes
are drilled upward from the galleries to small lenses or pockets of oil-
bearing sands.   To avoid gas explosions fans are provided and air-tight
doors with devices for rapidly opening and closing them are built at
suitable places.   Although the gas pressure in the sands worked underground had been greatly diminished by drilling the sands before they
were opened by galleries, there is nevertheless appreciable gas remaining
with the oil, and special precautions are taken to avoid explosions.

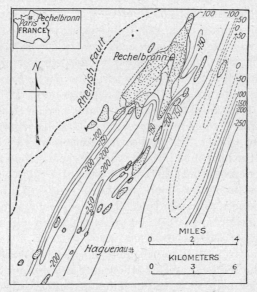

Fig. 356.—Map of Pechelbronn oil field, Alsace, France.   (*After Gigneaux and Hoffman.*)

About 40 per cent of the oil recovered from the field is obtained from
mines.[1]

In the Rhone Valley,[2] Department of Ain, asphalt is found in Urgonian
limestone and has been mined at several places near Seyssel.   This
formation carries asphalt at Val de Travers, Switzerland.   In eastern
France, near Grenoble, Isere, inflammable gas is found in Liassic marls
and limestones.   Near Bourg in Ain, a well in Triassic rocks 732 feet
deep yielded 3,531,000 cubic feet of gas per day.   Near Amberieu, 18
miles southeast of Bourg, a well drilled in 1921 struck gas in upper
Triassic beds.   This gas was used to light the town of Amberieu.

Near Servas and Anduze, in the Tertiary basin of Alais, Department
of Gard in southern France, asphalt is mined in Oligocene strata.   The

[1] DeLaunay, L., Gites mineraux et metalliferes, vol. 1, pp. 518–525, 609–614, 1913.
[2] Nicou, Le Calcaires asphaltiques du Gard, *Ann. mines*, ser. 10, vol. 10, pp. 513–568, 1906.
    Heim, A., *Petroleum Z.*, vol. 21, pp. 801–809, 1925.

rock mined is limestone with about 16 per cent bitumen. The asphalt carries 12 per cent sulphur. Asphalt is found also in fault fissures.

At Gabian,[1] Herault province, 30 miles west of Montpellier, a well was brought in 1924, flowing about 90 barrels of oil per day. The oil has

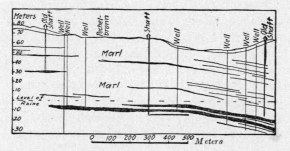

Fig. 357a.—Longitudinal section through the upper oil sands of Pechelbronn, Alsace The dark beds are petroliferous. (*After Andreae.*)

a gravity of 37.5° Bé. The rocks are faulted, dip south, and the oil is found in a porous dolomite of Keuper (Triassic) age which is encountered on the monocline about 350 feet deep. The gravity of the oil is about 37.5° Bé. The most productive of the Gabian wells yielded 38,410 barrels of oil to June 12, 1927.

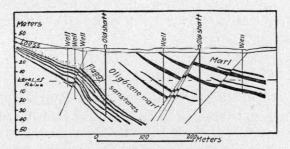

Fig. 357b.—Geologic cross-section through the Schwabweiler oil field, Alsace. The dark beds are petroliferous. (*After Andreae.*)

In southwestern France in the Departments of Basses Pyrenees and Landes, oil seepages and asphalt deposits are found at many places. The asphalt is found chiefly in Cretaceous rocks, although asphaltic sands of Miocene age have been mined at Bastennes, a village near Orthez, and at other places in this region.

[1] Martignan, P., Oil Developments in France, Production of Petroleum in 1924, "Petroleum Development Technology in 1924," Am. Inst. Min. Eng., pp. 208–214. 1925.

Powers, S., Am. Assoc. Pet. Geol. *Bull.*, vol. 9, pp. 346–348, 1925.

Duce, J. T., "Petroleum Development and Technology in 1927," Am. Inst. Min. Eng., p. 702, 1928.

In the Limagne,[1] Department of Puy de Dome (Auvergne) in the central plateau region, asphalt has been mined from small fissures in basalt and a well recently drilled found a little heavy black oil in Oligocene strata.   The Limagne is the upper part of the valley of the Allier.   This valley forms a lowland about 45 kilometers (28 miles) wide which structurally is a graben of downthrown Tertiary rocks which lies between crystalline rocks to the east and west.   The region has been intruded by volcanic rocks and other bodies of basalts in recent time.   A well near Crowell, southeast of Clermont Ferrand, sunk 836.3 meters (2,808 feet) all in Oligocene strata found small amounts of heavy oil at several horizons, but did not encounter commercial supplies and no sand more than 0.4 meters thick was encountered.   Other wells in the region near Clermont Ferrand encountered oil and gas in small amounts.

SWITZERLAND .

The Val de Travers[2] is in western Switzerland near the French boundary and northwest of Lake Neufchatel.   Asphalt has been mined in considerable amounts in a deposit near the Travers railway station. The asphaltic bed is of Urgonian and Aptien age of the Neocomian or Lower Cretaceous system.   The asphaltic bed is a limestone which dips at low angles and is worked underground.   Oligocene sandstone containing about 5 per cent of bitumen has been mined at Dardagny, 8 miles west of Geneva.

NETHERLANDS

At Corle,[3] 4 kilometers west of Winterswijk, Netherlands (Fig. 352), oil was discovered in 1924 in a well which penetrated 70 meters of Diluvium and Tertiary beds and entered the Buntsandstein; the Zechstein was met at a depth of 490 meters and the Carboniferous beds at 691 meters.   The Zechstein contains salt beds, potash beds, and some oil, the latter occurring in an anhydrite bed 27 meters thick at the base of the formation.   In the Carboniferous strata at a depth of 1,066 meters a sandstone carrying a green oil was encountered.   The rocks dip south and from Germany there probably extends into Holland a dome of older beds that lie beneath the younger formations that here form a plain. Information concerning the area was obtained by drilling in Germany near the border.

[1] WERENFELS, A., Exploration for Petroleum in the Limagne, France, Am. Inst. Min. Eng. *Trans.*, vol. 71, pp. 1351–1357, 1925.

[2] BREYNAERT, F., Le Gisement Asphaltique du Val de Travers, *Ann. mines*, ser. 11, vol. 2, pp. 316–347, 1912.

[3] WUNSTORF, W., *Petroleum Z.*, vol. 20, pp. 785–786, June 10, 1924.

GERMANY

In Germany[1] oil is found in three regions, namely, the North German, Rhenish, and Subalpine provinces. Of these the North German province is the most important. The Hanover fields of this province between 1874 and 1928 produced 12,815,308 barrels of oil and in 1927 produced 663,309 barrels, which was practically the entire German output.

The North German province is situated in a geosyncline which began to form in late Permian time. During the Mesozoic and Tertiary times more than 9,850 feet of strata were deposited in the basin. These sediments are chiefly marine or shallow sea deposits, but in late Tertiary time continental beds were formed. The section of this region is shown on page 624. The strata are folded and at many places salt anticlines and domes of salt rise to near the surface. The anticlines lie in two groups. One group strikes northwest parallel to the Hercynian alignment and the other strikes northeast parallel to the Rhenish alignment. Some of the domes are probably formed where these lines cross. The salt beds, which are associated with valuable potash deposits, are of Permian age. Some of the salt domes and anticlines are thrust upward through 10,000 feet of later strata. They have been extensively eroded and, above them, cap rocks of gypsum have accumulated by the hydration of anhydrite which is associated with the salt. The salt beds are highly folded and contorted. At places the domes are overlapped by Lower Cretaceous rocks. It is probable that some of the upthrust movements forming the domes took place as early as Jurassic time.

Brine springs, sink holes, the presence of halophytic plants[2] have led to prospecting for the salt domes. At certain places small bodies of Mesozoic rocks which have been thrust up with the salt crop out in the surrounding Pleistocene plain. The salt of the domes is of Upper Permian

[1] KAUENHAUEN, W., Oil Fields of Germany, Am. Assoc. Pet. Geol. *Bull.*, vol. 12, pp. 463–500, 1928.

BARTON, D. C., The American Salt Dome Problem in the Light of the Roumanian and German Salt Domes, Am. Assoc. Pet. Geol. *Bull.*, vol. 9, pp. 1226–1268, 1925.

KOCH, E., Beiträge zur Geologie des Untergrundes von Hamburg und Umgebung, Mitt. mineral. geolog. Staatsinstitut, Heft 9, 4 Karten, Hamburg, 1927.

KRAISZ, ALFRED, Geologische Untersuchungen über das Oelgebiet von Wietze in der Lüneburger Heide, Archiv. für Lagerstättenforschung, Heft 23, pp. 1–64, Preuss. Geol. Landesanstalt, Berlin, 1916.

STILLE, HANS, The Upthrust of the Salt Masses of Germany, Am. Assoc. Pet. Geol. *Bull.*, vol. 9, pp. 417–441, 1925.

STOLLER, J., Das Erdölgebiet Haenigsen-Obershagen-Nienhagen in der südlichen Lüneburger Heide, Archiv. für Lagerstättenforschung, Heft 36, Preuss. Geol. Landesanstalt, Berlin, 1927.

VAN WATERSCHOOT VAN DER GRACHT, W. A. I. M., The Structure of the Salt Domes of Northwest Europe as Revealed in Salt Mines, Am. Assoc. Pet. Geol. *Bull.*, vol. 9, No. 2, pp. 326–330, 1925.

[2] Plants that tolerate salty water.

age. This is shown by the fact that salt beds of the same character and showing the same stratigraphic order are found in middle Germany lying between Lower Permian and Lower Triassic beds. There are no limestone cappings above the salt plugs, and no oil is found in the gypsum cappings. The oil is found around the flanks of the domes, often where the oil-bearing rocks abut against faults, or at unconformities of petroliferous beds with the later strata.

The chief producing fields are Wietze, Nienhagen, Hänigsen, and Oberg. Formerly oil was produced at Oelheim, Hoheneggelsen, Sehnde, Hordorf, Klein-Schoeppenstedt, and Heide. Gas has been produced in large amounts at Neuengamme, near Hamburg, where no salt dome is found. Oil is known to be present in considerable amounts near the salt domes of Hope-Lindwedel, Sottorf near Hamburg, and at Gross-Vorlingen near Husum. The salt domes and oil fields of Hannover are shown in Fig. 358 after Stille.

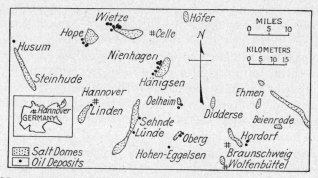

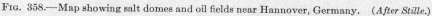

Fig. 358.—Map showing salt domes and oil fields near Hannover, Germany. (*After Stille.*)

The first oil well was drilled in 1859 in a tar pit at Wietze, but was not a commercial success. In 1881 several flowing wells were drilled near Oelheim, also near tar pits. In 1900 a new oil horizon yielding light oil was opened at Wietze at depths between 660 and 1,000 feet. In 1909 the production reached its maximum, which was 850,000 barrels. The oil came from Wietze, Hänigsen, and Oelheim. In 1922 a gusher yielding 1,500 to 2,250 barrels a day was completed in the northern part of the Hänigsen-Nienhagen field. Other large wells were brought in near by and this field soon surpassed Wietze. It now supplies the greater part of the German output.

The Wietze field, which produced 11,190,000 barrels of oil between 1874 and 1928, is at the northwest end of a salt dome. The salt is highly folded and the salt series is overturned to the north. The salt is capped by gypsum 82 to 164 feet thick. On the south side of the dome Jurassic and Lower Cretaceous beds dip away from the salt mass at low angles. On the north side of the mass they dip 70 degrees to the north and are

cut by a thrust fault that dips 20 to 35 degrees north (Fig. 359). Light
oil is found in the Upper Triassic (Upper Keuper) at depths of 1,155 feet
or less. It occurs in two sands, 63 and 8 feet thick, which are separated
by clay. The oil of the Upper Triassic strata is the deepest oil in the field
and is light, whereas the other oils are heavy. Oil is found also in the
Upper Dogger (Middle Jurassic), Lower Malm (Jurassic), and Upper

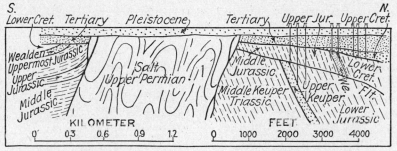

Fig. 359.—Geologic cross-section of the Wietze oil field. (*After Kraisz.*)

Malm (Jurassic). The fifth and most important horizon is the Wealden
(Lowest Cretaceous) where the oil is found in sand lenses at four horizons
which dip north about 45 degrees. This oil, when first discovered, was
associated with gas. After the gas pressure declined these horizons
were exploited through shafts and galleries run in the beds from the shafts.
A sixth horizon in the Upper Cretaceous is unimportant as are oil occur-

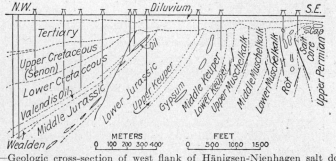

Fig. 360.—Geologic cross-section of west flank of Hänigsen-Nienhagen salt dome, Germany. (*After Stoller.*)

rences in the Tertiary and Pleistocene beds. The oil in the Triassic beds
has a gravity of 0.885 to 0.920. The oils in the younger rocks have
gravities between 0.935 and 0.950.

The Nienhagen-Hänigsen field southeast of Wietze is on the northwest side of a salt dome that strikes northeast. A section of the field
is shown by Fig. 360. The oil is found chiefly in Jurassic and Lower
Cretaceous strata. The main oil reservoir is in the Lower Cretaceous
which lies unconformably on the Middle Jurassic and is opened to depths

of 2,640 feet. The Upper Cretaceous (Senon) also carries oil. The Oelheim field southeast of Hänigsen produced oil from Jurassic and Lower Cretaceous strata. The Oberg field south of Oelheim is on the east flank of a salt dome. Light oil is found in the Jurassic (Lower Dogger) and heavy oil in the Lower Cretaceous (Wealden).

GENERALIZED STRATIGRAPHIC SECTION IN NORTHWEST GERMANY
(After Kauenhowen and others)

Series	Formation	Lithologic character	Facies	Average thickness	
				Feet	Meters
Pleistocene	Diluvium	Sands, gravels, boulder clay, loess, peat	Glacial, fluvioglacial, interglacial	330	100
Tertiary	Pliocene	Sands, gravels, clays, sandstones, lignites	Continental, piedmont, river and fresh-water deposits	1,300	400 max.
	Miocene	Clays, with mica, sands, lignites	Continental and marine	990	300 max.
	Oligocene	Clays with limestone nodules, greensands, sands, and marls with phosphatic concretions	Chiefly marine	800	250
	Eocene	Clays, volcanic ash, red sandstone	Marine and continental	160–330	50–100
	Paleocene	Limestones, conglomerates	Marine	230–660	70–220
Cretaceous	Senon	Light-colored limestones and chalk with flint nodules, conglomerates	Marine oil at Wietze, Nienhagen-Hänigsen	500–660	150–200
	Emscher	Chiefly gray marls	Marine	600–990	200–300
	Turon	Limestone and marls	Marine	990	300
	Cenoman	Marls and limestones	Marine	200	60
	Gault	Dark shales with siderite nodules	Marine	660–1,300	200–400
	Neokom (Wealden)	Blue and dark shales, sandstones, thin coal seams	Marine, brackish-water, estuarine, oil at Wietze, Nienhagen-Hänigsen, Oberg, etc.	660–1,300	200–400
Jurassic	Malm	Red shales, gypsum and rock salt beds, light limestones, and marls	Saline, brackish-water. Marine. Oil at Wietze, etc.	660–1,640	200–500
	Dogger	Dark shales, siderite nodules	Marine. Oil at Wietze, Oberg, Nienhagen	500–800	150–250
	Lias	Dark shales, marls, siderite nodules, oil shales, oolitic iron ores	Marine. Oil at Nienhagen-Hänigsen	600–980	170–300
Triassic	Keuper	Red and green clays and marls, gypsum, sandstones, coal sandstones	Saline and continental. Oil at Wietze	1,300 max.	400 max.
	Muschelkalk	Limestones and marls, anhydrite, and dolomite	Marine	600–980	170–300
	Buntsandstein	Red sandstones, sandy clays, colored clays and marls, gypsum and salt beds	Chiefly continental	2,300–3,300	700–1,000
Permian	Zechstein	Rock salt, potash salt, anhydrite, and other salt beds, salt clay, dolomite, limestone, bituminous shales	Marine	660–4,300	200–1,300
	Rotliegendes	Red sandstones and conglomerates, thin coal seams, porphyry	Continental	1,600–3,300	500–1,000

Natural gas was found near Neuengamme, 8 miles southeast of Hamburg, in 1910. During 10 years the well supplied about 200,000,000 cubic meters of gas which was used by the city of Hamburg for illumination. The gas, which is essentially methane, was encountered at a depth of about 247 meters on a dome-shaped uplift in sand in the Middle Oligocene clays.[1] The deposit is almost exhausted. Asphalt was once mined at Mount Schöppingen, 18 miles northwest of Münster and at Verwohle and near Hohdorf south of Hanover. At Heide, northwest of Hamburg, a chalk of Upper Cretaceous age carries oil.

On the west side of the Tegernsee in the Alpine foreland, in Bavaria, small amounts of oil have been recovered from sands and marls of either Eocene or Upper Cretaceous age. The oil was known as early as the fifteenth century and was sold for its medicinal properties. The strata containing the oil near Tegernsee are compressed to form isoclines that dip to the south at high angles.[2] Wells drilled in this region since 1819 have produced about 30,000 barrels of light oil.

The Pechelbronn field in Alsace (p. 618) derived its oil from Oligocene strata sunk in the Rhine graben. North of Pechelbronn in Germany, on the west side of the Rhine, small amounts of oil have been found at Buechelberg, Duerkheim, and Mettenheim north of Worms, and on the east side of the Rhine between Bruchsaal and Ubstadt south of Worms.

AUSTRIA

Since essentially the entire production of oil in Austria was derived from Galicia, the republic has produced practically no petroleum since 1919. The oil shales in northern Tirol are high in bituminous matter. At some places the content of bitumen amounts to more than 25 per cent. The average is about 5 to 7 per cent. During the war and the following years, some of the deposits were mined on a small scale.[3] In upper Austria, near Taufkirchen (Fig. 352), small deposits of oil are found. The Tertiary sediments rest on granite. The lowest Tertiary beds are conglomerates and sands of Miocene age. Above these are sandy marls and sands with marl conglomerates of upper Miocene age. Overlying the Miocene are Pliocene gravels and diluvium.[4] The Tertiary beds are

[1] HEILAND, C. A., Das Erdgasvorkommen von Neuengamme bei Hamburg, *Z. prakt. Geol.*, vol. 32, pp. 89–92, 1924.

[2] ENGLER, C., and H. HOEFER, *Das Erdoel*, vol. 2, p. 239, Leipzig, 1909.

[3] HRADIL, G., Ueber Oelschiefer und ihre Verbreitung in Tirol, *Petroleum Z.*, vol. 24, No. 3, pp. 87–100, 1928.

[4] PETRASCHEK, W., Die Gegend von Taufkirchen im oberoesterreichischen Innkreis und das dortige Erdoelvorkommen, *Petroleum. Z.*, vol. 21, pp. 1129–1134, 1925; also vol. 19, pp. 296–299, 1923.

FRIEDL, K., Die Erdoelfrage in Deutsch-Oesterreich, *Petroleum Z.*, vol. 20, pp. 1193–1199, 1256–1263, 1924; also vol. 23, pp. 189–241, 1927.

KALBE, O., Die tiefsten Bohrlöcher in Oesterreich, 1920–1926, *Petroleum Z.*, vol. 22, pp. 289–297, 1926.

folded and near Taufkirchen an anticline and syncline are found. A heavy asphaltic oil occurs in massive sands of the lower Miocene and shows some accumulation in the anticline. Artesian water with traces of oil is found in the syncline. This water is used for domestic purposes. Near Wels, 110 miles west of Vienna, on a structural dome in 1891 gas was encountered 330 feet deep in lower Miocene sands. The field produced about 2,400,000,000 cubic feet of gas in sands found at depths from 330 feet to 1,650 feet.

CZECHOSLOVAKIA AND HUNGARY

The Vienna basin[1] of Austria and Czechoslovakia is a structural basin about 200 kilometers long and 60 kilometers wide, which is filled with Tertiary sediments. The borders of the basin consist of crystalline schists, Paleozoic and Mesozoic sediments, and of the Flysch, the age of which is Upper Cretaceous, Eocene, and Oligocene. Miocene and Pliocene beds of considerable thickness are found in the basin and these are covered at many places by Quaternary gravels and loess. The chief oil fields are Gbely and Goeding (Hodonin) which to 1928 yielded 1,096,845 barrels of heavy oil.

Geologic Section at Gbely

Pontian:
    10 to 170 meters thick.
    Upper.   Fresh-water and lacustrine sediments.
    Lower.   Sands (Beienger sands).
Unconformity.
Sarmatian:
    Clays and marls, sands, glauconite; 140 to 160 meters thick at Gbely.

These rocks are thrown into folds and oil is found on a dome in the Sarmatian (Miocene) rocks at depths of 136 to 180 meters and at a second horizon at depths of 213 to 256 meters. Gas is developed at Kipcany, 4 miles south of Goeding.

In the eastern part of Czechoslovakia Upper Cretaceous and lower Tertiary rocks are exposed over large areas and oil seepages are known at many places but no commercial oil fields are developed. At Zboro a well sunk on a small anticlinorium in Eocene strata found small amounts of oil. The area showing indications of oil extends east to Körömezo.[2]

In northeast Hungary[3] a well drilled at Hajdu Szoboszlo, 13 miles southwest of Debraczen, in Tertiary rocks encountered gas.

---

[1] FRIEDL, K., Ueber die jüngsten Erdoelforschungen in Wiener Becken, *Petroleum Z.*, vol. 23, pp. 189–241, 1927.

[2] KETTNER, R., Zur Beurteilung der Erdoellagerstätten der tschecho-slowakischen Republik, *Petroleum Z.*, vol. 20, pp. 187–192, 1924.

[3] PAVAI, V., *Petroleum Z.*, vol. 23, pp. 1–8, 28–35, 1927.

YUGOSLAVIA

In Yugoslavia[1] wells drilled in Tertiary rocks near Ludbrieg encountered oil, and at Pitomacha, southeast of Ludbrieg, several oil sands were encountered in a well 2,667 feet deep. At Donya Tuzla gas and some oil were found in Miocene sands. At Vergorac, near the Adriatic Sea, considerable asphaltic limestone has been mined.

ALBANIA

In the southern part of Albania[2] Mesozoic and Tertiary rocks are thrown into strong folds that strike northwest. Oil seepages and asphalt deposits are found at several places and wells recently have found oil. At the village of Selenitsa, about 8 miles north of Avlona in southern Albania, deposits of bitumen, asphalt, and elaterite are found in Tertiary rocks probably of Pliocene age. The asphalt beds are found in conglomerates, in sandstones and in clay. According to Redfield, before the World War the mines yielded more than 7,000 metric tons annually. Certain Paris boulevards are paved with this asphalt.

Near Drashovista, 5 miles southeast of Avlona, in 1920 a well sunk on an anticline at a depth of 333 feet encountered a heavy black oil in Tertiary rocks; about 600 barrels were recovered. At Pahtos, about 8 miles north of Selenitsa and 15 miles northeast of Valona, in 1926 a well encountered heavy oil yielding 300 barrels a day. Near Lyushna, 18 miles north of Pahtos, oil films are found on a sulphur spring. A well is drilled at Ardenitsa, 7 miles north of Fieri and 12 miles northwest of Pahtos.

ITALY

The Apennine Range of Italy[3] is on an anticlinal chain flanked on either side by Tertiary strata in which the petroliferous deposits of Italy are found. The structure, even on the slopes away from the crest areas of the mountains, is very complicated and the oil occurs in highly tilted beds. Although oil has been exploited in a small way since before the

---

[1] WAAGEN, L., Die Erdoelhäufigkeit Jugoslawiens, *Petroleum Z.*, vol. 20, pp. 1313–1321, Berlin, 1924.

[2] NOWACK, E., Das Albanische Erdoelgebiet, *Petroleum Z.*, vol. 19, pp. 255–269, 1923.

REDFIELD, A. H., Petroleum in Albania, *Eng. Mining Jour.*, vol. 122, pp. 404–411, 1926.

GOUNOT, A., Mines de Bitume Exploitees en Albanie, *Ann. mines*, ser. 10, vol. 4, pp. 5–23, 1903.

[3] ZOPPETTI, V., Distretto di Milano, Revista del Servizio Minerario, pp. 205–230, 1880; pp. 191–235, 1891; pp. 171–198, 1892.

CAMERANA, E., L'industrie des hydrocarbons in Italie, Rome, 1907.

THIEL, GEORG, Das Asphaltkalkgebiet des Pescaratales am Nordabhange Majellas (Abruzzen), *Z. prakt. Geol.*, vol. 20, pp. 169–196, 1912.

ENGLER, C, and H. HOEFER, *Das Erdoel*, pp. 162–192, bibliography, 1909.

Christian Era, the total production of Italy is probably less than 2,000,000 barrels.   The production of 1927 is estimated to be 25,000 barrels.   The chief oil fields of Italy are Emelia, in the valley of the Po River, Chieti in Abruzzi, and Liri Valley on the west coast.

The Emilia region lies on the northeast slope of the Apennine Mountains between that range and the Po River.   Oil springs, salt springs, gas seeps, and small oil or gas fields are closely spaced in a belt 125 miles long and about 10 miles wide (Fig 361).   The oil is found in Eocene, Miocene, and Pliocene beds, which in general are tilted at high angles on folds that strike northwest.   The petroliferous strata are sandstones and thin limestone beds.   The oil is light and of high grade; in certain districts gas is developed and utilized in neighboring cities.

Fig. 361.—Map showing oil wells and gas emanations in Emilia district, Italy.   (*After Camerana.*)

In the Retorbido Rivanazzano district, 4 miles south of Voghera in the northwest part of the Emilia oil region, numerous shallow wells have yielded salt·water, gas, and small amounts of oil; at depths of 200 meters heavy oil is found in limestone.

At Montechino, 18 miles south of Piacenza, gas issuing from calcareous rocks associated with blue clays of Tertiary age led to the sinking of wells. The Tertiary beds are thrown into folds that strike southeast.   Wells from 300 to 1,400 meters deep have found oil at many horizons, but most of the oil is obtained from depths of 500 to 1,400 meters, probably in Eocene strata.   Certain wells yield initially about 300 barrels of oil a day but decline rapidly.   The oil is light and of high quality.

Velleia lies east of Montechino and is essentially part of the same oil field.   Salsomaggiore is a watering resort 15 miles east of Montechino. Warm salt water, which is used for baths, is found with gas and a little oil in the same strata at a depth of 760 meters. A few hundred barrels of oil are recovered annually. At Medesano Miano, southeast of Salsomaggiore, light straw-colored oil is found in Miocene and probably in Eocene beds. Ozzano, southeast of the Medesano Miano field produces oil with considerable gas. The gravity of the oil is 0.807. At Neviano de Rossi, south of Ozzano, light oil is found in Tertiary blue clays and sandstones. Some of the oil is said to come from Pliocene strata.

In the Chieti district, Abruzzi, the Tertiary strata are highly faulted. Asphaltic rocks are mined at many places in Eocene and Miocene beds. The mines are developed at Montepello, Letto Montepello, Abbategio, Roccamorice, and San Valentino and produce chiefly asphaltic limestone. Wells drilled for oil near San Valentino and Tocco have produced small amounts of light oil.

The Liri Valley district on the southwest side of the range contains asphalt deposits of similar character. Considerable deposits are developed on the east side of the district in Collo S. Magno and in Miocene limestone and sandstone at S. Giovanni Incarico. Near the latter place wells yielding 15 barrels of oil per day were drilled in 1915.

In Sicily[1] oil seepages are found in Tertiary and Quaternary rocks at many places. At Ragusa a limestone of Miocene age containing at places 10 per cent of asphalt has been mined in large amounts.

SPAIN

In northern Spain[2] on the flanks of the Cantabrian Mountains, which form the west extension of the Pyrenees, oil and asphalt are found at many places, although no commercial deposits of oil are developed. In Araya and at Penacerrada, 30 miles southwest of Araya, asphaltic limestone of Eocene age is mined. At Huidobro, 30 miles north of Burgos, oil rises from Lower Cretaceous strata, and a well was drilled on an anticline that strikes east and ends in a dome. At Robredo, north of Huidobro, a well drilled 2,569 feet obtained a little oil.

In the Aragon basin, near Manresa some 30 miles northwest of Barcelona, Eocene marl is impregnated with asphalt and similar deposits occur some 34 miles east of Manresa. At Margalef, 35 miles west-northwest of Tarragona, black oil flows from the walls of a cave.

Asphaltic limestone is found in Eocene beds at Manilva, 18 miles north of Gibraltar. At Grazalema, 46 miles north of Gibraltar, bituminous limestone of Lower Jurassic age has been mined. At Villamartin, 50 miles north-northwest of Gibraltar, a well drilled in 1907 obtained a little light oil. Near Conil, 45 miles west of Gibraltar, shallow wells have yielded a little light oil. At Lebrija, 65 miles northwest of Gibraltar, and at other places in Andalusia burning gas issues from salt springs.

[1] REDFIELD, A. H.. Federal Oil Conservation Board *Rept.* 3, Appendix C, p. 112, Washington, 1929.

[2] *Op. cit.*, p. 131.

PORTUGAL

At Cavilde, near Monte Real, near the west coast and about 95 miles south of Oporto, bituminous sandstone of Lower Jurassic age was formerly mined. At Torres Vedras, 55 miles south of Monte Real, asphalt has been distilled from Jurassic bituminous shale.

GREECE

In northwestern Greece[1] oil seepages occur in Miocene beds. At Dragopsa, 20 miles west-northwest of Yanina, a little oil and gas were found in hand dug wells sunk in Miocene strata. On the island of Paxos, off the coast of Epirus, Eocene limestone is impregnated with bitumen. At the south end of the island of Zante, also off the west coast of Greece, pitch springs are found in Pliocene beds, which are much broken. The ancient Greeks utilized the pitch for calking boats. Natural gas is found near Trikkala in Thessaly. This gas contains no gasoline vapor, is high in nitrogen, relatively low in methane, and, according to Georgalas, has probably formed by distillation of lignites.

TURKEY IN EUROPE

Near Ganos[2] on the west side of the Gulf of Marmora, oil is found in Tertiary strata, probably of Miocene age. The field extends southwest along the coast to near Sharkeui. Wells drilled in steeply folded Pliocene beds to depths of about 300 feet found small amounts of light oil in the Tertiary strata.

POLAND

The Carpathian Mountains[3] constitute a great S-shaped uplift, anticlinal in structure, formed late Tertiary time. This axis, according to

[1] REDWOOD, B., "A Treatise on Petroleum," vol. 1, p. 36, London, 1922.

GEORGALAS, G. C., Natural Gas in Thessaly, *Econ. Geol.*, vol. 19, pp. 92–95, 1924.

[2] ENGLISH, T., Coal and Petroleum Deposits in European Turkey, *Quart. Jour.* Geol. Soc., vol. 58, pp. 150–162, 1902.

[3] ZUBER, R., Die geologischen Verhältnisse der Erdoelzone Opaka-Schodnica-Urycz in Ost-Galizien, *Z. prakt. Geol.*, vol. 7, pp. 41–48, 1904; also vol. 12, pp. 86–94, 1904.

GRZYBOWSKI, J., Boryslaw, Une Monograph geologique. Internat. Acad. Sci. *Bull.*, pp. 87–127, Cracovie, 1907.

PAUL, C. M., and E. TIETZE, Neue Studien in der Sandsteinzone der Karpathen, Jahrb. k.k. Geo. Reich. Anst., vol. 29, pp. 189–304, 1879.

ENGLER, C., and H. HOEFER, *Das Erdoel*, vol. 2, pp. 268–298, 1909.

BOHDANOWICZ, K., "Tereny i zloza naftowe," pp. 136–179, 1923. In Polish.

DALTON, L. V., Sketch of the Geology of the Baku and European Oil Fields, *Econ. Geol.*, vol. 4, pp. 89–117, 1909.

REDFIELD, A. H., Federal Oil Conservation Board *Rept.* 3, Appendix C, Washington, 1929. (Includes bibliography of oil fields of Europe.)

HAYNES, W. P., Geological Work in the Carpathians, Am. Assoc. Pet. Geol. *Bull.*, vol. 6, pp. 523–532, 1922.

Suess (Fig. 362), probably extends across the Black Sea to the region of Taman and Kerch and in Russia becomes the Caucasus Range, at the end of which lies the Baku field. The principal oil fields of Galicia, Roumania, and Russia are on minor folds that are connected generically with the Carpathian and Caucasus ranges and were probably formed at about the same time.

A sketch map of the Carpathians, after Haynes, is shown in Fig. 363. A typical section showing the geology of the western part of the northern Carpathians is shown as Fig. 364, a block diagram of the region southwest of Nadworna in the central Carpathians is shown as Fig. 365, and a section west of Bacau (Fig. 366) shows the structure in the eastern part of the central Carpathians. The positions of the sections are indicated on Fig. 363. As shown by these and other sections, the faults and the

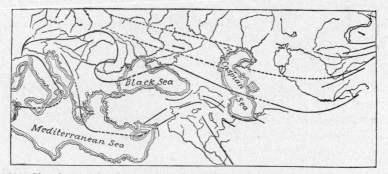

Fig. 362.—Sketch map showing structural axes in parts of Europe and Asia. (*Based on map by Suess.*)

axes of the folds dip in general toward the mountains, although a few of the folds, both in Galicia and in Roumania, dip away from the mountains. The faults and folds are overthrust. Nearly all of the oil in the Carpathian region is found on the outer side of the mountain folds.

There are said to be over 400 oil fields in Galicia, including certain undeveloped occurrences. Of these about 70 are in Cretaceous strata, 130 are in Eocene strata, 200 are in the Oligocene, and a few are in the Miocene strata.[1] The Boryslaw-Tustanowice group of oil pools is by far the most important; in these the oil is derived mainly from Eocene beds.

To the end of 1927 Poland produced 207,779,000 barrels of oil. Valuable deposits of ozokerite or mineral wax are associated with the oils, many of the deposits filling faults and fissures above the oil-bearing anticlines. Important centers of production include Boryslaw, Dwiniacz,

[1] MILLER, A., Galicia and Its Petroleum Industry, *Jour. Inst. Pet. Tech.*, vol. 8, pp. 312–347, London, 1922. (Includes a map showing age of strata in which the oil is found in the chief oil fields.)

GENERALIZED SECTION OF OIL REGION OF GALICIA

Miocene:
> Sandstones and limestone grading downward into saliferous and gypsiferous clays; oil bearing.

Oligocene:
> Sandstones, shales, hieroglyphic sandstones; includes Dobrotow beds with sandstones, shales, plant remains, etc.; oil bearing.
> Menilite shales. Dark bituminous shales with fish remains and Foraminifera.

Eocene:
> Hieroglyphic sandstone, green and red shales; oil bearing.
> Red clays, Nummulitic beds; oil bearing.

Cretaceous:
> Jamna sandstone; oil bearing
> Inoceramus (Ropianka) beds, shales, and sandstones (oil bearing) pass downward into bluish calcareous hieroglyphic sandstone; oil bearing.

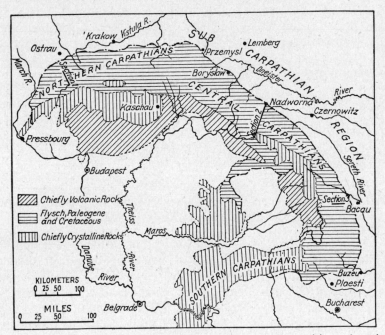

FIG. 363.—Geologic sketch of the Carpathian region, showing positions of sections on opposite page. (*After Haynes.*)

and Starunia.   To 1928 Galicia produced 233,616 metric tons of ozokerite,[1] about 741 tons being produced in 1927.

In western Galicia oil fields are numerous, although few of them have had large production.   The western fields produced 564,200 barrels of oil in 1927.   At Kleczany, at the west end of the western Galicia oil field (Fig. 367), an oil, rich in vaseline, is found in thin sandstone interbedded with marly clay of Upper Eocene age.   At Sekowa, southeast of

[1] REDFIELD, A. H., *op. cit.*, p. 116.

Gorlice, oil and gas are found in the Inoceramus beds of the Cretaceous system. At Siary, southwest of Sekowa, oil and gas are found in the Eocene and in Cretaceous beds. East of Gorlice, from north to south, are the Lipiuki, Kryg, and Mecina fields, which have produced oil chiefly from Eocene beds and, subordinately, from the Oligocene and Upper

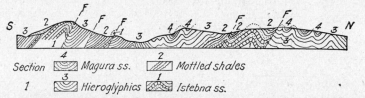

Section 4 ⬚ *Magura ss.*   2 ⬚ *Mottled shales*
1 ⬚ *Hieroglyphics*   3 ⬚ *Istebna ss.*

Fig. 364.—Geologic section near Ostrau and Zilina, section 1, Fig. 363. (*After Zuber.*)

Cretaceous beds. At Harklowa, 8 kilometers southwest of Jaslo, an anticline dips steeply northeast and more gently southwest. The Menilite beds of the Oligocene crop out. These consist of shales and

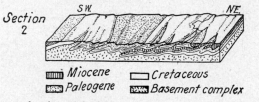

⬚ *Miocene*   ☐ *Cretaceous*
⬚ *Paleogene*   ⬛ *Basement complex*

Fig. 365.—Stereogram showing geologic structure near Nadworna, section 2, Fig. 363. (*After Zuber.*)

interbedded sandstone. Shallow wells sunk to the sand lenses produce oil. Wells about 600 meters deep pass through the Menilite shales to the Eocene oil sands, which are also productive. On the southwest side

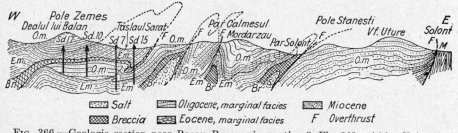

⬚ *Salt*   ⬚ *Oligocene, marginal facies*   ⬚ *Miocene*
⬚ *Breccia*   ⬚ *Eocene, marginal facies*   F *Overthrust*

Fig. 366.—Geologic section near Bacau Roumania, section 3, Fig. 363. (*After Voitesti.*)

of the field the Eocene beds are exposed, where they are faulted over the Menilite shales.

The Bobrka oil field, about 30 kilometers southeast of Jaslo, joins the Wietrzno field to the southeast and still further to the southeast are Rowne and Rogi. The four fields lie on a single anticline and form an oil field about 5 kilometers long. Bobrka was one of the first fields to be opened in Galicia, and in 1861 a well only 14 meters deep is said to have yielded 6 tons of oil an hour. In 1870 the monthly production was 800 tons. Modern drilling practice was introduced[1] in 1885. At Bobrka

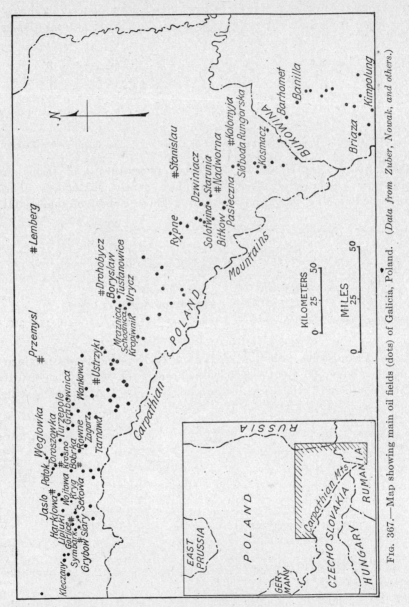

Fig. 367.—Map showing main oil fields (dots) of Galicia, Poland. (Data from Zuber, Nowak, and others.)

the anticline is very closely compressed. The oil is found in a porous Eocene sandstone which lies below red shale and the Menilitic shale.

[1] MITZAKIS, M.,"Oil Encyclopedia," p. 202, London, 1922.

The oil is associated with salt water containing iodine. At Rogi the fold is broader. Menilite shale crops out and wells are sunk to the Eocene oil sands.

The Potok oil field about 10 kilometers northwest of Krosno is one of the most productive oil fields in western Galicia. It lies on an anticline the axis of which trends west-northwest and plunges rather steeply west-northwest. Three groups of oil sands lie in gray, green, and red shales. The productive sands are of Eocene age. Gas is found at the top of the oil sand and had an initial pressure of about 28 atmospheres. The oil of Potok has a gravity of 35 to 45° Bé. Toroszowka field is southeast of Potok on the same anticline where the beds rise along the crest. The output of the field is small.

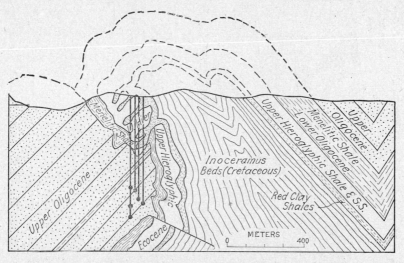

FIG. 368.—Cross-section of Wankowa oil field, Galicia. (*After Nowak.*)

In the Tarnawa-Wielopole field, 35 kilometers southeast of Rowne, sandstone of undetermined age, but probably Upper Eocene or Oligocene, crops out along a steep anticlinal axis, which strikes northwest and has smaller anticlines on each side of it. A heavy dark oil is found on faults at depths of about 650 meters in faults. In the Wankowa field, east of Zagorz (Fig. 368), oil is found in Oligocene strata on the southwest side of an overturned anticline.

The chief oil-bearing region of Galicia is the Boryslaw-Tustanowice group of oil fields which lie southwest of Drohobycz, which is about 75 kilometers southwest of Lemberg. This district has produced more than 75 per cent of the total production of Galicia and in 1927 yielded 4,316,000 barrels of the total of 5,195,000 barrels of oil produced by Poland. The field is an area of Cretaceous and Tertiary beds that strike northwest and are folded and faulted by strong overthrust faults. The faults and

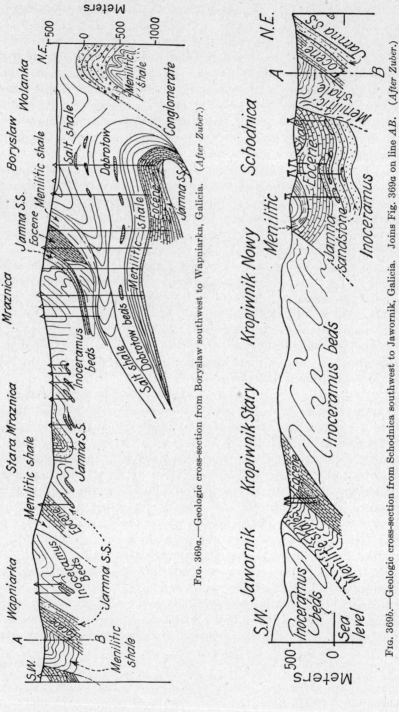

Fig. 369a.—Geologic cross-section from Boryslaw southwest to Wapniarka, Galicia.   (After Zuber.)

Fig. 369b.—Geologic cross-section from Schodnica southwest to Jawornik, Galicia.   Joins Fig. 369a on line AB.   (After Zuber.)

folds strike northwest. A cross-section[1] of the field from northeast to southwest is shown by Fig. 369.

The Boryslaw oil field which is about 5 kilometers southwest of Drohobycz is shown at the northeast end of the section. Closely spaced to the southeast are found the Tustanowicc and Truskawice fields. These three fields lie in an area that is by far the most productive in Galicia. The Boryslaw field was opened before 1850, when in an area of oil springs oil pits were dug by hand. It was drilled in 1896, when productive wells were secured. These wells found oil at depths of about 500 meters. Subsequently, wells were sunk about 1,500 meters or deeper and prolific oil zones were encountered. The productive zones are indicated on the section (Fig. 369) and include Saliferous shale (Miocene); the Dobrotaw formation, consisting of shale, sandstone, and conglomerate; the Boryslaw sandstone, which lies between the Eocene strata and the Menilitic shale; and from sandstone lenses and layers which lie in the Eocene strata and in the Jamna formation. The oil from this field is exceptionally high-grade light-gravity oil. The gas contains gasoline vapor and is utilized to produce natural gas gasoline. This and neighboring fields also produce ozokerite, which occurs in faults and fissures and is mined in shafts in several of the fields. A section of the field showing the faults which are largely filled with ozokerite is shown as Fig. 7.

In the Mraznica district, southwest of Boryslaw, oil is found in an infolded body of the salt shale formation (Meotic), which lies just below the Menilitic beds of the lower Oligocene, its position being due to a great overthrust fault. In the southwest part of the Mraznica field the oil is obtained from sand lenses in the Inoceramus beds of the Cretaceous system. Lenses of the same formation yield oil in the Wapniarka field.

The Schodnica field, which is shown on the section southwest of Wapniarka, produces oil from the Jamna sandstone of the Upper Cretaceous system and from the Eocene beds. It is part of a long belt of oil fields that strikes northwest and is followed to the northwest and southeast. A plan and sections of this area are shown by Figs. 370 and 371, after Zuber. The Opaka field to the northwest and the Urycz field to the southeast produce from Eocene beds; Kropiwnik field near the southwest end of the section produces from lenses of the Eocene.

The Bitkow district in eastern Galicia is 18 kilometers southwest of Nadworna and 55 kilometers west of Kolomyja. As shown by Nowak, the rocks strike northwest and are complicated by folding and overthrust faulting. The oil is found at four horizons at depths of about 450 to 900 meters and is obtained from Oligocene, Eocene, and Cretaceous strata.

---

[1] A section after Zuber has appeared in nearly all general texts and oil manuals. It has recently been revised and is included in Prof. Bohdanowicz text (in Polish) published in 1922. The section with transliterations and a few other changes is presented here. (W. H. E.)

At about 600 meters a particularly light oil is obtained.   Its density lies between 37 and 65° Bé.

At Pasieczna, about 8 kilometers east of Bitkow, an anticline strikes northwest, the beds dip northeast 35 degrees and southwest about 20 degrees.   Oil is found in an upper horizon in sandstones that lie below red shales and in a lower sandstone.   At Starunia, 6 kilometers north-

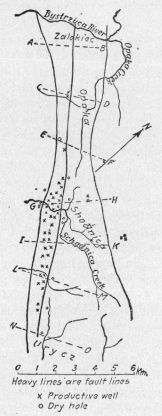

Fig. 370.—Plan of Opaka-Schodnica-Urycz oil fields Galicia.   The sections, *AB*, etc., are shown on Fig. 371.   (*After Zuber.*)

west of Nadworna, shallow workings formerly supplied considerable ozokerite.   Shafts sunk through diluvial beds encountered about 45 meters of light-colored clay shale below which is 8 meters of red clay shale.   Below the red clay unconformably lies a thick series of Salt Clay formation in which the ozokerite is found in elongated lenses and nests.   The Sloboda-Rungorska conglomerate is faulted against the Salt Clay and in it are found nests of high-grade ozokerite.   Oil is found in the western part of the field.

At Dzwiniacz, 20 kilometers north of Bitkow and 8 kilometers north-west of Starunia on the strike of the beds, ozokerite is found in lenses,

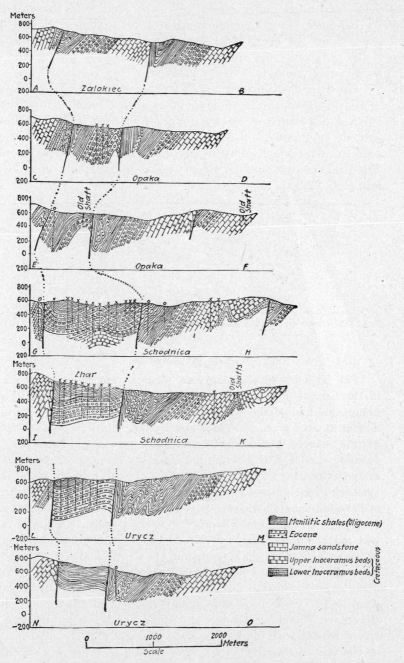

Fig. 371.—Sections of Schodnica oil field, Galicia, on lines shown on Fig. 370.

veins, and nests under conditions nearly similar to those at Starunia. At Kosmacz, 35 kilometers southwest of Kolomea, Eocene beds are exposed on the crest of an anticline that plunges northwest. Green shales of Eocene age are encountered in depth. The district has produced small amounts of heavy black oil.

The Sloboda-Rungorska[1] field, located about 16 kilometers southwest of Kolomyja, was at one time the most productive oil field in east Galicia. Oil was discovered in sinking wells for brine in 1771. Drilling began actively in this field in 1881 and in 1883 production had reached 550 barrels a day, which subsequently was increased to 1,600 barrels a day. The field, as described by Szajnocha, is located on a great overturned fold (Fig. 372).

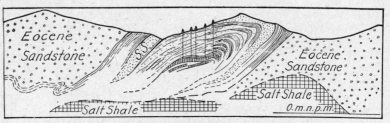

Fig. 372.—Geologic cross-section through Sloboda-Rungorska oil field. (*After Swider-skiego.*)

ROUMANIA

The oil fields of Roumania are situated on the outer or convex side of the Carpathian Mountains in the region of the foothill folds of the mountains and of the plains that slope southeast to the Danube River. The crest area of the Carpathians is made up of crystalline schists and granite which include metamorphosed strata of Paleozoic, Triassic, Jurassic, and Lower Cretaceous age. In the regions containing these systems there is evidence of two periods of great folding; one of Hercynian age took place in mid-Carboniferous time and is marked by a transgression of Permian conglomerates over pre-Permian strata, and a later one which took place at the close of Lower Cretaceous time. This later movement was marked by strong overthrusts which resulted in marking out the present Carpathian chain. Around the elevated area in a period between the end of the Lower Cretaceous and the end of the Oligocene in the lower areas surrounding the Carpathians, the strata of the Flysch series were deposited. These beds were strongly folded in Oligocene time and on the folded Flysch strata were deposited the Miocene and later series of strata which, with older beds, were strongly folded in the Miocene and at the end of Pliocene time. The folding of Pliocene and older strata was attended by great overthrust faulting.

[1] Szajnocha, L. W., Das Petroleumvorkommen von Sloboda-Rungorska in Ost Galizien, Verh. k. k. Geol. Reichanst., vol. 31, pp. 162–165, 1881.

As shown by Voitesti,[1] there are three great anticlinal axes in the later Tertiary strata of the Subcarpathian region. These are marked by great masses of salt that are squeezed upward along their crests. Between the chains of salt domes or salt anticlines there are synclinal basins of Miocene and Pliocene strata. In these strata the great oil deposits of Roumania are found, and, in general, the oil is accumulated near the salt masses in beds that dip away from the salt bodies or, to a less extent,

GENERALIZED GEOLOGIC SECTION OF THE SOUTHERN ROUMANIAN OIL FIELDS
(After Krejci)

Quaternary:
Gravels and sands (fluviatile).
Tertiary:
Pliocene:
Levantine. Gravels, sands, marls, fossiliferous, lignite seams at the base.
Dacian. Green and yellow marls, sands, sandstones and yellow and red sand lenses; oil bearing.
Pontian. Marls, sands, gravels, tuffs, lignite; oil bearing.
Meotic. Fresh-water stage; marls, clays, sands with big concretions, calcareous oolitic sandstone, thin coal layers; oil bearing.
Brackish water stage; marls, calcareous sandstone; oil bearing.
Miocene:
Sarmatian. Limestone, calcareous sandstone, sands, marls; oil bearing.
Tortonian. Limestone, marls, conglomerates.
Helvetian. Marls, micaceous sandstone, tuffs, gypsum, salt.
Burdigalian. Clays, conglomerates, tuffs, salt, gypsum.
Oligocene:
Massive sandstone, clays, limestone, and marls; gypsum salt; oil bearing.
Eocene:
Sandstone, limestone, marls.

[1] MRAZEC, L. and I. P. VOITESTI, Contributions à la connaissance des nappes du Flysch Carpathique en Rumanie, Annuarul Instit. Geol. al Romäniei, vol. 5, 1911, Bucarest, 1914.

MURGOCI, G. M., Tertiary Formations of Oltenia with Regard to Salt, Petroleum and Springs, *Jour. Geol.*, vol. 13, pp. 670–712, 1905.

VOITESTI, I. P., The Mode of Appearance of the Petroleum Deposits in the Carpathian Region with General Considerations of the Genesis of the Petroleum and the Salt of the Actual Deposits, *Jour. Inst. Pet. Tech.*, vol. 9, No. 38, pp. 291–311, London, 1923.

———, Geology of the Salt Domes in the Carpathian Region of Roumania, Am. Assoc. Pet. Geol. *Bull.*, vol. 9, pp. 1165–1206, 1925.

KREJCI, K., Der Bau der Rumänischen Oelgebiete, *Petroleum Z.*, vol. 21, pp. 1317–1323, 1925.

KRAUS, M., Das Oelfeld Campina (Bucea, Gahita) "Steaua Romana," *Petroleum Z.*, vol. 24, No. 1, pp. 1–21, 1928.

PUSTOWKA, A., Beiträge zur Kenntnis der Tektonik Rumäniens, *Neues Jahrb. Mineral.*, vol. 61, pp. 317–398, 1929.

CARDOS, I., and I. BASGAN, Das Oelgebiet von Moreni-Gura Ocnitzei, *Petroleum, Z.*, vol. 23, No. 4, pp. 139–146, 1927.

REDFIELD, A. H., Federal Oil Conservation Board *Rept.* 3, Appendix C, Bibliography, pp. 206–207, 1929.

in anticlines and domes, many of which have cores of salt below the
Miocene beds.

About 20 miles northwest of Ploesti (Figs. 373, 374) a great anticline
strikes east and brings to the surface the salt formation, and oil fields

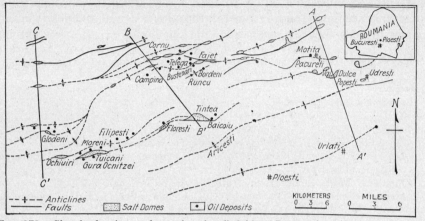

FIG. 373.—Sketch showing geology of main oil fields of Roumania. (*Data from Voitesti
and others.*)

are developed in folds and along the sides of the salt masses. These
fields include Campina, Telega, Bustenari, and Fajet. Along a lower
fold to the south of Bustinari are the Runcu and Bordeni fields. About

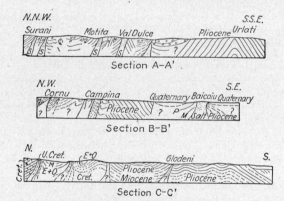

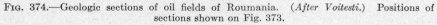

FIG. 374.—Geologic sections of oil fields of Roumania. (*After Voitesti.*) Positions of
sections shown on Fig. 373.

13 miles northwest of Ploesti three anticlines closely spaced strike northeast. These anticlines are broken at many places along their axes,
forming faults. On this group of anticlines are developed the oil fields
Ochiuiri, Moreni, Filipesti, Floresti, Baicoiu, and Tintea (Tsintea).
Southeast of this group is the Aricesti anticline which produces gas in
considerable amounts.

The Campina district, on the Prahova River, was the first large field to be developed and for many years was the leading oil field of Roumania. It contained many large flowing wells which produced oil chiefly from the Meotic, and Dacian series of strata. The structure of the field is shown in Fig. 375. The Telega field is a small field in gently folded beds that lies between Campina and Fajet-Bustenari. Fajet-Bustenari field is about 6 miles east of Campina. The oil is obtained from Oligocene and from Meotic (Pliocene) beds which are separated by a fault (Fig. 376).

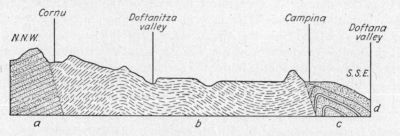

FIG. 375.—Section along Prahova River, Cornu and Doftanitza Valley. *a*, Flysch; *b*, Helvetian (Miocene salt series); *c*, Sarmatian; *d*, Pontian. (*After Stefanescu.*)

The Meotic beds are gently arched above a salt mass and in part of the field the beds are eroded from above the salt mass. The field produced high-grade light oil and for many years it maintained the highest production of any oil field in Roumania.

South of the Bustenari anticline the rocks dip gently to the south. At Runcu they rise to form a low anticline which strikes northeast to Bordeni. Important oil fields are developed at Runcu, Chiciura, and Bordeni. The Pacureti field is east of Bustenari and 16 miles northeast

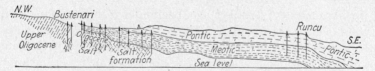

FIG. 376.—Cross-section from Bustenari to Runcu. (*After Mrazec.*)

of Ploesti. An anticline strikes east and plunges to the west. On the east side of the field Meotic petroliferous beds crop out and farther west the Pontic beds occupy the crest of the fold. The field yields a very light-gravity oil.

The Moreni field (Fig. 40), which is situated about 30 kilometers west and slightly north of Ploesti, has been the most productive oil field in Roumania. An elongated salt inlier strikes east and marks the crest of an anticline that is traced 35 kilometers from Ochiuiri to Tintea. The salt mass breaks through Pliocene beds and drilling has revealed against its sides and the whole Pliocene series, including from the surface down, the Levantine, Dacian, Pontian, and Meotic groups of strata.   The salt mass mushrooms at the top and at places leans over so that wells are drilled through the salt into younger beds.   On the north side of the salt mass, as shown in section Fig. 40, oil is found in the Meotic or the Lower Pliocene series and on the south side in the Dacian group of the Pliocene.   To the south of the salt mass is developed the Tuicani field which produces large amounts of asphaltic oil from the Dacian series. On the north side of the salt mass Stavropoleos field produces paraffin oil from the Meotic.   Gura Ocnitzei field lies on the west end of the salt mass.   On the north side of the mass on the extension of the Stavropoleos field oil is produced from the Meotic series, and on the south side of the salt mass oil is produced from the Dacian.   In the Ochiuiri field 2 miles west of Gura Ocnitzei oil is found in the Dacian and Meotic beds on the south side of a salt inlier in wells that are in general from 900 to 1,600 feet deep.   A well recently drilled about 3,000 feet deep found oil.

The Filipesti field is 5 kilometers northeast of the Moreni field.   The Dacian beds are brought to the surface on a relatively gentle fold, and wells sunk to the Meotic beds find oil rich in paraffin.

The anticline that strikes east from Moreni passes through Floresti, Baicoiu and Tintea fields, all of them located along salt masses.   At Baicoiu the mass has a mushrooming top and the Pliocene beds are thrust up along its sides so that they are locally vertical or overturned.   Wells producing large amounts of oil are drilled to the Dacian and lower series.   Tintea is east of Baicoiu on the edge of the same mass of salt. On the north side of the salt bed the Dacian series yields heavy black oil at depths of about 1,000 feet.

About 12 miles north of Buzeu which is 60 miles northeast of Ploesti, an anticline[1] strikes north-northeast and is followed 18 miles.   The fault involves rocks of Tertiary age, beginning with the youngest formation, the Levantine, through the Dacian and Pontian, to the oldest, the Meotic.   The Levantine consists of sands and marls with numerous seams of lignite, which reach a thickness of 6 to 7 inches in the lower part of the formation.   The underlying Dacian is estimated to be 3,000 to 3,500 feet thick.   Gray shales and arenaceous marls prevail.   Interbedded with them occur lenses and beds of hard yellow-red sandstone that is rich in fossils.

Beneath the Dacian lie the Pontian sediments, which occupy large areas in this district.   Four groups are distinguished, as follows: Yellow sandstones, more or less consolidated, 200 to 300 meters; gray clay marl, 200 meters; yellow sands and sandstones, the latter with spherical concre-

[1] PREISWERK, H., Ueber den Geologischen Bau der Region der Schlammvulkane und Ölfelder von Berca und Beciu bei Buzeu in Rumänien.   Z. prakt. Geol., vol. 20, pp. 86–95, 1912.

KRAUS, M., Petroleum, Z., vol. 24, pp. 1–21, 1928.

tions and ripple marks, 100 meters; gray clay marls, 100 meters. All of these divisions contain fossils.

The oil-bearing strata are in the Meotic, which has a thickness of about 600 meters. Marls and sands constitute the main mass of the

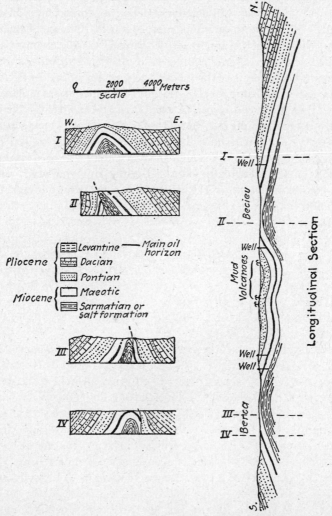

Fig. 377.—Sections through Berca and Becieu oil fields, Roumania. (*After Prieswerk.*)

formation. Interbedded with these are fairly hard sandstones, which make good horizon markers on account of their superior resistance to erosion. Toward the base of the formation they become more calcareous.

The Meotic formation is the lowest of the series described by Prieswerk as cropping out. Underlying it is the Sarmatian formation of Mactra limestone and rather coarse sandstones and conglomerates.

The structure of the district is shown in the accompanying sections (Fig. 377). The anticline is steep and asymmetric. Mud volcanoes are situated in the central depression which suggests a fault along the structure. The chief oil deposits are in the Meotic series.

In the Transylvanian basin[1] on the concave side of the Carpathian chain natural gas is found in Tertiary rocks in domes, some of which are salt domes. The domes in which gas is found include Sármás, Mesö-Sámsond, Mesö-Zah, Magyar-Sáros, Bázna, and Schemert. In the region of the gas fields gas seepages, hydrogen sulphide springs, and salt springs are numerous. Probably the gas developed is derived from the Sarmatian formation (Upper Miocene) which consists of sands, clays, and marls. Drilling was begun in 1908. In the Sármás field a well only 302 meters deep encountered an enormous flow of gas with a pressure of 384 pounds per square inch. The well could not be sealed properly, got out of control, and was sealed in July, 1911. Three months later it blew out, violently throwing debris ½ mile from the well. In general the open-flow capacities of the Transylvanian wells range from 1,000,000 to 30,000,000 cubic feet per day. The gas is essentially methane. No oil is found.

[1] CLAPP, F. G., Notes on Natural Gas Fields of Transylvania, Roumania, Am. Assoc. Pet. Geol. *Bull.*, vol. 8, pp. 202–211, 1924.

CHAPTER XX

RUSSIA

The chief oil-bearing regions[1] of Russia (Fig. 378) are (1) region surrounding the Caucasus Mountains including Baku, Grozny, and Maikop; in all of these fields the oil is found in Tertiary rocks. (2) Emba region north of Caspian Sea in which the oil is found in Jurassic rocks. (3) Extension of Baku field across the Caspian Sea including Cheleken Island and Oil Mountain in which the oil is found in Tertiary rocks. (4) Ferghana region of Central Asia in which oil is found in Tertiary and Cretaceous rocks. (5) Fields north of Emba and west of Ural Mountains in which oil is found in Permian, Pennsylvanian (?) and Devonian rocks. All of these fields have produced considerable amounts of oil, except the last-named group. At the end of 1927 European Russia had yielded 2,202,724,784 barrels of oil and Asiatic Russia had produced 33,420,419 barrels. Nearly all of this oil from European Russia was from fields around the Caucasus Mountains, the bulk of it coming from six fields located near Baku and from a single dome west of Grozny. The total production of all Russian fields in the operating year of 1927 to 1928 is estimated by Zavoico to be 83,700,000 barrels. Of this the production of the separate fields in millions of barrels is as follows: Baku fields 56.8, Grozny (Old and New Grozny) 23.7; Emba 2; Kouban (Maikop and neighboring fields) 0.65; Central Asia (Ferghana) 0.25, and Sakhalin 0.3.

The Caucasus Range is a great geoanticline. The central mass of the range is granite, which is skirted by basic rocks and these by metamorphosed Paleozoic sedimentary rocks. Above the latter in order are

[1] Golubjatnikoff, D. V., Productive Strata of the Apsheron Peninsula, Azerbaijan Neft. Khoz., Nos. 8, 9, (44, 45), pp. 42–55, Baku, September, 1925. In Russian.

Goubkin, I. M., The Oil Fields of the Grozny District, Neft, i Slattz., Khoz., vol. 4–7, pp. 28–42, Moscow, 1920.

Redfield, A. H., Federal Oil Conservation Board *Rept.* 3, Appendix C, pp. 122–130; bibliography, pp. 207–208, Washington, 1929.

Dalton, L. V., A Sketch of the Geology of the Baku and European Oil Fields, *Econ. Geol.*, vol. 4, 89–117, 1909.

Andrusov, N., Beiträge zur Kenntniss des Kaspischen Neogen, Com. Géol. *Mém.*, vol. 15, No. 4, 1902.

———, Die Südrussischen Neogenablagerungen, Russ. k. min. Gesell., *Verh.*, ser. 2, vols, 34, 36, 39, 1897–1902.

Adiassevich, A., The Russian Oil Fields, Am. Inst. Min. Eng. *Trans.*, 48, pp. 855–868, 1914.

Thompson, A. B., "The Oil Fields of Russia," London, 1904.

Triassic, Jurassic, Lower Cretaceous, Upper Cretaceous, and Tertiary strata. At the west end of the range are the peninsulas of Taman and Kertch and the east end is the Apsheron peninsula. These peninsulas are made up of Tertiary rocks and on the Apsheron peninsula are located the Baku oil fields. Cheleken Island, on the east side of the Caspian Sea, and Oil Mountain, on the mainland east of the island, are in line with the axis of the Caucasus Range. The Grozny and Maikop oil fields

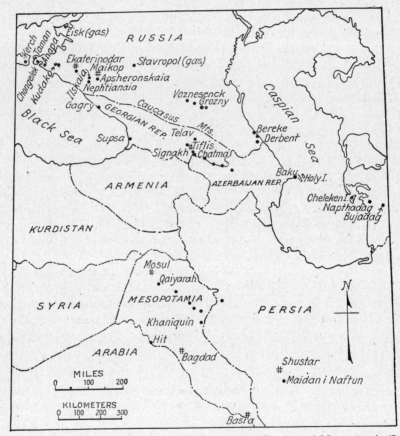

Fig. 378.—Map showing main oil fields (dots) of Russia, Persia, and Mesopotamia (Irak).

are on the northeast slope of the Caucasus. No considerable oil fields are developed on the southwest slope of the Caucasus nor in the peninsula of Taman and Kertch at its northwest end.

Kertch, Taman, and Maikop.—The peninsulas of Kertch and Taman lie between the Black Sea and the Sea of Azov. They project toward each other and nearly join, being separated by the Strait of Kertch. These peninsulas are made up of Oligocene and Miocene strata and are closely folded by folds that strike approximately east (Fig. 379). On the tops of some of the anticlines oil springs and mud volcanoes are found. The region has been drilled for oil, but only small production has been attained. Small wells have been drilled at Anapa on the south shore of Taman.

From Taman eastward to the Maikop district, which lies south of the town of Maikop, there is found along the northeast slopes of the Caucasus Mountains an almost continuous belt of oil indications, and in this belt several fields are developed. The chief operations are at Kudako, Ilskaia, Nephtianaia, and Shirvanskaia. Along this belt (Fig. 74) Miocene rocks crop out with dolomitic limestone at the top and a series of shales and sandstones below. These beds are about 1,000 feet thick, and they dip steeply northeast, but toward Maikop the dip flattens and the oil-bearing belt becomes wider. The Miocene beds overlie the Upper Cretaceous unconformably. The Kudako field is near the west end of this belt. The first gusher drilled in Russia was drilled in this district.

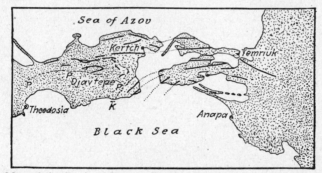

Fig. 379.—Map of the Strait of Kertch, Russia. The heavy lines indicate late Tertiary anticlines. (*After Andrussov.*)

The oil occurs in the Maikop sand of upper Oligocene and lower Miocene age. In the Ilskaia field east of Kudako oil has been produced from shallow wells for many years. These are sunk on a monocline that strikes northeast. The productive beds include the Maikop formation which yields light oil and an overlying dolomite which yields a heavy black oil. The dolomite is of Miocene age.

The Maikop oil field (Nephtianaia-Shirvanskaia), which is south of the town of Maikop and 50 miles northeast of Tuaspe, was worked by open pits at an early date, and the first flowing well was brought in by a Russian company in 1909. This well was followed by the drilling of several gushers, some of them producing large amounts of oil at depths of about 400 feet or less. The oil in the Maikop field is found mainly at the same horizon as at Kudako and Ilskaia, that is, near the bottom of the Miocene and top of the Oligocene series (Fig. 380). At Maikop the main oil horizon is associated with erosional valleys that are formed in the clays and marls of the upper part of the Middle Oligocene. These valleys

(Fig. 74) are filled in with the Maikop formation, which consists of dark shaly marls and beds of coarse sands, sandstones, and conglomerates. These beds are characterized by fish remains. Middle Miocene beds lie above the ancient valleys and are made up of shales with sand lenses, and the sands also carry oil.[1] The oil in the higher sands has a gravity of 0.940 and that of the lower sand channels about 0.840.

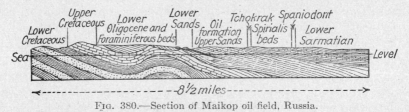

FIG. 380.—Section of Maikop oil field, Russia.

SECTION AT NEPHTIANAIA-SHIRVANSKAIA (MAIKOP)
(*After Charnotsky*)

Pliocene
  Meotic. Dolomitic limstone, dark shales at base (Congeria).
Miocene:
  Sarmatian:
    Upper. Conglomerates, sands, thin clays, partings of ferruginous sandstone, shell beds, gypsum (Mactra Caspia). Thickness, 25 to 30 meters.
    Middle *a.* Dark-gray shales, shell bed at top, typical fauna.
           b. Dark-gray shales, gray marls at base, Cryptomactra beds. Thin.
    Lower *a.* Shell limestone
           b. Dark-gray marls and thin gray shales, fish and plant remains. Thickness 400 to 500 meters.
Middle Miocene:
  a. Compact marly limestone with porous layers, Spaniodont beds. Thickness 10 to 15 meters.
  b. Dark shales and yellow gray marls, Spirialis beds. Thickness 200 to 400 meters.
  c. Chokrak. Sandy and Bryozoa limestone, shell beds, dark marls. Thickness 20 to 25 meters.
Miocene and Upper Oligocene:
  Maikop formation. Dark shales, coarse sands and sandstones, gravels, conglomerate, fish remains. Usually impregnated with oil. Thickness 225 meters at Nephtianaia; oil bearing.
Unconformity.
Middle Oligocene:
  White clays, marls, bituminous shales (Foraminifera). Thickness 200 to 800 meters.
Lower Oligocene:
  Green-gray clays. Pecten Bronni beds.
Unconformity.
Senonian:
  Chalk, marl, dark clay, coarse sandstone.
Unconformity.
Aptian:
  Dark sandy clays and sandstones, Ammonites.

[1] MADGWICK, T. G., Some Aspects of the Occurrence of Oil in Russia, *Jour. Inst. Pet. Geol.*, vol. 9, pp. 2–32, 1923.

Strata in Grozny Oil Field
(*After Kalickij*)

	Thickness, Meters
Akchagyl:	
Limestone, limestone conglomerate, sandstone, clayey sand, calcareous clay..	435
Unconformity.	
Middle Sarmatian:	
a. Bed with fish remains, gray shales with thin limestone.	
b. Cryptomactra beds: calcareous clays, limestone beds in upper part.	95
Lower Sarmatian:	
a. Mactra fragiles beds, calcareous clays with chalky marls.	
b. Syndesmya reflexa beds: calcareous shales with thin limestone beds.	43
Transition zone:	
a. Spaniodontella beds: shales, clays, clay sandstone calcareous clays and sandstones, limestone, water-bearing sandstone...............	50
b. Chokrak beds: shales, sandy clays, clay sandstone, sandstone, calcareous sandstone, limestone, limestone with concretions, dolomites, main oil-bearing series...	370
Mediterranean:	
Spirialis beds: black shales, limestones, black concretionary limestones, dolomite.	

Grozny.—The Grozny district is situated in the province of Terek in the foothill region of the Caucasus Mountains, about 300 miles southeast of Maikop and 100 miles west of Petrovsk, a port on the Caspian Sea. The field was opened by hand dug wells as early as 1823, and the first gusher was drilled in 1893 at a depth of 434 feet. The field has become

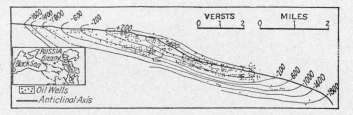

Fig. 381.—Map of Grozny oil field, Russia. (*After Kalickij.*)

the second in production in Russia. In the operating year of 1926 to 1927 it produced 22,700,000 barrels of oil, which is about 62,300 barrels per day. Old Grozny field is 10 miles northwest of New Grozny. Both of these fields are on elongated domes with long axes that strike southeast. A contour map of the Old Grozny field after Kalickij is shown as Fig. 381 and a section as Fig. 382. The rocks dip steeply to the northeast. To the southwest the beds dip 20 to 35 degrees. The fold brings the Lower Sarmatian beds (Miocene) to the surface, and these are surrounded by the Middle Sarmatian and Akchagyl (Pliocene) beds. The geological succession after Kalickij is shown in a table above. The main production is from the Chokrak series of beds which represent a transition from the Mediterranean to the Sarmatian series. The oil is found in a series of sandstones that are included in clays and shales of the Chokrak beds; 16 sands are productive. These beds are of Middle Miocene age and are younger than the Maikop oil-bearing strata.

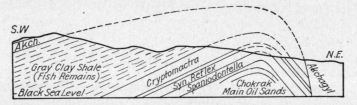

Fig. 382.—Geologic cross-section of (Old) Grozny oil field. (*After Kalickij.*)

About 64 per cent of the production of the Old Grozny field is obtained from flowing wells. Depletion begins with the encroachment of edge water under high pressure. The average thickness of the series of oil-bearing sands is 175 feet and the porosity is estimated to be 25 per cent.

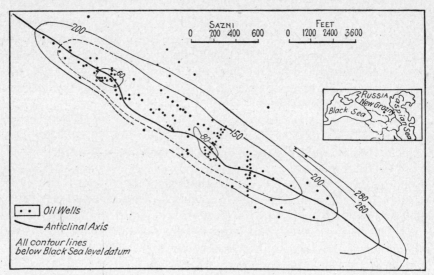

Fig. 383.—Map of New Grozny oil field, Russia. (*After S. Czarnockiego.*)

The production of oil[1] is 50 per cent of the pore space or 12.5 per cent of the volume of sand. The gas-oil ratio is 95 to 140 cubic feet of gas per barrel of oil, and the gas is mainly that dissolved in the oil.

In the New Grozny[2] field (Fig. 383), which also is located on a dome, the oil-bearing series consists of shales containing 22 sands, the entire

[1] LINDTROP, N. T., and V. M. NIKOLAEFF, Oil and Water Content of Oil Sands, Grozny, Russia, Am. Assoc. Pet. Geol. *Bull.*, vol. 13, pp. 811–822, 1929.

[2] LINDTROP, N. T., Outline of Water Problems in the New Grozny Oil Field, Russia, Am. Assoc. Pet. Geol. *Bull.*, vol. 11, pp. 1035–1044, 1927.

thickness of the series being 1,740 feet. Much of the oil is obtained from flowing wells. These yield large amounts of oil but are short lived owing to water encroachment. The field is under hydrostatic pressure and the gas-oil ratio is low, being about 100 to 250 cubic feet of gas per barrel of oil. The waters carry sulphates, chlorides, and carbonates and are altered residuary sea waters diluted by waters entering the outcrops of the sands. This water moves through a very deep syncline and its temperature is from 170 to 190° F.

Dagestan.—In the territory of Dagestan southeast of Terek, east and southeast of Grozny near the town of Derbent, oil seepages are found near the shore of the Caspian Sea at several places. At Bereke, about 15 miles north of Derbent, there was once a small production of oil (31° A.P.I.) from Pliocene strata. The Tertiary strata rest with angular unconformity on Upper Cretaceous beds. The field is located on an anticline that strikes northwest. The oil is associated with hot salt water that contains iodine and bromine compounds.[1] At Khosh Menzel, about 10 miles south of Derbent, oil exudes from mud volcanoes.

Baku.—The Apsheron Peninsula projects eastward into the Caspian Sea and lies approximately on the extension of the axis of the Caucasus Mountains. It is about 64 kilometers long and 22 kilometers wide and is a relatively low area with many small hills and ridges. Surface indications of oil abound and include mud volcanoes, oil seeps, gas seeps, and salt springs. This area was known to the ancient Persians who had a temple at Surakhani near Baku, where the altar fires burned natural gas and to which fire worshippers made pilgrimages. Hand dug borings were utilized to supply oil for many centuries. Active drilling began in 1873 when the first flowing well was brought in. This was soon followed by other wells, and, owing to the high gas pressure, the heavy flows of oil, and inadequate means for controlling the wells, large amounts of oil were lost. The district soon became the world's most productive oil field, and today its total production is unequaled by that of any other field of equal size. In the operating year 1926 to 1927 the total production of the Baku oil fields was 49,000,000 barrels, which is an average of 134,000 barrels per day. Practically all of this oil came from six centers, which, in order of productiveness, in 1927 are Surakhani, Bibi Eibat, Romani, Sabunchi, Balakhani, and Binigadi. All of these are towns that lie within a radius of 8 miles of Baku (Fig. 384).

The rocks of the Apsheron Peninsula are shown in a table that follows. Successively younger rocks lie to the east and Eocene rocks crop out in the area that immediately adjoins that shown in the northwest corner of Fig. 384. The east end of the peninsula is covered with Quaternary rocks except at Kala, where along an anticline the Pliocene beds are exposed.

[1] REDFIELD, A. H., Federal Oil Conservation Board, *Rept.* 3, Appendix C, p. 127, Washington, 1929.

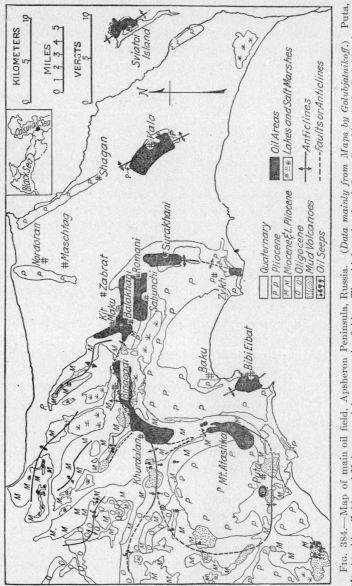

Fig. 384.—Map of main oil field, Apsheron Peninsula, Russia. (Data mainly from Maps by Golubjatnikoff.) Puta, Mt. Atashka, Zykh and Kala are mainly prospective fields. The chief production is from Surakhani, the Balakhani group, Binagadi, Bibi Eibat, and Sviatoi Island.

The structure of the Apsheron Peninsula has been worked out by Golubjatnikoff[1] and others. The area is thrown into sharp folds which strike in all directions and curve to outline structural basins. Bibi Eibat is on a short plunging anticline that is probably a dome, although the southeast end extends below the sea. The other large producing fields are all located on one system of anticlines that forms a semicircle around Baku.

SECTION OF ROCKS OF APSHERON PENINSULA

(*After Golubjatnikoff and Madgwick*, with correlations and additions from others)

Quaternary:
Littoral sediments, sands, gravel, clay, etc.

Pliocene:
Baku stage. Limestones, sandstones, sands, clays, conglomerate. Thickness 46 meters.
Apsheron stage. *a.* Limestone, limestone conglomerate, oolitic limestone, shell beds, sandy limestone, calcareous sandstone, sands, marls, clays. Limestones prevail in upper parts, sands in middle, and clays with volcanic dust in lower parts. Thickness 453 meters.
b. Dark clays with partings of sand and marl. Sands contain gas at Bibi Eibat. Thickness 76 meters.
Transition stage. Dark clays with partings of sand carrying gas. Thickness 11 meters.
Akchagyl stage (now regarded as Middle Pliocene, formerly as Meotic). Clays and shales with beds of limestone and sandstone. Contains gas at Bibi Eibat; some oil at Surakhani. Thickness 49 meters.
Fresh-water stage. Fossiliferous "fresh-water" beds, clayey beds with sands; part of main oil measures. Thickness 490 meters.
Unfossiliferous. Sandy beds with clay; part of main oil measures. Thickness 434 meters.
Kir Maku stage. Sands and sandstones, clay partings; part of main oil measures. Thickness 185 meters.

Unconformity (present in oil field areas).
Lower Miocene:
Spirialis beds. Sandy calcareous clay with ferruginous partings; carry oil.
Cedroxylon beds. Dark paper shales with siliceous concretions, petrified trees.

Oligocene:
Amphisyle beds. Dark shales with fish remains.

Oligocene (?):
Lamna beds. Green sandy shales with partings of siliceous sandstone and white marl; at places contain oil.

[1] The map (Fig. 384) is a composite sketch based on the original geologic map by Golubjatnikoff (1908) to which I have added the oil-bearing and prospective areas as outlined by Prof. Golubjatnikoff in 1923 and presented in a paper translated by Dr. T. G. Madgwick in the *Jour. Inst. Pet. Tech.*, vol. 9, p. 188, London, 1923. I have made a few changes in the map to agree with the later descriptions of structures by Golubjatnikoff that accompany his latest map. This map shows the oil fields but does not show the structural axes. Some of the rocks classed in the earlier reports as Miocene are now regarded by Prof. Golubjatnikoff as Pliocene. (W. H. E.)

Bibi Eibat.—The Bibi Eibat district lies about 2 kilometers south of Baku in a basin that opens to the sea and is rimmed by resistant beds of the Apsheron formation. The field lies on an anticline that strikes northwest and plunges northwest. The anticline is supposed to be a large elongated dome, but that is uncertain since the southeastern end of the axis passes into the sea. There are, however, two small upward

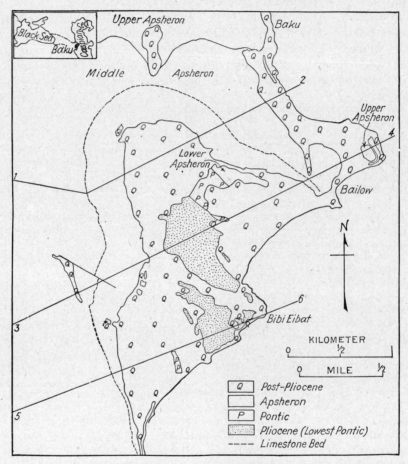

FIG. 385.—Map of Bibi Eibat oil field, near Baku, Russia. (*After Golubjatnikoff.*)

undulations on the crest of the axis in the productive part of the field. A plan of the field and cross-sections, after Golubjatnikoff are shown as Figs. 385 and 386. The top of the oil-producing zones is brought to the surface at the crest of the anticline, which is complicated by faulting. The oil is derived from beds which in the earlier reports are classed as Miocene but in the later reports as lower Pliocene. The productive series consists of numerous sands that are interlayered with clays and shales.

The field covers an area of about 2½ square miles and a considerable part of the field is on land reclaimed from the Caspian Sea. Salt water appears on the edges of the field. There are numerous productive sands and these are encountered in a thickness of 2,500 feet of strata. Sands above the oil-bearing series carry gas. The productive series of beds probably lie above a great unconformity. Recently a flowing well 3,470 feet deep was drilled. This well yielded 3,200 barrels of oil per day.

Surakhani.—The Surakhani district lies about 14 kilometers northeast of Baku. It is probably richer than any other oil field in the world of equal size. The Pliocene sediments form a broad gentle dome that strikes about north. The rocks dip 4 to 10 degrees to the west and 10 to 20 degrees to the east. The anticline dips north near the northern

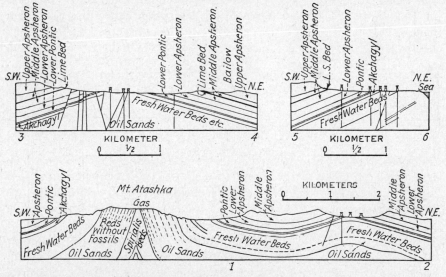

FIG. 386.—Sections of Bibi Eibat oil field near Baku, Russia. (*After Golubjatnikoff.*) Lines of sections shown on Fig. 385.

end of Surakhani lake. The southern end is concealed by a series of faults and the crest of the fold is faulted at many places. An east-west section of the field would closely resemble that of Bibi Eibat. The clays of the Akchagyl stage extend to depths of 550 to 650 feet. Below these are found the productive measures which extend to depths of 2,160 feet or more. These are the upper and middle portions of the productive measures. A light oil nearly white was found in the Akchagyl beds to depths of about 650 feet. A dark oil (40° Bé., sp. gr. 0.820) was found at a depth of 1,575 feet, below which the normal oil of the field was found.

Zykh.—The Zykh field is south of Surakhani near the coast and on the extension of the Surakhani anticline that here strikes a little west of south. The rocks dip about 6 to 12 degrees away from the crest of

the fold, and the fold plunges to the south.   At the crest of the anticline
Apsheron beds are exposed.   On this structure an eroded mud volcano
exhibits the fissures through which mud and many large stones were
thrown out.   Among the latter are recognized fragments of rocks of the
oil measures, which, as stated by Golubjatnikoff, indicate that the productive horizons are present.   Rocks a meter in diameter are noted, and
these are twice the width of the fissure, suggesting that the latter was
wider when the mud volcano was in eruption.   The field is not developed
but is classed as a productive area by the survey of the Geological Committee.[1]   The oil sands are said to lie at depths of 2,100 to 4,200 feet.

Balakhani.—Sabunchi, Romani, and Balakhani are three towns
located near the crest of the anticline which extends northwest from
the Surakhani field.   These towns are about 12 kilometers northeast
of Baku and are parts of a single oil field often called the Balakhani
field.   This field is one of the world's greatest oil pools and from 1882
to 1920, inclusive, its production was 183,232,000 metric tons of oil.

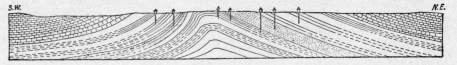

Fig. 387.—Section of Balakhani oil field near Baku, Russia.   (*After Barbot de Marni.*)

The oil field is probably located on the same anticline (Fig. 387) on which
is located the dome of the Sarakhani field.   The axis of the fold strikes
northwest through the great mud volcano Bog-Boga and branches, one
branch extending northwest through Kir-Maku, and the other extending
west to Binigadi.   The Balakhani or fresh-water series is found at
Balakhani at relatively shallow depths.   These sands lie deeper at
Sabunchi and still deeper at Romani.   According to Golubjatnikoff,
the sands worked in the field are in the upper division of the oil measures,
which is 2,400 feet thick and contains 34 producing sands.   The anticline plunges southeast and, consequently, lower beds are found to the
northwest.   The oil of Balakhani is heavy having a specific gravity of
0.927 to 0.937 and that of Romani is lighter with a gravity of 0.854.
In general the oils in the lower strata are heavier than oil found in the
higher strata.

Binigadi.—The Binigadi field is on a broad anticline that trends
east-west and that widens to the west to the mud volcano Keyzeky and
narrows and plunges east (Fig. 384).   Clays of Oligocene and Miocene
are brought up along the crest of the fold, which is marked by a strike
fault.   Pliocene and Miocene beds consisting of clays and sandstones
form the wings of the fold, and these are the productive measures.   On

[1] GOLUBJATNIKOFF, D. V., The Amount of Undeveloped Oil Land in the Baku
District, *Jour. Inst. Pet. Tech.*, vol. 9, pp. 185–207, London, 1923.

the south side of the fold the beds dip 15 to 35 degrees and on the north side 33 to 36 degrees. The fault throws the beds down to the north, and it dies out toward the east. A section on the south flank of the fold from top to bottom is as follows:

Series	Feet
A. Clays and sandy beds with Planorbis	181.5
B. Sands and coarse sands with small dark pebbles	684
C. Clays, dark, not laminated	65
D, E. Sands with thin clay partings	156
F. Clays, clay sands, pure sands, saturated with oil	396

These beds dip south and are opened by many hand dug pits. Oil is found in B, D, E, and F, but chiefly in F, in which there are 29 oil sands and of these 14 are highly saturated. The main production is from 4 sands. In recent years gushers have been drilled. The oil

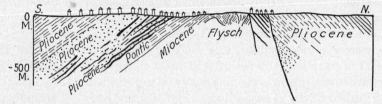

FIG. 388.—Geologic cross-section of Binigadi district, Baku region, Russia. (*After Zuber.*)

of Binigadi[1] is heavy, having a specific gravity of 0.913 to 0.925. According to Zuber, the accumulation of oil is due to deposition of tar and to lensing of the beds up dip. A section of the field, after Zuber, is shown by Fig. 388.

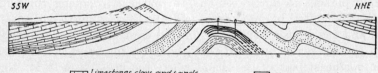

Limestones, clays and sands Apsherion (Pliocene)	Clays and marls
Marly shales and sands) Balakhany	Oil-bearing strata
Sands and sandstones ∫ (Miocene)	

FIG. 389.—Anticline between Puta and Perin-Agit Hill, Baku oil field, Russia. (*After Barbot de Marni.*)

West of Binigadi field the anticlinal axis bends and strikes south. Oil is recovered from hand dug pits sunk in the oil measures which are exposed at Khurdalan and at Hyokmali.

The Atashka field near Mount Atashka and west of Bibi Eibat is marked by strong gas vents ("Everlasting Fires") near the top of the hill and deposits of asphalt on its sides, Figs. 386 and 389. The field is on an anticline that plunges southwest. The relations of these beds to

[1] ZUBER, S., Die Erdoellagerungsverhältnisse in Binigady bei Baku genetisch betrachtet, *Petroleum Z.*, vol. 21, pp. 501–515, 1925.

sands of the Bibi Eibat field is shown on the section 1–2, Fig. 386. The beds dip 70 to 90 degrees on the east side of the fold and are locally overturned. On the west side they dip 65 degrees. The anticline plunges south, however, and fans out with more gentle dips of 15 to 25 degrees on the south part of the structure. Six oil-bearing series are present with 30 or more sands. The field is only partially explored.

The Kala field is on an anticline east of Surakhani and is marked by gas seepages. The oil-bearing strata lie 600 feet deeper than at Sura- khani. Oil and gas are found in the Apsheron and in the Akchagyl series and in the productive measures. The latter lie at depths of about 1,250 to 1,400 feet. Some of the oil in the district is a white light oil with a specific gravity of about 0.781. The productive measures are estimated to extend to depths of 4,200 feet. The area is much broken by faults. Six tests made in 1927 did not discover commercial production.

Sviatoi.—Sviatoi (Holy Island) lies in the Caspian Sea off the coast of the Apsheron Peninsula about 50 kilometers east of Baku. It has an area of about $3\frac{1}{2}$ square miles. Asphalt beds and oil seeps abound, and these were operated by hand dug wells by the Persians in ancient times. In 1903 a great gusher was brought in at a depth of 1,386 feet. Soon afterward several gushers yielding heavy oil were drilled. Holy Island is on a fold formed chiefly of post-Pliocene and Miocene beds. The upper parts of the Pliocene including the Apsheron and Akchagyl series, according to Golubjatnikoff, are not present on the anticline nor are the upper parts of the oil measures. The lower part of the oil measures is found at the top of an anticline the axis of which strikes N.21° W. The southwest side of the anticline dips at low angles and the northeast side is steeper. The fold plunges to northwest and to southeast, opening out fanlike. The dome is faulted by many cross-faults so that its north end is raised.

Oil and gas seepages are found on the crest of the fold, along faults and in asphalt sealed sands of the productive measures. Wells drilled on the northeast part of the island where the beds dip 4 to 12 degrees found heavy oil with a specific gravity of 0.944. A second anticlinal axis, also striking northwest, is developed near the dome. In the years 1915 to 1917 the Holy Island field produced considerable oil annually, but since then the production has decreased considerably. To 1920 the total production was 5,000,000 barrels.

In Georgia, south of the Caucasus Mountains, oil seepages are com- mon. At Chatma, southeast of Tiflis in the republic of Georgia, oil is found at two horizons the upper one of Sarmatian age. The rocks dip south and are folded, but the structure is complicated by thrust faulting.

At Ildokany[1] in the Telav district, northeast of Tiflis (Fig. 378), oil seepages are found in the Sarmatian (Miocene) and in the Eocene strata.

---

[1] MADGWICK, T. G., Some Aspects of the Occurrence of Oil in Russia, *Jour. Inst. Pet. Tech.*, vol. 9, p. 19, London, 1923.

In the Ozurgety or Supsa district on the Black Sea, northeast of Batum, oil is found in the Tertiary strata that are approximately equivalent to the Maikop and Chokrak formations, both of which produce oil on the north slope of the Caucasus.

Cheleken Island.– Cheleken Island is situated on the east side of the Caspian Sea about 300 kilometers (186 miles) east of Baku. It is a small island with steep shores and lies approximately in the strike of the extension of the axis of the Carpathian Mountains. At the surface there are numerous oil seeps, mud volcanoes, gas seeps, salt springs, and ozokerite deposits. These were known to the Persians who practiced surface mining at an ancient date. Under lease from the Russian Government, the first large wells were opened by the Nobel Brothers In 1904, who succeeded in establishing a considerable industry. The oil is of medium grade.

Near the center of the island there is a small hill (Chokrak) which forms the top of a structural dome. It is faulted by a system of faults that strike northeast and by another system that strikes northwest. Oil seeps showed on this hill and wells sunk on it have discovered oil in relatively small amounts. On the west side of the island there is a small structural dome extensively faulted. The beds dip 20 degrees to the northeast and about 30 degrees to the southwest, and highly productive wells were drilled on the southwest which is the steeper side. Some of the wells ceased to yield oil and the oil flow was followed by that of hot water at temperatures of about 52° C. The oil is found in and below the Akchagyl formation, chiefly in a formation of unknown age but probably Miocene. The fresh-water beds of the Apsheron Peninsula are probably eroded on Cheleken Island.

Naptha Dagh[1] (Neftiania Gora, Naphtedag, Oil Mountain) is situated on the mainland southeast of Cheleken Island and 33 kilometers southwest of Bala Ischem on the Central Asiatic Railway. This hill rises about 85 meters above the plain and covers an area of about 2½ square miles. It is marked by numerous oil and gas seepages, ozokerite deposits, and mud volcanoes. The field was drilled by the Central Asiatic Railway Company, and oil, obtained from shallow wells, was used for fuel. The field is a structural dome broken into a fault mosaic by closely set faults that strike east-northeast and southeast. The rocks dip in all directions from about 7 to 45 degrees. The rocks cropping out include gray and brown clay, red clay and gypsum, sands and sandstone. The oil is found in wells of relatively shallow depths in sandstone probably of Miocene or Pliocene age, which resembles the oil sands near Baku. The oil produced has a gravity of about 0.857 and contains 2 per cent paraffin.

Buja Dagh is 40 kilometers south-southeast of Bala Ischem and 30 kilometers from Aidan on the Central Asiatic Railway. A hill 10 kilometers long and 3 kilometers wide rises 150 meters above the plain.

---

[1] Sjögren, Hj., Jahrb. k. k. geol. Reichanst., p. 47, 1887.

The hill is an anticline like that of Naptha Dagh and has steep sides, although faulting is much less evident. Clay shales bedded with thin sandstones crop out on the hill, which shows oil springs, salt springs, and springs of hot water.

Emba.—West of Emba River and north of Caspian Sea, near the mouth of the Ural River, there is a great area of sedimentary rocks of the Permo-Triassic, Jurassic, Cretaceous, and Tertiary systems. These strata are thrown into anticlines and domes that are arranged along curved lines that are rudely parallel to the Ural Mountains. These anticlinal zones are faulted and along the faults are numerous oil seepages and deposits of asphalt. Indications of oil are noted at about 50 places. A map[1] of the area is shown by Fig. 390. In this region a flowing well was

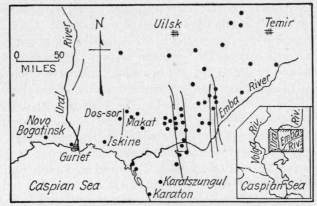

FIG. 390.—Map of Emba oil field, Russia, showing oil pools and indications of oil (dots). (*After Bohdanowicz.*)

drilled at Dos-sor in 1911, and to 1928 the total production of the Emba field was 19,323,150 barrels of oil. In the operating year of 1926 to 1927 the Emba field produced 1,825,000 barrels.

In the Dos-sor field, 60 miles northeast of Gurief, the chief production comes from a dome that is faulted down on the west side and that brings Jurassic rocks to the surface (Fig. 391).[2] The sands are found at four horizons in Jurassic rocks that lie at depths between 250 and 700 feet. Recently, according to a Moscow publication which is quoted by Olferieff, a sand some 50 feet deeper has been opened, and several wells have produced nearly 5,000 barrels per day from this sand. The Dos-sor oils have gravities between 16 and 35° Bé. and are very high in lubricants. The field produced about 86 per cent of the total production of the Emba

[1] BOHDANOWICZ, K., Tereny i zloza Naftowe, pp. 98–103, Warsaw, 1923. In Polish.

OLFERIEFF, T., Oil Possibilities in the Ural-Emba Region, *Oil Gas Jour.*, vol. 24, p. 76, Oct. 1, 1925.

[2] Figures 390 and 391 are redrawn and abridged from maps by the Russian Geol. Survey presented by Prof. Bohdanowicz.

region in 1927, and the Makat field east of Dos-sor produced most of the remaining portion. The Makat field is located on a structural dome that is much less complicated by faulting than the dome of Dos-sor. The oil is found at several horizons in the Jurassic strata.[1]

Valuable wells have recently been drilled near Gurief, near the mouth of the Ural River on the west side of the stream. About 10 of the other

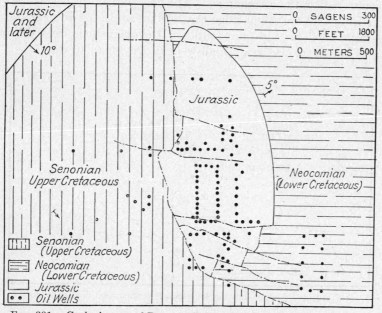

Fig. 391.—Geologic map of Dos-sor oil field, Russia. (*After Zamiatina.*)

fields shown on Fig. 390 have been drilled with indifferent success, and small wells are drilled at Tas Kuduk, 2½ miles north of Dos-sor, and at Novo Bogatinsk, 40 miles west of Gurief.

In Perm province in 1928 a well drilled by the Russian Government, 30 miles east-northeast of the city of Perm, encountered gas and oil in commercial amounts. A section[2] shown by the well is as follows:

	Feet
Alluvium	36
Marls and gypsum with some potassium-bearing salt beds, gypsum increasing with depth	525
Massive gypsum and anhydrite; anhydrite near base interlayered with dark bituminous shales	1,070
Anhydrite and dark shales with a little oil, passing into dark cherty limestone, probably of Pennsylvanian age, containing oil. On May 15, 1928, well made 15 barrels of heavy oil	1,080

[1] Mironov, S., Prospecting Operations in the Ural-Emba Oil fields, Comite Geologique of Russia, Applied Geol. ser. 3, pp. 1–60, Leningrad, 1928. Abstract in English.

[2] Zavoico, B. B., Am. Assoc. Pet. Geol. *Bull.*, vol. 13, pp. 859–860, 1929.

In Samara province, east of the Volga River and about 100 miles northeast of Samara, and in the drainage of the Volga River, bituminous sands of Permian age crop out. Attempts have been made to develop an oil field in this area but thus far without success.

The Ukhta field (Ust Uchta) is on the Izhma River a tributary of the Petchora River, and lies about 350 miles south of the Arctic Sea and east and somewhat south of Archangel. The field[1] lies on the east slope of the Timan Ridge, an anticlinal ridge that strikes southeast to near the Ural Mountains. Oil seepages are found in Devonian beds, and drilling in this area has developed very small wells in Devonian strata.

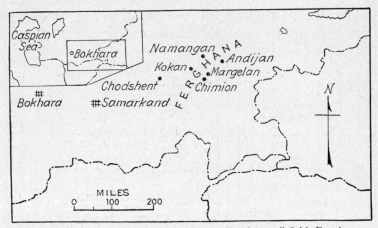

Fig. 392.—Sketch showing location of Ferghana oil field, Russia.

Ferghana.—The Ferghana[2] district (Fig. 392) is located in Russian Turkestan near the east end of the Central Asiatic Railway and about 400 miles east of Bokhara. Oil seeps and deposits of "kir" are found in this region and were utilized at an ancient date by Chinese and Turkomans. Oil seeps appear near the towns of Kokand (Kokan), Namandjan, and Chimion. Shallow shafts were sunk early in the nineteenth century and drilling began in 1898. The production of the field soon increased to about 240,000 barrels of oil a year, which is approximately the annual production of recent years.

In the valley north of the Alai Range the rocks dip north at high angles away from the mountains to the town of Chimion (Fig. 393).

[1] Maps and descriptions of the Samara and Ukhta regions are in a paper of K. Bohdanowicz, Tereny i zloza Naftowe, pp. 90–95, Warsaw, 1923. In Polish.

[2] GOLUBJATNIKOFF, D. W., Principaux resultats des travaux geologiques effectues en 1903 dans d'Apscheron, *Bull.* du Comite Geologique, vol. 23, 1904.

LEVAT, E. D., Possessions Russes en Asie Centrale, *Ann. mines*, ser. 10, vol. 3, pp. 303–307, 1903.

ROMANOWSKI. G., Materialien zur Geologie von Turkestan, pp. 42–45, St. Petersburg, 1880.

The geological section in this region is described by Lavat. In the mountains crystalline schists crop out. On the north side of the mountains these are covered with marls and other calcareous sedimentary rocks of Cretaceous age. The Cretaceous beds in turn are overlain by Lower Tertiary rocks known as the Ferghana stage, which in turn are covered by Aral-Caspian beds and Recent sands. A section of the area is shown by Fig. 393. Chimion is situated south of the railway near the town of New Margelan. The oil is found in the Ferghana stage of the Tertiary system (Eocene) and also in Cretaceous rocks. The Ferghana beds carry oil just south of the railway station Melnikovo, where production has been carried on for several years. According to Zavoico,[1] wells yielding 250 barrels a day at depths of about 650 feet were found in 1927 in the Shor-Sou field near the station Posetovka.

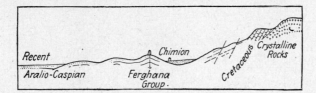

Fig. 393.—Section showing Chimion oil pool, Ferghana, Russia. (*After Levat.*)

At Maili-Sai, northeast of Namagan, according to Golubjatnikoff, the rocks exposed are as follows:

		Meters
Stage I.	Light brown sandy clay and conglomerate	1,000
	Brick-red clay, sandstone, and conglomerate	100
	Clay, sand, sandstone, and conglomerate alternating red, green, and blue gray	28
Stage II.	Red clay sand partings, sandstone, marl at top	58
	Green gray limy clays, marls, and limestones	26
	Shales, bituminous with fish remains, concretions near top	33
	Sand, sandy clay, basal conglomerate	10
Stage III.	Ferghana stage; marl, clay, sand, and conglomerate with three thick limestones	60
Stage IV.	Sand, clay, limestone, conglomerate at base[1]	150

[1] This section is reported by Madgwick in the paper cited. The original is not accessible. (W. H. E.)

According to Madgwick, the Lower Tertiary beds at Ferghana[2] lie in two nearly parallel belts on the north and south marginal sides of the valley, and the two belts come together at the east. Thus the basin which is underlain by the Ferghana oil-bearing series is one of considerable extent. These strata are said to be exposed also in large areas toward the frontier of Afghanistan.

[1] ZAVOICO, B. B., "Petroleum Development and Technology in 1927," p. 692, Am. Inst. Min. Eng., 1928.

[2] MADGWICK, T. G., Some Aspects of the Occurrence of Oil in Russia, *Jour. Inst. Pet. Tech.*, vol. 9, pp. 2–32, 1923.

CHAPTER XXI

OCEANIA AND ASIA, EXCEPT RUSSIA

PALESTINE

In Palestine no oil field is developed, although asphaltite and bituminous limestones are found at many places. Asphaltic deposits are found in the Jordan trough from near the Waters of Merom southward beyond

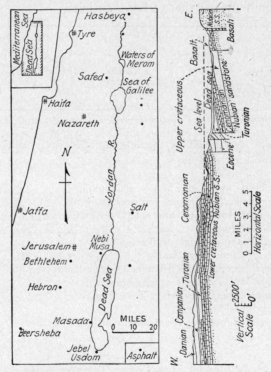

FIG. 394.—Map showing locations of occurrences of asphalt in Palestine. (*After Fohs.*) Section of Dead Sea. (*After Blanckenhorn.*)

the south end of the Dead Sea and in the plateau area of the Jordan trough. The country[1] is an area containing Paleozoic, Mesozoic, and Tertiary sedimentary rocks. All of these rocks are extensively folded

[1] BLANCKENHORN, M., Nutzbare Mineralien am Toten Meer, *Z. prakt. Geol.*, vol. 5, p. 360–361, 1897.

FOHS, F. J., Geology and the Petroleum and Natural Gas Possibilities of Palestine and Sinaitic Peninsula, Am. Assoc. Pet. Geol. *Bull.*, vol. 11, pp. 135–149, 1927.

and faulted, and in Cretaceous and Tertiary time the area was intruded by basalt. The distribution of the asphaltic deposits of Palestine is shown by Fig. 394. According to Fohs, there are possibilities of finding oil in the Lower Carboniferous sandstone and shale, in the Wadi Nasb limestone of the Upper Carboniferous, in the Upper Carboniferous sandstone above the latter, in the Nubian sandstone (Lower Cretaceous), in the Upper Cretaceous, and Eocene limestones.

PERSIA

Petroleum seepages and asphalt are found at many places in Persia[1] (Fig. 395) and have been known since ancient times.

Development on the modern scale began in 1903, and a few years later at Maidan-i-Naftun, near Shushtar, a well 1,100 feet deep came in and oil spouted 70 feet high, carrying away the derrick. Since then oil concessions covering most of Persia have been granted, and the Anglo-Persian Oil Company has developed an extensive field which is supplied with pipe lines and a refinery. The total production of Persia,[2] to April 1, 1928, was estimated to be 266,161,531 barrels. The oil of Maidan-i-Naftun has a mean specific gravity of 0.837 (37° Bé.) and contains 1.16 per cent sulphur and small amounts of asphaltic compounds. The chief oil field of Persia is the Masjid-i-Sulaiman field, which includes the Maidan-i-Naftun and neighboring pools near the town of Shushtar, about 280 miles southeast of Bagdad and 140 miles northeast of Basrah, a port at the head of the Persian Gulf and the terminus of the pipe line to the field. The country lies east of Irak (Mesopotamia). It is bordered on the west by a low desert area of alluvium east of which are parallel hill ranges and farther east the higher mountains of the Iranian chain. The rocks of this region are chiefly of Tertiary and Mesozoic age.

[1] RICHARDSON, R. K., The Geology and Oil Measures of Southwest Persia, *Jour. Inst. Pet. Tech.*, vol. 10, pp. 256–296, London, 1928.

BUSK, H. G., and H. T. MAYO, Some Notes on the Geology of Persian Oil Fields, *Jour. Inst. Pet. Tech.*, vol. 5, pp. 3–33, 1918.

PILGRIM, G. E., The Sulphur Deposits of Southern Persia, *Mem.* Geol. Survey India, vol. 53, pp. 343–358.

———, The Geology of the Persian Gulf and the Adjoining Portions of Persia and Arabia, *Mem.* Geol. Survey India, vol. 34, p. 344, 1908.

Op. cit., vol. 48, pt. 2, pp. 1–116, 1924.

SPIEKER, E. M., Petroleum in Persia and the Near East, *Eng. Mining Jour.*, vol. 110, pp. 316–323, 1920.

STAHL, A. F., "Persien, Handbuch der regionalen Geologie," vol. 5, pt. 6.

HARRISON, J. V., The Gypsum Deposits of Southwestern Persia, *Econ. Geol.*, vol. 19, pp. 259–274, 1924.

NICOLESCO, C. P., Petroleum in Persia, *La Revue Pétrolifère*, Nos. 277–288, 80 pages, 4 maps, Paris, 1928.

Review with geologic section by B. B. Zavoico in Am. Assoc. Pet. Geol. *Bull.*, vol. 13, pp. 396–399, 1929.

[2] DUCE, J. T., "Petroleum Development and Technology in 1927," p. 714, 1928

Deformation of the country took place in late Tertiary time. The folds and faults trend northwest. There is a noteworthy unconformity at the top of the Asmari limestone which marks a movement that was probably not profound, since discordances of bedding between the Asmari and Fars formations are slight. The Middle Fars overlaps the Lower Fars and rests on the Asmari limestone, showing that there was an erosion interval between them (Fig. 396). The Asmari limestone in general is hard and pure, but its upper part is highly dolomitic, friable, and cavernous, and it is in this part that the chief oil deposits lie. The Fars forma-

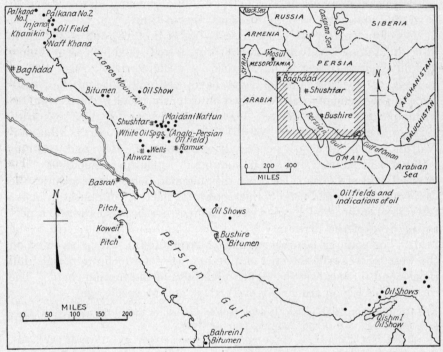

Fig. 395.—Map of parts of Persia and Mesopotamia (Irak), snowing oil fields and areas with indications of oil. (*Data from Mayo, Busk, Pascoe, Pilgram, and others.*)

tion overlies the Asmari limestone and consists of red beds, gypsum, anhydrite, salt, marl, and limestone. The lower part of the Fars consists partly of limestone derived from the Asmari, and at places the lower part of the Fars formation carries oil.

The deposition of the Fars formation was followed by a great period of deformation when the mountains were formed, and deformation continued during and after the period when the Bakhtiari beds were deposited. The steep limbs of the upfolds are on the southwest sides. The field was drilled as a result of the discovery of oil seepages in the Fars formation. The oil was found in the top of the Asmari limestone at depths between about 1,000 to over 2,700 feet. The wells spout oil under pressure, one of

SECTION OF SOUTHWEST PERSIA OIL REGION
(Mainly from Richardson)

Pliocene.

Bakhtiari. Conglomerates, sands, clays, grey limestone, thickness 15,000 ± feet.

Unconformity.

Miocene (Upper):

Upper Fars. Thick calcareous sandstone and limestone, red shale and marls, gypsum veins; thickness several thousand feet.

Miocene (Middle):

Middle Fars. Sandy limestone, calcareous sandstone, red and blue shales, thin beds of gypsum; thickness 2,500 ± feet.

Miocene (Lower):

Lower Fars. Red and blue shales, gypsum, anhydrite, salt, marl, some fragments of limestone; at places thin, in old basins 5,000 ± feet thick. Locally carries oil.

Unconformity.

Lower Miocene and Oligocene:

Asmari. Limestone, massive, thick bedded, hard, rich in Foraminifera locally porous at top; thickness 1,800 to 2,200 feet. At places the limestone is dolomitized, the magnesium content decreasing with depth; contains oil deposits of Maidan-i-Naftun.

Eocene:

Spatangid. Shales, blue green, splintery, contain some limestone; thickness 250 feet.

Upper limestone. Fine-grained, white, thin-bedded limestone with some shale, locally pink; conglomerate at base; thickness 900 to 1,600 feet.

Eocene and Cretaceous:

Blue shale. Shale, blue and purple, thin limestone near top, Eocene fossils; thickness 1,200 feet.

Lower limestone. Limestone, thin bedded white and gray, some shales thickness 700 to 1,000 feet.

Dasht-i-Gul. Limestone thick bedded; thickness 500 + feet.

them producing 12,500 barrels a day for a considerable period. Richardson states that the limestone is low in magnesium at certain outcrops,

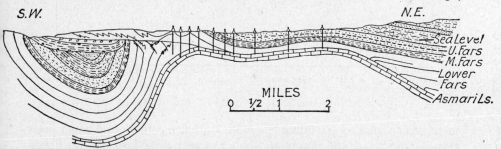

FIG. 396.—Cross-section of the Masjid-i-Sulaiman oil field near Shushtar, Persia. *(After Busk.)*

although the samples of the oil-bearing limestone carry 12 to 37 per cent magnesium carbonate. In this connection it is noteworthy that the amount of magnesium carbonate in the limestone in certain wells

decreases downward.   The oil is believed to have originated in the Asmari
limestone which is rich in foraminifera remains.   The structure of the
field is shown by Fig. 396.   It is probably domatic, although it is difficult
to interpret the structure, owing to the different behaviors under stress
of the massive limestone and the soft gypsum, salt, and shale series.
Richardson, who described the field in 1924 after several years of develop-

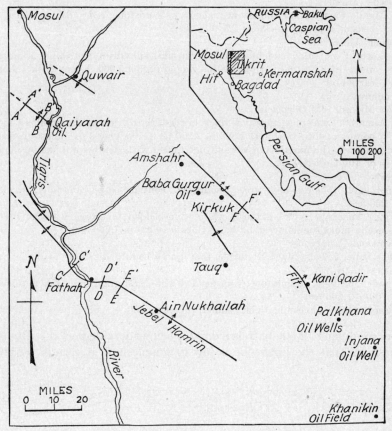

Fig. 397.—Sketch of part of Irak, showing anticlines and oil wells.   (*Data from Pascoe
and others.*)

ment with a view to extending the field, stated that there had never been
trouble from water and that no dry hole had been drilled, so that the limits
of the productive area were not known.   The original gas pressure was
about 400 pounds per square inch but has declined considerably.   The
gas is high in hydrogen sulphide.

An oil field has recently been developed at Khanikin, about 100 miles
northeast of Bagdad, by the Anglo-Persian Oil Company.

IRAK

The mountains and ridges of Persia extend into Mesopotamia[1] and are composed of strata similar to those in southwest Persia. Oil seeps are numerous and have been known for many centuries. A company, which is financed by Turkish, British, Dutch, French, and American capital,

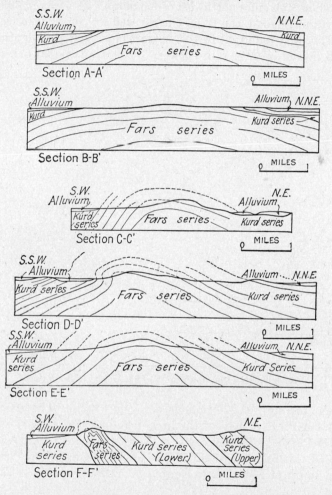

Fig. 398.—Geologic cross-section of Irak along lines indicated in Fig. 397. (*After Pascoe.*)

began operations in this area about 1923 and in 1927 had drilled several successful wells which derive their oil from Tertiary strata. These are

[1] Pascoe, E. G., Geological Notes on Mesopotamia with Special Reference to Occurrences of Petroleum, *Mem.* Geol. Survey India, vol. 48, pt. 1, pp. 1–90, 10 maps, 1924.

Milner, H. B., Mesopotamia, a Review of Its Geology and Petroleum Resources, *Min. Mag.*, vol. 27, pp. 89–90, 1922.

located in the villayets of Bagdad and Mosul.   At Injana, some 20 or 25
miles north of Khanikin, a large well was brought in.   A few miles north
of Injana the Palkhana No. 2 well encountered oil flowing 700 barrels
a day at a depth of 1,260 feet.   Northwest of this well the Palkhana
No. 1 found oil at 65 feet, and a 200 barrel flow at 1,320 feet.   Near
Kirkuk, about 100 miles northwest of Khanikin Figs. 397 and 398, and 150
miles north of Bagdad, the Baba Gurgur well was brought in October 14,
1927.   This well found oil in the Asmari limestone at a depth of 1,521
feet, and flowed oil at a rate between 35,000 and 95,000 barrels[1] a day

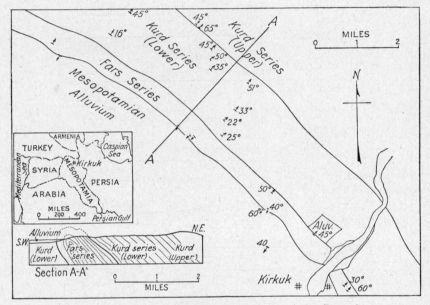

Fig. 399.—Map of area near Kirkuk, Irak.   (*After Pascoe.*)

with a gas pressure of 270 pounds per square inch.   The gravity of the
oil is 34.4 A.P.I.   A map of the area including Kirkuk is shown as Fig.
399, after Pascoe.   The survey (Fig. 399), was made before the well was
drilled and this fold is east of the fold on which the well was drilled.   At
Gaiyara, south of Mosul, a well rated at 5,000 barrels of oil a day was
drilled.

INDIA

Punjab.—In the Punjab[2], northwest India (Fig. 400), the Salt Range,
which strikes across the Indus River, exposes a thick geologic column.

---

[1] DUCE, J. T., "Petroleum Development and Technology in 1927," p. 713.

[2] WYNNE, A. B., Geology of Parts of the Punjab, *Records* Geol. Survey India,
vol. 6, No. 59; vol. 7, No. 64; vol. 8, No. 46, 1873–1875; also *Mem.* 11, pt. 2, 1875.

PASCOE, E. H., Petroleum in the Punjab and Northwest Frontier Provinces,
Mem. Geol. Survey India, vol. 40; pt. 3, 1914.

Beds of pure rock salt form great cliffs and ridges, and these are mined to supply the salt of northwest India. Subordinate folds, anticlines, and domes are found and, at places, associated with Tertiary strata, oil seeps occur. The Tertiary rocks exposed are stated below:

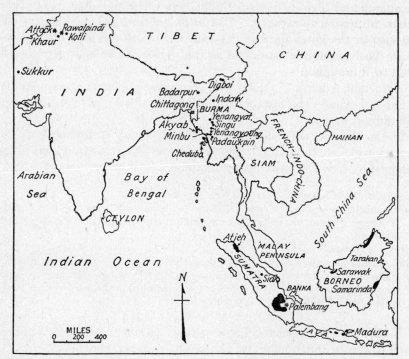

FIG. 400.—Map showing oil fields of India and of East Indies.

Recent:
  Sands, gravels, alluvium.
Pleistocene:
  Conglomerates and sands.
Pliocene:
  Upper Siwalik. Conglomerate and clays.
Miocene:
  Lower Siwalik. Sandstone and red clays.
  Murree. Greenish sandstone, a little red clay; oil-bearing.
Eocene:
  Nummulitic limestone.

Fox, C. S., A Contribution to the Geology of the Punjab Salt Ranne and Kohat, *Records* Geol. Survey India, No. 50, pt. 1, pp. 28–29, 1919.

Parsons, E., The Structure and Stratigraphy of the Northwest Indian Oil Field, *Jour. Inst. Pet. Tech.*, vol. 12, pp. 439–503, 1926.

Pinfold, E. S., Notes on the Structure and Stratigraphy of the Northwest Punjab, *Records* Geol. Survey India, vol. 49, p. 137.

Condit, D. D., The Permian in India, Am. Assoc. Pet. Geol. *Bull.*, vol. 9, pp. 1269–1276, 1925.

In the Punjab north of the Salt Range, oil is found in Upper Tertiary rocks, chiefly in the Murree sandstone of Miocene age.   The total production from 1880 to the end of 1927 was 1,643,952 barrels.   The chief production has come from the Khaur dome, about 50 miles southwest of Rawalpindi and 20 miles east of Pindi Gheb, where the upper part of the Murree formation is exposed.   The wells encountered oil about 1,600 feet deep in the lower part of the Murree.   Both Pascoe and Parsons regard the Nummulitic limestone as the source of the oil.   A pipe line is laid to Rawalpindi.

The Dhulian dome, $7\frac{1}{2}$ miles west-southwest of Khaur, is on a parallel flexure and exposes the Siwalik formation in its core.   A test 2,800 feet deep did not find oil.

In the Punch Valley near Kotli,[1] 50 miles east of Rawalpindi, the Tertiary rocks are faulted and folded near the Nar-Budhan dome, which is capped by Lower Siwalik beds; the following rocks are found:

Upper beds (Middle Siwalik):
  Soft sandstones and pale-colored shales, weathering into massive mural cliffs. Thickness exposed in the dome area immediately surrounding the core about 4,000 feet.
Lower beds (Lower Siwalik):
  Soft sandstones with scattered foreign pebble layers and with prominent brick-red shales and harder pseudoconglomerate beds, the last being especially developed below at the actual crest of the dome.   Thickness, so far as visible down to the lowest exposed beds, about 3,000 feet.

In the Indus Valley near Sukkur in Sind, 160 miles north of Hyderabad, a well drilled in 1894 found gas, probably in Eocene strata.

Assam.—In Assam and Bengal in northeastern India a great belt of Tertiary strata extends southwest along the Brahmaputra River to Chittagong and thence southward into Burma whence it extends south along the west flank of the Arakan Yoma.

The strata are thrown into folds, one system trending north, parallel to the Yunnan ranges, another east parallel to the Himalayas.   On anticlines and domes oil and gas seepages are numerous.   The production of upper Assam and Barak basin to the end of 1927 was 6,029,552 barrels of oil.

The Digboi[2] field lies on the Brahmaputra River 18 miles northeast of Jaipur.   The field is on a structural dome probably overfolded to the north-northwest.   The strata dip south about 40 degrees and the oil is found in the Tertiary coal measures (Miocene and Oligocene) at depths

[1] MIDDLEMISS, C. S., Possible Occurrence of Petroleum in Jammu Province, Preliminary Note on the Nar-Budhan Dome of Kotli in the Punch Valley, *Records* Geol. Survey India, vol. 49, pt. 4, pp. 191–213.

[2] PASCOE, E. H., The Petroleum Occurrences of Assam and Bengal, Geol. Survey India *Mem.* 40, pt. 2, pp. 270–324, 1914.

of about 2,000 feet. The field produced 3,500,000 barrels of oil between 1890 and 1923. The oil of Digboi has a gravity of 0.850, contains about 9 per cent paraffin, and tends to wax up the wells and sands.

Bappa Pung, 1 mile northeast of Digboi, is on a dome in line with the long axis of Digboi dome. Small amounts of oil are found in the "Coal Measures" series. Other salt licks or "pungs" in the region are said to be located, probably on domes. In the Makum Pani (creek) field, 8 miles south-southeast of Digboi station on the south side of Dihing River, gas and oil seepages are found in an area of the coal series. Shallow wells drilled in this area have yielded small flows of oil.

The Badarpur field is southwest of the Digboi field about 12 miles west of Silchar on the Barak River and near the junction of the Assam Bengal Railway and a short branch to Silchar. Sandy shales and sandstones, probably of Miocene age, form an anticline on which oil seeps are found. Drilling has yielded a heavy oil, some with gravity of 0.990, having the odor of camphor.

Near the town of Chittagong the Chittagong Hills trend north-northwest. The hills are formed by an anticline which brings the Tertiary coal measures to the surface. Gas seeps are numerous along the axis of the fold.

Burma.—The chief oil fields of Burma[1] lie in the Irrawaddy Valley which is a great synclinal trough of Tertiary rocks that is bounded on the east by the metamorphic rocks of the Shan Plateau and on the west by the pre-Tertiary rocks of the Arakan Yoma ranges (Fig. 401). The Tertiary rocks represent a great elongated delta and are made up of material washed into an ancient gulf from the north.

TERTIARY ROCKS OF BURMA

(After Pascoe)

Irrawaddian:
  Pliocene to Middle Miocene. Coarse fresh-water cross-bedded sands, no oil.
Peguan:
  Middle Miocene to Oligocene. Shales, sandstone, and conglomerate; mainly marine, but non-marine to north; 14,000 feet thick; consists of upper sandy or mixed group, main oil sands; middle clay group; lower sandy or mixed group (volcanic intrusions).
Eocene:
  Sandstones, shales, and conglomerate mainly marine, 12,000 feet thick; oil-bearing.

[1] PASCOE, E. H., The Oil Fields of Burma, Geol. Survey India *Mem.* 40, pt. 1, pp. 1–123, 1912.

STAMP, L. D., The Geology of the Oil Fields of Burma, Am. Assoc. Pet. Geol. *Bull.*, vol. 11, pp. 557–580, 1927.

———, *Geol. Mag.*, vol. 59, pp. 481–501, 1922; *Jour. Inst. Pet. Geol.*, vol. 13, pp. 21–70, London, 1927.

STUART, M., Suggested Origin of the Oil-bearing Strata of Burma Deduced from the Geological History of the Country During Tertiary Times, *Jour. Inst. Pet. Tech.*, vol. 11, pp. 296–304, London, 1925.

State Teachers College Library
Willimantic, Conn.

In general, at the north end of the delta non-marine beds predominate and at the south end marine beds predominate. At intervals, however, the conditions permitted marine invasions to the north end of the delta. From 1880 to January, 1928, the Irrawaddy Valley of Burma produced 170,272,646 barrels of oil. The production in 1927 was 7,025,228 barrels. The oils range from 21 to 62° A.P.I.

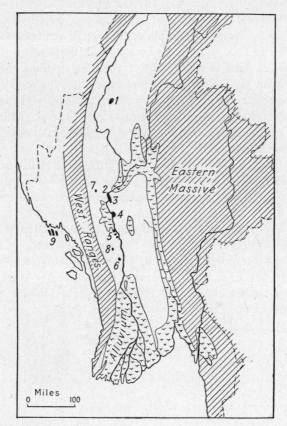

FIG. 401.—Map showing main oil fields of Burma. (*After Stamp.*) 1, Indaw; 2–3, Yenangyat-Singu; 4, Yenangyaung; 5, Minbu; 6, Padaukpin; 7, Ngahlaingdwin; 8, Yenanma; 9, Arakan Coast.

Along the west coast of Burma on the west flanks of the Arakan[1] Mountains (Yoma) there is a belt of closely folded Tertiary rocks that extends north to the Chittagong Hills already mentioned. The folds of the rocks are tight and closely packed; and, according to Pascoe, the region has relatively little promise. On Ramri and Cheduba islands and farther north on the islands near Akyab, oil and gas seepages and mud volcanoes are found at many places. Some of these mud volcanoes are

[1] Pascoe, E. H., Geol. Survey India *Mem.* 40, pp. 179–200, 1914.

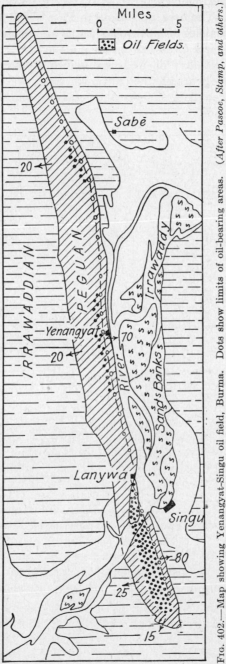

FIG. 402.—Map showing Yenangyat-Singu oil field, Burma. Dots show limits of oil-bearing areas. (*After Pascoe, Stamp, and others.*)

famous for their spectacular eruptions and the explosions are often accompanied by flame. The fires, according to Pascoe, are kindled by sparks generated from particles of hard rocks which are ejected from the vents. The flames are typical of and probably confined to eruptions that eject hard fragments. Shallow oil wells are drilled at many places in these islands and commonly are grouped along the crests of anticlines. Violent eruptions have taken place offshore under the sea, and some of these have built up small islands.

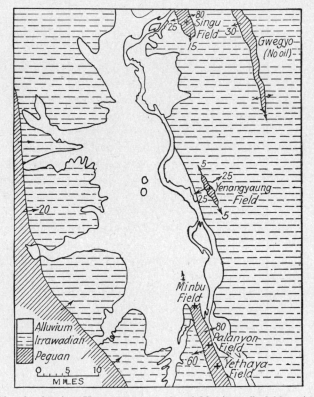

Fig. 403.—Sketch showing Yenangyaung and neighboring oil fields. (*After Stamp.*)

The locations of the oil fields are shown in Fig. 401. At Indaw at the north end of the belt, the oil is found in a sand series, probably marine, that lies between non-marine beds. The rocks are gently folded to form a dome in which the oil is found.

Yenangyat-Singu fields are on an anticline which crosses the Irrawaddy River. The fold is steep, particularly the east flank (Fig. 402). The oil is in the Peguan series which at the north end of the fold passes into non-marine beds. Three centers, each occupying a dome, are productive: Sabe, Yenangyat and Singu. The outcrop of the Peguan oil series is 39 miles long and 1 to $3\frac{1}{2}$ miles wide.   The structure is outlined by a red bed near the base of the Irrawaddian.   On account of the steep eastward dip the crest locus, according to Pascoe, bends strongly to the west.   Practically all of the production comes from wells that head west of the crest of the anticline on the side of the low dip of the fold.   On the domes on the anticline oil and gas are met at depths from 1,400 to 2,000 feet.   There are 10 or more sands that split and join others, making correlation difficult.   The gas rises above the oil in the structure.   Much of the oil is emulsified with water.

Ngahlaingdwin is a small field a few miles north of Yenangat.   It is located on a narrow anticline and derives its oil from the lower beds of the Peguan.

The Yenangyaung oil field is about 30 miles south of the Singu field (Fig. 403) on the east side of the Irrawaddy River.   Oil seeps in this field have long been known, and, before modern machinery was introduced by the British, the Burmese recovered small quantities of oil by sinking shafts.   Some of the companies still give permits to the natives to dig wells near the drilled wells, and there is still a small production from hand dug wells.   In 1888 when wells were drilled by modern machinery, the hand dug wells produced about 60,000 barrels of oil.   Since 1900 the field has produced about 75,000,000 barrels of oil from an area of a little more than one square mile.   The Yenangyaung field (Fig. 403) is a rather gentle elongated dome in which the Peguan strata occupy an area 6 miles long and 1 mile wide.   The Irrawaddian lies locally unconformably upon the Peguan (Figs. 404, 405), and both are cut by mud dikes that probably represent the conduits of old mud volcanoes that have been eroded.   The strata are cut by many small dip faults.   Most of the producing wells are scattered over a producing area of $1\frac{1}{4}$ by $1\frac{1}{2}$ square miles.   The main oil sands are in the Peguan and are called the 400-, 700-, and 1,000-foot sands.   Recently, oil was found at a depth below 3,000 feet more than a mile from the main producing area.   This district, which is the chief producing district of Burma, probably owes its productivity, according to Stamp, to the isolation of the fold and its consequent large gathering area.   The oil and gas of the field occupy the highest stratigraphic positions and the oil is accompanied by gas.   In general the deposits of gas lie above the oil.   Some of the wells spout oil and others yield gas at first which is followed by oil.

At Mimbu, 20 miles south of Yenangyaung, an anticline with a steep east limb and a gentle west limb brings the Peguan to the surface. The field is not highly productive, probably owing to the lack of porous sand beds in the part of the Peguan that is not eroded from the crest of the fold.   The production is from Mimbu town, where the fold plunges north, and Palanyon and Yethaya, where domes lie on the anticline.   At Mimbu there are famous mud volcanoes which are located along a fault.   One of them has built up a mound of mud nearly 100 feet high; others are simply broad pools of liquid mud through which large bubbles of gas rise and burst every two or three seconds.　Although oil is recovered from

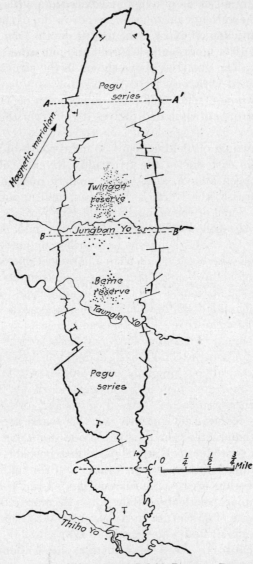

Fig. 404.—Sketch plan of Yenangyaung oil field, Burma.　Dots represent wells.　The heavy black line is the red bed at the base of the Irrawadian formation.　(*After Pascoe.*) For sections along *AA′*, *BB′*, and *CC′*, see Fig. 405.

hand dug wells at Mimbu, the deeper drilling had been disappointing. The closed structures of Palanyon and Yethaya have yielded most of the oil from the Mimbu field.　At Yenanma, southwest of Mimbu, the Peguan

rocks dip east 20 to 25 degrees.   Oil seeps are traced in a belt 40 miles
long and occur at horizons some 2,500 feet apart, one in the Upper Eocene
and another in the lower Peguan.   Stamp[1] believes that the oil deposit
is a pocket on a monocline, although Stuart considers it an accumulation
along a fault plane.

At Padaukpin, southeast of Yenanma (Fig. 401) the upper Peguan
beds are exposed in a small faulted dome.   A small production is derived
from sands found in the shales of the Pegu.

Off the Arakan Coast on Ramri Island, oil is derived from native
wells where it is associated with close folds.

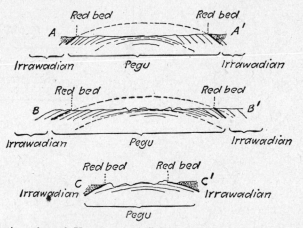

Fig. 405.—Sections through Yenangyaung oil field, Burma, along lines *AA'*, *BB'*, and *CC'*
in Fig. 404.   (*After Pascoe.*)

SIAM

In northwest Siam[2] in the valley of the MeFang River there are three
small tar seeps approximately in line.   These have been regarded as
indications of a possible oil deposit.   The Tertiary beds that carry oil
in Burma and Sumatra are not represented in Siam, nor, according to
Lee, are there any other probable source beds.   The Paleozoic rocks are
so highly metamorphosed that they are not regarded as favorable
reservoirs, and the Triassic are predominantly sandy and generally do
not offer favorable structural conditions.   It is possible that the tar is
derived from lignites in the Pleistocene in connection with igneous
intrusives, for basalts of late age are known to be present in northwestern
Siam and at several places in the MeFang Valley hot springs occur.

[1] STAMP, L. D., Am. Assoc. Pet. Geol. *Bull.*, vol. 11, p. 576, 1927.
    STUART, M., *Jour. Inst. Pet. Tech.*, vol. 11, pp. 481–485, 1925.
[2] LEE, W., Outline of the Geology of Siam with Reference to Petroleum, Am. Assoc.
Pet. Geol. *Bull.*, vol. 11, pp. 407–415, 1927.

SUMATRA

The island of Sumatra (Fig. 406) lies southwest of the south end of the Malay Peninsula and extends northwest and southeast about 1,100 miles. Its maximum width is about 250 miles. A high mountain range, which forms the crest of the island, is made up in part of gneisses, schists,

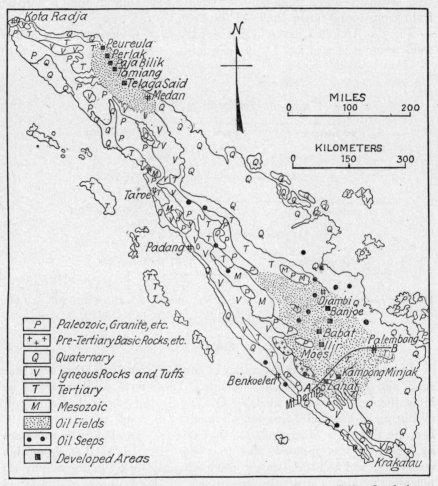

FIG. 406.—Map of Sumatra, showing oil fields. (*Data from Verbeek, Tobler, Landenberger, Brouer, Schmidt, and others.*)

and Paleozoic sedimentary rocks, commonly metamorphosed, which are intruded by granite, probably of pre-Carboniferous age. Upon these older rocks upper Carboniferous, Mesozoic, and Tertiary beds are laid down. In Tertiary and later times there was great volcanic activity attended by the extravasation of andesites, dacites, and other rocks. The oil fields of Sumatra[1] are near the north end of the island, north of Medan and in the south part of the island in Djambi and Palembang. The latter field is one of the largest oil fields of the East Indies. In 1927 Sumatra produced 6,122,000 barrels of oil.

TERTIARY STRATA IN SUMATRA

(According to Verbeek, Tobler, Van Es, and others)

Pliocene:

Upper Palembang—white, gray and blue tuffs, weathering pink and red, some lignite, lower part stratified. Thickness 2,000 feet.

Middle Palembang—clays and shales, sandstone and some lignite, no marine fossils. Principal oil-bearing strata in Palembang and probably in Djambi. Thickness 400 to 2,000 feet +.

Miocene:

Lower Palembang—green-blue clays, sandstones, sandy shale coral and glauconitic limestone, some lignite, marine, contain chief oil-bearing strata of northern Sumatra. Thickness 6,600 feet.

Telesa beds—compact, hard, gray and brown clays and shale, concretions, some limestone. Thickness, 3,280 feet.

Unconformity.

Eocene:

Sandstone, shales, clays, coals.

Conglomerate, breccias, sandstones, marl shales.

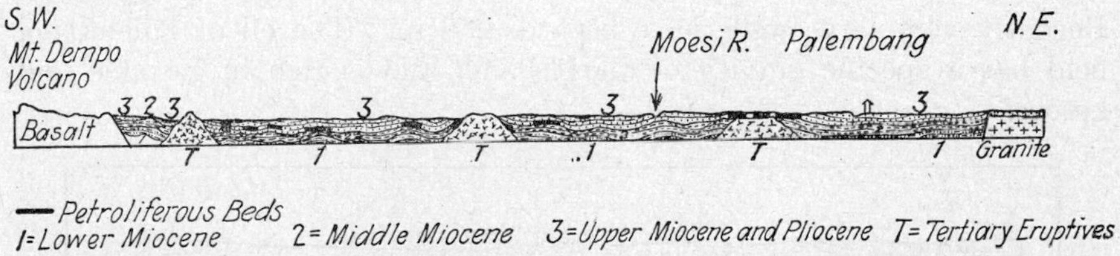

FIG. 407.—Section from Mount Dempo east to Palembang on line *AB*, Fig. 406. (*After Schmidt.*) Oil sands are black.

Eruptive rocks were extravasated near the close of Oligocene and at later periods. The strata are thrown into folds (Fig. 407) and the oil

[1] VERBEEK, R. D. M., Topogr 'en Geol. Beschrijving van un Gedulte van Sumatra's west kust, with atlas, Batavia, 1883.

TOBLER, A., Tijdschrift van het Koninklijk Nederlandsch Aardrijkskundig Genootschap, ser. 2, vol. 23, No. 2, p. 199, 1906.

———, Einige Notizen zur Geologie von Südsumatra, Naturforsch. Gesell. Basel *Verh.*, vol. 20, pp. 272–292, 1904. Reviewed in Inst. Min. Eng. *Trans.*, vol. 27, pp. 701–702, London, 1905.

CLEMENT, M., Le Petrole aux Indes Neerlandaises, *Ann. mines*, ser. 10, vol. 17, pp. 386–436, 1910.

SCHMIDT, C., Observations geologiques a Sumatra et Borneo, *Bull. Soc. Geol. France*, ser. 4, tome 1, pp. 260–276, 1901.

REDFIELD, A. H., The Djambi Oil Field of Sumatra, *Eng. Mining Jour.*, vol. 112, pp. 939–943, 1921.

ZWIERZYCKI, J., The Stratigraphy of the Coal and Oil Fields in the Netherlands East Indies, *Proc.* Pan-Pacific Sci. Cong., vol. 2, pp. 1572–1589, 1926.

is accumulated in the anticlines. Large deposits are developed in both Miocene and Pliocene strata. In the oil fields the strata are divided into Upper, Middle and Lower Palembang series. The Lower Palembang series are Upper Miocene and the Middle and Upper Palembang are of Pliocene age. In the region southwest and west of Palembang oil seeps are numerous and these commonly are found on anticlines. The greatest development centers around Moeara Enim, Kampong Minjak,

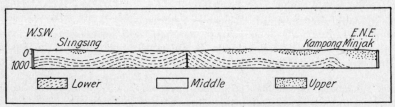

FIG. 408a.—Section *WSW* from Kampong Minjak oil field, Sumatra.

and Lahat. The Palembang field was drilled in 1898 when several wells were brought in. About 1900, flowing wells were drilled in the Kampong Minjak field (Figs. 408a and 408b) at depths of about 500 to 900 feet, and, subsequently, wells found oil at lower horizons. Soon afterward spouting wells were drilled near Moesi and Banjoe. Recently very large wells have been drilled in. The oil of Palembang field has a specific gravity of about 0.792 and is rich in gasoline and kerosene.

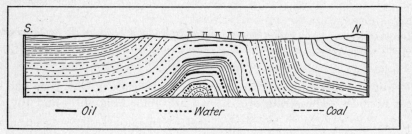

FIG. 408b.—Section through Kampong Minjak oil field, Sumatra. (*After Tobler.*)

Closely spaced anticlines[1] are mapped in Djambi and in Palembang. In the oil-bearing district, Moera Enim,[1] a little oil is found in the lower Palembang; but the principal producing horizon is the middle group in which the oil occurs in sands interbedded with clays which contain three oil horizons. The lowest is near the contact of the lower and middle Palembang series and in places is encountered 1,300 to 1,600 feet deep. It yields a light bright-green oil rich in gas, and the oil rests on salt water. Higher in the series is a second oil horizon which is the most produc-

[1] TOBLER, A., Topographische und geologische Beschreibung der Petroleum Gebiete bei Moera Enim, Tidschr. R. Ned. Aadr. Gen., vol. 4, pp. 199–315, 1906.

tive. It yields a dark-brown oil, heavier than the deeper one. The third horizon lies in a sand embedded in clays. The oil flows out under pressure that is well sustained.

In the Djambi Residency which lies north of Palembang, the Tertiary rocks are thrown into numerous folds that strike northwest and most of them expose upper Miocene beds along their crests.[1] In 1924 a spouting well yielding 200 to 250 barrels of oil was drilled on the Betoeng anticline. The Middle Palembang stage which includes the chief oil sands of Palembang Residency is thinner in Djambi than it is in Palembang. The Lower Palembang (Miocene) also is oil bearing in Djambi.

The north Sumatra field lies in Atjeh north of Medan along the east coast of the island. In this field a flowing well was drilled in 1885. Two wells yielding 375 barrels of oil per day were drilled near Telaga Said in 1892. A refinery was built in this region by the Royal Dutch Company. This company in 1890 drilled in several flowing wells near Perlak which encountered oil at depths of 420 to 770 feet. In 1901 the field yielded 150,000 tons of oil. The oil in the north Sumatra field is found on anticlines in Miocene and Pliocene strata. It is a medium light oil rich in gasoline and kerosene and has a gravity ranging from 33 to 53° A.P.I. The chief production is from the Lower Palembang (Upper Miocene) beds.

JAVA

The island of Java (Fig. 409) lies east of the south end of Sumatra and is on the great arc of Tertiary deformation that extends south from Burma through Andaman islands, Nicobar islands, and Sumatra. The island of Java is 600 miles long and 25 to 105 miles wide. It is very hilly, and its highest volcano has an altitude of more than 12,000 feet. Its longer axis trends nearly east and coincides approximately with the direction of the major folds.

Unlike the other large islands of the Sunda group, Java[2] is made up almost exclusively of Tertiary sediments and volcanic rocks. Pre-Cambrian rocks are absent altogether, although ancient schists crop out on Karimoen islands a short distance north of the north coast. In

[1] VAN ES, L. J. C., De tektonic van de westelijke helft den Oost-Indischen Archipel, Jaarboek van het Mijnwesen, vol. 46, pt. 2., pp. 5–140, Batavia, 1917.

[2] VERBEEK, R. D. M., and R. FENNEMA, Description geologique de Java et Madoura, 2 vol., Amsterdam, 1898.

———, and ———, Geologische Overzichtskaart von Java en Madoera, Geologische Beschrijving von Java en Madoera. (Detailed geologic map with closely spaced sections.)

———, Die Geologie von Java, Petermann's Mitteilungen, vol. 44, p. 25, 1898.

MARTIN, K., Die Eintheilung der versteinerungsführenden Sedimente von Java, Samml. Geol. Reichsmuseum, Leiden, ser. 1, vol. 1, pp. 135–245, 1899–1902.

PARSONS, E., Notes on the Geology of Java, Jour. Inst. Pet. Tech., vol. 11, pp. 426–447, 1925.

Java there are a few small patches of schists supposed to be Cretaceous. These rocks and the lowest Tertiary (Paleogene) probably cover about 1 per cent of the island. The upper Tertiary covers 38 per cent, the post-Tertiary strata 33 per cent, and the Volcanic rocks 28 per cent.

The Eocene strata consist of sandstone, clay, coal, and some limestone. The Oligocene includes eruptive rocks. The Miocene strata, which contain the chief oil deposits, are divided into (1) igneous breccias, in part water laid; (2) clays and sandstone, some lignite; (3) thinly bedded limestone with calcareous clays and gravels. The post-Tertiary time is characterized by great volcanic activity.

Java has produced oil steadily for many years, the production from 1893 to the end of 1927 being about 44,198,858 barrels. In 1927 the

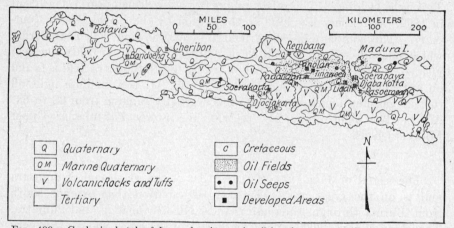

FIG. 409.—Geologic sketch of Java, showing main oil-bearing areas. (*Data from Verbeek, Fennema, and others.*)

yield, including Madura, was 2,314,837 barrels. In the latter years about 80 per cent of the total came from fields southeast of Rembang, including Panolan and Tinowun, and most of the remainder from the fields southwest of Sourabaya, including Lidah and Kutei. Samarang and Madura produced small amounts. All of the oil fields are characterized by oil seepages.[1] The oil is from Miocene rocks that are thrown into anticlines and domes. The chief production is from domes.

Southwest of Sourabaya the Tertiary rocks strike eastward and are thrown into folds with east-west axes. Oil and gas seeps are numerous. Near Lidah (Fig. 409) southwest of Sourabaya, and at several other places in this region, wells have encountered oil in the Tertiary strata. Some of the wells yield salt water rich in iodine, and at places the exploitation of the iodine led to the discovery of the oil.[2] The Miocene and Plio-

[1] SCHMIDT, C., *Bull*. Geol. Soc. France, vol. 4, p. 200, 1901.
[2] HOLZ, W., and L. RUTTEN, Ein Jod und Oel produzierendes Feld bei Soerabaja auf Java, *Z. prakt. Geol.*, vol. 23, pp. 162–167, 1915.

cene beds consist of conglomerates, sandstones, and volcanic tuff. Below these beds are clays, sands, calcareous sandstones, and limestones. The oil is near the axes of the anticlines, particularly where the latter are arched up to form domes. On the island of Madura the Tertiary strata are thrown into east-west folds. Oil seeps are numerous, but the wells drilled thus far have proved unprofitable.

DUTCH BORNEO

Borneo, which lies north of Java, is the greatest of the Sunda islands being about 830 miles long and 600 miles wide (Fig .410). A considerable part of the island is made up of schists, which are in part metamorphosed

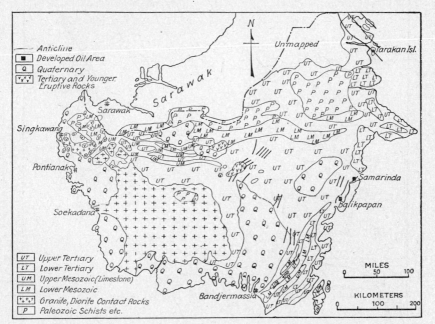

FIG. 410.—Geologic sketch of Dutch Borneo. (*Data from Hooze, Jezler, Redfield, and others.*)

Paleozoic rocks, and intruding granite. Above these are large areas of Mesozoic sedimentary rocks which are covered in turn by Tertiary sedimentary rocks. Petroleum is found in the Tertiary strata.

The southern and eastern part of the island is comprised in Dutch Borneo, near the east coast of which are located the Samarinda or Sanga Sanga oil field and its south extension the Balik Papan field. To the north the Tarakan oil field is located on Tarakan Island. These fields are among the greatest oil fields in Netherlands India, and in 1927 Borneo and Tarakan together produced 15,124,000 barrels of oil. The north and northwest part of the island are occupied by the three countries under British protection: British North Borneo, the sultanate of Brunei, and Sarawak.

Sanga Sanga.—The Sanga Sanga[1] (Samarinda) oil field is in Koetei, Dutch East Borneo, north of Balik Papan. Drilling began in this area

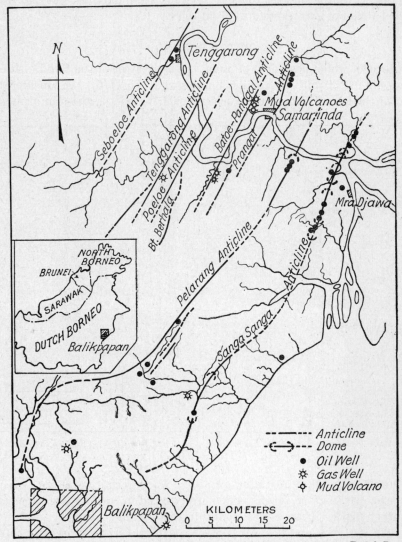

FIG. 411.—Sketch of Samarinda (Sanga Sanga), oil field near Balik Papan, Dutch Borneo. (*After Jezler.*)

in 1897 and the early efforts were successful; in 1911 the production had reached 495,124 tons. The country is an area of sharply folded Tertiary

[1] JEZLER, H., Das Oelfeld Sanga Sanga in Koetei (Niederl.-Ostborneo). *Z. prakt. Geol.*, vol. 24, pp. 77–85, 113–125, 1916.

rocks and oil seeps, and mud volcanoes are numerous. These guided
the early exploration, but later work was done on structures. The
Tertiary sedimentary rocks dip southeast away from the older sedi-

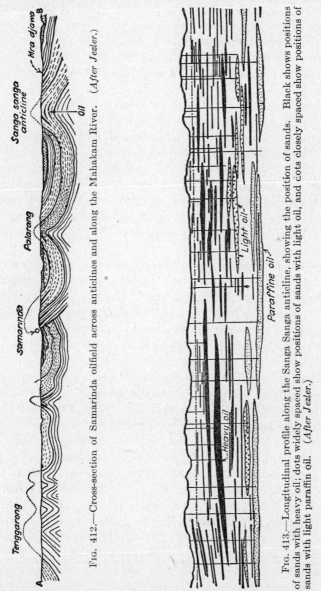

FIG. 412.—Cross-section of Samarinda oilfield across anticlines and along the Mahakam River. (*After Jezler.*)

FIG. 413.—Longitudinal profile along the Sanga Sanga anticline, showing the position of sands. Black shows positions of sands with heavy oil; dots widely spaced show positions of sands with light oil, and dots closely spaced show positions of sands with light paraffin oil. (*After Jezler.*)

mentary rocks that form the center of the island. They are thrown into
a series of long folds that are almost parallel and strike northeast almost
parallel to the coast. The eastmost folds which are on the basinward
side of the series are most productive.

The Sanga Sanga anticline is 80 kilometers long and probably plunges at both ends. It has an undulating crest (Fig. 411), and the oil fields are developed at high places on the crest. At the surface along the arch of the fold oil seeps and asphalt are found. Gas seeps are found also, and in 1888 when this region was visited by Hooze[1] the gas seeps were aflame. The crest of the anticline is nearly flat for about 1,000 feet. Near the crest the southeast limb dips gently, but farther to the southeast its dip increases to 35 degrees. The west limb is steeper, dipping at places 60 degrees.

The rocks are unconsolidated or poorly consolidated. The oil is found in Miocene strata, and oil seeps are found in Oligocene beds at places where these outcrop at the crests of folds, indicating that the Oligocene beds also are petroliferous. A cross-section of the area is shown as Fig. 412, and a section drawn along the Sanga Sanga fold as Fig. 413. The oil-bearing series is of the Burdigalian division of the Miocene. The petroliferous beds are sands which are included in clays and marls. Coals are found also in the oil-bearing series and at places coals form the cap rock of the oil sand. At other places the coal lies just below the oil sand.

The coals are lignites and their water content varies with depth. The Pliocene coals contain 30 per cent of water, the upper Miocene coals 20 per cent water, the lower Miocene coals 14 per cent water, and the Oligocene coals 10 per cent water. The water contents of the coals are so nearly uniform that they may be used to determine the age of the rocks. This observation was made by Hooze in 1887 and is confirmed by Jezler.

Three kinds of oil are produced in the Sanga Sanga field, namely, heavy, light, and paraffin. The heavy oil has a specific gravity of 0.96 to 0.89, the light oil 0.88 to 0.85, and the paraffin oil 0.86 to 0.84. The heavy oil is found at depths from 30 to 290 meters, the light oil at depths from 200 to 400 meters, and the paraffin oil at from 300 to 500 meters. The names are not well chosen, for analyses reported by Jezler show that the heavy oil contains as much paraffin as the paraffin oil, if not more, although the paraffin content of the light oil is much less than that of the paraffin oil that is found below the light oil. The heavy oil has obviously lost some of its lighter constituents by seepage to the surface. It yields no fraction below 150° C., although the other oils yield between 16 and 33 per cent. The deep light oil called "paraffin" oil has obviously undergone alteration as is suggested by the marked dehydration of the coals associated with it. Possibly it has undergone a natural "cracking" process. This is suggested by the high toluene[2] content and by other unsaturated hydrocarbons in the oils.

[1] Hooze, J. A., Ondzerzoek naar Kolen in het Rijk van Koetei, Jaarb. v.h. Mijnw in N. O. I., vol. 16, 2, s. 5–94, 1887.

[2] Kelway, J., The Crude Oils of Borneo, *Petroleum Times*, vol. 5, pp. 337–338, London, 1921.

In the Sanga Sanga field the oil recovered is, as already stated, in the Burdigalian, which contains coal with 14 per cent water. Although oil is not reported by Jezler from the Oligocene, which contains coal with 10 per cent water, the dehydration of coal with depth and the increase in the lighter constituents of oil with depth are noteworthy.

Jezler has calculated the amount of oil obtained from wells in each of the three oil horizons for the years 1901 to 1906 and has plotted the production of each with respect to the anticline. It is shown that the northwest or mountainward side of the fold, that is, the steep limb, yielded more light than the southeast limb. The basinward side of the fold, on the other hand, has yielded more paraffin oil, which, as noted, comes from deeper strata.

Tarakan.—Tarakan Island lies off the east coast of Borneo about 280 miles north of the Samarinda field. The Pliocene beds crop out on the island along an anticline that strikes northwest and on the main anticline are developed two structural domes. Oil seepages were noted on the island in 1863. Wells drilled 1,500 feet deep found large amounts of oil in the Pliocene beds and recently deeper oil-bearing horizons have been developed. The field produced 6,424,000 barrels of oil in 1927. In Tarakan the Pliocene beds represent a deltaic system in which sands and shales predominate. The series contains lignites and also fragments of coal derived from Miocene beds. The oil is found in the sand members of the Tertiary system and is comparatively uniform in composition. It has a gravity between 0.955 and 0.942, an asphalt base, and is distilled for making lubicating oil.[1]

Tertiary anticlines are found on the mainland west of Tarakan and on the islands of Boenjoe and Sebetik[2] north of Tarakan. Lately oil was discovered at Boenjoe.

NORTHWEST BORNEO

The mountains which form the backbone of the island of Borneo and occupy the boundary between Dutch Borneo and Sarawak consist of crystalline schists, igneous rocks, and Paleozoic sedimentary rocks which dip westward to the sea. The sedimentary rocks strike northeast nearly parallel to the coast. Possibly Mesozoic rocks lie above the Paleozoic sedimentary rocks. A wide belt of Tertiary and later sedimentary rocks lies to the northwest of the older sedimentary rocks. The Tertiary beds were folded in late Tertiary time by folds that strike northeast and oil seeps mark the surface of the Tertiary strata at many places.

In British North Borneo on the Klias Peninsula (Fig. 414), oil and gas seeps are found near Brunei Bay, and wells drilled on anticlines have

[1] KELWAY, J., The Crude Oils of Borneo, *Petroleum Times*, vol. 5, pp. 337–339, 1921.

[2] REDFIELD, A. H., Petroleum in Borneo. *Econ. Geol.*, vol. 17, pp. 313–439, bibliography, map, p. 321, shows Tertiary anticlines, 1922.

developed small amounts of oil and gas.   Near the axis of a steep anticline a short distance south of the south point of the peninsula, on Sept. 21, 1887, a great mud volcano[1] rose out of the bay and formed an island 750 feet long and 50 feet high which eventually was joined to the main-

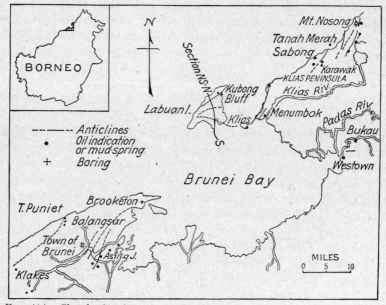

FIG. 414.—Sketch of region near Brunei Bay, North Borneo.   (*After Schmidt.*)

land.   On Labuan Island (Fig. 415), which is 8 miles west of Klias Peninsula small amounts of oil have been found.   Oil indications are numerous in Brunei on the southwest side of Brunei Bay.   The belt of Tertiary rocks that crop out in Brunei continue southwest into Sarawak and extend practically to the city of Sarawak.

FIG. 415.—Geologic section through Labuan Island, Brunei Bay, Borneo.   (*After Schmidt.*)

Exploration in Sarawak[2] was begun in 1911 by the Anglo-Saxon Petroleum Company.   Production gradually increased from 1911 to 1927, when the grand total production was 30,988,771 barrels.   In 1927 Sarawak produced 4,943,145 barrels and in 1929 about 5,591,392 barrels.   The Miri field is in north Sarawak on the Miri River.[3]   It

[1] STIGAND, J. A., A Discussion of a Paper by A. B. Thompson, Inst. Mining Met. *Trans.*, vol. 20, p. 262, London, 1911.

[2] REDWOOD, B., "A Treatise on Petroleum," vol. 1, p. 71, London, 1922.

[3] KELWAY, J., The Crude Oils of Borneo, *Petroleum Times*, vol. 5, pp. 338–339, 1921.

lies near the coast and also near the border of the sultanate of Brunei about 80 miles from Brunei Bay. According to Kelway, the field is on a clearly defined asymmetric anticline from which the rocks dip east at a much higher angle than they dip west. Oil is recovered from the west limb. The oil of Miri comes from Miocene beds. It is high in light products, yielding about 50 per cent gasoline and kerosene. Oil seepages are found in the Sadong field near the Sadong[1] River east of the town of Sarawak.

CERAM

Ceram is a small island of the Sunda group (Fig. 416), lying east of Celebes and is a colony of the Netherlands. The mountain range that forms the crest of the island consists of crystalline schists, graywackes,

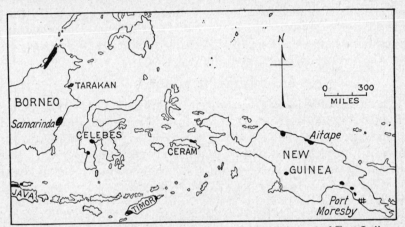

Fig. 416.—Map showing oil fields and certain prospects in part of East Indies.

limestones, and peridotites. On the northeast side of the island highly fractured rocks, probably of Jurassic or Triassic age, are overlain by Tertiary sands and shales, and the Tertiary beds are covered with coral limestone. Oil and gas seepages, mud volcanoes, and hot sulphur springs are found in this region. Wells were sunk in 1898 and a small oil field was developed. In 1927 Ceram produced 40,000 barrels of oil. The oil is recovered from Tertiary sands mainly from the lower Tertiary but, according to Thompson,[2] it may be derived from underlying Triassic strata.

TIMOR

Timor, near the east end of the Sunda islands chain, is about 300 miles long and about 60 miles wide and has an area of 12,500 square miles.

[1] ENGLER, C., and H. HOEFER, *Das Erdoel*, vol. 2, p. 540, Leipzig, 1909.
[2] THOMPSON, A. B., "Oil-field Exploration and Development," p. 489, London, 1925.

The northeast part is a colony of Portugal and the southwest part is a colony of the Netherlands. Permian strata, which rest upon a core of ancient rocks, consist chiefly of limestone. Triassic rocks also are found and Tertiary rocks form a fringe around the older rocks.

Oil and extensive gas seeps are found on the south coast in the east part of the island, and oil is obtained from hand dug wells. Thus far drilling has not developed an important field. According to Redwood,[1] the oil is found in Triassic and Permian beds. According to Engler and Hoefer,[2] it is derived from the Tertiary strata.

NEW GUINEA

In the British territory of Papua northwest of Port Moresby mud volcanoes and gas vents appear above anticlines in Tertiary strata and shallow wells have yielded a few thousand gallons of light oil.[3] On the north coast of the mandated territory near Torricelli and Prince Alexander ranges, oil seepages are found in folded Tertiary beds, and shallow wells near Aitape have yielded a little oil.

PHILIPPINE ISLANDS

The Philippine islands northeast of Borneo (Fig. 417) are made up of Tertiary sedimentary rocks which are folded, faulted, and intruded by igneous rocks.[4] The islands in the main are uplifted blocks which represent the high areas of mountain chains partly submerged. In the flanks of the major axis the rocks at places are only gently deformed. The Miocene beds include a great series of shales, and these shales at many places are marked by seepages of oil. Although conditions at places appear favorable for the accumulation of oil, the few tests that have been made have not resulted in the development of oil fields.

At Villaba, northwest end of Leyte, considerable residues of petroleum are found in sandstone and limestone of Upper Tertiary age. This material was once mined. In the southern part of the peninsula portion of Tayabas, south Luzon, oil and gas seepages are found over a considerable area. In Panay gas seeps are found and a well drilled for water at the town of Janiuay encountered salt water charged with gas. In Cebu, near Toledo, petroleum seeps occur in shales and a well drilled in 1896 near Toledo on a monocline found a little oil at a depth of 1,320 feet.

[1] REDWOOD, B. A., "A Treatise on Petroleum," vol. 1, p. 216, London, 1922.

[2] ENGLER, C., and H. HOEFER, Das Erdoel, vol. 2, p. 543, 1909.

[3] STANLEY, E. R., Oil Provinces of New Guinea, Proc. Pan-Pacific Sci. Cong. 1923, vol. 2, pp. 1248–1251, Melbourne, 1926.

[4] PRATT, W. E., The Occurrence of Petroleum in the Philippines, Econ. Geol., vol. 11, pp. 246–265, 1916; Am. Inst. Min. Eng. Trans., vol. 68, pp. 1091–1096, 1923.

SMITH, W. DUP., Petroleum in the Philippines, Am. Inst. Min. Eng. Trans., vol. 65, pp. 47–57, 1921; Mining Resources Philippine Islands, 1919–1920, pp. 55–64, Manila, 1922; Geology and Mineral Resources of the Philippine Islands, pp. 385–394. Manila, 1924.

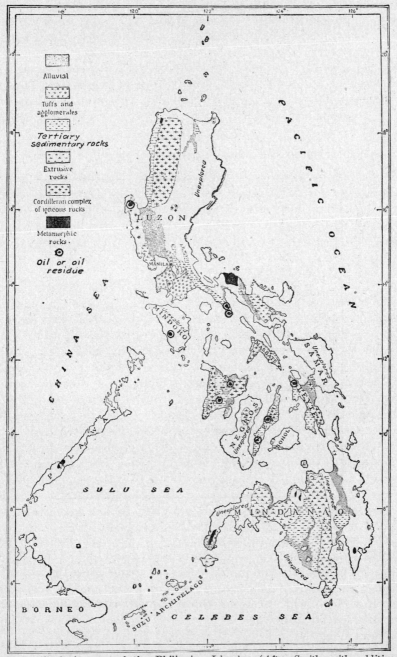

Fig. 417.—Geologic map of the Philippine Islands. (*After Smith, with additions by W. H. E.*)

JAPAN

The oil fields of Japan are in Hokkaido, the northern island of the four main islands of the empire; in the north part of the island of Honshu, the largest island in the group; and in the island of Taiwan (Formosa). The locations of the oil fields are shown by Fig. 418. All of the oil fields are in Tertiary strata and the main production is from Miocene beds. The total production of Japan was 1,785,073 barrels of oil in 1926 and about 1,700,000 barrels in 1927; the total production from 1874 to January 1, 1928, was 55,431,342 barrels. The prefectures of Echigo and Akita have produced about 98 per cent of the oil of Japan.

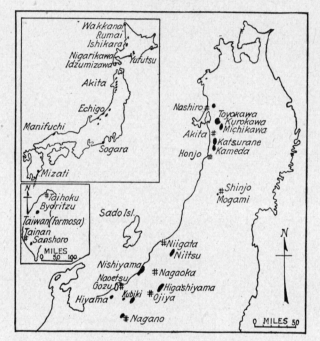

Fig. 418.—Map showing oil fields and prospective fields of Japan (black).

The main oil fields of Japan lie in a belt in the north part of Honshu near the west coast. It is a mountainous area and east of the oil fields Paleozoic sedimentary and granite rocks are found along the axis of the island. The Tertiary sedimentary rocks are found on the west side of the belt of older rocks. They are thrown into sharp folds and are faulted and intruded by many igneous masses. The chief oil fields[1] of Japan are found along the anticlines of the folded Tertiary beds.

[1] Iki, T., Some Studies of the Stratigraphy of the Tertiary Formation in the Echigo Oil Field, Japan, *Jour. Geol. and Geog.*, vol. 1, pp. 9–90, 1922.

Takahashi, J. R., The Marine Kerogen Shale from the Oil Fields of Japan, *Science Rept.* Tôhoku Imp. Univ., ser. 3, vol. 1, No. 2, pp. 63–156, Sendai, 1922.

The generalized geologic section after Iki is shown in Fig. 419. Although nearly all investigators of the oil field divide the oil measures into three parts, there is, according to Takahashi, some lithologic basis for a twofold division: (1) the upper part consisting of soft and friable shales, sandstones, and tuffs with remains of plankton including diatoms, sponges, and foraminifera; and (2) the lower part consisting of hard

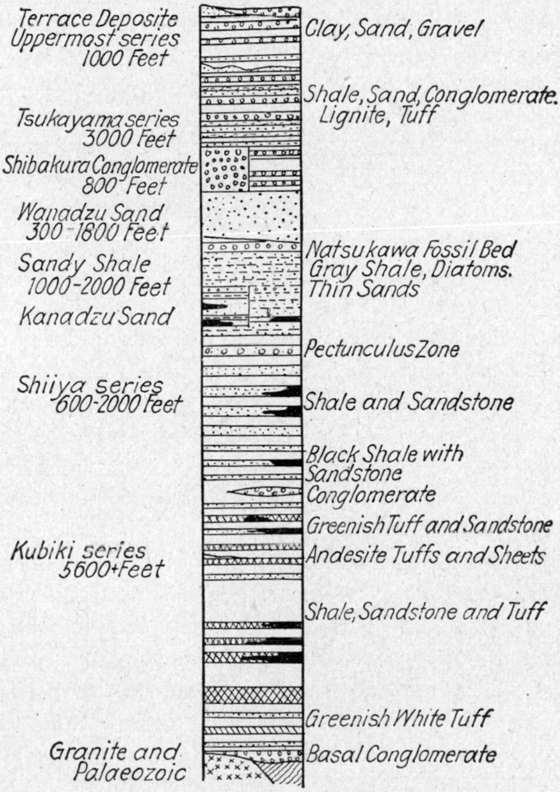

FIG. 419.—Generalized geologic section of Echigo oil field. (*After Iki.*)

mainly black shales, flinty, and marly shales with remains of diatoms and radiolaria.

The black shale series covers the granite and volcanic rock that at places form the cores of the anticlines. The lower part of the black shale series is an indurated banded shale which is commonly called quartzite. It contains globules of marcasite and layers of organic matter which

YOHE, H., Marine Tertiary of the Kwanto Mountain Land and of the Echigo and Akita Oil Fields, Japan, *Jour. Geol. and Geog.*, vol. 5, No. 3, pp. 95–106, 1927.

YOHE, H., and S. HANZAWA, Uhligina, a New Type of Foraminifera Found in the Eocene of Japan and West Galicia, *Jour. Geol. and Geog.*, vol. 1, No. 8, pp. 71–75, 1922.

discolors the shale. In the flinty varieties of the shale the matrix is opaline silica; some of it is a chalcedonic silica of secondary origin. As stated by Takahashi, the most flinty shales are diatomaceous. These shales were probably not deposited in deep waters but near shore in sheltered parts of the sea. Siliceous shales also are found in the lower part of the oil-bearing series. The siliceous shale grades into the black bituminous shale and also into marly and flinty shale. It is grayish black and is less vitreous than the flinty shale. This shale also contains remains of microorganisms of the plankton. The upper parts of the oil measures are less well consolidated. They include gray shales, marly shale, dark shales, sandstone, and tuff. This part of the series also contains bituminous matter with remains of diatoms, foraminifera, etc.

The oil-bearing rocks represent a series formed under rather closely similar conditions. They are marine shallow-water deposits formed in an area that was being alternately raised and lowered. Although there is no marked discordance in the lower and upper beds of the oil measures except at the base of the series, there are, according to Takahashi, hiatuses in both the lower and intermediate beds and the oil sands are commonly found at the unconformities. Nearly all of the fields are located on anticlines, although a few are on monoclines. Surface indications of oil are numerous. Oil and gas seepages and salt springs abound, and in the Akita field mud dikes occur.

The oil measures of Japan are of Miocene age and resemble rather closely the Monterey shale of California, particularly as to the fossil organisms in them. Sands are interbedded with the shales, but, according to Takahashi, there is relatively little gritty material or clay in much of the Japanese petroleum-bearing shales, the bulk of the shales being flint and "kerogen" of organic origin mingled at places with pyroclastic material. The oil, according to Takahashi, is derived in greatest amounts from the flinty shales which are most abundant in the lower parts of the oil measures, and, according to Iki, from the black shale near the base of the series in the Kabuki formation.

Echigo.—The Echigo[1] district (Fig. 420) is on the west coast of Japan about 150 miles northwest of Tokyo. It is an area of folded Tertiary beds, the folds striking northeast parallel to the coast. The oil is found in Miocene beds which commonly rest on igneous rocks. The oil ranges

[1] Iki, T., Preliminary Note on the Geology of the Echigo Oil Field, Geol. Survey Japan *Mem.* 2, pp. 29–57, Tokyo, 1910. In English.

Kobayashi, G., An Outline of the Geology of the Oil Fields of Japan, *Proc.* Pan-Pacific Sci. Cong., vol. 2, pp. 1180–1206, Melbourne, 1926; also *Econ. Geol.*, vol. 20, pp. 67–82, 1925.

Redfield, A. H., The Petroleum Supply of Japan, *Eng. Mining Jour.*, vol. 20, pp. 325–333, 369–375, 410–419, 1925.

Uwatoko, K., Sedimentary Natural Gases from the Oil and Coal Fields of Japan, Am. Assoc. Pet. Geol. *Bull.*, vol. 11, pp. 187–197, 1927.

in gravity from 15 to 45° A.P.I., and the heavier oils are in the higher strata. The Echigo district produced 41,651,760 barrels of oil to the end of 1927. The Tertiary rocks of the district are as follows: (1) black shale series; (2) tuff and sandstone within the black shale series; (3) shale and sandstone, locally present above the black shale series; (4) gray sandy shale sandstone; (5) shale, clay, sand, gravel tuff.

The Niitsu field 12 miles south of Niigata is one of the most productive in the district. It is on an anticline that brings the top of the shale and sandstone series to the surface. Heavy oil is produced from several horizons at depths between 480 and 1,500 feet. The Higashiyama field (Fig. 421) on an anticline east of Nagaoka produces from the black shale formation at depths to 2,000 feet. There are four producing horizons which yield oil with gravity between 20 and 30° Bé., the oil becoming progressively lighter with depth.

At the Urase[1] lease of the Higashiyama field the anticline strikes N. 30° E. and dips about 10 to 18 degrees northwest. The wells have a depth of about 940 feet and the oil sand is about 68 feet thick. The porosity of the sand is 25 to 30 per cent and the gravity of the oil 29.5° Bé. In 1919 the average production of the wells had reached about a barrel a day. Air was forced into the lower wells; this resulted in increased production, especially for wells with small yield.

In the Ojiya field (Fig. 422), some 15 miles southwest of Higashiyama, the lower black shale crops out on an anticline in the central part of the field and is overlain by the sandy shale series. The flanks of the anticline dip 30 to 40 degrees. The oil is derived from sandstone interbedded in the lower black shale. In depth the wells vary from 700 to 1,200 feet. The oil from Yamaya on the north has a gravity between 25 and 30° Bé., while that from Tokimizu on the south is of good quality with a gravity of 43 to 50° Bé. Gas is plentiful.

The Amaze field (Fig. 423) is on the coast northwest of Nagaoka. Conditions are closely similar to those at Niitsu. The rocks of the field consist of the lower black shale and intercalated thin fine bluish sandstones and tuffaceous sands, the latter having a thickness of 30 to 50 feet and being the chief oil-bearing strata. The limbs of the anticline dip nearly 30 degrees. The axis runs northeast-southwest along the coast and the oil wells located on its top are most productive. Oil occurs at several horizons; the uppermost is reached at a depth of only 30 to 36 feet. Some wells are said to have penetrated 12 oil horizons within 2,100 feet. At the opening of the oil field spouting wells were frequently brought in. The oil is of good quality, having a gravity of 38 to 42° Bé.

The Nishiyama field, southwest of the Amaze field, is one of the most productive oil fields of Japan. Small areas of black shale are exposed

[1] NIIYA, T., Result of Smith-Dunn Process Applied to Some Japanese Oil Fields Jour. Geol. Soc. Tokyo, vol. 29, p. 411, 1922.

along the crests of two parallel anticlines (Fig. 420).   The shale and
sandstone series is exposed along the flanks of the anticlines and in the
syncline between.   The beds dip from 10 to 30 degrees or more, and a
fault lies between the two fields.   The oil is segregated on the anticlines

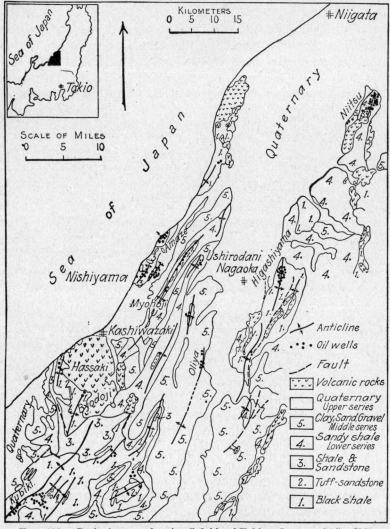

Fig. 420.—Geologic map of main oil fields of Echigo, Japan.   (*After Iki.*)

in the sands of the lower or black shale series.   The eastern subdivision
of the Nishiyama field is known as Negamine-Kamada field.   This field,
lying on the east anticline, was opened in 1898.   During the first 3 years
oil was obtained only from the first horizon at a depth of 720 feet.
Several spouting wells were drilled yielding over 120 barrels a day.   A

second horizon was encountered at 900 feet and a third at 1,500 feet. Some of the wells encounter much gas. A horizon below the third at depths greater than 1,500 feet contained gas under great pressure, so that tools were blown from holes and derricks wrecked. Some of the gas was piped to the refineries at Kashiwazaki southwest of the field. The oil

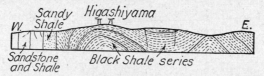

Fig. 421.—Cross-section of Higashiyama oil field, Echigo, Japan. (*After Iki.*)

from the first horizon is inferior in quality, having a gravity of 23.5 to 27° Bé., while those from the second and third horizons are light oils, 30 to 36° Bé. and 35° Bé., respectively. The western subdivision of the Nishiyama field is known as the Miyagawa field and is on the west anticline. This field also has produced large amounts of oil. The petroliferous strata lie deeper, being on the basinward side of the east fold. Wells

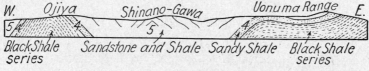

Fig. 422.—Cross-section of Ojiya oil field, Echigo, Japan. (*After Iki*).

at the upper horizons, about 1,300 feet deep, were not particularly prolific, but a bed at 2,040 feet deep yielded wells with 120 to 200 barrels daily, flush capacity. Oils from a depth of 1,500 feet have a gravity of 32 to 35° Bé. and are lighter than the average oil of the Nagamine-Kamada (east side) field; and that from the lower horizon of 2,000 feet

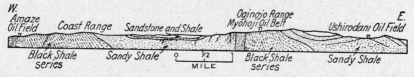

Fig. 423.—Cross-section of Amaze and Myohoji oil fields, Echigo, Japan. (*After Iki.*)

is of an excellent quality, having an average gravity of 44° Bé. and containing considerable paraffin.[1]

The Myohoji oil field lies on the east side of the Nishiyama field, extending north-northeast approximately along the crest of the Oginojo Range (Fig. 423). It is about 10 miles long with a breadth varying from 100 to 250 meters, embracing several areas with seeps known from early times. The rocks consist of the lower black shale intercalated with fine

[1] Isohe, Mashara, *Bull.* Japan Bur. Mines, prepared for San Francisco Exposition, p. 62, Tokyo, 1914.

bluish sandstone and tuffaceous sand. The strata are highly folded. An anticlinal axis lies a little west of the crest of the Oginojo Range and parallel to it. The flanks of the anticline are inclined at angles of 70 or 80 degrees and locally are overturned.

The Kubiki field is in the southwest part of the area about 25 miles southwest of Kashiwazaki (Fig. 424). The surface rocks are the black shale and its intercalated tuff-sandstone member. The tuff-sandstone is 100 to 200 feet thick and is the main oil-bearing stratum. The rocks dip north and are thrown into shallow anticlines and synclines with axes plunging steeply north. The wells vary in depth from 600 to 900 feet. At the opening of the field there were many wells yielding more than 50 barrels a day, but these soon declined to 10 barrels a day. The oil is of good quality with a gravity from 40 to 45° Bé.

The Gendoji oil field includes several scattered locations southwest of the Kubiki field. The rock composing the field is black shale overlaid in the southern part by the sandy strata. These sandstones carry oil, especially in the neighborhood of the anticlinal axis. The oil wells are from 420 to 800 feet deep or more. The oil has a gravity of 38 to 43° Bé.

FIG. 424.—Cross-section of Kubiki oil field, Echigo, Japan. (*After Iki.*)

The Yoneyama oil field embraces several oil-producing localities lying on the west side of the old volcano of Yoneyama, and is divided into two areas, the Byodoji and the Hassaki. The rocks include the black shale and the sandy shale. The oil is of good quality having a gravity of 46° Bé. The strata form anticlinal folds having dips of 20 degrees on both limbs and plunging to the south. The Hassaki field is situated south of Hassaki station. It extends about 2 miles north-south along the short anticlinal axis. The oil is of good quality, having a gravity of 46° Bé.

The Gozu field is half a mile west of Naoetsu, the chief shipping port in Echigo. The rocks composing the region are the lower, middle, and upper formations of the Tertiary series which form an anticline striking and plunging to the north. Toward the north the anticline, according to Iki, probably passes into a fault. The oil has a gravity of 40° Bé.

The Hiyama oil field is about 5 kilometers southwest of Takada. The lower black shale appears at the surface and is sharply folded. The oil is accumulated on the crest of an anticline. It has a gravity of 36° Bé.

Akita.—The Akita[1] district (Fig. 425) on the northwest coast of Honshu is about 125 miles north of the Echigo district. To January,

[1] CHITANI, Y., Geology of the Akita Oil Fields, *Proc.* Pan-Pacific Sci. Cong., vol. 2, pp. 1597–1609, map, p. 1607, Tokyo, 1926.

1928, the district produced 13,058,464 barrels of oil, ranking second to Echigo. The rocks are of Tertiary age and are thrown into folds that strike north. The oil is found in Miocene beds and is accumulated chiefly on anticlines and domes.

In the Kurokawa[1] oil field, north of Akita City, Tertiary rocks are found on the crest of a gentle anticline, and wells pass through a thick series of shales into siliceous shales which include beds of volcanic tuff and sand. Lenses of sand in both the shale series and in the siliceous shale series carry oil, and in general the oil is accumulated in the higher parts of the lenses (Fig. 426). Below the siliceous shales igneous rocks are encountered. These are in part gravels of igneous rocks that probably lie at a buried erosion surface. The gravels are locally 120 feet thick. Oil is accumulated at and near the contact of the igneous and siliceous shale and in the gravel beds. This horizon is the main oil-bearing zone of the field.

The Toyokawa field, northwest of Kurokawa, is on a structural terrace in the black shale, and the oil occurs in fractures in the shale. The Michikawa field is in gray shale which forms a dome trending north. different sands.

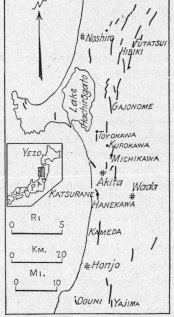

Fig. 425.—Map showing anticlines (lines) and oil fields of Akita district, Japan. (*After Chitani.*)

The oil is found in many

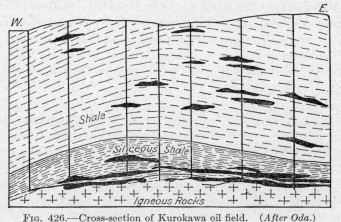

Fig. 426.—Cross-section of Kurokawa oil field. (*After Oda.*)

[1] Oda, R., The Kurokawa Oil Field, *Jour.* Geol. Soc. Tokyo, vol. **25**, pp. 239–395, 1918. In Japanese.

The Kameda[1] oil field occupies a belt 20 miles long and 2 miles wide extending along the northwest coast just south of Akita. The rocks are of Tertiary age and include:

Upper series:
  Sandy shale.
Middle series:
  Sandy shale and sandstone, locally tuffaceous.
Lower series:
  Shale, in part siliceous, interstratified with layers of sand, tuff and tuffaceous sand, and flows of basalt that are contemporaneous with the bed.

The field is thrown into folds and the anticlines plunge north so that in the south part of the field the lower beds are exposed and in the north part the upper beds. Faults, trending parallel to the coast, are numerous in the west part of the field. Oil sands and seepages are numerous. Sulphurous springs also are noted.

The Katsurane[2] field, 8 miles south of Akita, was the first oil field opened in the Akita region. The field is located on an anticline and the beds dip 15 to 20 degrees to the west, and 30 to 50 degrees to the east. Along the anticline the beds dip 5 degrees away from the field forming a dome. The core of the dome is intrusive basalt and at a depth of 3,000 feet the beds become steeper near the basalt. There are five oil sands in the field, four of them being in the Katsurane series within about 1,000 feet of the surface and a fifth being in tuff about 3,000 feet deep. The oil in the upper four sands ranges in gravity from 25 to 40° Bé., the lighter oils lying deeper, but the fifth sand contains oil of light gravity; this, according to Uwatoko, is due to the effect of the basalt intrusion. Edge water follows approximately the structure contours, although it is lower on the side of the field with the gentle dip. The third sand is most productive.

The Honjo[3] field lies south of the Katsurane oil field east of the town of Honjo. The geology of the area is similar to that of the Katsurane

[1] ODA, R., Japanese Geology Survey Explanatory Text of Oil Fields of Japan. Review by T. Iki in Japanese *Jour. Geol. and Geog.*, vol. 1, No. 2, pp. 225–226, 1922.

[2] UWATOKO, K., Geologic Structure and Oil Deposits in the Katsurane Oil Field. *Jour.* Geol. Soc. Tokyo, vol. 29, p. 498, 1922. Review by Iki in Japanese *Jour. Geol, md Geog.*, vol. 2, No. 2, p. 23, 1923.

UYENO, K., Katsurane Oil Field Worked Successfully under the Mudding Process, Author's abstract, *Jour. Geol. and Geog.*, vol. 2, No. 2, pp. 24–25, Tokio, 1923. Original texts of these two papers are in Japanese. Abstracts noted are in English.

[3] CHITANI, Y., The Geology of the Honjo Oil Field of Japan, Sec. 17, Geol. Survey Japan, 1922, with English resume by K. Inouye, Japanese *Jour. Geol. and Geog.*, vol. 2, No. 4, p. 22, 1923.

ISHII, K., The Mogami Oil Field, Prefecture of Yamagata, Explanatory Text of Map of Oil Fields of Japan, Sec. 18, 1922. Geol. Survey Japan, 1922. In Japanese. Author's abstract in English, Japanese *Jour. Geol. and Geog.*, vol. 2, No. 1, pp. 11–12, 1923.

INOUYE, K., Shinjo Sheet, zone 16, vol. 13, Geologic Map of Japan, Geol. Survey Tokyo, 1906.

field. The beds dip west from 10 to 30 degrees and in the east part of the field are steeply folded and faulted. Oil indications are numerous, but the wells drilled have not found commercial supplies.

Near Sagara on the east coast of Honshu, 110 miles southwest of Tokyo, the Tertiary beds are folded into many small anticlines. The district yields about 1,000 barrels of light oil annually.

Hokkaido.—In Hokkaido the northmost of the major islands of Japan, a belt of folded Tertiary rocks crosses the island from north to south. Oil is found on anticlines and domes at several places in this belt, but the total production of Hokkaido is small, amounting to 272,216 barrels to the end of 1927. A sketch after Kobayashi showing the anticlines of this area is shown by Fig. 427. At the north end of Hokkaido near Soya, a long anticline strikes south; the Koitoi field on this anticline has produced small amounts of oil. West of Koitoi field on another anticline is the Wakkanai field which has produced oil for many years. In both of these fields the gray shale series crops out on the crests of the anticlines.

In the Ishikari district north of Sapporo, two anticlines strike north. These bring to the surface the gray shale series of the Miocene and oil is found in the Miocene sands at depths from 700 to 1,300 feet; the fold farthest east is the most productive. Oil shows are found southeast of Teshio and also in Iburi southeast of Sapporo. In Oshima Province in southwest Hokkaido oil seeps are numerous in the Idzumizawa district.

Taiwan.—On the island of Taiwan (Formosa) an oil field is developed near Byoritzu, 60 miles southwest of Taihoku (Fig. 418) in Tertiary rocks and, recently, a well spouting 250 barrels of oil per day has been drilled. A small field is developed also at Sanshoro, southeast of Tainan.

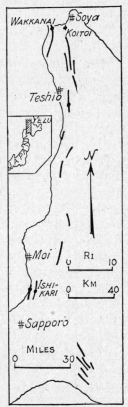

Fig. 427.—Map showing main oil fields of Hokkaido (Yezo) Island, Japan. Lines are axes of anticlines. (*After Kobayashi.*)

NORTH SAKHALIN

The east coast of North Sakhalin,[1] a region well known for its oil seeps, was drilled on the recommendation of Japanese geologists in 1919.

[1] KOBAYASHI, G., Preliminary Report on the Geology of the Oil Fields of North (Russian) Sakhalin; Am. Assoc. Pet. Geol. *Bull.*, vol. 10, pp. 1150–1162, 1925.

TOLMACHOFF, I. P., The Results of Oil Prospecting on Sakhalin Island by Japan in 1919 to 1925, Am. Assoc. Pet. Geol. *Bull.*, vol. 10, pp. 1163–1170, 1925.

The rocks of the region according to Kobayashi are shown in the table below.

Rock Formations of East Sakhalin Oil Fields

Quaternary:
    Alluvial and deluvial deposits.
Tertiary:
    Upper division.   Upper sandstone and conglomerate, 2,600 meters or less.
    Middle division.   Sandy shale series, passing downward into dark gray shale series, calcareous and conglomeratic, combined thickness 3,500 meters, oil seeps; sandstone series, upper part shaly, and contains coal beds, 1,700 meters; hard and soft shale series, oil seeps.
    Lower division.   Basal conglomerate and sandstone series; pebbles of igneous and Paleozoic rocks; 150 meters or less.
Unconformity.
Paleozoic.

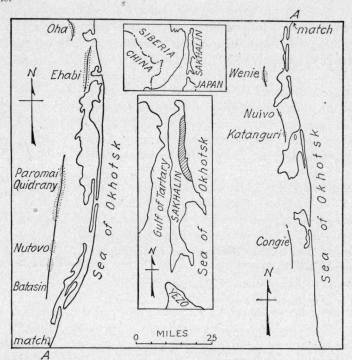

Fig. 428.—Map of Sakhalin; black lines are anticlines and stippled areas are oil bearing.
(*After Kobayashi.*)

The Tertiary rocks are of Miocene or Pliocene age and are of marine origin. They are thrown into north-south folds (Fig. 428) on which are located from north to south the following oil fields and prospective fields: Oha, Ehabi, Paromai-Quidrany, Nutovo, Wenie, Nuivo, Katanguri, Congie and others. The oil is found in nine sands in the Middle Division of the Tertiary, probably of Pliocene age. The production from 1921 to January 1, 1928, was 126,003 metric tons.

In the Oha field the sandy shale and dark-gray shale occupy the center of the axis. Oil seeps and asphalt lakes are common. The beds dip 15 to 25 degrees and the east flank dips are steepest. Fourteen wells are sunk on the west flank to depths of 1,000 meters or less and certain of these flowed 300 barrels a day. Four wells produced 41,741 barrels of oil in the first 6 months of 1925. The oil is found in quartz sand and in shaly sand and has a gravity of 0.934.

In the Ehabi field the anticline is steeper and two faults parallel the axis. Oil seeps abound. Wells sunk to depths of about 226 meters found little oil.

The Poromai-Quidrany anticline shows dips in general less than 40 degrees. A few oil seeps are found. The Nutova district is on a long anticline with a steep east flank. At places it is overturned. There are numerous oil seeps along the fold and a well yielding 20 barrels of oil a day was drilled. This well discovered a considerable flow of gas. A well with a flow of 10 barrels a day was drilled on the Katanguri anticline.

Fig. 429.—Map showing locations of main oil fields of China (black dots).

CHINA

In the province of Shensi, China,[1] about 450 miles southwest of Peking in a broad structural basin that lies west of the Huang-ho River, Paleozoic, Triassic, and Jurassic beds are folded, faulted, and at places covered by wind-blown sand. Shallow wells drilled near Yen Chwan (Yeng Chang) on the east side of the basin (Fig. 429) have yielded small amounts of oil

[1] CHU, T. O., The Oil Fields of China, Am. Assoc. Pet. Geol. *Bull.*, vol. 8, pp. 169–177, 1924; vol. 9, pp. 1295–1298, 1925.

FULLER, M. L., and F. G. CLAPP, Oil Prospects in Northeastern China, Am. Assoc. Pet. Geol. *Bull.*, vol. 10, pp. 1073–1117, 1926.

BLACKWELDER, E., Petroleum Resources of China and Siberia, Am. Inst. Min. Eng. *Trans.*, vol. 68, pp. 1105–1111, 1923.

SHING, T., and W. H. WONG, An Outline of the Power Resources of China, *Trans.* First World Power Conf., vol. 1, pp. 739–747, London, 1925.

for many years.   In 1915 deeper holes were drilled.   These wells obtain oil from Jurassic sandstone.   Oil is found also at Yenan and Chungpu. In 1917 the production amounted to 2,582 barrels.   Oil seepages are widespread in Shensi and are found also in the province of Kansu to the west of Shensi.

The province of Sze-chuan, which joins Shensi on the southwest, contains a great structural basin bounded by mountain ranges which is known as the Great Red basin.   This basin is made up largely of red sedimentary rocks.   The strata are of Mesozoic and Tertiary age and are thrown into numerous low folds.   For many centuries this area has been exploited for brine which was utilized for making salt.   The brine is from sands in Triassic and Jurassic beds.   Many of the wells produced gas and a little oil along with the salt.   The oil is decanted from the brine and used in lamps, and the gas is burned to evaporate the brine. The salt wells are widespread but the chief centers of the region are near Chia-ting (Kia-ting) and Tzu-ling-ching.   Oil shale has been mined at Fushun, 20 miles east of Mukden, south Manchuria.

NEW ZEALAND

On North Island, New Zealand, near New Plymouth,[1] Paritutu, Taranaki, Tertiary rocks chiefly Miocene and Pliocene are thrown into gentle folds which in general strike north-northeast.   Oil and gas seepages are numerous.   Several wells have been drilled, one of them 5,726 feet deep.   A small amount of light paraffin oil has been obtained at depths of about 2,000 feet from Pliocene strata.   The total production of the field was about 60,000 barrels to the close of 1925.   Gas, high in carbon dioxide, and salt water are associated with the oil.   Near Gisborne, north of Hawke Bay, North Island, oil seeps are found over a considerable area, and a little oil has been recovered from shallow workings in highly deformed Upper Cretaceous strata that are overlain unconformably by gently folded Tertiary beds.

In South Island in the Kotuku district, 20 miles southeast of Grey-mouth, a little oil has been obtained from pits in gravel which rests on Middle Tertiary mudstone and limestone which probably lie on a gentle anticline.   Wells drilled into the Tertiary rocks have found salt water and considerable CO_2 gas.

[1] CLARK, E. DE C., The Geology of the New Plymouth Subdivision, Taranaki Division, New Zealand Geol. Survey Bull. 14, pp. 1–47, 1912.

GRANGE, L. I., Petroleum in Taranaki, Proc. Pan-Pacific Sci. Cong. 1926, vol. 2, pp. 1595–1596, Tokyo, 1928.

MORGAN, P. G., Petroliferous Areas of New Zealand, Proc. Pan-Pacific Sci. Congress, vol. 2, pp. 1244–1247, Melbourne, 1926.

ONGLEY, M., and MACPHERSON, E. O., Oil-bearing Rocks of the Waiapu Sub-division, Proc. Pan-Pacific Sci. Cong. 1926, vol. 2, Tokyo, 1928.

CHAPTER XXII

AUSTRALIA AND AFRICA

AUSTRALIA

At Roma, in southern Queensland, Australia,[1] about 300 miles west of Brisbane, a well drilled for water in 1900 yielded gas from sandstone, probably Jurassic. A well drilled in 1908 yielded, at a depth of 3,702 feet, over 10,000,000 cubic feet of wet gas per day at a pressure of 200 to 300 pounds per square inch. This district is in a great basin of flat-lying Mesozoic rocks that are probably folded locally. The Jura-Triass of this region is non-marine, Lower Cretaceous marine, and Upper Cretaceous non-marine.

At Wolston, 13 miles south-southwest of Brisbane, a well found traces of oil in Triassic beds and a little gas was found at Beau Desert west of Brisbane.

At Price's Creek in the northeastern part of Western Australia, 28 miles southeast of Fitzroy Crossing, bituminous material is found in Carboniferous rocks. Wells drilled in this area found a little oil but no commercial deposit.

Near Latrobe northwest of Launceton in north-central Tasmania, Permo-Carboniferous oil shale is mined and oil shale is found at several other places. Oil scums are reported on pools of water in the Mersey Valley.

EGYPT

The oil fields of Egypt[2] are located about 150 miles southeast of Suez on the west shore of the Gulf of Suez (Fig. 430). This area was known

[1] ANDREWS, E. C., Prospecting for Petroleum in Australia, *Econ. Geol.*, vol. 19, pp. 157–168, 1924.

JENSEN, H. I., The Possible Oil Formations of Northeastern Australia, *Proc Pan-Pacific Sci. Cong.*, Australia, 1923, vol. 2, pp. 1254–1276, Melbourne, 1926.

WADE, A., The Search for Oil in Australia, *Jour. Inst. Pet. Tech.*, vol. 12, pp. 145–164, London, 1926.

CLAPP, F. G., A Review of Oil and Gas Prospects in Australia, Am. Assoc. Pet. Geol. *Bull.*, vol. 11, pp. 55–85, 1927.

[2] HUME, W. F., The Geology of the Egyptian Oil Field, *Jour. Inst. Pet. Tech.*, vol. 7, pp. 394–421, London, 1921.

——, *Geol. Mag.* Decade 6, vol. 4, pp. 5–9, 1917.

——, The Oil Fields of Egypt (with maps by John Ball), Govt. Press, vol. 54, pp. 315–320, Cairo, 1917.

BLANKENHORN, M., Aegypten, Hand. d. Regionalen Geol.. vol. 7, No. 9, pp. 1–57, 1921.

to the ancient Romans who exploited the oil seeps of Mons Petroleus (Gebel Zeit).   The chief producing centers are at Hurghada and Gemsah. A large part of the oil comes from Hurghada where the first well drilled yielded an initial production of 9,000 barrels a day.   The total production of Egypt in 1927 was 1,266,786 barrels.   Between 1875 and 1927 the production was 15,444,325 barrels.   Much of the oil of Egypt is emulsified with water and dehydrating plants are necessary to make the oil salable.   The bulk of the oil is heavy, having a gravity of about 22.5° Bé.

The oil-bearing area, as shown by Hume, consists of low granite ridges which trend northwest and are flanked by Nubian sandstone or

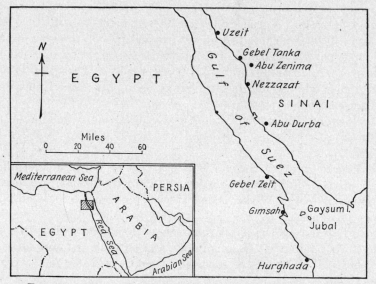

Fig. 430.—Map showing locations of oil fields in Egypt and Sinai.

later strata.   These strata were deposited around the granite ridges and later formations overlap the earlier ones.   The structures of the later rocks reflect the buried hills.[1]   A generalized section of the rocks is shown on a following page and a map and sections of the oil field as Figs. 431, 432, and 433.

Near Gebel Zeit (Jebel Zeit) at the north end of the oil field, granitic rocks appear and are flanked on the west side by Nubian sandstone and by limestone of Cretaceous age, which is overlain by Miocene gypsiferous beds.   Petroleum wells of small yield are dug on the side of the hill, but drilling has not yielded any important production.   At Gemsah, south of Gebel Zeit, wells sunk near the axis of an anticline have penetrated about 2,200 feet of salt.   Wells drilled to the east near shore have

[1] Powers, S., Reflected Buried Hills in the Oil Fields of Persia, Egypt, and Mexico, Am. Assoc. Pet. Geol. *Bull.*, vol. 10, pp. 433–442, 1926.

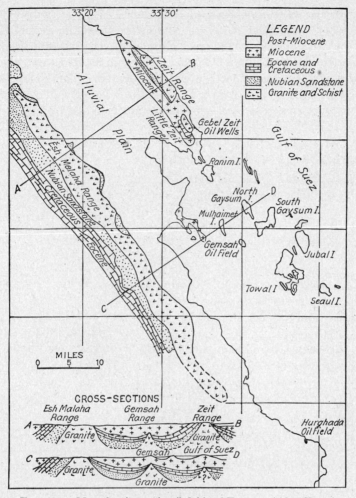

Fig. 431.—Map showing main oil fields of Egypt. (*After Hume.*)

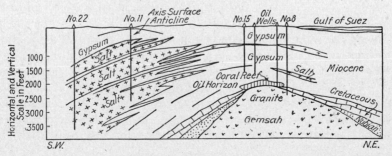

Fig. 432.—Cross-section of the Gemsah oil field, Egypt, showing the buried granite ridge surmounted by a coral reef, the oil-bearing horizon. (*After Hume.*)

penetrated limestone and gypsum, below which is an ancient granite
mass. Oil is found in a coral reef that lies above the granite and is
probably of Miocene age. This reef produced large amounts of oil when
first tapped. Owing to its porous character and small extent, the wells
declined rapidly and considerable water appeared. The oil of Gemsah

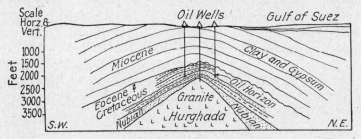

FIG. 433.—Cross-section of the Hurghada oil field, Egypt. (*After Hume.*)

is light, its gravity being about 39° Bé. In the Hurghada field southeast
of Gemsah wells drilled through Miocene and Cretaceous strata penetrate
a granite core at depths of about 1,670 to 2,000 feet. Oil is found in the
Cretaceous sandy shale, in Nubian sandstone, and in the weathered
surface of the granite. The Miocene strata are unconformable with the
Cretaceous beds and are less highly folded. Hurghada produces a heavy
oil with a gravity of 22.5° Bé.

GENERALIZED SECTION OF EGYPTIAN OIL FIELD
(*After Hume*)

Recent and Pleistocene:
    Raised coral reefs, Red Sea limestone.
Pliocene-Pleistocene:
    Marine gravel, limestone with Pecten.
Unconformity.
Plio-Miocene:
    Oyster beds.
Miocene:
    At places total thickness 1,000 meters.
  Upper Middle. Gypsum, clay, limestone; oil at Gebel Zeit.
  Lower Middle. Gypsum, salt, clays, and limestone.
  Lower Middle. Dolomite, coral reefs, oil horizon at Gemsah.
Unconformity.
Eocene:
    About 700 meters thick, at places wanting.
  Upper. Gypsiferous clays, conglomerates, phosphate beds.
  Middle and Lower. Limestone, coral reefs.
Upper Cretaceous:
  Upper. Limestone and sandstone.
  Lower. Nubian sandstone and other strata, oil bearing at Hurghada.
Unconformity.
Granite, schists, etc.

SINAI

Along the east shore of Red Sea, in Sinai,[1] to the southwest of Suez (Fig. 430), there are numerous seepages of oil. At Useit, 50 miles southeast of Suez, oil issues from a block of Eocene limestone that is bordered by Miocene strata. At Hammam Faraun, 4 miles southeast of Useit, oil impregnates beds probably of Miocene age. At Gebel Tanka, 19 miles southeast of Useit, seepages are found in Eocene beds. At Abu Zenima, 26 miles southeast of Useit, a limestone near the top of the Upper Cretaceous is saturated with oil. At Gebel Nezzazat, 13 miles southeast of Gebel Tanka, sands at the base of the Upper Cretaceous are impregnated with oil. At Abu Durba, 30 miles southeast of Gebel Nezzazat, a little oil has been obtained from Cretaceous sandstone.

TUNIS

Oil seepages are found at several places in Tunis, but no oil field is developed. At Ain Rhelal, 27 miles south of Bizerta (Fig. 353), oil seeps from the crest of an anticline which exposes Triassic beds. Near Teboura in the same region, a seepage of light oil is found on a dome in Lower Cretaceous limestone. Near Testour oil seeps from nearly vertical strata of clay of Middle Miocene age.

ALGERIA

In northwestern Algeria[2] the Ain Zeft district (Fig. 353), about 37 miles east and a little north of Mostaganem and about 70 miles east of Oran, has yielded small amounts of oil (28° A.P.I.). A little oil is now recovered at Tliouanet, 30 miles southeast of Mostaganem. In this region folds strike north of east and oil seeps are widespread. The oil is derived from Upper Miocene beds. The production of Algeria from 1904 to 1927 was 103,448 barrels, about 7,742 barrels being produced in 1927.

MOROCCO

In the Sebou Valley, which extends westward from Fez to the Atlantic Ocean, Jurassic, Cretaceous, and Tertiary strata are folded and faulted. At Jebel Tselfat and at many other places oil seepages are found. The wells of Sebou Valley are said to have produced about 73 barrels of oil per day in 1924.

[1] FOHS, J., Geology and Petroleum and Natural Gas Possibilities of Palestine and Sinaitic Peninsula, Am. Assoc. Pet. Geol. *Bull.*, vol. 11, pp. 135–150, 1927.

[2] DALLONI, M., Sur l'importance de certains types des structure dans les regions petroliferes et dans l'Afrique du Nord, Compt. Rendu Congres Internat. thirteenth Session, pt. 3, pp. 1345–1347, Liege, 1926.

DALLONI, M., La geologie du Petrole et la recherche des gisements petroliferes en Algerre, vol. 1, pp. 1–330, publié par l'Universite d'Alger.

BOHDANOWICZ, K. Z., Wycieczki Naukowej do Poludniowej Europy i Ponocnej Afriki, pp. 1–123, Warsaw, 1924.

ANGOLA

In Angola on the west coast of Africa oil seeps are noted at many places, where it issues probably from Cretaceous beds. About 50 miles southeast of Loanda a small amount of heavy oil was found at a depth of about 4,200 feet. Later discoveries of light oil are reported.

MADAGASCAR

Oil is found on the west coast of Madagascar[1] near the towns of Ampoza and Bemolanga, where exploration has been carried on by French engineers for several years. The developments are of unusual interest because of the great distance from the nearest producing fields. The

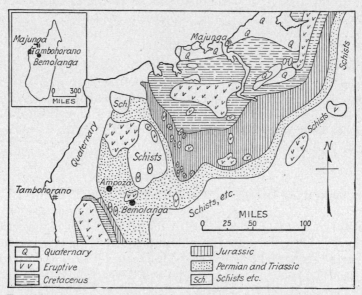

Fig. 434.—Map of Ampoza region, Madagascar. (*After Antoine Merle.*)

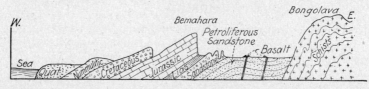

Fig. 435.—Cross-section of Ampoza region, Madagascar. (*After Antoine Merle.*)

oil-bearing strata lie in a valley flanked by mountains on either side. They dip away from crystalline schists and are overlain by Jurassic rocks and are believed to be of Permian or Triassic age. The relations are shown by Figs. 434 and 435. Oil sands crop out at many places. Although several wells have been drilled, no large deposits of oil have been discovered.

[1] MERLE, A., Petrole de Madagascar, *Ann. mines*, ser. 12, vol. 3, pp. 5–40, 1923.

INDEX

A

State Teachers College Library
Willimantic, Conn.